Finite Elements
in Geomechanics

WILEY SERIES IN NUMERICAL METHODS IN ENGINEERING

Consulting Editors

R. H. Gallagher, *School of Civil and Environmental Engineering, Cornell University*

and

O. C. Zienkiewicz, *Department of Civil Engineering, University College Swansea*

Rock Mechanics in Engineering Practice

Edited by K. G. Stagg and O. C. Zienkiewicz both of University College Swansea

Optimum Structural Design: Theory and Applications

Edited by R. H. Gallagher, Cornell University and O. C. Zienkiewicz, University College Swansea

Finite Elements in Fluids
Vol. 1 Viscous Flow and Hydrodynamics
Vol. 2 Mathematical Foundations, Aerodynamics and Lubrication

Edited by R. H. Gallagher, Cornell University; J. T. Oden, University of Texas; C. Taylor and O. C. Zienkiewicz, University College Swansea

Finite Elements for Thin Shells and Curved Members

Edited by D. G. Ashwell, University College Cardiff and R. H. Gallagher, Cornell University

Finite Elements in Geomechanics

Edited by G. Gudehus, Universität Karlsruhe

Finite Elements in Geomechanics

Edited by
G. Gudehus
Institut für Bodenmechanik und Felsmechanik
Universität Karlsruhe

A Wiley–Interscience Publication

JOHN WILEY & SONS
London · New York · Sydney · Toronto

Copyright © 1977, by John Wiley & Sons, Ltd.

Library of Congress Cataloging in Publication Data:

Main entry under title:

Finite elements in geomechanics.

  (Wiley series in numerical methods in engineering)
  Based on papers presented at an international symposium on numerical methods for soil and rock mechanics, held in Karlsruhe, Ger., in Sept. 1975.
  'A Wiley–Interscience publication.'
  Includes index.
  1. Engineering   geology—Mathematical   models—Congresses. 2. Soil mechanics—Mathematical models—Congresses. 3. Finite element method—Congresses.
I. Gudehus, G.
TA705.F54   624'.151'0184   77-792

ISBN 0 471 99446 4

Printed in Great Britain by J. W. Arrowsmith Ltd., Bristol BS3 2NT.

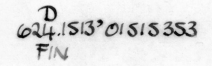

Contributing Authors

DR. P. K. BANERJEE

Department of Civil and Structural Engineering,
University College of Cardiff,
Newport Road, Cardiff, C2 TA, Wales, U.K.

DR. R. BUTTERFIELD

Department of Civil Engineering,
University of Southampton,
Southampton SO9 5NH, U.K.

PROFESSOR
C. S. DESAI

Department of Civil Engineering,
Virginia Polytechnic Institute and State University,
Blacksburg, Virginia 24061, U.S.A.

DR. J.-L. DESSENNE

Service Géologique National,
Bureau de Recherches Géologiques et Minières,
P.O. Box 6009,
F-45 018 Orléans. France.

B. FEUGA

Service Géologique National,
Bureau de Recherches Géologiques et Minières,
P.O. Box 6009,
F-45 018 Orléans, France.

PROFESSOR
R. H. GALLAGHER

School of Civil and Environment Engineering,
Cornell University, Hollister Hall, Ithaca N.Y. 14850,
U.S.A.

DR. C. GERRARD

Commonwealth Scientific and Industrial Research
Organization,
P.O. Box 54,
Mount Waverley, Vic. 3149, Australia.

DR. M. GOLDSCHEIDER

Institut für Bodenmechanik und Felsmechanik,
Universität Karlsruhe,
P.O. Box 6380, D-7500 Karlsruhe, West Germany.

PROFESSOR
R. GOODMAN

Department of Civil Engineering,
University of California,
Davis Hall, Berkeley, CA 94720, U.S.A.

PROFESSOR
G. GUDEHUS

Institut für Bodenmechanik und Felsmechanik,
Universität Karlsruhe,
P.O. Box 6380, D-7500 Karlsruhe, West Germany.

Contributing Authors

C. HUMPHESON — Department of Civil Engineering,
University College Swansea,
Singleton Park, Swansea SA2 8PP,
Wales, U.K.

DR. K. KOVÁRI — Institut für Strassen- und Untertagebau ETH,
Clausiusstrasse 33, CH-8006 Zurich,
Switzerland.

DR. R. W. LEWIS — Department of Civil Engineering,
University of Wales, Swansea,
Singleton Park, Swansea SA2 8PP,
Wales, U.K.

DR. C. LOUIS — Service Géologique National,
Bureau de Recherches Géologiques et Minières,
P.O. Box 6009,
F-45 018 Orléans, France.

G. N. PANDE — Department of Civil Engineering,
University of Wales, Swansea,
Singleton Park, Swansea SA2 8PP,
Wales, U.K.

DR. I. M. SMITH — Simon Engineering Laboratories,
University of Manchester,
Manchester M13 9PL, U.K.

PROFESSOR A. VERRUIJT — Department of Civil Engineering,
Delft University of Technology,
Geotechnical Laboratory,
Stevinweg 1, Delft, Netherlands.

PROFESSOR E. L. WILSON — College of Engineering,
Department of Civil Engineering,
Division of Structural Engineering
and Structural Mechanics,
University of Berkeley,
Berkeley, CA 94720, U.S.A.

H. WINTER — Institut für Bodenmechanik und Felsmechanik,
Universität Karlsruhe,
P.O. Box 6380, D-7500 Karlsruhe, West Germany.

PROFESSOR W. WITTKE — Institut für Wasserbau, Grundbau
und Bodenmechanik,
Technische Hochschule Aachen,
Mies-van-der-Rohe-Strasse,
D-5100 Aachen, West Germany.

Contributing Authors

DR. C. P. WROTH

University of Cambridge,
Engineering Department,
Trumpington Street,
Cambridge CB2 1PZ, U.K.

PROFESSOR
O. C. ZIENKIEWICZ

Department of Civil Engineering,
University of Wales, Swansea,
Singleton Park, Swansea SA2 8PP,
Wales, U. K.

Preface

Among civil engineers, mining engineers, engineering geologists and with other engineering sciences the uniform term of 'geomechanics' is gradually becoming accepted. It distinguishes the science of (macroscopic) displacements and forces in the technically relevant part of the earth's crust. The range of application of geomechanics is therefore considerable and, because of the technical expansion, difficult to define. Geomechanics is more complex than other branches of technical mechanics, for instance hydraulics or the theory of elasticity, because of the relevant properties of the materials involved. Soil and rock can quite justifiably be listed among the substances whose structure and reactions are most complex. Geomechanics therefore represents an inexhaustible source of mathematical problems: a large spectrum of applied mathematics is being used and is still proving insufficient time and again.

The rapid emergence of computer methods must have impressed anyone who is using geomechanics. Finite-element-methods (FEM), in particular, are gaining more popularity each year. Does this not finally supply the key to the diversity of questions and problems of mathematical and mechanical nature in geomechanics which is so difficult to survey? In fact, the number of enthusiastic defenders of FEM is equalled by the number of disappointed heretics.

This state of affairs occasioned an international symposium on numerical methods for soil and rock mechanics which was held in Karlsruhe in September, 1975. A number of well-known experts were invited to make main contributions on the latest stage reached in their field. In order to make this discussion a fertile one, not more than 150 participants were invited to give a number of notified short papers. The course of this symposium exceeded previous hopes.

It was agreed to make the main contributions available to as large a readership as possible in a partially supplemented and reviewed form. The result is this book. Parallel to this the short papers and discussions of the symposium are being published as proceedings by the Institut für Bodenmechanik und Felsmechanik, Universität Karlsruhe.

Preface

This volume is intended for readers both from research establishments and industry who have already had some experience with FEM. It may also be of interest for practitioners in adjacent subjects like chemical engineering, metal plasticity, terramechanics or concrete technology. As has been shown, FEM can make a vital contribution towards the integration of theory and practice.

The first chapter represents a kind of state-of-the-art report: a systematic synopsis is given to aid the reader's comprehension of the following chapters. The stress is on the physical–mechanical base, while only a few hints are given in regard to the mathematic–numerical aspect. Discontinuities in rock are not dealt with.

The second chapter provides a synopsis of input data, fabric and history. In this volume this represents the link with engineering geology. Chapters 3 to 10 concentrate on soil mechanics. Several new constitutive laws are put forward with arguments of an experimental–analytical (Chapter 3) and numerical (Chapters 4 and 5) nature. Chapters 6 and 7 contain examples of practical application from foundation engineering, while Chapters 8 and 9 deal with several peculiarities in time-dependent processes.

Chapter 10 provides a link with rock mechanics, which is the subject of Chapters 11 to 14. Chapters 10 and 11 concentrate on special FEM techniques for discontinuities.

Chapters 12 and 13 demonstrate the application of elastic–plastic FEM for rock cavities.

Percolation of rock fissures is the subject of Chapter 14.

A discussion of numerical error sources can be found in different chapters; e.g. in Chapters 3, 8 and 10. Chapter 15 additionally provides a systematic synopsis and demonstrates that output interpretations can also represent a considerable source of error.

Although the symposium was not limited to FEM, it again proved the dominant nature of FEM among numerical methods. An alternative which is proving promising for several uses is the integral equation method. Being a boundary element method, it is related to FEM and therefore discussed in this book in Chapter 16.

This last chapter may prevent an over-estimation of FEM. It clearly shows that a greater application of mathematical analysis can be enormously economical. Obviously, FEM can never replace field and laboratory measurements, or the engineer's intuition, either, but may be accepted as furthering these considerably.

Acknowledgments

The editor wishes to express his gratitude for the financial support of the

Preface

Deutsche Forschungsgemeinschaft (German Research Community) for the symposium on numerical methods for soil and rock mechanics held in Karlsruhe. He is also grateful to the authors for having prepared their contributions under a rather tight time-schedule.

Contents

Contents

Chapter 1

Some Interactions of Finite Element Methods and Geomechanics: A Survey

G. Gudehus

1.1 INTRODUCTION

Geomechanics and finite element methods (in the followihg occasionally abbreviated to FEM) have exerted a mutual influence in their recent development. Undoubtedly, soil and rock mechanics provide a wealth of problems for the numerical mathematician. Conversely, the speedy emergence of computer methods has transmitted many impulses to geomechanics. At the present stage of development it is probably impossible to gauge the correlation of both subjects with any accuracy. The present synopsis therefore only attempts to illustrate the present state of affairs in a systematic manner. In view of the vast diversity of both areas this system can only provide a framework; the reader will be partly able to fill the gaps in the subsequent chapters. No claim to completeness is being made.

The main theme of the discussion is formed by a classification of typical boundary value problems of geomechanics, according to thermodynamic criteria. In the scheme in Table 1.1 four categories are distinguished, according to their rate of dissipation. Some cyclic processes are also included although they do not strictly fit into the scheme. Attempts are made to deduce the mechanical and numerical formulae from variational principles. A separate publication is planned with regard to the physical basis and explanation of these principles. Variational principles can be helpful for finite element methods, although they are not indispensable. Thus a number of known and some new formulae result. The reader should not expect a universal theory, however: as can be anticipated, dry friction, among others, does not fit into this thermodynamic concept.

Sections 1.2 to 1.5 deal with the four categories in detail. A reasonable knowledge of basic continuum mechanics and some acquaintance with some finite element methods is assumed. The complexity of the problems dealt with according to Table 1.1 increases *grosso modo* from left to right and from top to bottom. The rate of practical relevance takes the same directions

1

Table 1.1   A survey of boundary value problems in geomechanics

	Rate of Dissipation		
Zero Equilibrium states	Constant Stationary processes	Decreasing Stabilizing transitions	Increasing De-stabilizing transitions
Elastic*	Elastic vibration*†	Transient vibration*†	Plastic collapse†‡
Pseudo-elastic*†	Potential flow*	Diffusion*	Plastic softening†‡
Elastic with	Plastic flow†‡	Consolidation†	Brittle failure†‡
limit condition*†	Viscoplastic flow†‡	Elastic-ideally-plastic deformation*†	Liquefaction†‡
		Plastic hardening†‡	
		Creep-relaxation†‡	
		General coupling‡	

State of development of finite element methods (1975):
  * FEM exist and are applied in practice.
  † FEM exist and are applied in research.
  ‡ FEM are being prepared in research.

which illustrates the problem which we find ourselves facing today. Each section is concluded with a very brief summary.

Section 1.6 deals with the input data. As opposed to other branches of applied mechanics, geomechanics maintain a special position here. The condition of a natural body of soil or rock is the product of its geological past. As a rule we do not know this past and cannot completely investigate the condition.

As far as numerical requirements are concerned, the few remarks in Section 1.7 should suffice. Several excellent informative volumes deal with the relevant finitization of space and time. Mention need only be made that nearly all the most important numerical criteria–convergence, stability, economics–in geomechanics in particular, can only be found empirically.

In the last section of this chapter, results from finite element methods are compared with results from small- and large-scale tests in soil mechanics. This comparison is essential because of possible faults in the mechanical formulation of the problems and their numerical execution. At best, a finite element method can be verified in this way, but often its result has to be corrected or calibrated subsequently. In other cases it has to be rejected as useless, after its 'moment of truth'.

1.2 EQUILIBRIUM STATES

A state of equilibrium can be recognized thermodynamically (or rather thermostatically in this instance) by the following properties: A certain set of *state variables* satisfies *equations of state* typical of the material as well as *conservation laws* not correlated to the material. Equivalent to this condition is that a relevant *Gibbs' function* of the state variables is stationary in an equilibrium.

Mathematically this can be expressed as

$$\delta G_t = \delta \int_B G_B \, dB = \delta \left\{ \int_S G_S \, dS + \int_V G_V \, dV \right\} = 0 \qquad (1.1)$$

i.e. the first variation with regard to the state variables of the total Gibbs' function G_t of the system disappears. We assume sufficient continuity of the total Gibbs' function G_t to result as body integral (subscript B), divided into a surface portion (subscript S) and a volume portion (subscript V) *via* the relevant specific values G_B, G_S, G_V. Equation (1.1) is the most general form of an equilibrium condition. The term with G_S contains the (so-called natural) boundary conditions.

With regard to the state variables, explicit or implicit *side conditions* can apply, which are holonomic in any case. The task lies in arriving at the equilibrium values of the state variables. Normally, this is a 'well-posed' problem, i.e. existence and uniqueness of the solution are assured and slight alterations of the input data merely result in slight changes in the solution. Nothing is stated about the progress of the state variables within a certain time up to a state of equilibrium or afterwards.

We intend to clarify these abstract statements with an example from geomechanics. In this, we assume the analysis to be carried out with the aid of finite elements. The state variables may be assumed to be stresses and strains. The required result may be assumed to be the displacements and stresses in the surrounding zone of a tunnel opening (Figure 1.1).

With the selection of a grid and the element-relevant shape functions, a finite set of state variables results. It is not proposed to follow up the thermodynamic background of this finitization here. With the deformation method predominantly used, the nodal displacements **q** are the state variables. Together with the elastic material matrix **D**, the body force **b**, and the boundary stresses $\mathbf{t}_S$ (assumed to be conservative), the specific Gibbs' functions result

$$G_V = \tfrac{1}{2} \boldsymbol{\varepsilon} \mathbf{D} \boldsymbol{\varepsilon} - \mathbf{b} \mathbf{u} \qquad G_S = -\mathbf{t}_S \mathbf{u} \qquad (1.2)$$

wherein the displacement **u** and strain $\boldsymbol{\varepsilon}$ are connected as usual.

Conversion to nodal displacements, application of the variational principle Equation (1.1) and calculation of the variation with regard to the finite set of variables **q** results in the familiar equations of the FEM. The kinematic boundary conditions can be regarded as explicit side conditions. Constant density can be considered as a further side condition which is not explicit.

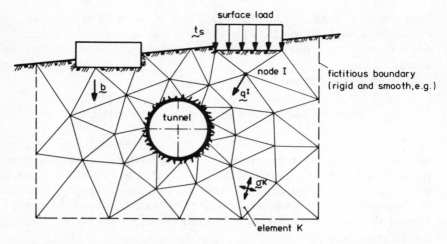

Figure 1.1   Equilibrium state around an excavated tunnel: finite set of variables

Instead of Equation (1.2), the complementary work (enthalpy) can also be used and varied with regard to stress. This is the less frequently used force method.

Some advantages and drawbacks of the finite element methods are clearly recognizable. Irregularities of geometry, loads and characteristic values of materials can be computed easily in principle. Although the side and lower boundaries have to be fixed arbitrarily, the error which is thus produced can generally be kept sufficiently low, as has been demonstrated in comparative calculations.

Mechanically, the problem is particularly well-posed, which therefore makes the success of the numerical computerization less surprising. It is all the more regrettable that such solutions have fairly small relevance for geomechanics. States of equilibrium as described above may only occur in very competent rock with few fissures in which case a detailed calculation is unnecessary anyway. With most of the cases occurring technically (e.g. of the type Figure 1.1) other conditions are also present.

It is the intention in this Section to concentrate further on such formulations, modified according to practical requirements, which can also be considered as equilibrium methods. The set of state variables can be extended, the equations of state can be further adapted to the peculiarities of soil or rock, and additional side conditions can be introduced.

If the modifications are correct thermostatically, the problem remains well-posed, but the gain in practical relevance is low. Thus, temperature and water content can, for instance, be introduced into the situation shown in Figure 1.1 as additional state variables. In a state of equilibrium, the thermal and hygroscopic potentials have to remain constant (no-flow condition); a solution which may be the correct one in theory, with a fixed outer boundary, but certainly irrelevant in practice.

If the elastic specific energy is regarded as non-quadratic function of strain, correct, non-linear material laws can result. The displacement equations also become non-linear with corresponding numerical impediments. This approach may be of interest for rubbery substances, but soil and rock have been proved through experience not to be elastic any more, if they do not react in a linear manner. The application of non-quadratic elastic energy representations is therefore of merely academic interest in geomechanics.

It is a different matter with regard to the so-called pseudo-elastic material laws, which have found particularly widespread application in the FEM, in geomechanics. For certain monotonous stress histories of a rate-independent material, deformation is an ordinary function of stress (or *vice versa*). Apart from the case of linear elasticity, as dealt with above, such a law only holds for certain stress paths. This has far-reaching consequences which are not always considered:

(1) Laboratory tests are only relevant if the stress paths occurring in the earth body are simulated.

(2) Pseudo-elastic material laws are not equations of state and therefore no thermostatic equilibrium problem exists.

(3) In particular, there is no stationary Gibbs' function any longer; nothing further can be said about existence and uniqueness of the solution.

(4) The finitized displacement equations generally no longer follow from a variational principle and are no longer symmetrical therefore.

Obviously, one is no longer faced with a well-posed problem: this is the normal state of affairs which has to be accepted in geomechanics.

What consequences can be drawn by the user if he wants to be able to judge the method? Here, as well as with the finite element methods to be discussed below, there are the analytical and the empirical methods.

The analytical method has to approximate the formulation more closely to that of a well-posed problem. Taking a pseudo-elastic constitutive law an equilibrium problem for this cannot longer be correctly formulated.

This therefore enforces use of a transition process (third column, Table 1.1), i.e. with an elastic-plastic formulation, for instance. More about this in Section 1.4.

The empirical method is simpler to understand but by no means without problems. To permit transfer to cases which are not precisely ascertained (for which a FEM may be helpful), a general postulate of continuity is always required. Contradicting formulations (postulates apart) should not be accepted. For the equilibrium problem with the pseudo-elastic constitutive law this reads: The displacement equations generally have to be written with the aid of the principle of virtual work and not of a variational principle. The numerical solution occurs iteratively, because of the non-linearity. As a means of control the calculated stress–strain paths for chosen elements are to be compared with those on which the finite constitutive law was based. If the deviations—according to a norm determinable in advance—are 'slight', the error in the solution will also be 'slight', as far as the above postulate of continuity applies. More details on this in Section 1.4 and Chapter 3 of this book.

During checking, it may happen that stresses occur locally which are physically impossible. This results in another possibility for modifying the formulation of the equilibrium problem: the supplementary condition is added that stresses $\boldsymbol{\sigma}$ may not break a strength condition anywhere:

$$F(\boldsymbol{\sigma}) \le 0 \qquad (1.3)$$

As this is not an equation but an *inequality* one is no longer dealing with a problem of equilibrium, which can be correctly formulated thermostatically. The existence of a solution is obviously no longer certain; a rupture may be present. As soon as the Condition [Equation (1.3)] applies as an equation for at least one element, uniqueness is generally lost as nothing is stated by such a condition on the stress–strain behaviour in a state of limit equilibrium. Only solutions which are statically admissible, i.e. those which do not violate conditions of equilibrium and strength anywhere, can therefore be arrived at (Koiter, 1963). We shall now investigate two methods of this kind in more detail.

A special case of the Condition [Equation (1.3)] relevant to rock is the no-tension condition

$$\max \sigma \le 0 \qquad (1.3a)$$

If calculation is made with a step-by-step increase of loads, those zones with $\max \sigma \doteq 0$ for each subsequent step can be omitted (as is similarly the case when calculating excavation processes). In the zone which is still load-bearing, the uniqueness of stresses and displacements is maintained because each iteration step represents an elastic problem. The no-tension zone can be imagined as fissured. This, however, is only one interpretation: the real extent of the fissures does not necessarily have much relation to this because it is subject to additional constitutive laws.

The condition of shear failure

$$\max |\tau| - \tau_0(\sigma) \le 0 \qquad (1.3b)$$

of the Mohr–Coulomb type is particularly suitable for soil and rock. Since shear failure zones are known not to disintegrate, the introduction of additional conditions for such zones cannot be avoided. Wittke and his co-workers (see Chapter 13 of this publication) assume that the normal stresses on surfaces with limiting shear stresses (so-called slip surfaces) maintain the values which result from an elastic solution without the Condition [Equation (1.3b)]. By super-imposing elastic eigenstress fields the validity of Condition [Equation (1.3b)] everywhere is ascertained. A compatible strain field is thus obtained because the superposition of compatible fields again results in a compatible field, providing infinitesimal strains. Because a statically admissible stress field can be arrived at by the superposition of different eigenstress fields the method is not unique.

In judging this, two approaches can again be taken. The analytical approach leads to the third or fourth column in Table 1.1. Uniqueness of stresses and displacements can be obtained by adding a flow rule to the strength condition; the formulation is then elastic–plastic. On the basis of collapse theorems, statically admissible stress fields can be constructed without consideration of kinematic compatibility and information on stability is obtained in this manner. The empirical approach, which will be further discussed in Section 1.7, is impeded by the fact that a postulate of continuity can no longer apply (as with the pseudo-elastic method): as soon as zones occur with a state of limit equilibrium, proximity to a correct solution cannot be expected any more. Statements on error norms are impossible in such a case.

A summary of the particularly important points in judging finite element methods for equilibrium states now follows.

Problems of equilibrium which have been formulated correctly thermostatically can be computed particularly easily, but are of little practical relevance. The behaviour of soil and rock is better represented by pseudo-elastic material laws or added strength conditions, or a combination of both, at the expense of having to accept sources of errors which cannot be easily rectified. With analytical improvements the framework of equilibrium problems has to be left behind.

1.3 STATIONARY PROCESSES

Stationary vibrations and stationary transport processes have the following similarity: the entropy production per period or per unit of time, respectively, does not alter. From this fact arise some parallels with the equilibrium problems for finite element methods. A stationary transport process is therefore also referred to as a *flow equilibrium*. Certain variational principles can be formulated. Although a perfectly stationary process hardly ever occurs in practical problems it is relevant as an asymptotic case.

First of all, we will consider a *stationary vibration* from Figure 1.2, taken from Haupt (1977). A solid wall is imagined, for the purpose of screening off surface vibrations. An equilibrium problem can be obtained in complex variables, with all its advantages. However, several points have to be mentioned which lessen the simplicity of the problem:

(1) By dividing it into a grid, the body is provided with characteristic lengths which it does not physically possess: this can lead to artificial eigenfrequencies and false dispersion.

(2) By fixing the outer boundary arbitrarily the results can vary between unacceptably wide limits. Agreement has not been fully reached on the adequate springs and dashpots which could replace half space.

(3) The kinetic conditions at the boundary which determine the dynamic excitation are even more debatable. Should stresses or displacements be assumed for this fictitious boundary?

Attempts to overcome these problems by an increased number of elements fail again and again because of computer limitations. Combinations with the analytic half-space theory can be considered. Regarding this, the boundary element method (see Chapter 16 of this book) can be mentioned as a promising alternative.

Some hope is being attached to the finite element method because of the considerable importance of dynamic problems in practical geomechanics. Luckily for the user of this method the physical basis is quite well safeguarded: unlike any other process in soil or rock, the linear elastic material law can be recommended with stationary vibrations (although it is never precisely valid). Still lacking is a finitization which is simultaneously more economically viable and nevertheless safeguarded by the half space theory.

We will now move on to the transport processes. These processes are governed by the conservation laws for momentum, mass and energy. Following a proposal of Lebon and Lambermont (1973) it is possible to replace the conservation laws by a variational principle that is analogous to the thermostatical equilibrium condition of Equation (1.1), reading

$$\delta \int_B (\dot{G} - D)\, \mathrm{d}B = \delta \left\{ \int_V (\mathbf{v}\, \mathrm{grad}\, G_V - D_V)\, \mathrm{d}V + \int_S (\dot{G}_S - D_S) \right\} \mathrm{d}s = 0 \tag{1.4}$$

Here G is the Gibbs' function as introduced for Equation (1.1). The symbol D is the *dissipation potential* for the forces associated with irreversible fluxes. The volume portion D_V of this potential depends on the type of material and flow and results in a classification of the processes.

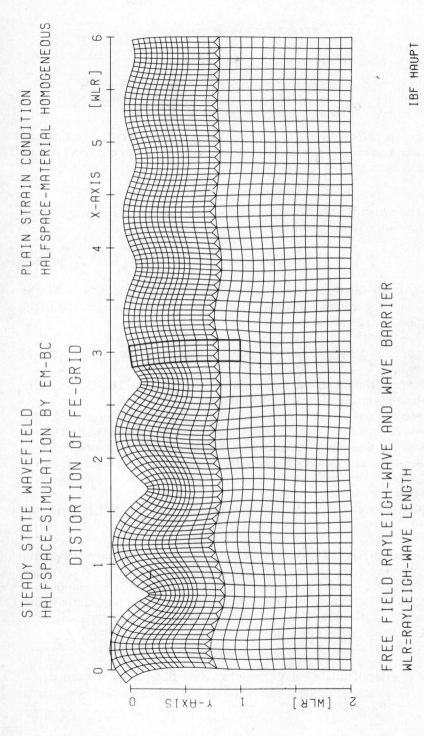

Figure 1.2 Free field Rayleigh-wave and wave barrier; after Haupt (1976) (WLR = Rayleigh-wavelength)

The variation has to be carried out with respect to:

Velocity **v**, yielding the conservation law of linear momentum.
Chemical potential(s), yielding the conservation law of mass(es).
Temperature, yielding the conservation law of energy.

There are two main types of stationary flow, mathematically speaking: the dissipation potential D_V can either depend on a vectorial transport rate or on the tensorial strain rate

$$\dot{\boldsymbol{\varepsilon}} := \tfrac{1}{2}(\text{grad } \mathbf{v} + \text{grad }^T\mathbf{v})$$

With the *potential flows*, being most important among the first type, D_V is a quadratic form of the gradient of a scalar potential ϕ:

$$D_V = \frac{1}{2} a_{ij} \frac{\partial \phi}{\partial x_i} \frac{\partial \phi}{\partial x_j} \qquad (1.5)$$

$a_{ij} = a_{ji}$ holds for thermodynamic reasons. Through Equation (1.4), the variation being carried out with respect to the only scalar potential ϕ itself, Equation (1.5) gives the more familiar expression

$$\delta\left\{ -\int_V \frac{1}{2} a_{ij} \frac{\partial \phi}{\partial x_i} \frac{\partial \phi}{\partial x_j} \, dV + \int_S n_i v_{iS}\phi \, dS \right\} = 0 \qquad (1.6)$$

which is equivalent to the conservation law of mass. The surface term contains the surface normal n_i and velocity v_{iS}.

In geomechanics this formulation is particularly relevant for groundwater flow and also for electrical or thermal conduction. This is a linear, well-posed problem and thus numerical successes in this area are not surprising.

Otherwise, finite element methods for potential flows are not dealt with in this Chapter. They are only of interest in this section in comparison with other boundary value problems.

With the *stationary plastic flow*, the dissipation potential D_V, defined by

$$\boldsymbol{\sigma} = \partial D_V / \partial \dot{\boldsymbol{\varepsilon}} \qquad (1.7)$$

cannot be represented in a quadratic way any longer as will be more clearly recognizable below; extreme non-linearity is present instead. The stresses have to fulfill a flow condition, Equation (1.3). Because of the stationarity condition, no hardening or softening can take place, the elastic strain rate disappears and the flow is isochoric ($\dot{\varepsilon}_{kk} = 0$). The strain rate depends on the stress as shown by the flow rule

$$\dot{\boldsymbol{\varepsilon}} = \dot{\boldsymbol{\lambda}} \, \partial Q / \partial \boldsymbol{\sigma} \qquad (1.8)$$

The plastic potential Q may or may not coincide with the flow function F in the Condition [Equation (1.3)]. In the former case, the flow rule is associated. The positive factor λ remains uncertain for the time being because Equation (1.8) only describes the local slip mechanism of the material. For the boundary of the flow area, stresses or velocities have to be allocated in a suitable manner. As opposed to the potential flow, a theorem of existence unfortunately does not apply: this is why the boundary conditions have to be formulated by guesswork.

This type of boundary value problem occurs in the practice of extrusion but seldom in geomechanics. The difficulties which may occur in the application of finite elements are demonstrated with the example of the flow in a silo (Figure 1.3)—(the example has not been completely calculated for

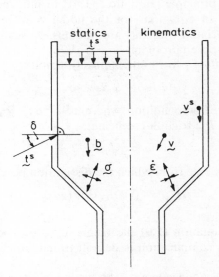

Figure 1.3 Steady hopper flow of an earth material: principal situation

that very reason). For simplicity's sake, we shall consider a axi-symmetric problem with isotropic material. The flow rule, Equation (1.8), then produces a coaxiality of σ and $\dot{\varepsilon}$ as well as volume constancy. For the flow condition we distinguish the two cases (*a*) cohesion only and (*b*) friction only.

(*a*) *v. Mises-flow condition*. The dissipation potential, reading

$$D_V = \sqrt{(\tfrac{8}{3})}c\sqrt{[\mathrm{tr}\,(\dot{\varepsilon}\dot{\varepsilon})]} \tag{1.9}$$

can be calculated for an elementwise linear velocity field (c = cohesion).

This leads to

$$\boldsymbol{\sigma} = \partial D_V / \partial \dot{\boldsymbol{\varepsilon}} = \sqrt{(\tfrac{8}{3})} c \, \dot{\boldsymbol{\varepsilon}} / \sqrt{[\mathrm{tr}\,(\dot{\boldsymbol{\varepsilon}}\dot{\boldsymbol{\varepsilon}})]} \tag{1.10}$$

which realizes flow condition and associated flow rule.

$$\dot{G}_t = \int_V \mathbf{v}\mathbf{b}\,\mathrm{d}V + \int_S \mathbf{t}_S\mathbf{v}\,\mathrm{d}S \tag{1.11}$$

supplies the rate of the total Gibbs' function G_t with conservative volume and surface forces $\mathbf{b}$ and $\mathbf{t}_S$ respectively. As is characteristic for stationary transport processes, a material constituent is not present in $\dot{G}_t$.

The variational principle [Equation (1.4)] in finitized form leads to a *non-linear* system of equations for the nodal velocities. The numerical complications associated with this are obvious. Nevertheless, this can be accepted as a well-posed problem.

(*b*) *Friction condition*: the mathematically simplest expression

$$F(\boldsymbol{\sigma}) := S_{ij}S_{ij} - k\sigma_{kk} \tag{1.12}$$

is established for the flow condition; wherein $S_{ij} = \sigma_{ij} - \tfrac{1}{3}\sigma_{kk}\delta_{ij}$ represents the stress deviator and k a friction coefficient.

$$\dot{\varepsilon}_{ij} = \dot{\lambda} S_{ij} \tag{1.13}$$

is a reasonable flow rule from which the dissipation potential

$$D_V = \sqrt{(\tfrac{8}{3})} k\sigma_{kk} \sqrt{[\mathrm{tr}\,(\dot{\boldsymbol{\varepsilon}}\dot{\boldsymbol{\varepsilon}})]} \tag{1.14}$$

results.

In contrast to Equation (1.9) the mean stress σ_{kk} occurs in Equation (1.14). With this a complication is demonstrated which is related to dry friction:

In order to establish the velocity field, the mean stress field needs to have been established first. This is only possible with so-called statically determined problems with suitable boundary conditions, (plane or spherically symmetrical), among which the silo problem demonstrated above cannot be included. In general, the problem is therefore not well-posed. The case could arise then that the assumption of stationary flow is physically insupportable; a case in point could be the pulsating hopper flow. No way out of this problem is known so far. Nothing can therefore be achieved at present by pursuing the calculation of stationary plastic flow processes in frictional material with the aid of finite elements.

The stress in *visco-plastic flow* correlates with the value of $\dot{\boldsymbol{\varepsilon}}$ contrasting with for instance, Equation (1.10). In the ordinary graph of τ against $\dot{\varepsilon}$, the course according to Figure 1.4 is typical. As a comparison the curves for the linearly viscous and the ideally plastic flow are also plotted (the latter

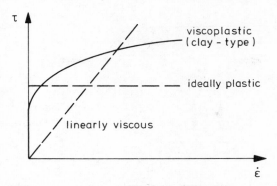

Figure 1.4   Stress–strain rate behaviour of a visco-plastic material

recognizably extremely non-linear). According to more recent investigations (see Chapter 3 of this publication) a dependence in the form

$$\tau = \tau_0(\dot{\varepsilon}_0) + \sigma_e\theta \, \log\,(\dot{\varepsilon}/\dot{\varepsilon}_0) \qquad (1.15)$$

is justified for clays. Here, $\dot{\varepsilon}_0$ represents an arbitrary reference strain rate, τ_0 a plastic portion dependent on $\dot{\varepsilon}_0$ (possibly vanishing as $\dot{\varepsilon}_0$ tends to 0), σ_e the stress equivalent to the void ratio e and θ a viscosity parameter. The appropriate dissipation potential now also obtains a viscous term in addition to the plastic term, viz.

$$D_V = D^p + D^v = \sqrt{(\tfrac{8}{3})}\tau_0[\mathrm{tr}\,(\boldsymbol{\varepsilon}\boldsymbol{\varepsilon})]$$

$$+ \sqrt{(\tfrac{8}{3})}\sigma_e\theta\frac{\sqrt{[\mathrm{tr}\,(\dot{\boldsymbol{\varepsilon}}\dot{\boldsymbol{\varepsilon}})]}}{\dot{\varepsilon}_0}\left\{\log\frac{\sqrt{[\mathrm{tr}\,(\dot{\boldsymbol{\varepsilon}}\dot{\boldsymbol{\varepsilon}})]}}{\dot{\varepsilon}_0} - 1\right\} \qquad (1.16)$$

By the same differentiation as for Equation (1.10), the generalised form of Equation (1.15) is derived from D_V, i.e. it represents—as must be the case—the potential for σ with respect to $\dot{\boldsymbol{\varepsilon}}$.

Again an example from geomechanics is considered (Figure 1.5). The flow of soft, clayey soil past a pile is considered; a problem important in foundation engineering lies in calculating the transverse force exerted on this pile by the soil. The outer boundary is fictitious, but at a sufficient distance from the pile this assumed boundary certainly cannot cause serious errors. The process of calculation according to the FEM is as follows (results cannot yet be presented): The v-field is to be constructed as volume-preserving and elementwise linearly distributed (throughout or *via* penalty function). Having inserted Equations (1.11) and (1.16) into the variational principle [Equation (1.4)], we arrive at a non-linear system of equations for

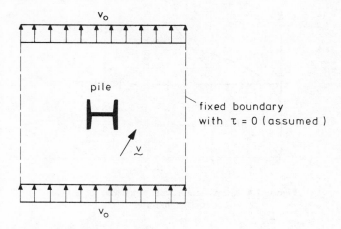

Figure 1.5   Stationary flow of a soft soil past a pile

the nodal velocities. The problem can be quoted as well-posed, but not altogether plain numerically.

A summary with regard to the stationary processes now follows: apart from certain systems with dry friction the stationary flow problems can be correctly formulated thermodynamically. The finite element method therefore represents a suitable aid. With non-quadratic potentials numerical difficulties occur, because of non-linearity. Caution is necessary in the introduction of fictitious finite boundaries for stationary vibrations only.

1.4   STABILIZING TRANSITIONS

In the third column of Table 1.1 are summarised transitions which do not result in collapse. They are distinguishable by a dissipation power which, as a rule, decreases in time. They are non-stationary, i.e. the state variables alter their values in the course of time. The term transition is used because an equilibrium or flow equilibrium can exist at the beginning and end of the process. It is appropriate to keep these reference states in mind, although they are often not even reached, particularly in practical geomechanics. This is so because it has emerged that much of the equilibrium methods can be adopted—with the application of finite elements, too—although not correctly in all cases.

Again the cyclic processes will be dealt with first, because they do not quite fit into the thermodynamic context. Some peculiarities in the application of finite elements are explained in Chapter 9 of this publication. In addition to what has been stated in Section 1.3 on stationary vibration, difficulties arise from the finitization of the time. With linear-elastic systems it is at least possible to calculate an optimum finitization analytically. Transient vibrations in geomechanical systems which are not linearly-elastic are ranged among those processes which have hardly been dealt with analytically and which appear at present unsuitable for treatment with finite elements.

The monotonous processes listed in the third column of Table 1.1 have some common characteristics which will be explained in advance. Again, the variational principle as introduced by Lebon and Lambermont (1973) for linear chemical systems appears to be promising for the application in geomechanics

$$\delta_f \int_t \int_B (\dot{G} - D)\, dB\, dt = 0 \qquad (1.17)$$

The symbols G and D designate, as before, Gibbs' function and dissipation potential. The symbol δ_f means a restricted variation: during the process of variation the dependence of $\partial G/\partial t$ on rates of state variables and of grad G on gradients of state variables is to be kept frozen. With this restriction, the Euler–Lagrange equations of Equation (1.17) are again the conservation laws of linear momentum, mass and energy.

Contrary to equilibrium and flow equilibrium, Equation (1.17) does not generally mean that a certain integral is stationary for the real process. As the restricted variation may cause some errors it is recommended, to be on the safe side, to determine the Euler–Lagrange equations in each special case. Restricted variational principles having a formal resemblance to Equation (1.17) were also proposed by Desai (1972) for finite element methods in geomechanics. Both from the aspect of numerics and of thermodynamics, it is advisable to use restricted variational principles with some caution.

The variational principles Equation (1.1) for equilibrium and Equation (1.4) for flow equilibrium are contained in Equation (1.17) as special cases. Equilibrium: a quasi-static transition from one equilibrium to the other is assumed to occur without dissipation power; $\int_t \dot{G}\, dt = G$ in Equation (1.17) can then be integrated (except for an irrelevant reference value), and Equation (1.1) is obtained. For flow equilibrium, because of the stationarity, the integration with respect to t can be omitted in Equation (1.17) and Equation (1.4) is obtained immediately. From the connection between Equations (1.1), (1.4) and (1.17) it can already be seen that equilibrium and flow equilibrium can be relevant limiting cases of transition processes.

The initial or final states exert a contributory influence on the transition processes because of the assumed monotony. As a rule, mechanical processes in soil and rock—as far as they are of technical interest—are dissipative. Only the momentary values of the state variables are relevant for the process in the particularly simple, stationary dissipative process, and not their differences from former or future values. In other words, the memory of the past can be completely wiped out. From this can be concluded that the final condition with many processes of geomechanical interest affects results more strongly than the initial one. Confer also Chapter 3. Further classification of the transition processes will now depend upon the characteristics of the materials.

With the *linear diffusion* process the transport rates have scalar potentials. The correlation between our variational principle (1.17) and better known equations is demonstrated for the chemical diffusion. For simplicity's sake only one spatial variable x and one chemical admixture is considered.

The only independent state variable is the chemical concentration c. If the barycentric velocity **v** is neglected, the following portions for the Gibbs' function and the dissipation power, which depend on the concentration c, are obtained:

$$G_V = -\frac{1}{2}kc^2 \qquad D_V = \frac{1}{2}d\left(\frac{\partial c}{\partial x}\right)^2 \qquad (1.18)$$

with two material constants k and d for the chemical portion of energy and dissipation power, respectively.

The variational principle [Equation (1.17)] takes the special form

$$\delta_t \int_t \int_V \left(\frac{\partial G_V}{\partial t} - D_V\right) dV\, dt = 0 \qquad (1.19)$$

wherein the variation is to be carried out with respect to the chemical potential c, keeping $\partial c/\partial t$ constant. This restricted variation yields the Euler–Lagrange equation

$$-k\frac{\partial c}{\partial t} + d\frac{\partial^2 c}{\partial t^2} = 0 \qquad (1.20)$$

which is the familiar diffusion equation. The extension to three dimensions is straightforward.

The formulation of finite element methods can now take place in two ways which applies for all transition processes: by finite time differences or by applying a variational principle for the time-dependence. The former method is used more frequently (compare Chapters 8 and 9 of this publication), but the errors possible with this are difficult to ascertain. On the other hand the latter method poses bigger formal problems and is rarely applied therefore.

The chemical diffusion can be calculated quite well with the aid of finite elements but is of no particular interest in geomechanics. It should be kept in mind, though, that the variational principle (1.17) and its finite transformation is also useful for other diffusion processes, like unsaturated pore flow, swelling, heat conduction, electro-osmosis, and the combination of such processes. Since all these processes obey potential laws the outlook for finite elements is favourable. Several of the necessary constitutive parameters are already quite well known in soil physics.

Consolidation of a poro-elastic subsoil is the transition process which has been dealt with most thoroughly in geomechanics. For the purpose of improved intelligibility the one-dimensional process will be considered only here. In this case the piezometric height $h = z + u/\gamma_w$, depending on height z and pore pressure u, is the only scalar potential (formally being a chemical potential). If, as usual in the theory of consolidation, compressibility of water and velocity effects of the porous matrix are neglected, one obtains the relevant terms

$$G_V = -\frac{1}{2E_S}(\sigma')^2 \qquad D_V = \frac{1}{2}k\left(\frac{\partial h}{\partial x}\right)^2 \qquad (1.21)$$

The materials constants E_S and k stand for elasticity and permeability respectively. The negative sign for G_V is required because an increase of effective stress means a decrease of potential energy of the fluid phase.

Inserting $\sigma' = \sigma_0 - u = \sigma_0 - (h - z)\gamma_w$ for effective stress and carrying out the restricted variation as in Equation (1.19) yields

$$-\frac{\gamma_w}{E_S}\frac{\partial^2 h}{\partial x^2} + k\frac{\partial h}{\partial t} = 0 \qquad (1.22)$$

and this is the conservation law for the mass of pore fluid, which is the familiar equation of consolidation.

The process of generalization to three dimensions is straightforward. It should be noted that our principle Equation (1.19) does not generally coincide with other formulations which are proposed for finite elements (Gallagher *et al.*, 1975).

If a deviation from the elastic material behaviour occurs with this, all the complications mentioned in Section 1.2 are valid. The use of such non-elastic constitutive laws for consolidation is therefore strongly advised against, unless they are analytically or empirically proven (preferably both). This is the case with isotropic and K_0-consolidation, but unfortunately not for most other modes of deformation.

Elastic–plastic deformation will now be discussed. This is considered as a transition process and not, as is often assumed, a problem of equilibrium.

The peculiarity lies in the fact that no time variable occurs but merely the chronological sequence: a plastic process can be speeded up or slowed down as required, without—by definition—affecting the result. This condition is unsatisfactory in a physical sense and also causes numerical problems. A way out may be obtained with the re-introduction of the real-time variable.

The typical problems arising in connection with the finite element method will be demonstrated in two examples (Figures 1.6a and 1.6b). These are the bearing capacity problem and the cavity problem. For the time being, a

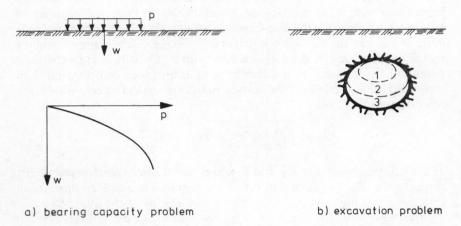

a) bearing capacity problem

b) excavation problem

Figure 1.6 Two examples of elastic–plastic processes beneath the ground

linearly-elastic, ideally-plastic material will be assumed. The problem is well-posed for a cohesive substance (e.g. as shown by Koiter, 1963), if the following information is available:

(1) The law of elasticity, flow condition and flow rule for the material.
(2) The initial stress field, the sequence of the body and surface forces as well as the sequence of the boundary displacements for the body.

It has to be remembered that rather more information is required here than for equilibrium or flow equilibrium. If the material is not purely cohesive, but shows friction, the same information should be needed but a proof for the uniqueness of this solution is not known.

The correct formulation of the constitutive laws represents no difficulties on principle. If the simplest formula is taken in each case, Hooke's law is obtained as well as the von Mises flow condition, coaxiality of σ and ε, and plastic incompressibility. The initial stress field is of considerable importance for both examples: even if the initial vertical stress σ_z^i corresponds to the overburden, the horizontal stress σ_x^i is statically possible within wide limits. σ_x^i considerably affects the result, because only this determines the initial limits of elasticity. The elastic-plastic level of σ_x^i can only be calculated if the past history can be retraced to a stress-free initial state.

While the body forces in both cases of Figure 1.6 are trivially the same the sequences of the boundary forces show considerable differences. With the bearing capacity problem the obvious method is to prescribe a uniform increase of the surface load or the displacement on an area of the surface. The conditions at the edge of a cavity are less trivial, as this really concerns a variable boundary which follows the extent of the excavation. Only an indication of the entire course of the excavation would be the correct elastic-plastic boundary condition; any data regarding stresses or displacements along the final cavity edge prior to the end of excavation must be arbitrary.

The FEM is quite suitable for solving such problems, as proven by successful calculations (see Chapter 12, for instance). The incremental version is preferable because of its mechanical formulation. The extended Newton methods (initial stress or initial strain method), are very suitable for non-linear elastic or pseudo-elastic problems, but can lead to contradictions of the flow rule; as with the modified equilibrium problem (see Section 1.2) uniqueness is not generally certain.

An incremental formulation also results from the application of our variational principle [Equation (1.17)] with the interval $(t, t + \Delta t)$ in conjunction with the mean value theorem of integral calculus:

$$\delta \int_t^{t+\Delta t} \int_B (\dot{G} - D)\, \mathrm{d}B \, \mathrm{d}t \doteq \delta \int \left[\frac{G(t + \Delta t) - G(t)}{\Delta t} - D\left(t + \frac{\Delta t}{2}\right) \right] \Delta t \, \mathrm{d}B$$

$$= \delta \int_B (\Delta G - \Delta t \,.\, D)\, \mathrm{d}B = 0 \qquad (1.23)$$

More precise mean values can lead to half-step methods. A time-independent variational problem remains whose formulation is similar to the flow equilibrium. This appears to justify reference to a series of equilibrium states, which is not correct thermodynamically, though. Equation (1.23) fails for the flow condition of dry friction. This problem can be overcome by formulating the incremental equilibrium instead, through the principle of virtual work, which results in a non-symmetrical matrix. It may be assumed that Equation (1.23) is correct, but that understanding of dry friction is not sufficient yet. It is pointed out that dry friction also causes contradictions with analytical mechanics (Painlevé, 1895).

The calculated load-settlement curve (Figure 1.6a) is non-linear, because the extent of plastic zones changes through the process. With an increasing load, eigenstress fields develop in order to counterbalance unbearable elastic stresses. These cause a hardening of the system which has a lot in common with the possible hardening of the material which will be considered now.

The stress-strain curve of a *plastically hardening* material is very similar to the graph of Figure 1.6a. This can be explained thermodynamically by the change in certain *inner variables* ξ. Apart from the particularly simple case of density hardening, which provides the base for the Cam-clay theory among others, these are hidden variables; this is the whole problem. The eigenstress field corresponds to the inner variables in the global hardening of a body which consists of an elastic-ideally plastic material. Presumably the inner variables ξ represent the structure of a hardening material. The growth law for these inner variables, i.e. the hardening law, is also required for a complete formulation of the problem. This occurs as a further contributory factor to the rate of Gibbs' function, in the variational principle [Equation (1.23)]. Owing to its independence of time, the growth law could have the form

$$\dot{\xi} = \mathbf{A}\dot{\xi} \tag{1.24}$$

for continuous constitutive behaviour.

A main problem of plasto-mechanics (and therefore the related thermodynamics) is finding expressions for ξ and $\mathbf{A}$, which are based on physical facts, determined by measuring techniques and which can be applied practically. Part of this is to represent flow condition, flow rule and Gibbs' function as dependent on the variables ξ.

How far is this state of knowledge relevant for finite element methods in geomechanics? Hidden variables should be left aside for practical problems at present. Obtaining the necessary information for the ideally-plastic problem is difficult enough. However, the FEM is very useful for purposes of research in testing one or the other hardening law for its usefulness.

In *creep-relaxation*, all problems mentioned above can occur simultaneously, and these processes are often of practical importance. For sake of clearness we make the following restrictive assumptions:

(1) Volume changes are excluded, i.e. the soil or rock is to be supposed saturated and more or less impervious. This eliminates consolidation or swelling.

(2) All non-mechanical effects ar excluded, i.e. temperature, chemical composition and electrical potentials are assumed constant.

(3) The (time-independent) component of the constitutive behaviour is to be taken as elastic or pseudo-elastic. This limits investigation to certain stress-strain paths and maximum amounts of them.

(4) The strains are to be low enough to be linearized geometrically.

The simplest constitutive model suitable for creep-relaxation is a linear Kelvin body. The stress $\boldsymbol{\sigma} = \boldsymbol{\sigma}_e + \boldsymbol{\sigma}_v$ is composed of an elastic portion $\boldsymbol{\sigma}_e$ and a viscous portion $\boldsymbol{\sigma}_v$:

$$\boldsymbol{\sigma}_e = \mathbf{D}\boldsymbol{\varepsilon} \tag{1.2 bis}$$

$$\boldsymbol{\sigma}_v = \mathbf{M}\dot{\boldsymbol{\varepsilon}} \tag{1.25}$$

where $\mathbf{M}$ represents the (usually isotropic) viscosity matrix. A linear system of equations is obtained from the conservation law of linear momentum. The FEM is suitable and has been used in different forms. Unfortunately, the practical relevance to geomechanics is low, since the viscous behaviour of soil and rock is distinctly non-linear in most cases.

In Chapter 3 of this volume, a finite visco-plastic constitutive law is given for clayey soil, which is based on experiments:

$$\tau = \tau_p + \tau_v = c_u \sqrt{\varepsilon/\varepsilon_p} + \sigma_e \theta \log{(\dot{\varepsilon}/\dot{\varepsilon}_0)} \tag{1.26}$$

The plastic constituent is not constant here, as in the case of Equation (1.15), but plotted as a function of the strain ε. The expression $\tau_p(\varepsilon)$ is pseudo-elastic and only applies up to a certain peak strain ε_p; beyond this, stationary flow or softening apply. Non-quadratic expressions matching Equation (1.26), analogous to Equation (1.2) and (1.16) can be made for the pseudo-elastic energy G_V and the dissipation potential D_V:

$$G_V = \sqrt{\tfrac{8}{3}} c_u [\mathrm{tr}\,(\boldsymbol{\varepsilon}\boldsymbol{\varepsilon})]^{3/2} - \mathbf{bu} \tag{1.27}$$

$$D_V = \sqrt{\tfrac{8}{3}} \sigma_e \theta \frac{\sqrt{[\mathrm{tr}\,(\dot{\boldsymbol{\varepsilon}}\dot{\boldsymbol{\varepsilon}})]}}{\dot{\varepsilon}_0} \left(\log \frac{\sqrt{[\mathrm{tr}\,(\dot{\boldsymbol{\varepsilon}}\dot{\boldsymbol{\varepsilon}})]}}{\dot{\varepsilon}_0} - 1 \right) \tag{1.28}$$

Attempts to apply the variational principle [Equation (1.17)] have failed as yet because of certain thermodynamic difficulties. However, one can write down the governing conservation law of linear momentum directly. Transfer to finite elements is quite possible but results in non-linear equations. Calculations are at present under way for certain creep problems (Borm, 1976). Closed-form solutions of special cases are available as a control for the complicated, non-linear method of calculation, see Chapter 3.

If the pseudo-elastic representation [Equation (1.27)] is discarded for the reasons stated in Section 1.2, the formal difficulties increase enormously. Very recently, however, two different approaches which promise an outcome have been developed independently: as demonstrated by Zienkiewicz and Pande in Chapter 5 of this book, the elasto-plastic finite element calculation can be supplemented with viscosity terms. This simplifies the iteration which is necessary because of the non-linearity, i.e. the viscosity contributes a numerical advantage. Leinenkugel (1976) demonstrates through tests and with the aid of the rate process theory that clay soil really represents a viscous fluid. Plastic behaviour of clays is really time-dependent, but the strain rates under constant load can be so low that they are more or less unnoticeable.

If the rate-independence of plasticity is dropped, certain contradictions between plastomechanics and thermodynamics can possibly be removed. With this is given hope for a unified concept, supported by and advantageous to geomechanics and finite element methods.

Hardly anything can be said on the *general coupling processes*, as practicable analytical or numerical methods are still unavailable. The fact that such processes are often of practical importance is characteristic of the present situation of geomechanics. Excavation of a tunnel can be taken as an example: by tunneling in bad, so-called 'interesting' rock, a creep-relaxation is triggered off, combined with loosening, swelling, temperature changes and disturbance of electrochemical fields. If such processes should ever be calculable numerically, which is rather doubtful, the only method not resulting in complete confusion should start from variational principles such as Equation (1.17).

To summarize again: many stabilizing transitions can be correctly and uniformally formulated through a variational principle and dealt with through the FEM. The process of finitization of time *via* finite differences can lead to violations of variational principles which are difficult to gauge. Plastic and viscous constitutive behaviour leads to non-linear displacement equations. Processes with material plastic hardening or linked non-mechanical influences or both have not yet been analysed sufficiently to be dealt with numerically in practical cases.

1.5 DESTABILIZING TRANSITIONS

A transition is regarded as destabilizing, when the dissipation potential D increases with time. This case undoubtedly occurs with a collapse. The inequality $D > 0$ therefore represents a necessary, but by no means sufficient, instability condition. The process may again be guided by a variational principle, but does not result in an equilibrium or a flow equilibrium. Processes with $D > 0$ and $D < 0$ can alternate if certain constitutive or boundary conditions or both prevail. The transition from primary to tertiary creep may be considered as an example. The focus will therefore be on the actual collapse processes.

Collapse theorems are available for the *plastic collapse* (Koiter, 1963). The static theorems will be dealt with first:

(1) No collapse can occur if any statically admissible stress field exists for the given loads.

(2) Collapse does occur if no statically admissible stress field exists for the given loads.

Because of their purely static character, both theorems do not give any information on the kinematics of a possible collapse. The first one, linked to the condition of normality, suffices for stability: the second is necessary for instability. To apply them, stress fields have to be constructed and varied; the variation is an economical necessity in the first case, while it is a matter of safety in the second (Gudehus, 1972).

It is little known that finite elements can be useful with the construction of admissible stress fields (which is very difficult both graphically and analytically). The equilibrium method with limiting condition discussed in Section 1.2 may be analytically incorrect, but can be used to obtain useful stress fields for the above collapse theorems, if used skilfully. The displacements obtained at the same time do not necessarily relate to any possible failure mechanism, but can also be quite realistic in their level and trend (with empirically proven suitable additional assumptions).

The construction of stress fields without displacements can be more consistent. With the aid of the boundary conditions the collapse theorems have to be interpreted as being extremum statements, and empirically founded additional information can be inserted as above. The stress field is constant elementwise, interrupted by statical discontinuities. The simplex algorithm can be used in determining extremum values. A first geotechnical application of this promising method is due to Schmitt (1974). Different from the method of characteristics frequently used in earth statics the stresses do not fulfill the limiting strength condition everywhere, but do not violate it anywhere either.

The kinematic collapse theorems are as follows:

(3) If any failure mechanism which is kinematically possible and which has a calculated excess of kinetic energy, occurs anywhere, collapse takes place.

(4) If no calculated excess of kinetic energy occurs in any failure mechanism which is admissible kinematically, no collapse takes place.

This situation is quite parallel to that with the static theorems. Here, nothing is said on the stress distribution in a possible collapse. The third theorem, linked with the condition of normality, is sufficient for a collapse, the fourth is necessary for stability. Failure mechanisms have to be constructed and varied for their application; in proving stability, the variation is a necessity for safety, in proving instability (e.g. for terramechanics) a necessity for economy.

Again it is hardly known that failure mechanisms can also be constructed with the aid of finite elements. A geomechanical example was worked out by

Frémond and Salençon (1973). With the usual division into triangular elements the result can be a long way from the correct one known here. The introduction of elements with different degrees of freedom therefore becomes necessary, as is being done successfully in a graphical method (Goldscheider and Gudehus, 1974). There are therefore definite hopes for different new finite element methods.

The methods discussed give no information on the actual sequence of a collapse. Substitute solutions are being constructed in the sense of the variational principle [Equation (1.17)], which may oversatisfy the required (restricted) stationarity to a certain extent. This is no real calculation of instability, as, for instance, a bifurcation problem. This is impossible anyway, because the second variation of energy expressions does not occur. Finite element solutions of correctly formulated bifurcation problems in geomechanics are not known to the author. The analytically correct solution of a semi-inverse bifurcation problem with experimental verification is meanwhile available (Vardoulakis *et al.*, 1977). The following points will provide a guide on what to consider in future finite element calculations of bifurcation problems:

(1) Special elements and special constitutive laws are necessary for kinematic discontinuities.

(2) The follower laws for boundary forces have to be known.

(3) The geometric terms play a decisive part.

Although relevant correct finite element methods are not yet available, several destabilising processes will be listed for which attempts at numerical treatment have already been made.

In the *plastic softening* of soil or rock the gradual or sudden development of fissures is a typical symptom. The partial result of a finite element calculation by Lee and Lo (1973) is reproduced in Figure 1.7. A pseudo-elastic equilibrium method with limiting strength condition was applied. The solution is kinematically incorrect as it does not contain the flow rule of the material and it gives little information on the failure mechanism, but it does give some idea of the softening process. In practice, the position is made more complex by the fact that softening is often time-dependent, owing to soil viscosity and pore water flow. No numerical methods have been developed for this as yet.

Brittle failure is closely related to plastic softening but can be even more complex because of acceleration effects and temperature influence. Finite element methods have also been used in fracture mechanics, but without sofar, to the author's knowledge, affecting geomechanics.

Liquefaction of saturated sand is difficult to tackle as an elastic–plastic process with coupled pore-water flow. The spontaneous liquefaction can

λ = relative mobilization of shear strength

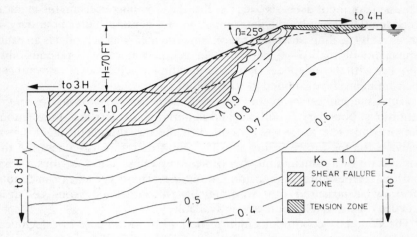

Figure 1.7   Shear stress level contours for a 70 ft slope for $K_0 = 1$; after Lee and Lo (1973)

also be regarded as bifurcation collapse and the successive one as fatigue. Constitutive equations for plastic hardening and softening are needed for the correct coupled formulation. For the reasons mentioned in Section 1.4 the finite element programs available sofar cannot be considered practically applicable for liquefaction.

Summarizing, this indicates the following for destabilizing processes: mechanically correct finite element methods for the description of a collapse in soil or rock are not available yet. On principle, stability bounds for the plastic collapse can be obtained *via* finite elements. For collapse processes as important as visco-plastic softening, brittle failure or liquefaction, finite element methods which are sufficiently reliable for practical geomechanics have not yet been found.

1.6   INPUT DATA AND HISTORY

Chapter 2 of this book contains an extensive discussion of the roles of fabric and stress history. This section can therefore suffice with a fairly brief survey, augmented by the scheme in Table 1.1. Obtaining geomechanical input data is not cheap; the user therefore ought to know as precisely as possible what he can and wants to achieve. There should really be no doubt on the importance of the input data for every geomechanical calculation. To start with, here are several characteristics common to all input data.

The most important decision to make—which is often overlooked with a discussion of input data—is over the classification into a certain mechanical category. This includes the determination of a fictitious outer boundary, if one is really dealing with a half space. Since no mechanical model is an exact equivalent of reality—in particular in geomechanics—the responsibility here lies with the engineer. Only after deciding which data are relevant can their influence be examined in more detail.

For a mechanical problem, the input data can be classified as initial conditions, boundary conditions and material characteristics; the sections can overlap. The *history* is contained in the initial state insofar as it is relevant for the future behaviour. The point therefore is to describe the initial state by a sufficient number of field variables—e.g. velocities, stress, density, temperature, composition, structure. These variables can fundamentally be measured (otherwise they have been defined wrongly), but in practice only a small proportion is available.

The boundary conditions ought to be known in the case of a technical problem at the free boundary. With the FEM fictitious boundaries at the sides and underneath often are added, of which nothing is known technically. It is therefore desirable to establish the boundary conditions applying here analytically. Since this does not often succeed, arbitrary, at best empirically supported boundary conditions must be added as input data.

The constitutive properties usually provide the most important data. There are two alternatives for determining these. With the *in situ* methods a mechanical process is created in the natural underground; from its analysis the constitutive parameters can be obtained in retrospect. This procedure is correct if one is dealing with a well-posed problem, which unfortunately is the exception in geomechanical practice. The FEM can again be applied in their interpretation, if the expense is justified.

With laboratory methods, the sample always has to be returned to its natural local initial state and then be subjected to the locally occurring process. This is the ideal requirement: in fact, the local initial state is not sufficiently well known and can rarely be reproduced faithfully enough, which also applies for the subsequent process. It is not relevant here to give more information on the laboratory research into constitutive equations, nor is there sufficient space. It may only be stated that the FEM can also be employed with this.

The, often quite considerable, *spatial scattering* in the constitutive properties is characteristic of geomechanics. It is obvious to employ statistics in this case (see Chapter 2), which has become quite common lately. Since the results and not the input data are the ones which are really required, statistical mechanics should be preferably applied. This opens a wide scope for finite element methods: in the manner of the Monte Carlo method the distribution of the constitutive parameters can be varied systematically in certain ranges of scattering and their effect be noted from the result. This can certainly only be done with well-posed problems and very simple boundary conditions.

A discussion of the individual categories in Tale 1.1 now follows. With the equilibrium problems no basic difficulties arise, if the correct thermostatic conditions are fulfilled; however, this is hardly ever the case. Adding the limit condition [Equation (1.3)] is mostly without problem as far as the input data are concerned, since the determination of the strength parameters is comparatively safe. Some more difficulties are experienced with the anisotropy which is often supplied, but this is not worth too much trouble: in favourable circumstances the calculated displacements can be correct in their sequence and tendency in the equilibrium method with limit conditions, and in that case anisotropy does not carry much importance.

The complete uncertainty of the pseudo-elastic approach, on the other hand, is conformed by the associated input data. If the constitutive behaviour really is elastic–plastic, the initial conditions have to be exactly known. The effects caused by stiffness which is otherwise faulty are discussed in Chapter 3. In addition, the following has to be noted: the actual stress-strain path is not known at all beforehand; this has to be guessed for the time being and can at best be corrected later. Particular caution is therefore advisable with the pseudo-elastic method.

The stationary processes provide the least difficulties with regard to the input data. Actual boundary conditions have to be transformed into a form which is suitable for stationary processes. The conditions at the fictitious lower and lateral boundaries present a problem only with oscillations. Stationary processes have again to be produced in laboratory tests to arrive at the constitutive parameters. The history problem is avoided because the memory with stationary processes is swept out as far as possible. The decisive input obviously consists in the confirmation that a stationary process exists at all.

The transition processes require considerably more input data than are normally available. This can be demonstrated with plastic hardening. For the elastic-ideally plastic body, the initial, so-called primary stress field is required as well as the constitutive characteristic values. As the chances of measuring *in situ* are very limited, the initial stress field usually has to be estimated or constructed through an assumed past history.

It need not be further explained that the results can be manipulated within considerable limits in this way. For a material with non-trivial hardening, i.e. hardening which is not only attributable to compaction, the initial distribution of the hidden variables is also needed. For this, sediment-petrography offers several procedures for assessing structure data, but while a translation into a correct mechanical formulation is not available, a relevant finite element calculation is of little purpose.

With creep-relaxation the additional problem may arise that the conditions at the fictitious boundary are needed for the entire process. A closed-form solution discussed in Chapter 3 illustrates that such cases exist. No solution to this problem is known yet.

The problem may be somewhat simpler for collapse if only the application of the collapse theorems is considered. Fairly reliable data for flow condition and flow rule can be obtained, but if frictional strength is essential, and the boundary conditions do not even allow an approximate statical determination, the initial inner stress field is needed; this again presents the same problem as the one with the plastic hardening. Boundary data, especially the follower law of the boundary forces, are frequently missing in the calculation of actual collapse processes.

Altogether, the difficulties in obtaining the necessary input data again increase in the problems in Table 1.1, *grosso modo* from left to right and from top to bottom. In many cases the finite element method therefore has to be ignored or a rather simpler problem tackled instead. The user is most obliged to estimate considerable proportions of the input because of an unknown geological past and the technical and financial limits of the measuring techniques.

1.7 NUMERICAL REQUIREMENTS

As far as numerical techniques are concerned, geomechanics has to make extensive use of outside help. This section only contains a very brief discussion for this reason.

For the required *finitization* of the space, the techniques from other branches are being successfully applied, as is particularly demonstrated in Chapter 10 of this book. Geomechanics has made some contributions for rock fissures, as can be seen in Chapter 11. The development of special elements for propagating cracks in soil and rock is still in its initial stages. Finitization of time is usually done by the difference method. In Chapter 8, linear problems are discussed in detail. Investigation of non-linear viscosity typical of soil has not yet been undertaken. Chapter 15 demonstrates that the interpretation of the output is by no means a trivial component, but one which is very important for a technical evaluation of the results of the FEM.

Numerical convergence and *uniqueness* can rarely be judged analytically; this book does not offer any contributions for these. At most variational principles may permit statements on convergence in the mean. If a problem is not well-posed mechanically, numerical convergence and uniqueness cannot usually be expected either. In individual cases numerical tests are recommended as a minimum requirement. This would be the case for the method illustrated in Chapter 13, for example.

The *economics* of the numerical methods are very important for the whole of geomechanical practice. Non-linearity and complicated geometry often cause the finite element methods to be quite expensive, if not too expensive. A summary of the results—as far as this is possible—in replacement formulae, diagrams and tables is therefore of considerable importance. All iterative techniques for non-linear problems (see for instance Chapters 4 and 13) have to stand the economic test as a very important criterion.

1.8 FINITE ELEMENT METHODS VERSUS REALITY

Finite element methods not only have to be economically sound but also precise enough in their technical information. This can only be checked through comparison of the results with actual cases. Such a comparison should be undertaken very carefully.

The ideal comparison should result in *verification*; this only succeeds after very thorough analyses and model tests which have been checked throughout. Analysis is necessary for the definite separation of what is to be verified. If only few data are chosen, a chance coincidence can easily cause the wrong inferences. Only a complete set of data for a certain case, and a well analysed, well-posed problem can therefore result in a real verification.

Obviously, a real verification is only possible in the laboratory. Here is an example. A finite element programme for the volume-conserving creep of saturated soft clay is assumed. Section 1.4 demonstrated that this problem can be formulated numerically, but has problems due to its non-linearity. The following procedure—which can obviously be applied for other cases— is recommended:

(1) The finitization of the space should be defined with reference to another problem which is related as closely as possible, but better understood. Here, an equilibrium problem with non-linear elastic constitutive behaviour is an obvious choice.

(2) The finitization of the time and the iterative solution of the non-linear equations needs to be new because of the special constitutive law. However, as closed-form solutions are available for special cases (see Chapter 3), these provide a comparable standard. The next step can only be taken if this comparison has been positive.

(3) The material has to be able to be reproduced at any time and therefore needs to be remoulded and reconsolidated. The most detailed investigation of the constitutive parameters takes place in bi-axial tests, but without rotation of principal axes.

(4) The same material has to be used for model tests, preferably with two-dimensional or axial-symmetrical deformation. Inner displacements can be measured with the lead-shot technique (e.g. Nahrgang, 1974).

At best, a satisfactory coincidence for the entire field results. What does this verify? Obviously at most the acceptability of the input assumptions, i.e. mainly the generalization of the constitutive law [Equation (1.26)] into Equations (1.27) and (1.28), for example.

This proves, as it should in other cases, that special constitutive assumptions can be verified with the FEM, which is very helpful. The FEM itself can only be verified analytically.

Such an extensive verification cannot be made for technical large-scale tests. A typical situation is described in Chapter 6. With any natural example, the input data are not completely available, but several have to be guessed. Measured data are only available for few points for a comparison with the calculation results. If the finite element calculation is part of a genuine prediction, a verification can still result, although not in the sense of natural science but of engineering. The lack of precise data and physical laws, for the judgement of the output is augmented by the engineer's estimate, which is perfectly legitimate and necessary.

From this stage there is only a small step to the *empirical modification* of finite element methods, if results do not at first coincide with reality. This much used and understandably popular method is not always legitimate, but often apparently unavoidable. That part of input data which has to be guessed or assumptions of mechanical laws can be modified. With repeated practical application, a FEM which has actually been incorrectly formulated can be successively improved empirically; Chapter 13 defends the success of this procedure. However, great caution is recommended for a transfer to different cases. Fundamentally, this procedure can and should result in a mechanically correct formulation.

Finally, the comparison with reality can prove so bad that the relevant FEM has to be *discarded*. An improvement of input data, mechanical and numerical formulation then could be undertaken, but in spite of all the computer method euphoria it has to be kept in mind that finite elements are by no means the only aid in geomechanics, nor are they always the best.

Acknowledgements

The review presented herein was prepared with the partial help of Dr P. Bloch (physics) and Mr H. Winter (mathematics), Karlsruhe, with financial support of the Volkswagenwerk Foundation, Hanover. The author also wishes to thank his sister, Gesa Beales, B.Ed., for the major portion of the English translation.

REFERENCES

Borm, G. W. (1976). 'Viscoplastic constititutive matrix corresponding to the hyperbolic sine creep law', *Proc. 2nd Intern. Conf. Num. Meth. Geomech., Engng. Found. Conf., ASCE Blacksburg.*

Desai, C. S. (1972). 'Overview, trends and projections: theory and applications of the finite element method in geotechnical engineering', State-of-the-Art Paper, *Proc. Sympos. Appl. of FEM in Geotechn. Engng.*, C. S. Desai (Ed.), USA Eng. Waterways Experiment Station, Vicksburg.

Frémond, M. and Salençon, J. (1973). 'Limit analysis by finite element methods', *Proc. Symp. on the Role of Plasticity in Soil Mechanics, Cambridge*, A. C. Palmer (ed.), 297.

Gallagher, R. H., Oden, J. T., Taylor, C., and Zienkiewicz, O. C. (Eds.), (1975). *Finite Elements in Fluids*, Vol. 1, Viscous Flow and Hydrodynamics, John Wiley, London.

Goldscheider, M. and Gudehus, G. (1974). 'Verbesserte Standsicherheitsnachweise', *Vorträge Baugrundtagung, Dtsche. Ges. f. Erd-und Grundbau, Essen* 99.

Gudehus, G. (1972). 'Lower and upper bounds for stability of earth-retaining structure', *Proc. 5th Europ. Conf. Soil Mech. and Found. Engng., Madrid*, 21.

Haupt, W. A. (1977). 'Influence Matrix Boundary-Condition for the Analysis of Dynamic Problems by FE-Method', *Proc. Vol. II Sympos. Num. Methods Soil and Rock Mech.*, Karlsruhe.

Koiter, W. T. (1963). 'General theorems for elastic–plastic solids', *Progress in Solid Mechanics*, Vol. 3, North Holland, Amsterdam.

Lebon, G. J. and Lambermont, J. H. (1973). 'Generalization of Hamilton's principle to continuous dissipative systems', *Journ. Chem. Physics*, **59**, 6, 2929.

Lee, C. F. and Lo, K. W. (1973). 'Stress analysis and slope stability in strain-softening materials', *Géotechnique, London*, **23**, 1–11.

Leinenkugel, H. J. (1976). 'Deformations- und Festigkeitsverhalten bindiger Erdstoffe unter Berücksichtigung der Viskosität', *Veröffentl. Inst. f. Bodenmech. und Felsmech., Universität Karlsruhe*, **66**.

Nahrgang, E. (1974). 'Verformungsverhalten eines weichen bindigen Untergrundes', *Veröffentl. Inst. f. Bodenmech. und Felsmech., Universität Karlsruhe*, **60**.

Painlevé, P. (1895). 'Lecons sur le frottement', *Comptes Rend. Acad. Sci., Paris*, **120**, 596.

Schmitt, G. P. (1974). 'Ein Beitrag zur Klarung des Tragverhaltens einfach verankerter Baugrubenwände'. *Mitt. d. Versuchsanst. f. Bodenmech. u. Grundb., TH Darmstadt*, **14**.

Vardoulakis, I. *et al.* (1977). 'The formation of slip bands in sand bodies as a bifurcation problem', submitted for publication in *Int. J. Num. and Anal. Meth. in Geomech.*

Chapter 2

Background to Mathematical Modelling in Geomechanics: The Roles of Fabric and Stress History

C. M. Gerrard

2.1 INTRODUCTION

The aim of this paper is to review briefly the background understanding of applied geomechanics problems that is essential to the successful formulation of mathematical models. Some of the aspects mentioned, particularly those relating to the roles of fabric and stress history, have not been adequately incorporated into existing mathematical models. In this sense the paper highlights areas in which improvements to mathematical models should be made in the future. Because of the wide scope of this task no attempt is made to compile a comprehensive treatise and many aspects such as dynamic effects and temperature effects are excluded altogether. Examples are chosen from the literature to illustrate the points considered most relevant. In the introductory section of the paper the various factors defining a particular geomechanics problem are discussed as input data to mathematical models. The difficulties arising from the variability of such data are also discussed. The main section of the paper is devoted to several aspects of the mechanical properties of earthen materials and in the final section a brief assessment is made of mathematical models in terms of their ability to incorporate these aspects. This is done in a qualitative way since detailed formulation of models is covered in other chapters in this book.

Four basic points of philosophy permeate the discussion and should be stated initially:

(1) That soil mechanics and rock mechanics are complementary aspects of a wider subject 'geomechanics'. Tsytovich (1975) defines geomechanics as '*the science that deals with the mechanical processes that take place in the earth's crust due to both natural factors and the influence of human activities*'. In this chapter the term *earthen materials* is used to describe those materials comprising soil and/or rock masses.

(2) That variability and fabric are important in geomechanics problems, these being often ignored or inadequately treated in many analyses. The variability applies not only to material properties but also to man-induced and natural loads and to environmental factors. The term *fabric* is considered to include a variety of features in the structure of earthen materials covering a wide range of scales. It is therefore analogous to the definition of petrofabrics given earlier by Friedman (1964) as '*the study of all structural and textural features of a rock as manifest in every recognizable rock element from the configuration of the crystal lattices of the individual mineral grains up to and including large-scale features which require field investigation*'. Fabric is intimately related to the deformation and stress history of an earthen mass and can be considered as 'inherent' i.e. including all deformations up to the process being studied, and 'induced', i.e. modifications caused by the process being examined. Friedman points out that in the interpretation of fabric two complementary approaches can be used: kinematic, based on the deformations associated with fabric change; and dynamic, based on the nature of the stresses at the time of deformation. The relationship between these two approaches is shown in Figure 2.1.

(3) That mathematical (or physical) modelling can provide the key to orderly and scientific advances in geomechanics when applied correctly as one component in an integrated cycle. Such a cycle has been proposed by

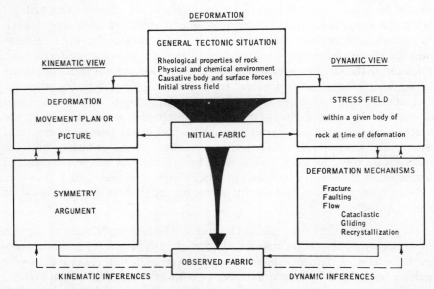

Figure 2.1　Kinematic and dynamic approaches to fabric interpretation. (After Friedman, 1964; Figure 1)

Aitchison (1973) for studies on expansive soils but is equally applicable to any geomechanics problem (see Figure 2.2). The features of the cycle are the establishment of hypotheses of material behaviour (constitutive relationships), the quantification of the various types of input data, the prediction and observation of full-scale performance of the engineering development,

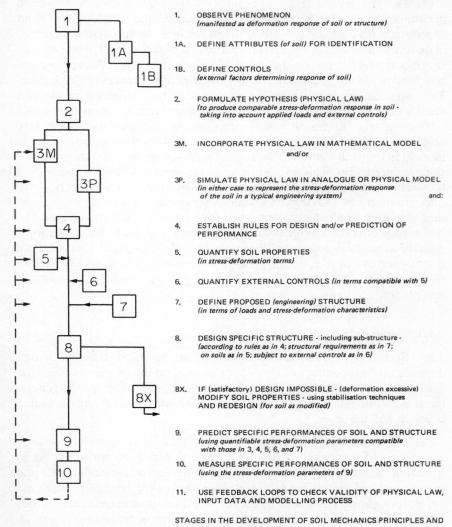

1.   OBSERVE PHENOMENON
    (manifested as deformation response of soil or structure)

1A.   DEFINE ATTRIBUTES *(of soil)* FOR IDENTIFICATION

1B.   DEFINE CONTROLS
    (external factors determining response of soil)

2.   FORMULATE HYPOTHESIS (PHYSICAL LAW)
    (to produce comparable stress-deformation response in soil -
    taking into account applied loads and external controls)

3M.   INCORPORATE PHYSICAL LAW IN MATHEMATICAL MODEL
    and/or

3P.   SIMULATE PHYSICAL LAW IN ANALOGUE OR PHYSICAL MODEL
    (in either case to represent the stress-deformation response
    of the soil in a typical engineering system)   and:

4.   ESTABLISH RULES FOR DESIGN and/or PREDICTION OF
    PERFORMANCE

5.   QUANTIFY SOIL PROPERTIES
    (in stress-deformation terms)

6.   QUANTIFY EXTERNAL CONTROLS *(in terms compatible with 5)*

7.   DEFINE PROPOSED *(engineering)* STRUCTURE
    (in terms of loads and stress-deformation characteristics)

8.   DESIGN SPECIFIC STRUCTURE - including sub-structure -
    (according to rules as in 4; structural requirements as in 7;
    on soils as in 5; subject to external controls as in 6)

8X.   IF (satisfactory) DESIGN IMPOSSIBLE - (deformation excessive)
    MODIFY SOIL PROPERTIES - using stabilisation techniques
    AND REDESIGN *(for soil as modified)*

9.   PREDICT SPECIFIC PERFORMANCES OF SOIL AND STRUCTURE
    (using quantifiable stress-deformation parameters compatible
    with those in 3, 4, 5, 6, and 7)

10.   MEASURE SPECIFIC PERFORMANCES OF SOIL AND STRUCTURE
    (using the stress-deformation parameters of 9)

11.   USE FEEDBACK LOOPS TO CHECK VALIDITY OF PHYSICAL LAW,
    INPUT DATA AND MODELLING PROCESS

STAGES IN THE DEVELOPMENT OF SOIL MECHANICS PRINCIPLES AND
SOIL ENGINEERING PRACTICES

Figure 2.2   Components in an integrated geomechanics study. (After Aitchison, 1973; Figure 2a).

and feed-back to check the validity of the physical laws, input data and modelling process.

The plea for an integrated approach to completing the scientific cycle is not new but is still largely ignored. This leads to the unbalanced and wasteful development of some components in the cycle.

(4) That the desired degree of accuracy in the prediction of the full-scale performance provides an important constraint in the development of an appropriate mathematical model. Models are by their very nature approximate representations of material response and hence a proof of the inaccuracy of a model is merely a statement of the obvious. The real questions are how inaccurate the prediction is and what the consequences of this will be. Two extreme approaches to the problem of the definition of desired accuracy can be thought of as that of the 'engineer' and that of the 'scientist'.

The engineer's approach, when extrapolated to its logical conclusion, is to employ within the time-scale of the project that level of sophistication in modelling that will minimize the total cost (investigation, design, construction, maintenance). This implies that the engineer will think in terms of a hierarchy of models in which the more sophisticated (and hence expensive) ones are used when savings of a commensurate nature are likely to accrue. Since in most applied problems the objective is to prevent or limit the occurrence of certain movements, the engineer is likely to be preoccupied with the accurate prediction of these. On the other hand, the scientist is not constrained to a time-scale and seeks to understand all aspects of behaviour to an extremely high level of prediction, e.g. 95 or 99 per cent levels of acceptance.

2.1.1　Input data to mathematical models

The effectiveness of mathematical modelling in applied geomechanics depends on the adequacy of the input data and on the degree to which the mathematical formulation reflects the realities of the prototype. In general there are four interacting factors that define any applied geomechanics problem and these are:

(1) *The properties of the earthen mass (and those of the materials comprising associated structures).* Although earthen materials comprise the broad spectrum of hard rock, broken rock, weathered rock, residual soil and transported soil, certain fundamental characteristics of mechanical response apply throughout. These include the role of fabric symmetries in anisotropic response and fabric changes in non-linear and stress dependent response. Similar patterns of behaviour at failure are observed with dilatancy and the general application of criteria of the Coulomb–Navier type. The presence of

moisture affects mechanical response in terms of the effective stress law, flow laws, and the hydration of minerals.

(2) *The loadings imposed by the engineering development or natural phenomena.* These vary greatly in their nature, intensity and duration. External loads may be static, such as dead weight, tectonic stresses or hydrostatic pressure, or transient as in the case of wheel loads, wind, wave and earthquake. Internal loads can result from self weight, static and transient pore pressures and inhibited swelling or shrinkage associated with pore fluid or temperature variations. In the past, mathematical models have required severe idealizations on the representations of loads. The effect of these idealizations on the accuracy of predicting behaviour should be determined so that improved idealizations can be introduced for cases where the accuracy should be improved.

(3) *The overall geometry.* The main categories of external geometry are the surface loaded mass, the slope and the underground opening, these occurring either separately or in combination. Internal geometry corresponds with macro-fabric elements and includes the location and continuity of folds, faults and joints and the strike, dip and dimensions of beds, layers and zones.

(4) *The environment.* The main environmental factors relevant to geomechanics problems are the initial total stress and pore pressure conditions, the time patterns of rainfall and temperature changes and the nature of the pore-fluid electrolyte.

The techniques for the *in situ* measurement of positive pore pressures are well developed and equipment is now available for reliable measurement of *in situ* suctions (e.g. Richards, 1971). Many difficulties have been experienced in attempts to measure the *in situ* state of total stress in earthen materials. These are due to the problem of inserting a measuring device in a manner to cause minimal, or at least predictable, disturbance and to the apparent variability of values, partly due to topography and internal geometry, and to discontinuities across fabric features such as faults, joints and fissures. Techniques are better developed for rocks than for soils and, as an example, Worotnicki, Alexander, *et al.* (1975) list the results from several *in situ* stress measuring techniques associated with the case study of an underground copper mine. With regard to soils the use of the pressuremeter, particularly the self boring type (e.g. Hughes, Wroth, *et al.*, 1975) appears to hold great promise as a reliable method of *in situ* stress measurement.

Geological history is of great importance in the understanding of current *in situ* stress states and their relationship to previous stress values. The occurrence of relatively high *in situ* lateral stresses is common in deposits of earthen materials and may result from a variety of mechanisms such as change in total stress (e.g. removal of overburden), change in pore water pressure (e.g. water table elevation, pumping, desiccation due to plant life), and fabric changes (e.g. secondary compression, weathering). As an example, the cutting of a river valley can lead to the development of large stress concentrations as predicted by Worotnicki (1969). The case shown in Figure 2.3 is for a 90° V notch where initially the horizontal and vertical stresses are equal. Poor estimation of the *in situ* lateral stresses (Dodd and Anderson, 1972), or the maximum previous vertical stress (Diaz-Padilla and Vanmarke, 1973), can cause serious errors in subsequent predictions of behaviour of slopes and building foundations respectively.

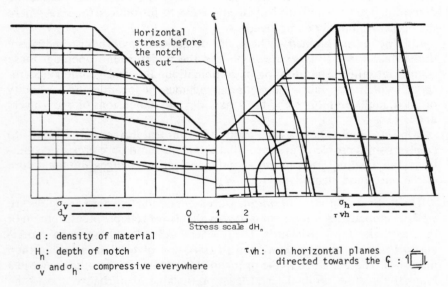

Figure 2.3   Influence of a valley on *in-situ* stresses. (After Worotnicki, 1969; Figure 11)

The accuracy of prediction of a mathematical model depends very largely on the adequacy and relevance of the input data. Since the properties of earthen materials are, in general, stress-path dependent, it is of considerable value to examine the way in which principal stress magnitudes and orientations vary from their initial conditions as typical engineering developments proceed. These are shown in Figure 2.4 for the three categories of external geometry. For the case of the sealed pavement, the changes in the dry subgrade are produced by seasonal climatic factors (Southern Hemisphere, temperate), whilst in all other cases the changes are produced by the placing additional load or by further excavation. It will be noted that in a given

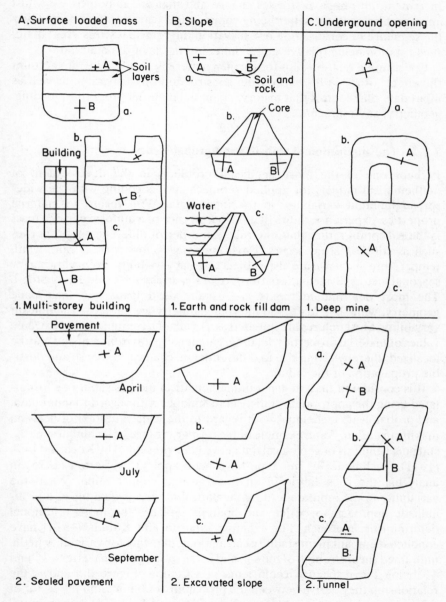

Figure 2.4 Field stress paths for geomechanics problems (surface loaded mass, slope, underground opening

increment, all principal stresses change and that one may increase whilst another decreases, the latter being common in excavation situations. Over the sequence of construction or excavation the principal stress axes rotate, such rotation being relative to the 'inherent' fabric of the material.

Constitutive relationships for earthen materials should take into account the effects of stress history, during construction or excavation, as well as input data that control that history, i.e. initial material properties, loading, geometry, environment.

2.1.2 The application of statistics and probabilistics

Perhaps one of the most significant problems in the development of mathematical models for applied geomechanics is coping with the widespread inherent variability in the input data. With regard to material properties, experience shows that the occurrence of a uniform earthen mass is the exception rather than the rule. An order of difference in properties such as stiffness often occurs. Environmental factors such as rain, wind, temperature and wave are also subject to great variability, even allowing for seasonal factors. Systematic patterns of *in situ* stresses are seldom recorded. The most determinate inputs are usually dead loads and man-made geometry, while live loads and internal geometry are subject to significant variability. Most failures are initiated as a result of a combination of extreme values of material properties, loading, geometry or environment and may be localized, thereby giving rise to differential mechanical response and possible propagation of the failure.

It is considered that, in general, mathematical models should be formulated using the appropriate statistical techniques with regard to input data, and probabilistic techniques with regard to the wider question of decision making in design. As an example of the former, a range of techniques for the statistical analysis of geological data have been presented by Koch and Link (1971). Techniques of this type have been applied by Barton (1975) in analyzing the rock fabric in an underground copper mine. When the variability in the input data to mathematical models is quantified, a probabilistic approach to design and analysis replaces the more traditional deterministic approach. For example, Matsuo and Kurada (1974) have conducted embankment stability calculations, allowing for variability in the undrained shear strength of the soil and in the mobilized shear stress, V_c and V_s being the respective coefficients of variation. Figure 2.5 shows the relationship they derive between the probability of failure and the factor of safety for various levels of the coefficients V_c and V_s. In another example, Fraser and Wardle (1975) have used program FOCALS (Wardle and Fraser, 1975), to analyze the loaded rectangular raft resting on a layered strata

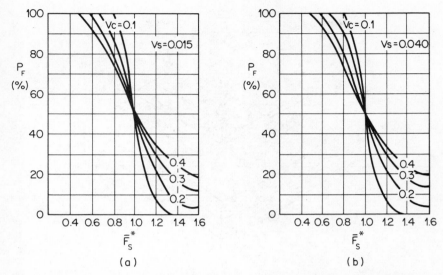

Figure 2.5 Probabilistic embankment analysis—factor of safety versus probability of failure. (After Matsuo and Kurada, 1974; Figure 17a, b)

shown in Figure 2.6a. Coefficients of variation for the modulus of the raft, the modulus of the soil and the loads were adopted as 0·1, 0·3 and 0·14 respectively. The bending moments at point A in the raft were calculated by allowing each of the moduli or loads to vary in turn and the results are shown in Figure 2.6b. In this figure M_x indicates average values of the independent variables and σ_{M_x} indicates the standard deviation.

In recent years it has become popular to apply Bayes' theorem to decision theory in geomechanics design and analysis (e.g. Folayan, Hoeg, *et al.*, 1970). The method relies on the assessment of prior probabilities and it is here that the method is most open to abuse, particularly in cases where prior probabilities are assumed rather than being based on data. This warning has been sounded by Pahl (1975) who states that '*when prior assumptions are made about values of parameters in any mathematical model the biases in the conclusions are unknown. The credibility of the conclusions will always be suspect until confirmatory objective evidence is made available*'. He further suggests that errors of this type are less likely to occur in applying the second moment reliability index proposed by Hasofer (1974a, b). However, to apply this index, enough replicates to give reasonably good estimates of the means, variances and correlations will always be required.

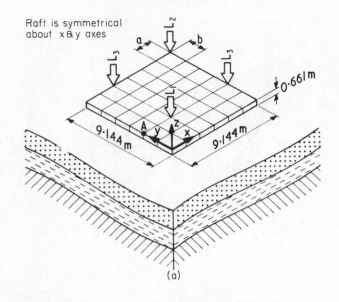

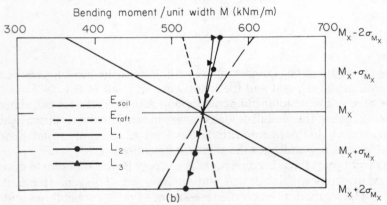

Figure 2.6 Bending moments in a raft—variable loads and moduli: (a) raft, layered deposit and loads, (b) effect of variation on bending moment. (After Fraser and Wardle, 1975; Figures 11 and 14)

2.2 MECHANICAL PROPERTIES OF EARTHEN MATERIALS

Of the four main inputs to mathematical models emphasis is given in this paper to the mechanical properties of earthen materials particularly highlighting the importance of fabric and stress history. The following major aspects of mechanical properties are studied by reference to illustrative examples:

(1) The symmetries in the fabrics of earthen materials and their reflection in geometric and mechanical anisotropies.

(2) An example of the relationships between geological history, *in situ* stress patterns, and mechanical properties.

(3) The influence of initial fabric and stress induced fabric changes on the degree of anisotropy and magnitude of the mechanical stiffness.

(4) Creep as a fabric change phenomenon.

(5) Strength and dilatancy related to fabric.

(6) The role of pore fluids.

2.2.1 Fabric of earthen materials—geometric and physical anisotropies

The fabrics of earthen materials are intimately related to the mechanical processes occurring during their formation or test loading. These processes can be examined in terms of the deformations that occur (kinematic) or the stresses that are acting (dynamic) (Friedman, 1964, see Figure 2.1). Studies linking the fabrics and the processes have been conducted for some time in rocks (e.g. Knopf, 1957; Turner and Weiss, 1963) and have been applied more recently by Lafeber (Barton, 1973) with regard to soils. Typical deformations that occur include folding, faulting, sliding, sedimentation and consolidation. In simple terms these can be associated with combinations and permutations of the three fundamental types of stress: tension, compression, and/or shear.

Strains that will accompany the stresses will depend on an interaction between the symmetry of the applied stress and the symmetry of the defects that are relevant to the straining process and its scale. In a small laboratory sample of marble these defects may be micro-fissures associated with the preferred orientation of the crystallographic planes of calcite, while in a radical jacking test in the field they may be joints and fissures at spacing of the order of 0·3 m. If the strain is continued to relatively high levels, the initial arrangement of the defects is suppressed and the symmetry of the new defects becomes closely related to the symmetry of the applied stress system.

Based on a combined kinematic (deformation) and dynamic (applied stresses) consideration, the symmetry patterns that may be produced in the fabric of earthen materials are as follows (see Figure 2.7).

Triclinic

This system has no plane or axis of symmetry and would be produced by complex deformations. For example, a triclinic symmetry may arise from compression in direction 1, with differential restraints in directions 2 and 3,

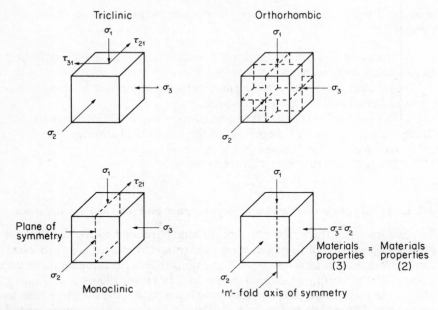

Figure 2.7 Common symmetry types—triclinic, monoclinic, orthorhombic and n-fold axis

accompanied by shear components acting in directions 2 and 3 on the plane having its normal to axis 1.

Monoclinic

In this there is a single plane of symmetry such that any two directions symmetric with respect to this plane are equivalent. A symmetry such as this would be produced by, for example, compression in direction 1 with differential restraint in directions 2 and 3, accompanied by a shear component in the direction 2 acting on the plane having its normal to axis 1. Typical examples are given in Figures 2.8 and 2.9.

For the deposit of pebbles and cobbles shown in Figure 2.8, the stream direction is indicated, and this case is typical of the comprehensive study of sedimentary deposits carried out by Johansson (1965). He found that monoclinic or near-monoclinic symmetries were usual, and that the direction of orientation of long axes depended on the nature of process involved in the formation of the deposit. When particles were transported in contact with a stable frictional substratum they tended to be aligned transverse to the direction of movement. However, if they were moved in a transporting medium without contact with such a substratum, or involved in a mass movement due to gravity, then the long axis tended to be aligned parallel with the direction of movement.

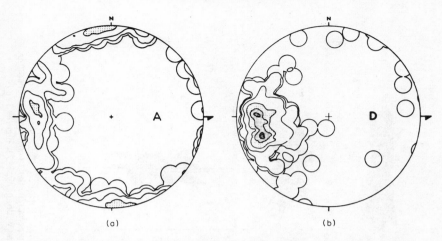

Figure 2.8 Monoclinic symmetry in the arrangement of pebbles and cobbles in a stream deposit: (a) long axis orientation, (b) dip of flat pebbles and cobbles. (After Johansson, 1965; Figure 8)

The example shown in Figure 2.9 is for a beach sand reported by Lafeber and Willoughby (1971). This case is instructive in that if the particle orientations alone are considered (Figure 2.9b) then a higher order of symmetry is suggested. However, because of the angle between the imbrication and the bedding (Figure 2.9a), the overall fabric must be described as monoclinic with a vertical plane of symmetry normal to the coastline.

Orthorhombic

Here there are three mutually perpendicular planes of symmetry and this would be produced, for example, by compressions of different magnitudes in the three directions parallel to the normals to the three planes. An example of this (Figure 2.10) was produced from the analysis of the joint orientation of a columnated granite porphyry (Berger, 1966). Two intersecting joint sets are prominent, these being near vertical and approximately at right angles to each other.

n-fold axis

For this case there is an axis of symmetry such that any direction normal to the axis is equivalent. An example of how this could be produced is by compression in the direction of this axis, the material properties and deformation restraints being equal in all normal directions. An aspect of the fabric of a marble is chosen as an example. Thill, Willard, *et al.* (1969) show that preferred orientation of the calcite *c* axes in Yule marble has an *n*-fold

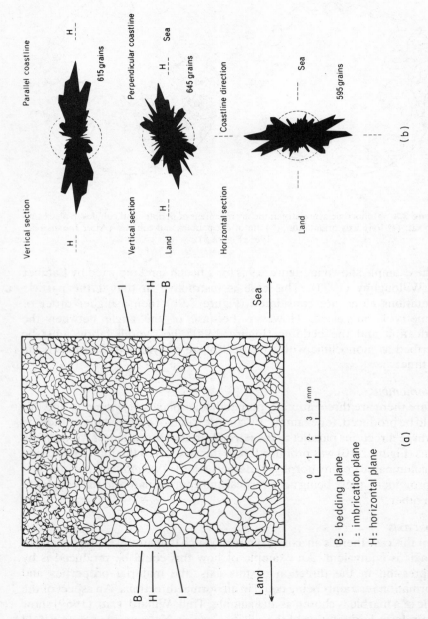

Figure 2.9 Monoclinic symmetry in the fabric of a beach sand: (a) vertical cross-section perpendicular to coastline. (B = bedding, I = imbrication), (b) preferred orientation of long axes (5° intervals). (After Lafeber and Willoughby, 1971; Figures 3 and 4)

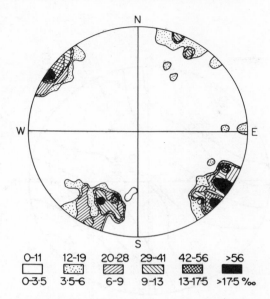

Figure 2.10　Orthorhombic symmetry in the orientation of joints in granite porphyry (×3200). (After Berger, 1966; Figure 2)

axis of symmetry (Figure 2.11a), while in later work (Thill, Bur, *et al.*, 1973) it is shown that the microcrack pattern in Tennessee marble also exhibits *n*-fold axis of symmetry, this being parallel to the pattern of the *c*-axes.

Spherical

All directions are equivalent and such cases rarely occur in nature. It requires that there be no dominant direction with regard to deformations and stresses during the formation of the earthen material. (Earthen materials having spherical symmetry in all of their fabric elements would be expected to behave in an isotropic fashion.)

Soils and rocks usually undergo several different formation processes and there is a tendency for the resultant fabric to retain some aspects of the symmetries of all such processes. This leads to the development of low orders of symmetry so that the fabrics of many natural earthen materials are triclinic or monoclinic (e.g. Knopf, 1957; Turner and Weiss, 1963; Friedman, 1964; Barton, 1973; Johansson, 1965). The fabrics of laboratory prepared samples of earthen materials or earthen-like materials will reflect the high order of symmetry usually associated with laboratory formation processes. Extreme care is therefore needed in extrapolating the results of

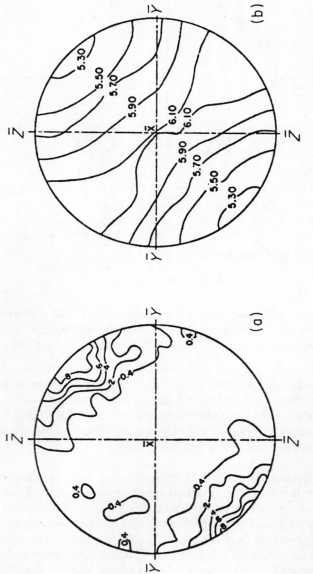

Figure 2.11 '*n*' fold symmetry in the fabric and mechanical response of Yule marble: (a) preferred orientation of calcite *c*-axes, (b) longitudinal velocity variations with direction of propagation. (After Thill, Willard, *et al.*, 1969; Figures 5 and 6)

tests on such materials to field situations where low orders of symmetry are the rule.

Natural fabrics reported in the literature are probably biased away from the lowest orders because of the difficulty in recognition and analysis, particularly in view of the fact that different elements of a fabric are often associated with different scales. When the symmetry and scale of fabric elements are common to various deformation processes these become most pronounced in the resultant fabric. However, a 'fading memory' mechanism also exists whereby, other factors being equal, the effect of the more recent formation process takes precedence. This can be clearly seen from the work of Lafeber (1969) who examined the orientation of planar pores in two samples of heavy montmorillonitic clay, one of which had been subject to the action of heavy vehicular traffic load. The equal-area projections of the normals to the planes are shown in Figure 2.12. The untrafficked sample (Figure 2.12a) shows a predominance of subhorizontal planar pores, while for the sample subject to the traffic load (Figure 2.12b) there are two sets of planar pores dipping at 30°–40° in opposite directions. These two sets of planes have dip directions trending sub-parallel with the traffic direction. The combination of vertical and shear loads applied by traffic would produce stress patterns in the soil that conform to the observed patterns of discontinuities in the trafficked sample.

Another example of a superimposed deformation on an original fabric is given by Dreyer (1972) who quotes results for the stressing of marble with non-equal principal stresses. The fabric diagrams are shown in Figures 2.13a and 2.13b for the undeformed and deformed states respectively. In Figure 2.13b the correlation with the symmetry of the imposed stress pattern is clearly evident, although some remnants of the original fabric can also be seen.

Different fabric elements at similar or at different scales may have similar or different orders of symmetry. Several workers have reported cases where the symmetries in large scale fabric elements have been reflected in the mechanical behaviour during tests on smaller-scale samples. (Boretti-Onyszkiewicz, 1966; Paulmann, 1966; Maurino and Limousin, 1966). This implies that the symmetries in the small-scale fabric elements that control behaviour during such tests are similar to those observed at large scale. The sandstone examined by Boretti-Onyszkiezicz (1966) had open macro-fractures oriented parallel to older calcite-filled macro-fractures, both sets being oriented at large angles to the bedding. Unconfined compression tests were performed on unfractured material so as to promote planar fractures normal to the bedding but free to occur in any azimuth with respect to the bedding. The fractures induced by this test loading trended parallel to the main sets of macrofractures as shown in Figure 2.14.

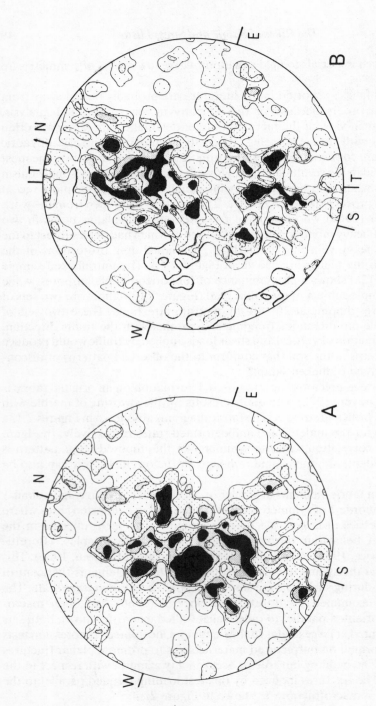

Figure 2.12 Planar pore patterns for trafficked and untrafficked clay: (a) sample outside wheel track, (b) sample within wheel track. (After Lafeber, 1969; Figure 6)

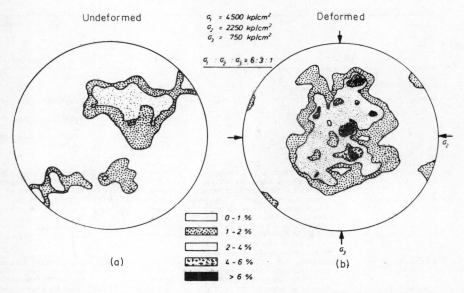

Figure 2.13 Fabric patterns for marble: (a) Undeformed, (b) Deformed by non-equal principal stresses. (After Dreyer, 1972; Figure 38)

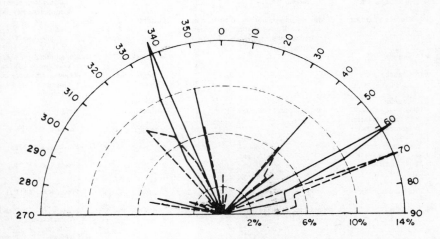

Figure 2.14 Correlation between directions of field macro fractures (solid line) and fractures induced by testing (dashed line). (Reproduced, by permission, from Boretti-Onyszkiewicz, 1966; Figure 4)

Finite Elements in Geomechanics

Table 2.1   Stress–strai

Material	Fabric Description	Symmetry	Test method
(a) QUARTZOFELDSPATHIC ROCKS			
1.1 Barre granite			Longitudinal and shear wave velocities
		Isotropic	Uniaxial compression = 0
1.2		'n' fold axis parallel to direction of uniaxial stress (axis 3)	Uniaxial compression = 40 MPa
1.3 Barre granite	Orthorhombic with the three planes of symmetry being those of least cleavage resistance (rift), intermediate (grain), and greatest resistance (hardway). The normals to these planes are respectively the directions of 3, 2 and 1. Concentration of microfractures in the rift plane	Orthorhombic—planes of symmetry in stiffness properties similar to those for microfractures	Laboratory tests—oriented samples uniaxially loaded to 67 MPa at a rate of 6·7 MPa/min. Strains recorded by bonded strain gauges. Results quoted are secant moduli
1.4 Stanstead granite			
1.5 Laurentian granite	One principal axis of stiffness coincides with rift axis but the other two are offset by 60° from the grain and hardway axes	Orthorhombic?	
1.6 Alvarenga	Joint systems often in two or three intersecting steeply dipping sets. In some cases the two intersecting sets are at right-angles, suggesting an othorhombic structure	Orthorhombic in some cases. Axis 3 i.e. approximately vertical and approximately parallel to the joints is often direction of least stiffness. Axes 1 and 2 in some cases are approximately normal to the joint sets	Laboratory tests—oriented samples uniaxially loaded to 19·6 MPa. Strains recorded by bonded strain guages. Results quoted are secant moduli
1.7 granite			
1.8 Altolindoso			
1.9 granite			
1.10			
1.11 Vilarinho gneiss–			
1.12 granite			
1.13 Granite Alto Rabagao Dam	Microfissures on horizontal plane. Axis 3 is vertical	Orthorhombic?	Laboratory tests on prisms, together with field plate loading tests in galleries
1.14 Granite Vilar Dam	Microfissures on horizontal plane. Axis 3 is vertical, axis 1 is horizontal in the direction of the river, axis 2 is normal to river	Orthrhombic?	
1.15 Granite		Isotropic	Longitudinal and shear wave velocities on cube samples
1.16 Granite		Orthorhombic (axes 1, 2, 3)	Resonant frequency and ultrasonic pulse tests on oriented cores
1.17 Granite		Orthorhombic?	
1.18 Granite gneiss	Layering parallel to plane 12	Orthorhombic?	Field tests with radial jack. Pressure ≈ 5 MPa
1.19 (Average of three)			Pressure ≈ 5 MPa
1.20 Granite gneiss			
1.21 (Compact)			
1.22 Gneiss with shale			Pressure ≈ 2·5 MPa
1.23 (Average of two)			
1.24 Gneiss (slaty)			Pressure ≈ 4 MPa
1.25			
1.26 Mylonite gneiss			Pressure ≈ 1.5 MPa
1.27			
1.28 Gneiss	Layering parallel to plane 12. Slightly fissured	Orthorhombic	Laboratory compression tests on oriented samples — Pressure = 0–2 MPa
1.29			Pressure = 49–59 MPa
1.30 Gneiss		Orthorhombic?	
1.31 Gneiss		'n' fold axis?	

proerties of earthern materials

Test sample size (mm)	GPa						ν_{12} (ν_{21})	ν_{13} (ν_{31})	ν_{23} (ν_{32})	Reference
	E_1	E_2	E_3	G_{23}	G_{13}	G_{12}				
100 dia. × 100 long	36.7		36.7	18.3		18.3	0.036			Nur and Simmons (1969)
	43.6		56·2	24·2		20·1	0·086	0·070 (0·085)		
29 dia. × 43 long	46·8	36·6	33·7							Douglas and Voight (1969)
	47·5	35·5	25·9							
50 × 50 × 150 prisms	78·0	42·8	30·2							Peres Rodriques (1966)
	37·5	17·5	24·3							
	37·3	42·8	30·4							
	49·8	36·2	28·5							
	26·4	34·2	41·2							
	48·0	42·2	38·3							
	48·5	34·6	36·3							
	3·62	3·07	1·58							Serafim (1963)
	14·4	5·99	3·24							
	81·9			33·5						Alexandrov, *et al.* (1969)
54 dia. × 305 long	42·4	44·5	30·3	17·2	16·9	19·6	0·168 (0·176)	0·203 (0·146)	0·209 (0·141)	Duvall (1965)
	27·4	44·2	30·4							Obert and Duvall (1967)
2200 dia. × 2000 long	53·0		15·0							Lauffer and Seeber (1961), Seeber (1970)
	(41·0)		(11.0)							Unbracketed figures correspond to recovered deformation, bracketed figures correspond to total deformations
	32·0		23·0							
	(28·0)		(21·0)							
	37·0		6·1							
	(28·0)		(3·1)							
	14·6		6·0							
	(9·8)		(2·0)							
	6·9		2·1							
	(5·9)		(0·93)							
10 × 10 × 30 prisms	17·3	15·1	7·3	6·2	6·4	7·6	0·005	0·058	0·087	Tremmel and Widmann (1970)
	40·7	42·7	36·2	12·1	15·2	18·5	0·318	0·367	0·351	
	23·1	12·4	18·6							Obert and Duvall (1967)
	48·9		9·0							Stepanov and Batugin (1967)

Table 2.1—*continued*

Material	Fabric description	Symmetry	Test method
1.32 Gneiss	Layering parallel to plane 12	'n' fold axis (axis 3)	Uniaxial unconfined tensile tests of oriented samples. Tangent moduli taken at half strength
(b) BASIC/LITHIC			
2.1 Basalt		Isotropic	Longitudinal and shear wave velocities on cube sample
2.2 Basalt		Isotropic	Resonant frequency and ultrasonic pulse methods
2.3 Basalt 2.4 2.5	Preferred orientation of mineral grains with optical axes oriented perpendicular to direction of tectonic compression, parallel to direction of tension	'n' fold axis parallel to the direction of tectonic compression (axis 3)	Laboratory tests— longitudinal and shear wave velocities
2.6 Peridotite			
2.7 Dunite	Strong concentration of Olivine a axes and girdles of b and c axes	'n' fold axis of symmetry parallel to a axes (i.e. axis 3)	Longitudinal and transverse wave velocities. Confining pressures from 0·1 GPa to 1·0 GPa
2.8 Dunite	Strong concentration of all three Olivine axes (a, b, c)	Orthorhombic $\begin{pmatrix} a \text{ axis} = \text{axis 3} \\ b \text{ axis} = \text{axis 2} \\ c \text{ axis} = \text{axis 1} \end{pmatrix}$	Longitudinal and transverse wave velocities. Confining pressures from 0·1 GPa to 1·0 GPa Results quoted are for a confining pressure of 0·4 GPa
2.9 Dunite		Orthorhombic	Longitudinal and shear wave velocities on cube samples
2.10 Olivinite		Orthorhombic	Longitudinal and shear wave velocities on cube samples
2.11 Enstatite		Orthorhombic	Longitudinal and shear wave velocities on cube samples
2.12 Andesite		Isotropic	Laboratory tests—uniaxial compression and tension tests, together with torsion tests. Strain gauges attached to samples
2.13 Hornbendite		Orthorhombic	Longitudinal and shear wave velocities on cube samples
2.14 Eclogite	Preferred orientation of pyroxene grains relative to axis 3	'n' fold axis parallel to axis 3	Longitudinal and shear wave velocities on cube samples
2.15 Zoisitic prasinite		Orthorhombic	Longitudinal and shear wave velocities on cube samples
2.16 Bandera			Ultrasonic longitudinal and shear wave velocities. Sample subject to range of hydrostatic pressures— ≈0·0 MPa pressure
2.17 Sandstone	Preferred orientation of cracks parallel to bedding plane		68·9 MPa pressure
2.18 Berea			≈0·0 MPa pressure
2.19 Sandstone			68·9 MPa pressure
2.20 Sandstones (average of 2)	Bedding plane is plane 12	Orthorhombic?	
2.21 Siltstone	Direction of bedding coincides with maximum wave velocity, minimum velocity perpendicular to bedding (i.e. axis 3)	'n' fold axis perpendicular to bedding?	Laboratory tests— longitudinal and shear wave velocities
2.22 Tuffaceous sandstone			
2.23 Arkansas sandstone	Breaks along bedding at iron oxide deposits spaced 50–150 mm apart. Bedding is plane 12	Orthorhombic	Triaxial compression tests

Test sample size (mm)	GPa						v_{12} (v_{21})	v_{13} (v_{31})	v_{23} (v_{32})	Reference
	E_1	E_2	E_3	G_{23}	G_{13}	G_{12}				
9.7 dia. × 68 long	$5E_3$		E_3							Barla and Goffi (1974)
	62.9			31.4						Alexandrov, *et al.* (1969)
5 × 76 × 54	98.0						0.28			Kaarsberg (1968)
60 dia. × 120 long	42		40		18	18	0.16	0.14		Skorikova (1965)
	53		49		21	22	0.20	0.22		
	46		34		16	20	0.15	0.20		
	94		53		21	34	0.38	0.31 (0.28)		Skorikova (1965)
25 dia. × 60 long	155	155	176.8	70	70	62	0.240	0.400	0.308	Christensen and Ramananantoandro (1971)
25 dia. × 60 long	190	156	216	75	80	74				Christensen and Ramananantoandro (1971)
	101.0	87.4	62.0	24.1	23.8	36.2	0.185	0.258	0.329	Alexandrov, *et al.* (1969)
	171.0	160.0	151.0	73.2	70.4	68.4	0.314	0.333	0.274	Alexandrov, *et al.* (1969)
	157.0	148.0	134.0	51.6	55.6	60.9	0.261	0.244	0.270	Alexandrov, *et al.* (1969)
	32			14			0.153			Nishimatsu (1970)
	115.0	106.0	98.0	36.4	38.0	42.5	0.278	0.276	0.317	Alexandrov, *et al.* (1969)
	142.0	142.0	178.0	58.5	58.5	55.4	0.283	0.204	0.204	Alexandrov, *et al.* (1969)
	135.5	125.0	113.0	63.5	51.1	45.5	0.228	0.354	0.364	Alexandrov, *et al.* (1969)
	18.6		12.4		7.3	8.1	0.14	0.25 (0.16)		King (1968)
	28.9		26.2		12.0	12.7	0.14	0.19 (0.18)		
	19.3		14.5		7.0	8.5	0.14	0.30 (0.22)		
44 dia. × 89 long	34.4		34.4		14.6	14.6	0.18	0.18 (0.18)		
	8.7	10.1	6.5							Obert and Duvall (1967)
60 dia. × 120 long	42		39		17	17	0.23	0.28		Skorikova (1965)
	71		57		28	28	0.27	0.25 (0.02)		
9 dia. × 38 long	31.2	32.8	19.4				0.14 (0.15)	0.21 (0.14)	0.18 (0.11)	Chenevert and Gatlin (1965)

Table 2.1—*continued*

Material	Fabric description	Symmetry	Test method
(c) PELITIC CLAY			
3.1 Sandy clay shale	Two fracture systems: (a) dip 30°–90°, strike SSE (b) dip 30°–90°, strike SW	Orthorhombic fabric but not aligned with orthorhombic symmetry of test.	Field tests—cube samples in the invert of test adit. Horizontal loads by flat jacks in slots, vertical loads by hydraulic jacks
3.2	Joint distance of the order of 30 mm	Plane 32 only common symmetry plane to both systems	
3.3• Clay shale			
3.4 Colorado oil shale	Strong bedding in plane 12	'n' fold axis of symmetry perpendicular to bedding planes	Resonant frequency and ultrasonic pulse methods
3.5 Clay shale (average of 3)	Bedding plane is plane 12	'n' fold axis? (axis 3)	
3.6 Sandy shale (average of 3)	Bedding plane is plane 12	'n' fold axis? (axis 3)	
3.7 Pennsylvanian shale	Plane of laminations is plane 12	'n' fold axis normal to laminations?	Drained triaxial compression tests. Initial moduli quoted curve is concave upward
3.8 Shale	Sound, non-fissured with sub-horizontal stratification (i.e. plane 12)	'n' fold vertical axis?	Field test—Rocha flat jack method on cube sample
3.9 Shale	Layering (plane 12)	'n' fold axis?	Field tests—Rocha flat jack method
3.10 Marl	Layering (plane 12)	'n' fold axis?	
3.11 Opoka marl	Pronounced stratification plane 12	'n' fold axis?	Laboratory tests—uniaxial compression tests oriented so that symmetry elements were common to the samples and the applied stress tensor. Stress rate 0·98 MPa/s
3.12			
3.13			
3.14 Marl			
3.15 Mudstone	Horizontal bedding—3 main joint sets (a) parallel to bedding (b) steep dip, strike SE (c) steep dip, strike NE	'n' fold axis perpendicular to bedding planes (i.e. planes 12)	Field test—seismic refraction—91·5 m spread with geophones at 15·2 m spacing. Two shots beyond either end of spread and one at centre of spread. Longitudinal and transverse wave velocities
3.16 Sandstone and siltstone			
3.17 Siltstone	Partially metamorphosed thin bedded sediments; parallel planes of stratification (planes 12)	'n' fold axis of symmetry (axis 3)	Wave tests
3.18 Coarse phyllite			
3.19 Fine phyllite			
3.20 Phyllite	Layering parallel to plane 12	Orthorhombic	Field test with radial jack pressure ≈ 3 MPa
3.21			
3.22 Calcareous slate			Pressure ≈ 5·5 MPa
3.23 Slate			
3.24 Slate	Laminations parallel to plane 12	'n' fold axis parallel to axis 3	Longitudinal and shear wave velocities on cube samples
3.25 Slate	Axis 3 is normal to the plane of foliation	Orthorhombic	Uniaxial compression and tension tests together with torsion tests. Strain gauges attached to samples

Test sample size (mm)	GPa						v_{12} (v_{21})	v_{13} (v_{31})	v_{23} (v_{32})	Reference
	E_1	E_2	E_3	G_{23}	G_{13}	G_{12}				
000 × 1000 × 1000	0·93	0·15	1·37				0·04 (0·03)	1·07 (0·01)	2·77 (0·08)	Lögters and Voort (1974)
	0·73	0·69	9·80				0·05 (0·21)	0·5 (0·11)	1·0 (0·32)	
	0·48	0·83	1·22				0·06 (0·08)	0·49 (0·06)	1·0 (0·09)	
	49·9	49·9	36·2	15·3	15·3	19·7	0·266 (0·266)	0·144 (0·199)	0·273 (0·198)	Kaarsberg (1968)
	19·3		9·7							Stepanov and Batugin (1967)
	45·3		29·6				0·10	0·29 (0·19)		Stepanov and Batugin (1967)
88 dia. × 76 long	0·062		0·034							Mesri and Gibala (1972)
1000 × 1000 × 1000	10·8		4·9							De Beer, *et al.* (1974)
1000 × 1000 × 1000	12·2		7·3							Rocha and Silva (1970)
50 × 50 × 50	57·8		30·8							Lozinska-Stepien (1966)
	3.03		2.25							
	1.71		1.86							
	3.62		1.76							
	2·54		1·17							
	6·6	6·6	4·5	1·4	2·1		0·64	0·12 (0·08)		G_{12} assumed = $1·5G_{23}$ Wiebenga, *et al.* (1964)
	12·9	12·9	7·2	3·0	4·5		0·44	0·53 (0·29)		G_{13} assumed = $0·75G_{12}$
	60·7		55·5	22·4	25·0		0·215	0·28		Lekhnitskii (1966)
	72·4		46·4	25·7	28·4		0·27	0·53		
	73·5		55·7	28·6	29·2		0·26	0·37		
2200 dia. × 2000 long	6·6 (3·4)		1·7 (0·7)							Lauffer and Seeber (1961) Seeber 1970) Unbracketed figures correspond to recovered deformation, bracketed figures correspond to total deformation
	15·9 (13·4)		8·1 (3·8)							
	114·0	114·0	53·0	19·8	19·8	53·5	0·067	0·328	0·328	Alexandrov, *et al.* (1969)
	71·5	63·0	82·1	26·9	27·9	24·9	0·218	0·380	0·284	Nishimatsu (1970)

Table 2.1—*continued*

Material	Fabric description	Symmetry	Test method
3.26 Hard blue Pehrhyn slate	Slaty cleavage associated with preferred orientation of micaceous and chloritic components in the rock. 'Planes of elastic and velocity symmetry are coincident with the planes of fabric and tectonic symmetry	Orthorhombic Stiffest along axis 1 ≡ direction of cleavage dip and maximum fabric extension	Ultrasonic longitudinal and shear waves
3.27 Green Pehrhyn slate		Least stiffness along axis 3 ≡ normal to planar features and direction of maximum fabric shortening	
3.28 Chloritic slate	Direction of bedding coincides with maximum wave velocity, minimum velocity perpendicular to bedding (i.e. axis 3)	'n' fold axis perpendicular to bedding?	Laboratory tests— longitudinal and shear wave velocities
3.29 Very altered slate	Axis 3 is normal to the plane of foliation	Orthorhombic?	Laboratory tests—oriented samples loaded to 9·8 MPa
3.30 Little altered slate			Strains recorded by bonded strain gauges. Results
3.31 Sound slate			quoted are secant moduli
3.32 Green River shale	Thinly banded, finely laminated. Bedding is plane 12	Orthorhombic	Triaxial compression tests
3.33 Permian shale	Thinly banded, finely laminated. Bedding is plane 12	Orthorhombic	

(d) PELITIC (MICA)

Material	Fabric description	Symmetry	Test method
4.1 Muscovite mica schist	Laminations parallel to plane 12	'n' fold axis parallel to axis 3	Longitudinal and shear wave velocities on cube samples
4.2 Schist	Foliation surfaces: strike NS (axis 1) dip 30° E Stratification surfaces: strike NS dip 30° W	Monoclinic, axis 1 is normal to the plane of symmetry	Laboratory tests—uniaxial compression of cylinders oriented with their axes parallel to NS, EW, and vertical stress up to 15 MPa
4.3 Schist (Phyllades de Revin)	Horizontal foliation surface lineation in one horizontal direction (axis 1)	Orthorhombic axes 1, 2, 3 are normals to planes of symmetry	Laboratory tests—uniaxial compression of cylinders oriented in the three orthogonal directions up to 30 MPa
4.4 Biotitic mica schist	Axis 3 is normal to the plane of schistosity	Orthorhombic?	Laboratory tests—oriented samples loaded to 9·8 MPa. Secant moduli quoted
4.5 Schist I	Pronounced stratification parallel to plane 12	'n' fold axis (axis 3)	Laboratory tests—uniaxial compression tests arranged
4.6 Schist II			so that one of the test planes was parallel to the axis of
4.7 Schist III			the samples while the other two test planes were inclined. Strain gauges attached to samples in various orientations
4.8 Serpentine Schist	Laminations parallel to plane 12	'n' fold axis (axis 3)	Uniaxial unconfined tensile tests of oriented samples. Tangent moduli taken at half strength
4.9 Mica schist	Layering parallel to plane 12	Orthorhombic?	Field tests with radial jack pressure ≈ 2 MPa
4.10			
4.11 Greywacke schist	Medium weathering; strongly folded	'n' fold axis perpendicular to schistosity planes (i.e. planes 12)	Field tests in adits—modulus *measured* at a range of angles. G_{23} calculated in the assumption that $v_{13} = 0$
4.12	Slight weathering; strongly folded		
4.13	Highly weathered; strongly folded		
4.14 Schist	Stratification parallel to planes 12	'n' fold axis? (axis 3)	Field tests in 2 m × 2 m gallery 30 m deep. Plate load tests parallel and perpendicular to stratification. Load to 3·4 MPa

Test sample size (mm)	GPa						v_{12} (v_{21})	v_{13} (v_{31})	v_{23} (v_{32})	Reference
	E_1	E_2	E_3	G_{23}	G_{13}	G_{12}				
5, 10, 15 × 64 × 90	46·3	44·1	30·1	10·6	15·4	16·0	0·426	0·426	0·439	Attewell (1970)
	40·5		23·9	8·1	8·1	13·9	0·469		0·462	
50 dia. × 120 long	130		81		35	49	0·33	0·28 (0·17)		Skorikova (1965)
50 × 50 × 150 prisms	34·8	55·4	7·8							Peres Rodriques (1970)
	63·8	54·1	11·3							
	85·2	90·7	30·4							
19 dia. × 38 long	35·2	35·0	29·4				0·15 (0·16)	0·18 (0·28)	0·19 (0·18)	Chenevert and Gatlin (1965)
	35·4	31·6	24·4				0·17 (0·18)	0·21 (0·13)	0·21 (0·13)	Chenevert and Gatlin (1965)
	77·7	77·7	60·9	25·2	25·2	33·5	0·159	0·246	0·246	Alexandrov, *et al.* (1969)
96 dia. × 192 long	49·0	26·5	14·5				0·29 (0·15)	0·33 (0·14)	0·35 (0·33)	Masure (1970)
96 dia. × 192 long	120	100	28·5				0·24 (0·14)	0·56	0·60	Masure (1970)
50 × 50 × 150 prisms	69·2	75·6	43·1							Peres Rodriques (1970)
	95·4		74·5		27·2	37·6	0·268	0·270 (0·211)		Pinto (1970)
	76·9		41·0		20·5	31·4	0·219	0·271 (0·145)		
	63·4		20·0		7·9	27·9	0·134	0·212 (0·067)		
29·7 dia. × 68 long	2·5E_3		E_3							Barla and Goffi (1974)
2200 dia. × 2000 long	57·0		3·8 ← recovered deformation							Lauffer and Seeber (1961)
	(53·0)		(1·9) ← total deformation							Seeber (1970)
	38·0		8·1	1·3						Pinto (1970)
	12·2		4·7	1·0						
	5·1		1·2							
	∼20		∼8·5							De Beer, *et al.* (1968)

Table 2.1—*continued*

Material	Fabric description	Symmetry	Test method
(e) SALINE/CARBONATE			
5.1 Clay limestone	Pronounced stratification	'n' fold axis? (axis 3)	Laboratory tests—uniaxial compression tests oriented
5.2			so that symmetry elements were common to the samples and the applied stress tensor. Stress rate 0·98 MPa/s
5.3 Clayey limestone	Sub-horizontal strata (i.e. plane 12)	'n' fold axis normal to stratification?	Field tests (a) rigid plate
5.4			(b) flexible plate
5.5			(c) good man jack (d) microseismic velocities in the rock mass
5.6			
5.7 Limestones	I. Almost horizontal dense bedding—	'n' fold axis	Field tests—radial jacking
5.8 (Cherkei damsite)	II. cryptocrystalline limestone interbedded	perpendicular to	device, 1·8 m dia. × 1·47 m
5.9	with marl and marl-clay—near-vertical	bedding planes?	long—internal pressures up
5.10	III. tectonic cracks opening to 20 mm and	(axis 3)	to 9·78 MPa with up to
5.11	IV. filled with calcite and marly clay— near-vertical lithogenic fissures opening to 1 mm		three cycles
5.12 Limestone	Axis 3 is normal to bedding	Orthorhombic?	
5.13			
5.14 Marble		Orthorhombic	Longitudinal and shear wave velocities on cube samples
5.15 Marble	Bedding plane is plane 12	Orthorhombic?	
5.16 Yule marble	Preferred orientation of the (c) axes of calcite indicates in 'n' fold axis of	'n' fold axis of symmetry parallel	Longitudinal wave velocities (G_{12} assumed 1·1 G_{13}).
5.17	symmetry. Thill, *et al.* (1969) show that wave velocity patterns have the same symmetry	to *c* axes of calcite grains (axis 3)	Static compression, 0·254 mm/min strain
5.18			Uniaxial compression tests
5.19 Rock salt	Bedding plane parallel to plane 12	'n' fold axis parallel to axis 3	
(f) SANDS			
6.1 Natural beach sand	Bedding dips seaward at 5°. Sand contains some platy grains, one long axis parallel to coast while other dips landward at 10°. (axis 2 parallel to coast, axis 3 vertical)	Monoclinic. Symmetry plane is vertical and normal to coast	Drained triaxial compression tests (secant moduli taken at half failure)
6.2 Earlston sand	Laboratory samples prepared by dropping in air. Short axes of sand grains vertical	'n' fold vertical axis of symmetry	Triaxial test (low strain)
6.3	(Willoughby, *et al.*, 1968)		Torsional triaxial test (low strain)
6.4 Leighton Buzzard sand	Laboratory prepared samples by dropping in air	'n' fold vertical axis of symmetry (i.e. axis 3)	Compression tests on oriented cube samples. Confining stress = 0·055 MPa. Secant moduli at 1 per cent strain
(g) CLAYS			
7.1 Krasnozem silty clay	Planar pore pattern relates to terrain slope which strikes N 29° E. (axis 1 is EW, axis 3 is vertical)	Monoclinic symmetry plane is vertical and normal to the strike of the slope	Undrained triaxial compression on partly saturated samples. (Secant moduli taken at half failure)
7.2 Foliated clay	Layering parallel to plane 12	Orthorhombic?	Field test with radial jacks.
7.3			Pressure ≈ 2 MPa
7.4 Neo Comian clays	Severe jointing coinciding with horizontal bedding direction. Symmetry of	'n' fold vertical axis (axis 3)	Laboratory triaxial compression tests
7.5 Meso-Cenozoic clays	anisotropic modulus coincides with symmetry of anisotropic swelling		

Test sample size (mm)	GPa						v_{12} (v_{31})	v_{13} (v_{31})	v_{23} (v_{32})	Reference
	E_1	E_2	E_3	G_{23}	G_{13}	G_{12}				
50 × 50 × 50	1.27		2·06							Lozinska-Stepien (1966)
	3·13		1·86							
Plate dia. = 280	12·7		4·3							Arambury (1974)
Plate dia. = 1000	12·3		5·5							
	5·6		4·8							
	18·6		14·7							
	13·9		2·96							Evdokimov and
	13·6		5·96							Sapegin (1964)
	13·5		6·43							
	5·62		2·30							
	6·24		1·83							
	40·9	37·2	33·4							Obert and Duvall
	56·4	61·8	69·4							(1967)
	84·7	80·1	74·8	29·7	30·7	32·6	0·314	0·353	0·306	Alexandrov, *et al.* (1969)
	63·1	71·6	49·3							Obert and Duvall (1967)
12·7 × 12·7 × 25·4	74·2	74·2	53·9	16·5	16·5	29·0	0·27	0·36 (0·26)	0·36 (0·26)	Ricketts and Goldsmith (1972)
	56·0	56·0	49·2	13·1	13·1	22·5	0·246	0·258	0·258	
25 × 25 × 50	59·7	59·7	38·8							Lepper (1949)
	42·9	42·9	46·4	12·7	12·7	15·0	0·296 (0·296)	0·206 (0·218)	0·206 (0·218)	Dreyer (1972)
101 dia. × 203 long	0·035	0·040	0·054							Lafeber and Willoughby (1971)
102 dia. × 203 long	0·017		0·034			0·0064	0·33	−0·41		Morgan and Gerrard (1973)
	0·0041		0·0083	0·0037		0·0016	0·33	0·39		(E_1/E_3 and v_{12} obtained from cube sample tests)
100 × 100 × 100	0·015		0·018							Arthur and Menzies (1972)
101 dia. × 203 long	0·0043	0·0071	0·0097							Lafeber and Willoughby (1971)
	1.28 (0·82)		0·59 ← recovered deformation (0·29) ← total deformation							Seeber (1970)
	0·032		0·016					0·08 (0·04)		Rogatkina (1967)
	0·121		0·062					0·23 (0·18)		

Table 2.1—*continued*

	Material	Fabric description	Symmetry	Test method
7.6	London clay (Ashford) — 20 m deep	Heavily overconsolidated clay with orientation of fissures predominantly horizontal together with some concentrations at high angle dips. Patterns vary from pseudo-orthorhombic to 'n' fold axis (Skempton *et al.*, 1969)	'n' fold vertical axis (i.e. axis 3)	Undrained triaxial compression tests with oriented samples cut in various directions from blocks. Analysed assuming saturated and no volume change. Secant moduli. taken at half ultimate
7.7	(Ashford) —35 m deep			
7.8	London clay (High Ongar Oxford Circus)			Drained triaxial compression tests with samples cut from blocks. In the analysis E_1/E_3 assumed 1·8
7.9	London clay (Barbican Arts Centre)			Laboratory compression. Drained and undrained triaxial and plane strain tests. Parameters quoted are effective stress values
7.10	Kaolinitic clay	Laboratory prepared samples from slurry. One-dimensional consolidation to 0·39 MPa	'n' fold axis parallel to consolidation direction (i.e. axis 3)	UU triaxial tests. OCR = 1
7.11				Constant OCR = 10
7.12				volume OCR = 15
7.13				assumed in OCR = 20 analysis. Secant moduli at 3 per cent strain
7.14	Florida clay $\sigma = 0.55\ K_0 = 0.48$	Test materials prepared by one-directional consolidation from slurry with the pressure increasing from 0 to 0·23 MPa over 90 hours. Subsequent one directional consolidation under different cell pressures thereby producing different degrees of anisotropy. The first two clays are almost pure kaolinite, while the third contains some illite σ in the first column indicates the cell pressure in MPa during the second stage of consolidation	'n' fold axis parallel to consolidation direction (i.e. axis 3)	Laboratory tests—16 undrained hollow cylinder torsion tests performed on each material in compression and extension. For any test the rate of true stress and the principal stress inclination were fixed. Tests at constant volume with samples fully saturated
7.15	Florida clay $\sigma = 0.41\ K_0 = 0.47$			
7.16	Florida clay $\sigma = 0.275\ K_0 = 0.49$			
7.17	Hydrite clay $\sigma = 0.41\ K_0 = 0.52$			
7.18	Hydrite clay $\sigma = 0.275\ K_0 = 0.52$			
7.19	Grundite clay $\sigma = 0.41\ K_0 = 0.69$			
7.20	Fulford clayey silt	Preconsolidation pressure 47 KPa exist. Overburden effective stress 20 KPa ∴ lightly overconsolidated K_0 about unity	'n' fold vertical axis (i.e. axis 3)	Multi-stage compress. undrained triaxial compression and extension tests. Secant extens. moduli at 1 per cent axial strain
7.21				

(h) MISCELLANEOUS

	Material	Fabric description	Symmetry	Test method
8.1	Coal	Bedding parallel to plane 12, major cleats parallel to plane 23, minor cleats parallel to plane 13	Orthorhombic	Oriented cylinders loaded in triaxial compression to failure. (Confining pressures 0·34 to 4·1 MPa). Tests also on oriented cubes
8.2	Bituminous concrete	Vertical kneading compaction of laboratory samples	'n' fold axis parallel with compaction direction	Triaxial compression, simple shear and torsional tests Confining pressure = 0·28 MPa Load time = 5 s Temperature = 26·7 °C

Test sample size (mm)	GPa						ν_{12} (ν_{21})	ν_{13} (ν_{31})	ν_{23} (ν_{32})	Reference
	E_1	E_2	E_3	G_{23}	G_{13}	G_{12}				
38 dia. × 76 long	0·088		0·042		0·018	0·046	−0·04	1·04		Ward, *et al.* (1959), Ward, *et al.* (1965), Gibson (1974)
	0·145		0·084		0·037	0·064	0·13	0·87		
38 dia. × 76 long							−0·04	0·28		Simons (1971), Gibson (1974)
	0·022		0·011			0·011	0·0	0·38 (0·19)		Atkinson (1975)
	0·0022		0·0027		0·0006	0·0007	0·58	0·42		Bhaskaran (1975)
	0·0018		0·0022		0·0005	0·0006	0·60	0·40		
	0·0017		0·0017		0·0004	0·0006	0·50	0·50		
	0·0015		0·0012		0·0002	0·0003	0·49	0·61		
Hollow cylinder 71 (outside dia.) 51 (inside dia.) 142 (long)	0·903		1·0		0·465	0·583	0·55	0·45		Saada and Ou (1973) *N.B.* Results for E_1, G_{13}, and G_{12} are given as ratios of E_3 Compression tests unbracketed, extension tests bracketed
	1·80				(1·14)	(1·59)	(0·115)	(0·885)		
	0·567		1·0		0·402	0·331	0·717	0·283		
	1·36				(1·235)	(1·03)	(0·322)	(0·678)		
	0·578		1·0		0·354	0·337	0·712	0·288		
	1·33				(1·102)	(1·00)	(0·335)	(0·665)		
	0·670		1·0		0·279	0·402	0·665	0·335		
	2·12				(1·41)	(2·24)	(−0·057)	(1·06)		
	0·534		1·0		0·342	0·308	0·734	0·266		
	1·75				(1·30)	(1·55)	(0·127)	(0·873)		
	0·845		1·0		0·481	0·538	0·576	0·424		
	1·084				(0·838)	(0·745)	(0·458)	(0·542)		
38 dia. × 76 long	$0.32E_3$		E_3		$0.65E_3$	0·84	0·16			
	$2.3E_3$		E_3		$0.48E_3$	−0·15	1·15			
55 dia. × 110 long (cylinders)	3·16	2·24	2·24	0·61	0·44	0·38	0·43 (0·21)	0·37 (0·16)	0·26 (0·21)	Ko and Gerstle (1972)
101 (cubes)										
25 × 25 × 50	0·65		0·98	0·13		0·22	0·49	0·43 (0·39)		Busching, *et al.* (1967)
12·7 × 12·7 × 54										
28·5 dia. × 12·7 long										

Strong correlations have been observed between the geometric and physical anisotropies for all earthen materials. Geometric anisotropies are defined by the symmetry elements present in the fabric, while physical anisotropies are made manifest by variations with direction in the magnitude of mechanical properties such as stiffness, strength, wave propagation velocities and permeability. Because of the multi-phase character of earthen materials, anisotropy needs to be defined on a statistical basis rather than on the point concept used in mathematical theory (Lafeber, 1966). Several examples of correlation between geometric and physical anisotropies are as follows:

(1) Thill, Willard, *et al.* (1969) found that the symmetries in the longitudinal-velocity anisotropies in three rocks coincided with relevant fabric element symmetries. In Yule marble, a fabric feature is the preferred orientation of calcite optic axes and the symmetry is an n-fold axis. For a pumice the feature was flattened elongate vesicles, while in a granite it was micro-fractures in the quartz grains, both of these cases exhibiting orthorhombic symmetries. The fabric and longitudinal velocity diagrams for the Yule marble are shown in Figures 2.11a and b. Khalevin and Koshkina (1966) have examined a wide range of metamorphic rocks in which the main fabric elements were the cleavage and sets of parallel rock pores or lineations oriented at right-angles to the cleavage. Significant differences in the longitudinal velocities in the orthogonal directions were noted in the following order of magnitude: parallel to cleavage and perpendicular to lineation > parallel to cleavage and parallel to lineation ≫ perpendicular to cleavage.

(2) Kirkpatrick and Rennie (1973) and Saada and Ou (1973) (see also Table 2.1) both report that when clay is consolidated from a slurry state under the action of a stress state having an n-fold axis of symmetry, then a clay fabric and mechanical properties are produced having the same symmetry system. This is due to the preferred orientation of packets of clay particles in planes that are normal or near normal to the compression (Matsuo and Kamon, 1973).

(3) Lafeber and Willoughby (1970, 1971) show that for a beach sand the fabric of the deposit (see Figure 2.9), the orientation of the failure surfaces of tested specimens and three-dimensional pattern of secant modulus all have in common a single vertical plane of symmetry perpendicular to the coastline. In addition, the failure planes in triaxial tests intersect along lines which are either parallel or normal to the bedding-imbrication plane dip. These writers suggest that monoclinic symmetry is likely to be found in any deposit that has been subject to uni-directional transport in the (near) horizontal plane (cf. Johansson, 1965).

(4) Ruiz (1966) reports correlation between rock fabric features and diametral deformation in a pressure chamber test of 2·2 m diameter and 6·0 m in length. The rock was a sound schistose gneiss with some joints. The location of the test, a stereographic representation of the schistosity and joints and the diametral deformations before and after grouting are shown in Figure 2.15. For the ungrouted case at low pressure the deformation was governed by the joints with maximum elongation on axis 3. At higher pressure the joints closed and the deformation pattern was governed by the schistosity with maximum elongation on axis 2. The results for the grouted case confirm this mechanism with the deformations at all pressure levels being controlled by the schistosity of the rock.

(5) The relationship between soil and rock fabric and anisotropies in permeability has been often reported. This will be discussed briefly in a later section.

2.2.2 Removal of overburden related to *in situ* stresses and properties

Important in any geotechnical investigation is the relationship between geological history and the fabrics, present *in situ* stresses and mechanical properties of the earthen materials involved (cf. 'dynamic' analysis of fabric suggested by Friedman (1964). To illustrate this relationship the relative simple case of London clay is chosen for study.

London clay is marine deposit of the Eocene age and has been subsequently heavily overconsolidated. It has an almost constant clay mineralogy with illite and montmorillonite being the major components, and lesser amounts of kaolin and minor quantities of chlorite (Gilkes, 1968). However, some variations occur and Skempton, Schuster, *et al.* (1969) report illite and kaolinite as the predominant minerals with subsidiary montmorillonite at Wraysbury.

The maximum current thickness of the deposit is about 180 m, while the pre-existing overburden is estimated to be about 200 m in central London (Skempton and Henkel, 1957) and about 400 m at Ashford (Bishop, Webb, *et al.* 1965). London clay exhibits a remarkably uniform lithology and dips rarely exceed three degrees. Under these conditions it would be expected that the consolidation process would produce a microfabric pattern in which the packets of clay particles are aligned parallel to each other and with their flat faces lying normal to the direction of consolidation. Such behaviour certainly occurs in kaolinitic clays (Kirkpatrick and Rennie, 1972).

An examination of the fabric patterns of the joints and fissures in the London clay at Wraysbury and Edgware has been conducted by Skempton, Schuster, *et al.* (1969). They found that joints in the principal sets were spaced at 0·06 to 5·0 m (average 2 m) and were near vertical and with

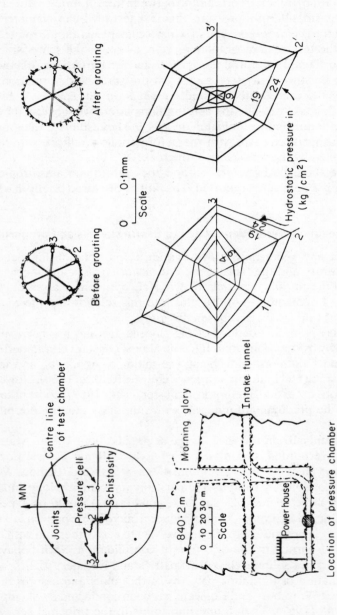

Figure 2.15 Correlation between fabric and diametral deformation in a pressure chamber test. (Reproduced, by permission, from Ruiz, 1966; Figure 3)

preferred orientation in the planes N 60° W and N 30° E. An orthorhombic fabric is suggested with these two planes and the horizontal plane being planes of symmetry. Rowe (1972), in an examination of London clay at Ardleigh, reports vertical joints spaced 60 to 75 mm in one direction and 25 to 40 mm in the orthogonal direction. The patterns of fissures at Wraysbury and Edgware showed a typical spacing of 25 to 75 mm with the dips of most fissures tending parallel to the bedding. A minority of fissures formed a girdle at large-angle dips. All samples suggest a horizontal plane of symmetry. Some samples appear orthorhombic with a moderate degree of anisotropy within the horizontal plane, while other samples appear to possess an n-fold vertical axis of symmetry. Another important aspect of the fabric associated with the bedding has been reported by Rowe (1972), again in relation to the London clay at Ardleigh. Microscopic studies revealed medium to fine silt on bedding planes spaced at 12 to 25 mm apart, with occasional sand to coarse silt veins. Stereographic plots of the joint orientations and fissure orientations (depth 1·7 m) observed by Skempton and Hutchinson (1969) are shown in Figures 2.16a and b respectively.

The effect of overconsolidation, or the removal of overburden, in producing a major set of fissures sub-parallel to the bedding direction has been found in a variety of cretaceous sediments (Fookes and Denness, 1969) and even in granite (Todd, Simmons *et al.*, 1973). Fookes and Denness found a secondary girdle of fissures trending perpendicular to the bedding, while Todd, Simmonds, *et al.* report secondary concentrations of cracks in two sets of planes at right angles, both of these being normal to the horizontal (rift) planes.

It appears likely that the strong pattern of fissures, which develops parallel to the bedding in overconsolidated materials, is associated with the relatively high compressive stresses in this direction that are brought into action by the overconsolidation process. The magnitude of these stresses has been studied by Brooker and Ireland (1965) who took several natural soils, remoulded them to a wet state, and then subjected them to a cycle of loading and unloading without permitting lateral strain. The loading represents primary consolidation and the unloading represents over-consolidation. The relationships obtained between the axial stress and lateral stress, during both stages of the cycle for London clay, are shown in Figure 2.17a, while the ratio of lateral stresses to axial stress K_0 is plotted against the effective angle of internal friction for a range of clays and a sand in Figure 2.17b. In this plot the over-consolidation ratio is varied from 1 to 32 and the ϕ' value of 35° represents the sand, while London clay has the ϕ' value of about 17·5°. The results of Figure 2.17b suggest that for a wide range of highly overconsolidated earthen materials, *in situ* lateral stresses of two to three times the overburden stress could be expected. Since the major principal stress is

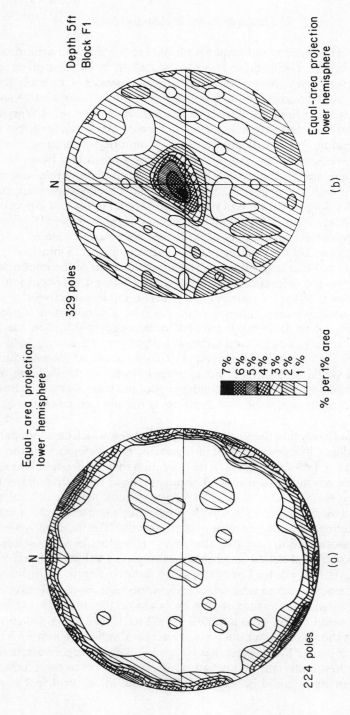

Figure 2.16 Orientation of joints and fissures in London Clay at Wraysbury: (a) joints (b) fissures. (After Skempton *et al*., 1969; Figures 7 and 15a)

Depth 5ft
Block F1

Equal-area projection
lower hemisphere

(b)

329 poles

7%
6%
5%
4%
3%
2%
1%

% per 1% area

Equal-area projection
lower hemisphere

(a)

224 poles

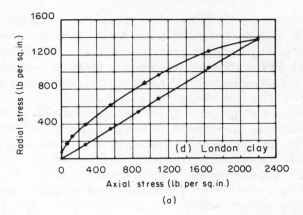

(a)

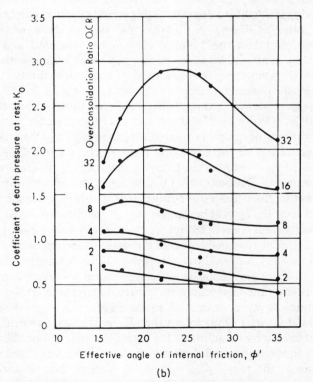

(b)

Figure 2.17 Relation between axial and lateral stresses during overconsolidation: (a) loading and unloading for London clay, (b) effect of OCR and ϕ' on K_0. (Reproduced by permission of the National Research Council of Canada from Brooker and Ireland, 1965; Figures 4 and 9)

acting parallel to the bedding, it is reasonable to expect that fractures in this direction will result, especially in a clay having both silt seams and pronounced preferred orientation of the packets of clay particles. Other writers have pointed out that the stress conditions in the upper sections of natural deposits of overconsolidated clays approach that theoretically required to cause passive failure (e.g. Singh, Henkel, *et al.* 1973).

The mechanical properties of the London clay have been measured by Ward, Samuels, *et al.* (1959) and by Ward, *et al.* (1965). In the first series of tests, samples were taken from boreholes in the London area, and subsequent undrained laboratory tests indicated that the stiffness in the horizontal direction E_h was about 1·6 times that in the vertical direction E_v. In the later series test samples were obtained from blocks obtained from Ashford, and a similar but more exaggerated behaviour was found with $E_h/E_v \approx 2$. Gibson (1974) attributes this difference to the greater depth of overburden originally overlying the Ashford deposit, as this would produce a higher overconsolidation ratio. Gibson, in considering the analysis of immediate settlements, has taken the London clay to be saturated and therefore incompressible. Further, he assumes the clay to be elastic with an n-fold vertical axis of symmetry. The condition of incompressibility reduces the number of elastic parameters from five to three, i.e. E_h, E_v and G_{vh}. The first two of these were measured directly by Ward *et al.* (1965), while the last was determined by Gibson, by making use of the measured value of the undrained stiffness of samples oriented with their axes at 45° to the bedding. The average values of the constants were $E_h/E_v = 1\cdot84$, $G_{vh}/E_v = 0\cdot38$, $\nu_{hv} = 0\cdot92$ and $\nu_{hh} = 0\cdot08$. Anisotropy in the stiffness of London clay has also been shown by Simons (1971) in a series of drained tests in which the material was therefore treated as being compressible. If it is assumed that for the drained tests E_h/E_v will be similar to that for the undrained tests, then Simons' results yield $\nu_{hv} = 0\cdot28$ and $\nu_{hh} = -0\cdot04$ as 'undrained' parameters (see Table 2.1). The reasonableness of this assumption has been shown from test results recently reported by Atkinson (1975). A series of drained and undrained tri-axial and plane-strain compression tests was conducted on London clay from the Barbican Arts Centre. From these tests the effective stress parameters were estimated to be $E_h/E_v = 2$, $\nu_{hv} = 0\cdot38$, $\nu_{hh} = 0$. Ward, Samuels *et al.* (1959) found that E_h was greater than E_v for both loading and unloading. In addition, the undrained unconfined shear strength was greater in the horizontal direction S_h then in the vertical direction S_v, but the ratio of the two S_h/S_v, was not as high as that pertaining to the stiffness anisotropy E_h/E_v, being about 1·4 compared with about 1·8.

It is important to note that in all of the analyses of laboratory tests on London clay, it has been assumed that the horizontal plane, or bedding plane, is a plane of isotropy. This assumption is probably valid in terms of the 'packets' of clay particles, and in terms of the pattern of fissures, such as that shown in Figure 2.16b. However, the pattern of joints in the London clay appears to be orthorhombic in nature (Figure 2.16a). If this symmetry is reflected at smaller scales, then the assumption of a plane of isotropy will be invalid. Even if the plane of isotropy does exist at the smaller scale, it will still mean that the mechanical performance predicted from small scale tests is unlikely to be valid for large scale field problems.

It is instructive to compare London clay with other clayey soils with regard to the relationship between over-consolidation and the stiffness and strength anisotropies measured in undrained tests. Several results are summarized in Table 2.2.

Table 2.2   Comparison of characteristics of some clayey soils

Material	Stress history	E_h/E_v (compression)	E_h/E_v (extension)	S_h/S_v (compression)	Reference
Kaolinite	Light overconsolidated	0·6		0·9	Mitchell (1972)
Kaolinites	Normal consolidated	0·5 to 0·9	1·3 to 2		Saada and Ou (1973)
Clayey silt	Light overconsolidated	0·3	2·3	0·83	Parry and Nadarajah (1974)
London clay	Highly overconsolidated	1·8	1·6	1·4	Ward *et al.* (1959) Ward *et al.* (1965)
Kaolinite	Normal consolidated	0·8		0·8	Bhaskaran (1974)
	Medium overconsolidated (OCR = 10)	0·8		1	Bhaskaran (1975)
	Highly overconsolidated (OCR = 20)	1·4		1·2	

The following trends are evident from Table 2.2:

(1) As the overconsolidation ratio is increased, both E_h/E_v (compression) and S_h/S_v (compression) are increased, and both can become greater than unity at high over-consolidation ratios. S_h/S_v appears to pass through unity at a lower OCR than E_h/E_v. This point is well illustrated by the work of Bhaskaran (1975), who has conducted oriented undrained compression tests on a kaolinitic clay for a range of overconsolidated ratios. The stress–strain curves obtained in these tests are shown in Figure 2.18.

(2) The value of E_h/E_v in extension tests appears to be greater than unity for all values of the over-consolidation ratio.

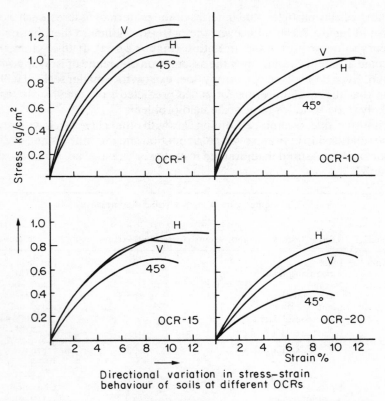

Figure 2.18   Directional variation in stress-strain behaviour of a kaolinitic clay at various overconsolidation ratios. (After Bhaskaran, 1975; Figure 1)

Both of the above aspects of behaviour are considered to be due to the tendency to develop fissures parallel to the bedding during unloading in the direction normal to the bedding.

2.2.3   Anisotropy and stress dependence of stiffness

The inherent fabric of earthen materials closely correlates with the inherent stiffness anisotropy. Subsequent stress induced changes in fabric are reflected in changes in stiffness and stiffness anisotropy. Some aspects of these topics are outlined below.

Many records of measured stiffness anisotropy are summarized in Table 2.1 where earthen materials have been divided into several categories, including sand, clays and the rock groups of quartzofeldspathic, basic/lithic, pelitic (clay), pelitic (mica), and saline/carbonate (Franklin, 1970). Other relevant information is also included in the table where available, e.g. dominant fabric features, test methods and test dimensions. For ease of comparison all measurements have been analyzed in terms of the linear elastic theory. This was done with some reluctance as it is acknowledged that while this theory may be relevant to wave propagation tests on 'intact' samples of rock, it is difficult to apply to those earthen materials where the application of the test load changes the properties from their initial values. This problem was reflected in the fact that complete sets of anisotropic stiffness data were seldom recorded in field tests, more frequently in laboratory compression tests and often in wave propagation tests. In addition fewer records appear to exist for soils than for rocks. Both partial and complete sets of data have been listed in terms of any or all of the direct moduli, E_1, E_2, E_3, the shear moduli, G_{23}, G_{13}, G_{12}, and the Poisson's ratios, ν_{12}, ν_{13}, ν_{23}. It was considered that patterns in these components would be more easily comprehended than patterns in the components of the stiffness tensor, although there are sound arguments for increased use of the latter, particularly where the 'stress path' approach to mathematical modelling is being employed. In order to avoid any confusion the shear moduli and Poisson's ratios are defined below through the examples G_{23} *and* ν_{23}:

G_{23} is the modulus relevant to shear stress and strains in the plane 23.

$-\nu_{23}$ the ratio of the direct strain in the 3 direction to the direct strain in the 2 direction when a direct stress in the 2 direction is the only non-zero stress component.

For most of the cases recorded in Table 2.1, a parallel set of planar defects was reported as a dominant fabric element. These defects were in the form of bedding, stratification, layering, schistosity planes, foliation, fissuring or jointing. In all of these cases, axis 3 was taken as the normal to these planes. For the remainder of cases, whenever the presence of an n-fold axis of symmetry was stated or implied this was taken to be axis 3.

The following general comments can be made with regard to Table 2.1:

(1) The very large differences in direct moduli from hard rock (up to 200 GPa) to soft soils (down to 0·0013 GPa).

(2) The moduli decrease as the scale of the sample increases, e.g. Evdokimov and Sapegin (1964) report that the modulus of Chirkei limestone measured in laboratory compression tests is 30 times that measured in a pressure-chamber test. This behaviour is related to the likely inclusion of relatively weaker defects in large samples. However, the pattern can be modified or even reversed for soft or loose soils where sampling disturbance can result in laboratory values of stiffness being smaller than those determined *in situ*.

(3) The moduli of rock samples were higher when tested by wave propagation methods than by laboratory compression tests. Clark (1966) reports ratios of these moduli varying between one and three, depending on rock type. The higher values were associated with the pelitic rock types.

(4) That the various rock groups could be approximately ranked from least to greatest in terms of stiffness anisotropy: basic/lithic, quartzofeldspathic, saline/carbonate, pelitic (clay), pelitic (mica).

(5) Rocks exhibited more extreme stiffness anisotropy than soils.

(6) Many of the orthorhombic cases reported were pseudo n-fold in that $E_1 \approx E_2 \neq E_3$, $G_{23} \approx G_{13} \neq G_{12}$, and $\nu_{23} \approx \nu_{13} \neq \nu_{12}$.

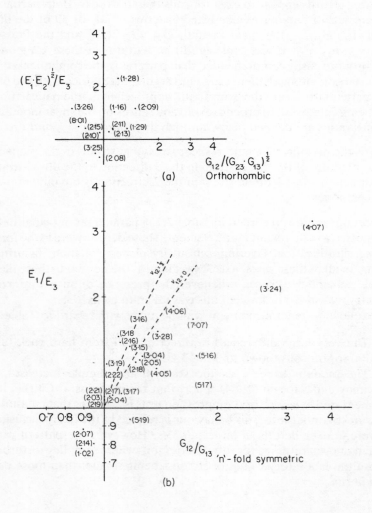

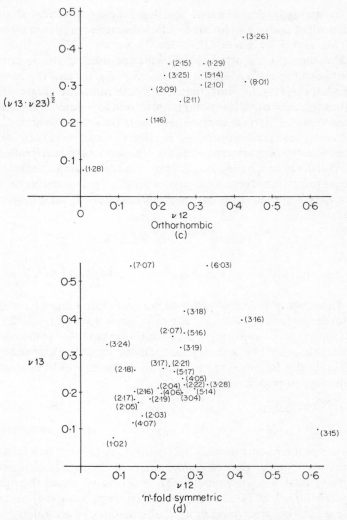

Figure 2.19 Plots of 'elastic' parameters for a variety of soils and rocks: (a) Ratio of E^s against Ratio of G^s, orthorhombic, (b) Ratio of E^s against Ratio of G^s, 'n' fold, (c) Poisson's ratios, orthorhombic, (d) Poisson's ratios, 'n'-fold

(7) For almost all rocks possessing planar defects, and for heavily over-consolidated soils, the ratio $E_1 \times E_2 / E_3^2$ is greater than unity, indicating lower stiffness in the direction normal to these defects.

(8) For some basic igneous rocks and for rock salt $E_1 \times E_2 / E_3^2$ is less than one, and this correlates with the preferred orientation of mineral crystals.

(9) For normally consolidated and lightly overconsolidated soils, for beach deposited sands, and for artificial sand samples prepared by dropping through air, $E_1 \times E_2/E_3^2$ is less than one.

(10) For the vast majority of the cases reported, a strong correlation exists between the ratio of direct moduli $E_1 \times E_2/E_3^2$ and the ratio of the shear moduli $G_{12}^2/G_{23}G_{13}$ such that either both ratios are greater than one, or both are less than one. This point is illustrated in Figures 2.19a and b. For cases where planar defects control behaviour (in general where $E_1 \times E_2 > E_3^2$), the analytical model proposed by Berry, Crea, *et al.* (1974) can be compared with the experimental results. These workers have followed the work of Walsh (1965a, b) and Brady (1969) in considering a rock composed of isotropic material but containing a parallel set of planar defects or fissures. For the case when these fissures are open the following relationship can be derived:

$$\frac{G_{12}}{G_{13}} = \frac{1+(E_1/E_3)+2\nu_{12}}{2(1+\nu_{12})}$$

This function has also been plotted on Figures 2.19a and b for ν_{12} values of 0 and 0·5.

(11) The range of scatter of values of Poisson's ratios is not large as can be seen from the plots of $(\nu_{23} \times \nu_{13})^{1/2}$ versus ν_{12} shown in Figures 2.19c and d.

(12) One aspect of anisotropic behaviour often ignored is the magnitude of the shear moduli relative to those of the direct moduli. This can be gauged by examining the following six factors. all of which would be unity if the materials were isotropic:

$$E_1/[2(1+\nu_{12})G_{12}] \qquad E_2/[2(1+\nu_{21})G_{12}] \qquad E_3/[2(1+\nu_{31})G_{13}]$$

$$E_1/[2(1+\nu_{13})G_{13}] \qquad E_2/[2(1+\nu_{23})G_{23}] \qquad E_3/[2(1+\nu_{32})G_{23}]$$

An analysis of the results showed that on average the first two factors were near unity as would be expected since many of the cases exhibited n-fold symmetry or near n-fold symmetry. The average values of the other four factors were 0·97, 1·20, 1·22 and 0·98 thereby suggesting that compared to isotropic rocks the shear moduli in anisotropic rocks are relatively lower than the direct moduli. Although there was considerable scatter this tendency was most pronounced for slates, schists and coal so that relatively low shear moduli appear to be associated with the degree of development of sets of planar discontinuities.

It should be emphasized that any of the above conclusions, based on Table 2.1, which relate to shear moduli and Poisson's ratios are biased in favour of the wave propagation tests, and to a lesser extent the laboratory tests, since these components were rarely measured in field tests.

The variation of direct modulus with orientation has been examined by several workers. Usually, compression tests on oriented cylinders or prisms were conducted, although there are examples of field compression tests and laboratory tension tests. In general, two basic forms of variations have been found as shown in Figures 2.20a and b. Although these particular curves relate respectively to a schist and a greywacke schist (Silveira, 1966), they have application to a wide range of earthen materials. For the first type (type A, see Figure 2.20a) the modulus in any inclined direction is always intermediate between the extreme values at 0° and 90°. However, in type B (Figure 2.20b) there is a wide range of angles over which the modulus in the inclined direction is lower than the smaller of the two principal moduli. Reported measurements of the type A and type B variations of modulus with angle are listed below in Table 2.3 together with references to Table 2.1.

Table 2.3   Variations of modulus with angle with reference to Table 2.1

Type A		Type B	
Barre granite	(1·3)	Very altered slate	(3·29)
Alvarenga granite	(1·8)	Little altered slate	(3·30)
Altolindoso granite	(1·9)	Sound slate	(3·31)
Vilarinho gneiss granite	(1·10)	Biotitic mica schist	(4.4)
Gneiss	(1·32)	Schist I	(4·5)
Beach sand	(6·1)	Schist III	(4·7)
Leighton Buzzard sand	(6·4)	Serpentine schist	(4·8)
Lightly overconsolidated		London clay	(7·6, 7·7)
Fulford clayey silt	(7·2)	Normally consolidated	
		and overconsolidated	(7·10, 7·11,
		kaolinitic clay	7·12, 7·13)

It will be noted from Table 2.3 that the type B variation is related to earthen materials in which a dominant set of planar discontinuities has been well developed. The point was raised previously by Silveira (1966), Mello Mendes (1971), and Bhaskaran (1975). The analytical model developed by Berry Crea, *et al.* (1974) for a parallel set of planar discontinuities or fissures does predict this pattern of behaviour if some of the fissures are assumed to be open and others closed. Gibson (1974) has pointed out by using tensor transform theory that the direct modulus at an inclination of 45° to a pair of axes is closely related to the shear modulus referred to these axes. It would therefore appear that the occurrence of the type B variation of modulus with inclination is linked with the relatively low shear modulus phenomena mentioned previously in the discussion of Table 2.1.

Changes in the effective stresses applied to earthen materials usually produce a fabric reorganization, with associated changes in stiffness

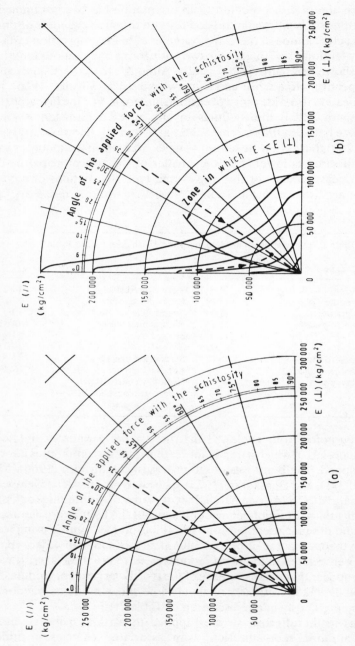

Figure 2.20   Variation of direct modulus with orientation: (a) $E_1 > E_\theta > E_3$; (b) $E_1 > E_3 > (E_\theta)_{min}$. (After Silveira, 1966; Figures 3 and 4)

anisotropy and magnitude. It has been recognized for some time that the mechanical behaviour of rock material is usually governed by the pattern of defects, e.g. Thill, Bur, *et al.* (1973) in testing dry and saturated rock spheres conclude that *velocity anisotropy arises mainly from preferred orientation of microcracks rather than from that of mineral constituents.* Depending on the magnitude and orientation of the applied stress system relative to the rock fabric symmetries, some microcracks will tend to close while others will open. In a granite with an apparently random orientation of microfissures, and related isotropic stiffness, Nur and Simons (1969) developed anisotropic stiffness response by uniaxial loading. On the other hand there are many reports (e.g. Voight 1968; Tremmel and Widmann, 1970; Todd, Simmons, *et al.*, 1973) where initially anisotropic rock becomes less anisotropic as a result of uniaxial loading as shown in Figure 2.21. In both cases the likely explanation is the closure of fissures that are oriented approximately normal to the direction of loading. Some care is needed in the interpretation of tests in which the degree of anisotropy is apparently decreased by uniaxial loading. Todd, Simmons, *et al.* (1973) point out that at about one-half of the fracture strength, cracks are initiated or propagated parallel to the stress axis, leading to a decrease in stiffness perpendicular to this direction.

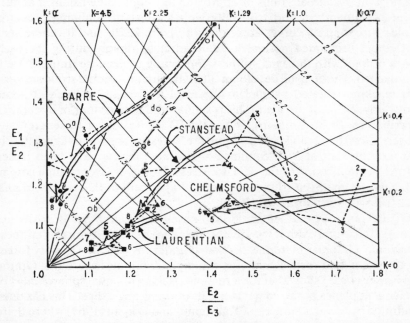

Figure 2.21 Decreasing anisotropy in granite with increasing load. (After Voight, 1968; Figure 4)

However, cracks normal to the direction of stress continue to close, so that the axial stiffness may increase with stress right up to near failure. Under these conditions the material fabric and stiffness will be anisotropic. By taking samples of rock from different orientations and testing them to high uniaxial stress levels, an apparent isotropy may be produced, but in reality this is nothing more than comparing the maximum moduli of materials that are essentially different because of the different patterns of stress-induced fissures.

The effect of de-stressing a rock mass in allowing pre-existing cracks or joints to open, thereby lowering the stiffness, has been recognized for some time (e.g. Alexander, Worotnicki, *et al.*, 1963; Panov, Sapegui, *et al.*, 1970) have considered this process of joint opening for the case of pressure chamber tests in tunnels. They conclude that under certain conditions the high level of anisotropy observed in diametral deformations is influenced to a greater extent by the opening of cracks associated with stress relief than by the inherent anisotropy of the rock in its virgin stress state.)

The change in stiffness with applied stress in an 'artificial' rock mass has been examined by Rosengren and Jaeger (1968). An aggregate of very low porosity was produced by the thermal cracking of calcite to produce an interlocking system of grains of approximately equal dimensions. Samples were subsequently tested tri-axially with a constant confining pressure. Typical stress–strain curves are shown in Figure 2.22a, and it can be seen that cracks orientated normal to the load close rapidly during the early stages of load with the axial stiffness continuing to increase until failure is approached. The delayed development of the circumferential strain suggests that cracks orientated parallel to the axial load begin to open at about two-thirds of the failure load. This is similar to the behaviour of intact rock described by Todd, Simmons, *et al.* (1973). The results of Rosengren and Jaeger (1968) for a range of confining pressures are shown in Figure 2.22b, and indicate that at high confining stress most cracks have been closed before the application of the deviator stress. However, even at high confining pressures the axial stiffness was only 30 per cent of that of the original rock (i.e. without thermal cracking).

Of the range of earthen materials, uncemented granular deposits are amongst those that exhibit the greatest influence of stress history on stiffness behaviour. Granular materials deposited under the action of gravity forces develop an n-fold vertical axis of symmetry in their fabric patterns. Graton and Fraser (1935) show that for a random packing of equal spheres most of the tangent planes of the contacts will have small-angle dips. This has been confirmed by the experiments of Kallstenius and Bergau (1961) where there was a greater density of spheres in vertical sections than there was in horizontal sections. For an artificial sand deposited by dropping through

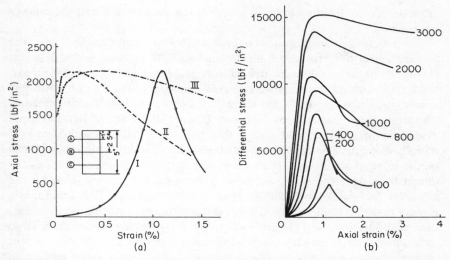

Figure 2.22. Stress-strain properties of a low porosity aggregate in triaxial compression: (a) typical axial and circumferential strains, (b) axial strain for different confining pressures. (After Rosengren and Jaeger, 1968; Figures 3 and 5; reproduced by permission of the Institution of Civil Engineers)

Parkin, Gerrard *et al.* (1968) show that again an *n*-fold vertical axis of symmetry is produced in the fabric pattern, the long axes of the grains lying predominantly in horizontal planes. Naturally occurring sands are usually deposited under the action of horizontal as well as vertical forces and a vertical monoclinic symmetry plane is produced containing the line of action of the horizontal force. The long axes of the grains are oriented at small dips (see Figure 2.9). A common pattern of vertical stiffness greater than horizontal stiffness has been observed in the above cases: by El Sohby (1964) for the spheres, by Biarez (1961), Parkin, Gerrard, *et al.* (1968) and El Sohby and Andrawes (1973) for artificial sand tested in hydrostatic compression, and by Lafeber and Willoughby (1970) for beach sand.

The effect of increasing the hydrostatic pressure applied to the artificial sands is to decrease the degree of anisotropy exhibited (Parkin, Gerrard, *et al.*, 1968; Karst, Legrand *et al.*, 1965). The results of Parkin, Gerrard *et al.* indicate that as the pressure is increased from zero to 0·073 MPa, the ratio of the incremental horizontal strain to the incremental vertical strain decreases from about 6 to 2·5. Most of the irrecoverable strain that occurs during hydrostatic pressure loading is in the horizontal direction (El Sohby and Andrawes (1973)) as would be expected, considering that strain in this direction would be facilitated by the preferred orientation of long axes of grains in horizontal directions. The recoverable portion of the strain tends to be isotropic.

The progressive development of anisotropy in granular media during the application of deviator stress has been discussed by Barden and Khayatt (1966). In further analytical work, Hardin and Black (1966) conclude that a sand mass with a fabric having spherical symmetry would exhibit stiffness anisotropy when subject to any stress field other than hydrostatic pressure. The analysis and experimental work of Biarez (1961) was related to simple assemblies of spheres and shows that the stress induced anisotropy of initially isotropic assemblies assumes the same planes of symmetry as those of the applied stress tensor. Furthermore, the anisotropic structure produced by a deviator stress of given orientation will be modified by the application of a deviator of different orientation, so that the resultant fabric is more resistant to the changed applied stress tensor. Tests on cube samples of sand reported by Morgan and Gerrard (1973) show how an initial 'n'-fold axis (axis 3) of symmetry in the stiffness properties can be changed to orthorhombic symmetry by the application of a stress tensor having an 'n'-fold axis (axis 1) of symmetry, this axis being at right angles to the initial axis of symmetry in the stiffness properties. During the first stage of loading, the stresses $\sigma_1 = 31$ kPa, $\sigma_2 = 10\cdot3$ kPa and $\sigma_3 = 10\cdot3$ kPa were built up in proportion. In the second stage σ_3 was increased without change in σ_1 or σ_2 and it was found that the strain developed in the 2-direction during this stage was about double that in the 1-direction.

The effect of applied stress magnitudes on the stiffness magnitudes of granular materials has been extensively examined. In general, increased modulus is observed with increased confinement, while decreased modulus is associated with increased shear. Such observations have led several workers (e.g. Holden, 1967; Richards, 1975) to suggest constitutive laws in which the stiffness increases with octahedral normal stress but decreases with octahedral shear stress. In a series of replicate triaxial and torsion triaxial tests, Gerrard (1967) has shown that the stiffness of sand depends on stress history as well as stress level. The results are shown in Figure 2.23 as plots of axial strain ε_1 and volume strain ε_{vol} against axial stress. For the first series of tests, A, a confining pressure was first applied, followed by a deviator stress. The axial strain and volume strain at the end of both these load stages is plotted on Figure 2.23. In the second series, B, the ratio of the stresses σ_1 and σ_3 was constant ($\approx 2\cdot8$), and at the end of loading the stresses were exactly the same magnitude as those at the end of the A tests. The curves for the B tests on Figure 2.23, compared with the points for the A tests, indicate that the low ratio of σ_1 to σ_3 applied during the early stages of the A tests has resulted in a much stiffer and less dilatant behaviour.

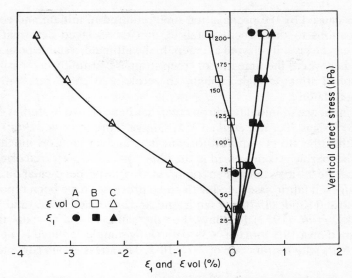

Figure 2.23 Stress-strain response of sand for different stress histories. (Test A σ_3 constant, Test B σ_1/σ_3 constant, Test C $\tau/\sigma_1/\sigma_3$ constant)

In the third series of tests, C, the direct stresses were applied in exactly the same fashion as in the B tests. However, a torsion was also applied in such a manner that its magnitude was proportional to the direct stresses at all stages. This meant that the octahedral normal stresses in tests B and C were the same at all stages, but the octahedral shear stresses in the C tests were larger than in the B tests. It will be noted from Figure 2.23 that the axial stiffness in the C series is significantly lower and that the volume behaviour is much more dilatant.

The effect of the intermediate principal stress on the axial (axis 1) secant modulus of sand has been examined by Bishop, Green, *et al.* (1973) in a series of tests on cube samples. These show that as σ_2 is increased from σ_3 towards σ_1, there is initially a sharp increase in modulus followed by a flattening where further increase in σ_2 has little effect. This behaviour is shown to be in contrast with that predicted by the linear elastic theory.

The above discussion relating changes in effective stress to changes in stiffness magnitude and anisotropy highlight the need in practical applications to take into account the stress paths followed during engineering development in the field.

2.2.4 Creep

In many earthen materials, changes in effective stress produce both an instantaneous change in fabric and deformation, and a delayed change. The delay is caused by the propagation time required to initiate and complete modifications to the structural fabric, and the delayed deformations or strains can be broadly classed as creep. In the ultimate, a stable position may be reached where the time rate of creep strain is constantly decreasing or, if the applied stress is high enough, an accelerated creep rate will result, leading to failure.

The influence of initial fabric on creep has been shown in studies on Yule marble (Griggs, Turner, *et al.*, 1953; Griggs, Turner, *et al.*, 1960). It was found that the stress required to indicate transient creep is much higher when the marble is compressed in the direction of the preferred orientation of the calcite '*c*'-axes than when compressed in the perpendicular direction.

Changes in fabric associated with creep processes have been reported by Hoshino and Koide (1970) for sandstone, and by Vyalov (1969) and Vyalov, Zaretsky, *et al.* (1973) for clays. For the sandstone, a tri-axial test was performed on a 19·5 mm dia. × 39·0 mm long sample confined at a pressure of 150 MPa with a strain rate of $2·7 \times 10^{-6}$. The stress–strain curve together

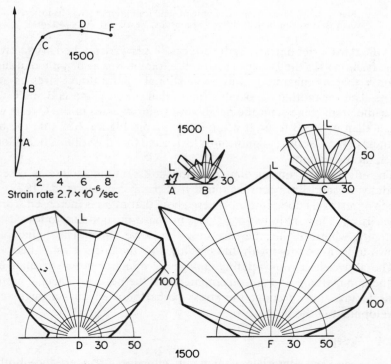

Figure 2.24   Triaxial test of sandstone—stress–strain curves and rose diagrams of microfractures. (After Hoshino and Koide, 1970; Figures 1 and 2)

with the rose diagrams, showing the number and preferred directions of the microfractures produced at various stages of the test, are shown in Figure 2.24. These micro-fractures were observed to occur along grain boundaries, or in the grains of quartz and calcite, or within the matrix of the rock. The path CDF is essentially one of constant stress and took approximately 40 minutes to traverse. The deformations occurring during this time interval could therefore be regarded as creep strains. The rose diagrams for points C, D and F indicate both the increasing number of micro-fractures associated with increasing strain and the gradual change in orientation distribution from peaks near the directions of maximum shear stress to a peak in the axial load direction.

The investigations of Vyalov were on a remoulded Jurassic clay described as being highly dispersed and highly plastic. The tests were performed in simple shear on hollow cylindrical samples loaded by various constant torques. The soil fabric was examined by petrographic and electron microscope methods. Typical strain *versus* time curves are shown in Figure 2.25, together with schematic representations of the soil fabric at various points on the curve. These curves correspond to the two ultimate conditions mentioned earlier, low applied stress leading to stability, and high applied stress leading to failure. Before deformation, rigidly cemented micro-aggregates of the original clay material occupied about 70 per cent of the area of the microsection. The surrounding space was filled by a 'randomly' oriented clayey mass. During stage OA of curve II and OD of curve I, the

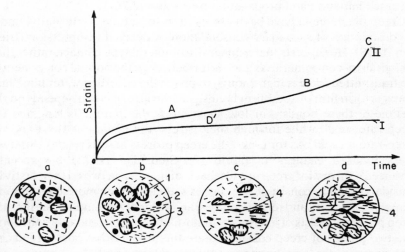

Figure 2.25   Creep test on remoulded clay—strain-time curve and schematic diagrams of fabric. (After Vyalov, 1973; Figure 1)

deformation is largely recoverable, and the number and size of cavities and voids is reduced with compression and stretching in the direction of shear. A closer packing is produced, some defects are healed, others are initiated. In the long term increased soil strength is produced. For the case of higher shear stress, the next stage of deformation (AB on curve II) is marked by continued healing of defects, but with the break-up of the micro-aggregates and the orientation of clay particles in the direction of shear, together with associated fissuring in this direction. The process of defect healing gradually falls behind the process of defect initiation and propagation, so that the creep deformation accelerates (section BC, curve II). Macrofissures oriented parallel to the shear direction develop and failure follows.

The hypothesis that creep in rocks is a stress-aided crack propagation phenomenon, is based on the 'structural' theory of creep (e.g. Charles, 1958; Scholz, 1968), this theory being successfully applied by Cruden (1971) to analyse creep test results of Pennant sandstone and Carrara marble. Lama (1974) uses an argument based on the high surface energies of rocks compared with metals, to conclude that structural theories are more relevant to creep in rock than dislocation theories. The strength tests of Houpert (1974) and John (1974) at different strain rates show that for several rock types the strength is higher for faster strain rates, again suggesting the importance of the time required for fractures to fully develop and propagate. The stress dependent nature of the creep of saturated Westerly granite is shown by Wawersik (1974) who shows that, for the same level of shear, increasing confinement decreases the creep strain rate by apparently inhibiting crack initiation and propagation (see Figure 2.26).

Creep phenomena have been observed in soils, clays particularly, under the description of secondary consolidation or delayed compression (Bjerrum, 1973). He suggests that a mineral-to-mineral type contact, rather than a mineral-to-non-mineral contact, is formed when the normal component of the transmitted force is high enough to pierce the adsorbed water film. Such contacts form firm or semi-firm bonds, and the rate of creep depends on the lifetime of these bonds. For low shear stress the lifetime is long and the creep-rate small, while for high shear stress the lifetime is short and the creep-rate is rapid. As for rocks, the creep process in soils relates closely to stress induced changes in fabric. Ter-Stepanian (1975) has recently advanced a theory for creep in soils that is of interest on two counts: firstly he considers creep to consist of two phases rather than the more conventional primary, secondary and tertiary phases, and secondly he emphasises that the creep process consists of a series of 'jump-like' reorganizations of soil fabric. The two phases of creep considered are the mobilization phase, replacing the primary phase, and the rupture phase, replacing both the secondary and tertiary phases. During mobilization, re-orientation occurs so as to develop

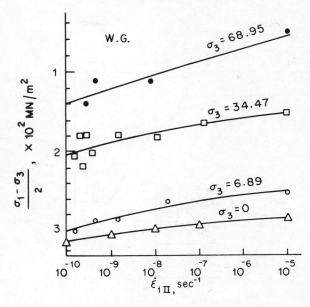

Figure 2.26 Secondary creep rate of water saturated wester-
ley granite as a function of $\sigma_1 - \sigma_3$ and σ_3. (After Wawersik,
1974; Figure 5; reproduced with permission of the National
Academy of Sciences)

the maximum possible frictional resistance. If this is insufficient to oppose
the applied shear stress, a mobilization limit is reached, and a transition
occurs to the rupture phase.

The results of Ter-Stepanian indicate the absence of the so-called secondary or steady creep phase, this being supported by the results of Bishop
(1966), Feda, Kamenov, *et al.* (1973) and Liam Finn and Shead (1973).
Figures 2.27a, and b show the results of a typical creep test on a highly plastic
sensitive, overconsolidated lacustrine clay, tested in a ring shear apparatus.
For Figure 2.27a the time-scale is linear, while in Figure 2.27b it is
logarithmic. In Figure 2.27c, in which log strain rate is plotted against log
time, the location of the mobilization limit is highlighted. Liam Finn and
Shead (1973) show that for a range of deviator stresses applied to a normally
consolidated clay, the respective mobilization limits (i.e. points of transient
minimum strain rates) fall on a line when plotted on a log strain rate *versus*
log time basis (see Figure 2.28 and cf Figure 2.27c). The curve for the test
with a deviator stress of 42·8 lbf/in^2 (295 kPa) runs parallel to and lower
than the line joining the mobilization limits, suggesting that the rupture
phase will not be initiated in this case. The mobilization phase–rupture

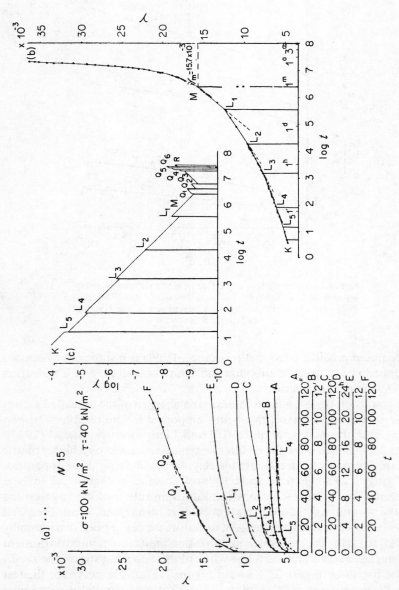

Figure 2.27 Creep tests on undisturbed clay showing mobilization limit. (After Ter-Stepanian, 1975; Figure 4; reproduced by permission of the Institution of Civil Engineers)

phase concept of Ter-Stepanian is more fundamentally satisfying than the previous primary-secondary-tertiary concept, since the arbitrary secondary stage is eliminated. It will be of considerable interest to examine whether the same approach can be applied to creep in rocks.

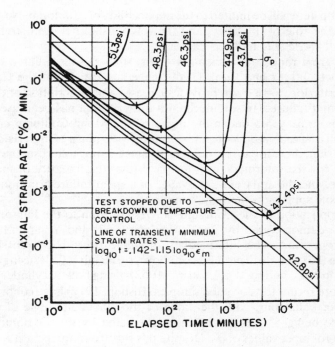

Figure 2.28 Mobilization limits for a range of deviator stresses. (After Liam Finn and Shead, 1973; Figure 4)

The other main point raised by Ter-Stepanian is the jump-like changes in strain rate produced by discrete reorganizations of fabric. The scale of these reorganizations would need to be comparable to that of the sample if they are to be manifest on the stress-strain curve. In rocks, acoustic emission rates have been found to correlate with creep strains (Mogi, 1962; Hardy, Kim, *et al.*, 1970) and this release of energy is probably associated with reorganizations of the microfabric.

In conclusion, it is suggested that creep is a stress-induced fabric change phenomenon, initially proceeding so as to mobilize maximum shear resistance. It is of great practical significance, particularly in slope stability, where creep and/or 'progressive' failures are commonly observed in both soils and rocks (Saito, 1965; Skempton and Hutchinson, 1969; Broadbent and Ko, 1972).

2.2.5 Strength

Discussion here will be limited to the applicability of 'Coulomb–Navier type' criteria, the role of dilatancy, and the relationship between strength and 'inherent' fabric and 'induced' fabric.

For a great range of earthen materials, such as soils, jointed rock and intact rock, Jaeger and Cook (1969) have suggested that the Coulomb–Navier criterion, $\tau = c + \mu\sigma$, provides a reasonable description of the stress condition at failure. (In soil mechanics this criterion has been used extensively for some years under the name of the Mohr–Coulomb criterion.) Although a large number of test results for a wide range of materials support this criterion, there are three major criticisms relating to its use: the inability to allow for the intermediate principle stress, the linearity of the failure envelope, and the apparent irrelevance of a shear failure criterion to cases where axial splitting is the failure mode.

The application of the Coulomb–Navier criterion to the failure of clays has been demonstrated by Wu, Lo, *et al.* (1963) and Yong and McKyes (1971). For sands, the intermediate principle stress has been shown to influence the strength. This has been shown by Habib (1951), using cylindrical torsion tests, and by Wu, Lo *et al.* (1963), using hollow cylinder tri-axial tests. More recent tests on cube samples (Bishop, 1972) have confirmed this pattern of behaviour, with the value of the maximum angle of shearing resistance being 5° greater than that predicted by the Coulomb–Navier criterion for most values of σ_2. Despite this shortcoming, the test results fall much closer to the Coulomb–Navier criterion than the extended Tresca criterion or extended von Mises criterion. In describing the sliding of jointed rock, Jaeger (1959) found the analogue of the Coulomb–Navier criterion to be in good agreement with experiments for low stresses. More recently, Ladanyi and Archambault (1969) have proposed a general failure model for an irregular rock surface, in which allowance has been made for components to the strength arising from dilatancy and shearing of the asperities. This model is analogous to that proposed for sands by Rowe (1962) in which it is suggested that components of strength arise from true interparticle friction, particle rearranging, and dilatancy.

For intact rock, Hoek (1965) analysed the results of a large number of tests and showed that the modified Griffith criterion, with a range of μ values between 0·5 and 1, gives a better fit to the data than the extended Griffith criterion or the original Griffith criterion. For higher stresses, the modified Griffith criterion is essentially the same as the Coulomb–Navier criterion under triaxial stress conditions. Biaxial tests have been conducted by Brown (1974) on Wombeyan marble showing a maximum increase in strength of about 15% above the uniaxial compressive strength. This occurs when $\sigma_2 \approx 0\cdot4\sigma_1$. Brown notes a splitting mode of failure in this tests and hence the difficulty, in such a case, of applying criteria based on shear stress conditions.

In contrast with stiffness behaviour of earthen materials, it appears that for a wide range of conditions the strength behaviour is almost independent of the stress path to failure. This has been shown, for example, by Campanella and Vaid (1973) for a sensitive marine clay, and by Swanson and Brown (1971) for a range of rock materials.

Deformation processes leading to failure in earthen materials are always associated with the tendency to dilation (e.g. Figures 2.22 and 2.23). This occurs irrespective of whether the failure takes place due to axial cleavage, or whether an *en-echelon* shear zone is etablished in which deformation can be considered as a series of separation modes linked by an alternating series of sliding modes, e.g. the saw-tooth models used to describe rock-joint sliding. The tendency to dilation is made manifest either by volume expansion in stiff and/or brittle materials (e.g. Rosengren and Jaeger, 1968), a decrease in the rate of volume compression in compressible materials, or the development of high lateral stresses for constrained materials (e.g. Hayashi, 1966). In many materials, the onset of failure is often signalled at an early stage by changes in the dilation behaviour associated with propagation or development of the pattern of defects (e.g. Bordia, 1971).

The *en-echelon* pattern of defects developed in granular materials in direct shear has been investigated by Borowicka (1973) and Murayama and Matsuoka (1973). The results of these studies show that the symmetry of the fabric changes from orthorhombic to monoclinic as shearing proceeds, with the distortion at peak strength being greater than when residual strength is reached. Typical results obtained by Borowicka (1973) are shown in Figure 2.29, where the frequency of grain contacts are plotted against the perpendiculars to the tangent planes of the contacts. The number of contacts increase in the range 0–90° with a maximum at 60°, while the contacts in the range 90°–180° are decreased, particularly at intermediate values. This suggests a pattern of separation of contacts in one quadrant, and the development of sliding contacts in the opposite quadrant.

Some of the earliest discussion of the strength of anisotropic earthen materials was due to Casagrande and Carillo (1944). They distinguish between 'inherent' anisotropy as that being initially possessed by the material, and 'induced' anisotropy as that being due to the strain associated with the applied stresses. The 'inherent' anisotropy in earthen materials is produced as a result of the stress systems prevailing at the time the material

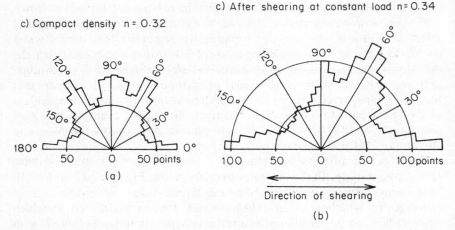

Figure 2.29 Shear tests on sand—frequency of contacts versus orientation of the normals to the tangents to the contacts: (a) Before shearing, (b) After shearing. (After Borowicka, 1973; Figures 3 and 4)

was formed. (The term 'stress' is used here in its broadest sense to include physico–chemical and thermal effects.) The magnitude and symmetry of these stresses will determine the nature of the 'inherent' fabric and the bonds by which it is maintained. If, in a subsequent strength test, the applied stresses are much lower than the formation stresses, then dominant features in the fabric will persist throughout the test and remain to influence the anisotropy observed in the strength. On the other hand, if the stresses applied in the test are high relative to the formation stresses, then the 'inherent' fabric is gradually reorganized during the test. At failure, only remnants of the 'inherent' fabric remain and the fabric is dominated by 'stress-induced' features (e.g. see Figure 2.13). The symmetry of this 'induced' fabric will relate to the symmetry of the applied stress system. When the test stresses and the formation stresses are of the same order, then significant aspects of both the 'inherent' fabric and 'induced' fabric will influence the anisotropy observed at failure. It can be seen that for the engineering range of applied stresses it would be expected that the failure of soft soils may usually be influenced by 'induced' fabric, while for hard rock 'inherent' fabric would dominate, these cases representing the opposite ends of a spectrum.

Where the 'induced' fabric controls the failure it is reasonable to assume that strength tests performed on samples of various orientations may yield similar strength values, if the applied stress system is the same. This is due to a gradual reorganization of the fabric with the significance of 'inherent' features diminishing, and the 'induced' features becoming more important. Examples of this are the reports of 'isotropic' strength by Morgenstern and Tchalenko (1967), following direct shear tests on clay, by Kirkpatrick and Rennie (1972), from tri-axial tests on clay, and by Green and Reades (1975), based on tri-axial and plane strain tests on sand. In such cases the following points should be noted:

(1) The fabric and stiffness of any sample approaching failure will be highly anisotropic with symmetries related to those of the applied stress tensor.

(2) The stress-strain characteristics of samples from different orientations are extremely dissimilar, this being of great importance in any field involving the gradual establishment of a failure surface.

(3) For clays, the pore pressure parameter A is generally anisotropic so that the undrained strengths are anisotropic.

The 'inherent' fabric of most earthen materials has some influence on failure under conditions relevant to engineering, in general this being greater for rocks than for soils. The effect of 'inherent' fabric on the failure of a sand deposited by dropping through air can be seen from the results of Arthur and Menzies (1972). As discussed previously, a horizontal plane of isotropy is produced in the fabric and tests were performed on cube samples with the major principal stress being inclined at angles of $0°$, $20°$, $30°$, $40°$ and $90°$ to this plane. The test results shown in Figure 2.30a and b indicate the variation of strains ε_1 and ε_3 with stress ratio and angle of inclination. In all tests $\sigma_2 = \sigma_3$ and axis 2 was the axis of rotation of the fabric relative to the applied stress system. The greatest strength was found when the principal stress axis coincided with the 'n'-fold axis of symmetry in the fabric, the least strength when these axes were perpendicular to each other, with a monotonic change in strength with angle of rotation. Anisotropic strength was also found by Lafeber and Willoughby (1970) in a beach sand. The drained tri-axial tests performed showed that the monoclinic fabric pattern gave rise to significantly greater strength when tested in the vertical direction than in a horizontal direction. The influence of the fabric on the orientation of the failure planes in this case has been discussed previously.

For many earthen materials the 'inherent' fabric is often dominated by a set of parallel planar features as can be seen from the data in Table 2.1. Lo and Morin (1972) have tested two clays having this type of fabric and have shown that, in effective stress terms, the strength is anisotropic. St Vallier clay and St Louis clay are sensitive marine clays, the first containing layers of sandy silty clay and silty clay, while the second contains bands of fine sand and silt. Their estimated overconsolidation ratios are respectively 2·5 and 2·2. Samples for tri-axial tests were cut from blocks of the materials with the

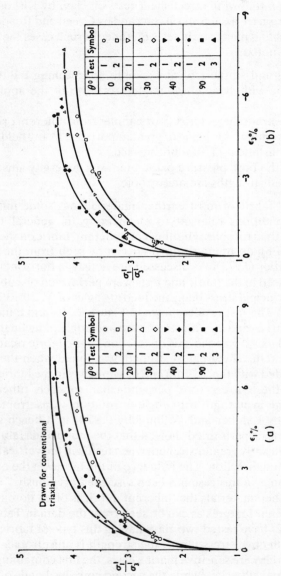

Figure 2.30 Strength tests on sand—principal stress axis inclined to 'n' fold fabric axis: (a) σ_1/σ_3 versus ε_1, (b) σ_1/σ_3 versus ε_3. (After Arthur and Menzies, 1972; Figures 21 and 22; reproduced by permission of The Institution of Civil Engineers)

axes of the cylinders being inclined at angles i of 0°, 45°, 60° and 90° to the normal to the layering or banding planes. The results of undrained tests are shown in Figure 2.31a for the St Louis clay and Figure 2.31b for the St Vallier clay, the stress paths to failure for $i = 90°$ being shown in Figure 2.31b. The patterns for the two clays are clearly similar, with the minimum strength being 0·54 to 0·70 times that in the vertical direction at low to intermediate stress levels. At higher stress levels orientation of the samples appears to have little effect on the strength. It appears that at low stress levels the 'inherent' fabric dominates, giving significant differences of

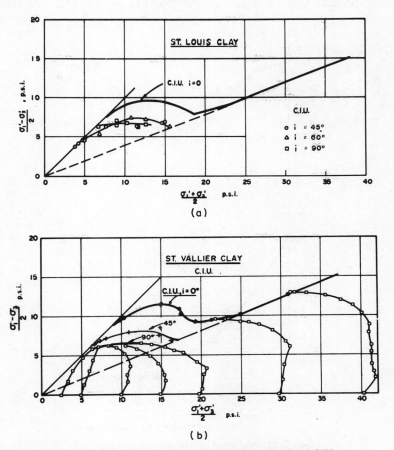

Figure 2.31　Anisotropy in strength of sensitive marine clays from CIU tests: (a) St. Louis Clay, (b) St. Vallier Clay. (Reproduced by permission of the National Research Council of Canada from Lo and Morin, 1972; Figures 8 and 9)

strength with orientation, while at high stress levels the stress-induced fabric produced in the failure zones in sample dominates the behaviour. At intermediate stress levels, a transition between the two occurs. This explanation is supported by the observation that at low stresses the failures are brittle and often involve a splitting mechanism, while at high stress the failures are ductile. Anisotropic strength, in effective stress terms, has also been found by Sangrey (1972) in a naturally cemented sensitive clay.

Several workers have performed tri-axial tests on rocks having dominant planar features in their fabric. Examples are Donath (1972), who tested a slate, a phyllite and a schist, Chenevert and Gatlin (1965), who tested a

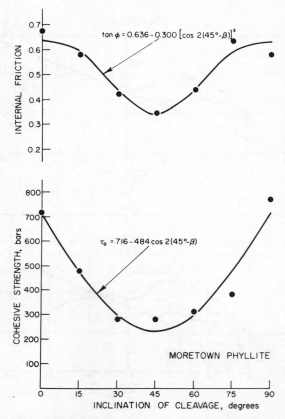

Figure 2.32 Variation of cohesive strength and coefficient of internal friction in Moretown Phyllite as a function of inclination of cleavage. (After Donath, 1972; Figure 4; reproduced by permission of the Geological Society of America)

sandstone and several shales, and Akai, Yamanoto, *et al.* (1970) who tested two schists. The variation of strength with the angle of inclination of the major principal stress, relative to the fabric planes, shows a smooth variation in all cases. This is in contrast with the discontinuities in the characteristic curve, predicted by the single plane of weakness theory suggested by Jaeger (1960). This discrepancy may be due to Jaeger's assumption that ϕ did not vary with orientation. Subsequent test results (e.g. Donath, 1972) show that this assumption is incorrect, as can be seen in Figure 2.32, where the angle of friction and cohesive strength of Moretown phyllite are plotted against the inclination of cleavage.

Direct shear tests on a model material representing a single system of parallel planar joints have been conducted by Hayashi (1966). It is important to note that because of the monoclinic symmetry of this test arrangement, joint-plane inclinations over a range of 180° need to be considered, rather than the range of 90° considered when a tri-axial test is used, e.g. Chenevert and Gatlin (1965), Donath (1972). A positive joint system is defined by Hayashi as where the angle between the direction of the shear and the joint planes is between 0° and 90°, while for a negative joint system this angle is between 0° and −90°. Two sets of tests were conducted and in the first the direct stress normal to the shearing direction was held constant during shearing, while in the second the direct strain normal to the shearing direction was held constant. The results for the first set of tests, as shown in Figure 2.33, indicate a greater strength for positive joint systems, largely due to the cohesion component, since the friction factor is marginally greater for negative joint systems. For the second set of tests, i.e. for constant, normal, direct strain, the pattern of strength behaviour was reversed and was much greater for negative joint systems than for positive joint systems. This was due to the fact that for negative joint systems, compared with positive joint systems, a much larger normal direct stress was required to prevent expansive normal direct strains. Further direct shear tests on model materials containing patterns of parallel planar joints, both continuous and intermittent, have been conducted by Kawamoto (1970). The normal direct stress was held constant, and the normal direct strains showed greater extension for negative joint systems than for positive joint systems, this being in accordance with the pattern of dilatancy restraining forces observed by Hayashi (1966). The patterns of variation of strength, with orientation found by Hayashi and Kawamoto, were similar with maxima at about 60° and at about −30° and minima at 0° and about −60°. Differences could be attributed to different C and ϕ values. Kawamoto found that the effect of intermittent joints compared with continuous ones was to increase strength, generally decrease dilatancy, and to decrease the degree of anisotropy.

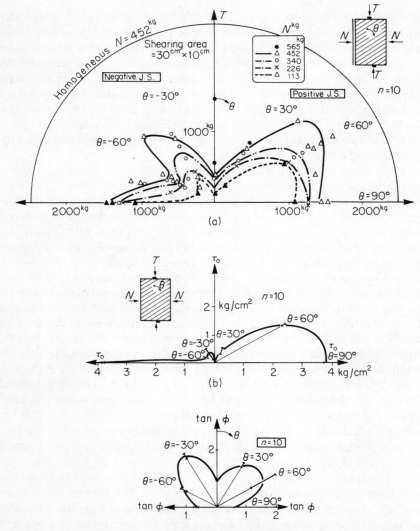

Figure 2.33 Strength tests on model layered material—direct shear tests with constant normal stress: (a) Total strength variation with orientation, (b) Apparent cohesion variation with orientation, (c) Apparent internal friction factor variation with orientation. (Reproduced by permission from Hayashi, 1966; Figure 12)

The shear strength properties of an earthen material containing two dominant sets of defects have been examined by Morgenstern and Noonan (1974). The material was a coal from Alberta, Canada, and a fabric analysis indicated that bedding consisted to thin horizontal bands, and that a single set of parallel joints or cleats was oriented at right angles to the bedding. The average joint spacing was about 20 mm, with most joints being continuous and closed for several feet. The results of direct shear tests, together with the respective orientations of the bedding, the joint (fracture) planes, and the shear test plane are shown in Figure 2.34. For the four test and fabric configurations shown the shear strength parameters were:

	A	B	F	G
c (MPa)	0·41	0·52	0·17	0·34
ϕ (degrees)	41	42	68	65

It is of interest to note that the value of ϕ measured on pre-cut planes was 30°.

The above examples show that strength data should always be accompanied by descriptions of the test configuration, the symmetries of the applied stress system, and the 'inherent' fabric of the earthen material tested.

2.2.6 Role of pore fluids

Soil and rock masses are porous media comprised of solid, liquid and/or gas components. Pore fluids influence the mechanical response of earthen materials in the following ways:

(1) Pressures in these fluids cause the effective stresses acting between solid particles to be different from the total applied stresses. The shear strength and volume change characteristics related to these effective stresses rather than tot*$\dot{a}$* stresses.

(2) Spatial differences in the soil–water potential will result in flow, which may be steady-state or transient, depending on the boundary conditions.

(3) A range of silicate and alumino-silicate minerals have a physico-chemical reaction with moisture. Access to water in these cases can lead to a weakening and/or softening effect.

The concept of effective stress for saturated soils was proposed by Terzaghi (1923) in the form $\sigma' = \sigma - u_w$, where σ' is effective stress, σ is total stress, and u_w is pore water pressure.

Extensive experimental evidence has confirmed the validity of this effective stress in controlling the shear strength and volume change characteristics of saturated soils. For stiffer materials Skempton (1961) has shown the need to allow for relative increases in effective stress for cases where the contact area becomes significantly large and/or where the compressibility of the porous material is relatively low. There is, however, considerable

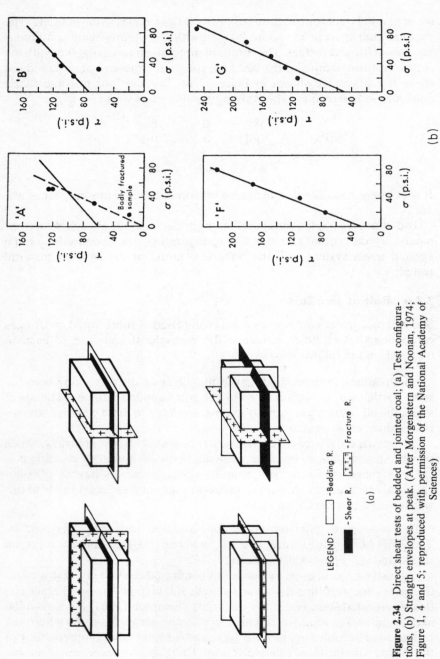

Figure 2.34 Direct shear tests of bedded and jointed coal; (a) Test configurations, (b) Strength envelopes at peak. (After Morgenstern and Noonan, 1974; Figure 1, 4 and 5; reproduced with permission of the National Academy of Sciences)

difficulty in evaluating the components of the modified effective stress law for rocks (Robin, 1973) and recent tests indicate that the simple Terzaghi law can be adequate in certain conditions, e.g. Byerlee (1966): sliding of westerly granite; Handin, Hager, *et al.* (1963) and Brace and Martin (1968): peak strength of sedimentary rocks and low porosity crystalline rocks; Cornet and Fairhurst (1972): elastic limit of Berea sandstone. The application of the effective stress law to rocks is complicated when the pore space is not interconnected as found by Cornet and Fairhurst (1974) from tests on Indiana limestone. The strength was not significantly affected but the post-peak slope was much flatter than for material with interconnected pores.

In undrained shear tests pore-pressure changes are induced in saturated earthen materials. This has been well established in soils and Ohnishi and Goodman (1974) have measured pore pressures of up to 20 per cent of the peak shear stress in tests on artificial joints in sandstone. This behaviour may partially explain the often reported 'apparent' decrease in shear strength when rock is saturated.

For partly saturated materials, Skempton (1961) proposed that the term be replaced by $u_a - \chi(u_a - u_w)$ where u_a is the pore air pressure, χ is an experimental coefficient and is zero for dry material and unity for saturated. For soils in which high suctions occur, Aitchison (1973) has discussed the difficulty of measuring the components in this effective stress law, and proposes the following mechanistic statement

$$\sigma' = \sigma + x_m P''_m + x_s P''_x$$

where P''_m is matric suction $= u_a - u_w$, the symbol P''_s is solute suction, and x_m, x_s are factors with values between zero and unity, depending on stress path. Since x_m and x_s cannot yet be simply determined, Aitchison suggests that the effective stress principle can only be correctly applied by using stress path testing in which the three components σ, P''_m and P''_s are applied in the correct magnitudes and sequences. The influence of each of these components on the one-dimensional deformation of a pleistocene clay is shown in Figure 2.35. In each case, one component is varied whilst the other two are held constant. The highly significant influence of solute suction on deformation for low values of applied stress is apparent. High suctions can also occur in argillaceous rocks (e.g. Chenevert, 1969), and affect behaviour in the manner described by the effective stress law.

The proper application of the effective stress law to strength and volume change considerations of earthen masses can only be achieved if the nature and scale of the fabric components of such masses are recognized and understood. As pointed out by Aitchison (1973) in discussing structurally unstable soils, '*The stress response of a system could well be determined by the*

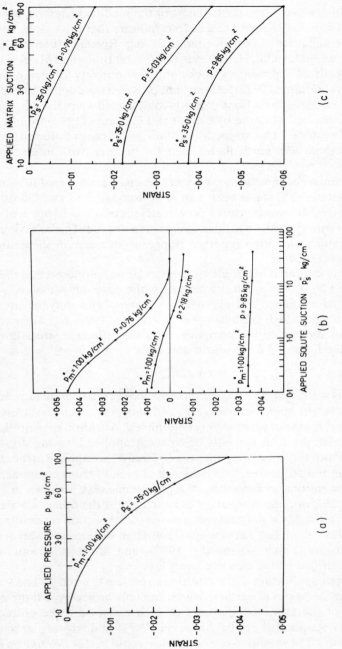

Figure 2.35 Comparative effects of applied pressure, matrix suction, and solute suction in a partly saturated clay: (a) Applied pressure vs. strain, (b) Solute suction vs. strain, (c) Matrix suction vs. strain. (After Aitchison, 1973; Figure 5)

stress level within a critical phase of the system rather than by the average stress level throughout the system'.

Fluid flow through the pores of earthen materials may cause excessive seepage, material transport with the possiblity of piping failure, or redistribution of pore pressure and hence changes in effective stresses. The permeability or hydraulic conductivity is closely related to the fabric in terms of the geometry of the pore spaces. In a number of cases, e.g. Marshall (1958) for soils (see Figure 2.36a), and Rocha (1972) for jointed rocks (see Figure 2.36b), workers have derived expressions for permeability on the basis of the pore geometry. Subsequent testing has demonstrated the validity of such expressions, particularly with regard to the dominant effect that relatively few large pores can have if they are continuously connected. Other important factors are the orientation of pores and the degree of spatial uniformity in the pore pattern. The mean spacing of the pores relative to the overall dimensions of the earthen mass will determine whether a 'pseudo' continuum approach can be adopted, or whether each major pore will have to be modelled in detail.

Anisotropies in fabric patterns are reflected in permeability anisotropy which, for a given earthen material, is usually of higher order than the related stiffness anisotropy. In a jointed rock, Rocha (1972) suggests a hundredfold difference in permeability with direction (see Figure 2.36b) while for London clay Rowe (1972) shows the horizontal permeability to be much greater than the vertical permeability due to the presence of horizontally bedded permeable inclusions (see Figure 2.37a).

Flow in earthen materials may be laminar, as described by Darcy's law, or turbulent, for those cases where the Reynolds number is sufficiently high. Non-laminar flow only occurs in soils for the rare cases of fluid flow at high velocity or gas flow at low velocity (Lambe and Whitman, 1969). Laminar and turbulent flows in jointed rocks have been studied by Louis and Maini (1970) and although the quantity of flow is relatively less in the case of turbulence the pore pressure patterns are similar.

Changes in effective stress cause changes in the pore geometry and hence changes in the permeability If the stress change tends to close pores the permeability decreases [e.g. Rowe, 1972 (silty clay); Brace and Martin, 1968; (granite); Rosengren and Jaeger, 1968 (cracked marble)], while shear stress increase may open pores and increase permeability (Sharp and Maini, 1972 (jointed rock)). These investigations highlight the potential danger of investigating flow patterns on the basis of site investigations on the materials in their *initial* effective stress state. The variation in permeability of a sample of London clay with effective vertical stress is shown in Figure 2.37a, while the variation of permeability of a partly saturated clay with variation in suction is shown in Figure 2.37b. For an artificial rock joint in sandstone

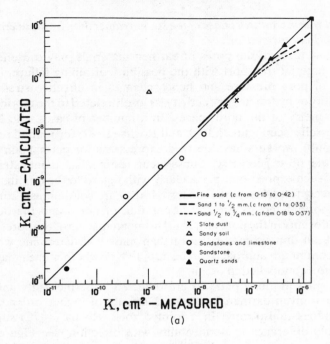

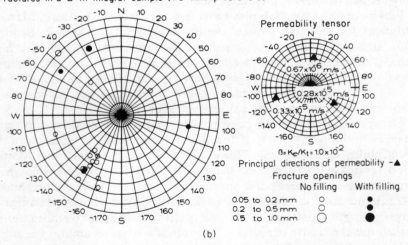

Figure 2.36 Relation between pore geometry and permeability: (a) Soils, (b) Jointed rock. (After Marshal, 1958; Figure 2; reproduced by permission of Oxford University Press; and Rocha M, 1972; Figures 9 and 11)

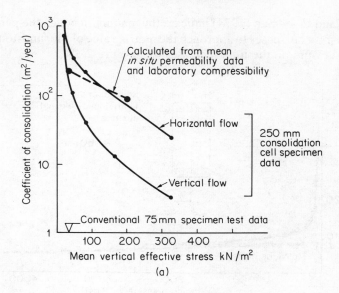

(a)

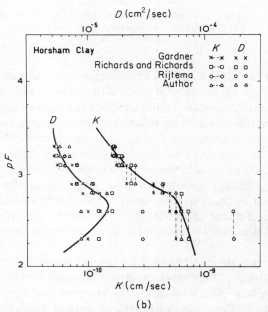

(b)

Figures 2.37 Change in permeability with stress in soils: (a) Saturated clay, (b) Partly saturated clay. (After Rowe, 1972; Figure 32; reproduced by permission of the Institute of Civil Engineers; and Richards, 1967; Figure 3)

Ohnishi and Goodman (1974) indicate the manner in which the permeability of the joint decreases to approach the matrix value of the sandstone as the normal pressure on the joint increases (see Figure 2.38).

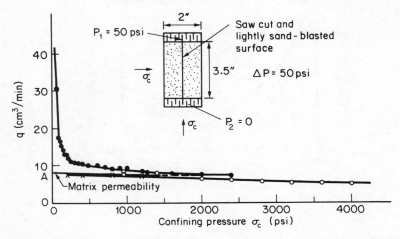

Figure 2.38 Change in rock joint permeability with normal stress. (After Ohnishi and Goodman, 1974; Figure 13; reproduced with permission of the National Academy of Sciences)

The physico-chemical reactions of moisture with earthen materials fall into several categories, the chief of which is the shrink–swell phenomenon in clays. The mechanism involved is described by the Gouy–Chapman double-layer theory and the potential for this behaviour to occur is closely linked to the magnitude of the specific surface of the mineral involved, typical values being montmorillonite ($1000 \, \text{m}^2/\text{g}$), illite ($100 \, \text{m}^2/\text{g}$), kaolinite ($10 \, \text{m}^2/\text{g}$), $0 \cdot 1 \, \text{mm}$ sand ($0 \cdot 03 \, \text{m}^2/\text{g}$) (Lambe and Whitman, 1969). Softening in clays is due to increased moisture content, and in partly saturated materials this is inversely related to suction. The results of Richards and Gordon (1972) show how the resilient modulus of a remoulded partly saturated soil decreases with decrease in suction, i.e. increase in moisture content (see Figure 2.39).

The influence of fabric on the swelling of a range of clays has been shown by Rogatkina (1967). These clays contained predominant sets of horizontal bedding joints often filled with sand. The structure varied from thin laminated to schistose. Both the deformation modulus and the potential for swelling were greater in the direction normal to the bedding than parallel to the bedding. The latter phenomena arises from the relatively easy penetration of water along the joints.

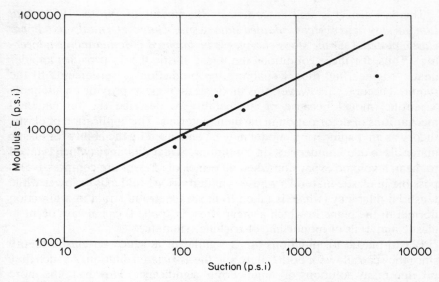

Figure 2.39 Change in resilient modulus of partly saturated clay with suction. (After Richards and Gordon, 1972, Figure 3)

The weakening effect of the hydration of silicate minerals in rocks has been raised by Nur (1974). He suggests that this may explain the observations of crack growth and fracture of quartz in the presence of water. Nur also raises the question of the dehydration of hydrated minerals at extremely high pressure (e.g. serpentine → olivine, talc, water). The release of water causes an apparent drop in strength because of the reduction in the effective confining stress.

2.3 DISCUSSION OF MATHEMATICAL MODELS

The development of mathematical models in applied geomechanics must be related to four basic aspects:

(1) The nature of the four interacting inputs relevant to geomechanics problems, i.e. material properties, imposed loading, overall geometry and environmental factors.

(2) The natural variability that is usually associated with these inputs, particularly the material properties and the environmental factors.

(3) The dependence of the properties of earthen materials on their fabric and complete stress history.

(4) The distinction between the criteria for an adequate 'scientific' model and an adequate 'engineering' model.

This last aspect is well illustrated by the finding of Wroth (1972) '*that London clay in its overconsolidated state* in situ *behaves essentially as a linear elastic material for the stress changes to be imposed in foundation engineering*'. Thus, for these conditions the linear elastic theory provides an adequate 'engineering' model enabling the prediction of settlements to the required accuracy. However, this theory is unlikely to provide an adequate 'scientific' model because of its inability to describe the fundamental mechanisms of deformation in earthen materials. The application of elastic theory as an 'engineering' model may be enhanced by the ability for elastic materials to dilate under certain conditions. Scalar dilatancy (which is taken to mean a volume expansion when all principal stresses are compressive) is possible in elastic materials whose symmetry is 'n'-fold axis or lower while tensorial dilatancy (which is taken to mean extension strain in a direction normal to the plane in which a shear stress is applied) can always occur in elastic materials of monoclinic or triclinic symmetry.

Elasto-plastic formulations are a significant advance on elastic theory since they can allow for both failure and the associated dilation. As such they provide many solutions of 'engineering' significance. However, the more simple formulations can be criticized on the basis that stress history cannot be allowed for in the elastic phase, and in the plastic phase it is difficult to represent the true dilation characteristics of earthen materials. The concepts of hyper-elastic, hypo-elastic, and simple materials, as discussed by Truesdell and Noll (1965), appear to be relevant to geomechanics problems but have had little application to date. The hyper-elastic material has some restrictions in that while it can deform in a way analogous to the development of 'induced' fabric, it still relies on the concept of a stored energy function. Hypo-elasticity is less restrictive than hyper-elasticity but still implies recoverability of deformation on load removal. The concept of simple material with fading memory may provide a satisfactory basis for the development of a 'scientific' mathematical model for applied geomechanics. Another promising development in 'scientific' models is that of the blocky model (e.g. Byrne, 1974). In this approach the discrete nature of most earthen masses is recognized from the outset and attention is focused on the nature of the contacts.

The development of 'scientific' mathematical models, for practical geomechanics problems, should be based on the accumulation of data relating to the mechanical response of earthen materials when subject to the range of practical stress paths (e.g. Figure 2.4). In order to avoid spurious discussion related to the problems of mathematical expediencies rather than real behaviour, mathematical formulation should not proceed until a balanced and reliable bank of data is available for all of the relevant inputs. The following components are considered essential in a 'scientific' model:

(1) The definition of input data in stochastic, rather than deterministic form. Information on the variance associated with each component of input data is essential, previous studies usually indicating that this is underestimated.

(2) The application of probabilistics to achieve the required degree of certainty in the prediction by balancing the uncertainties in the input data and the uncertainties involved in the modelling process itself.

(3) The geological processes relevant to the formation of the deposit and their correlation with observations of 'inherent' fabric, prior stress history, current stress patterns and anisotropies in the mechanical properties. These are often ignored in current mathematical models which assume a 'random' distribution and/or orientation of contacts, pores, fissures or joints. Fabric patterns of this type occur extremely rarely in *natural* earthen materials. However, it is not a simple matter to recognize and quantify those fabric elements that will be relevant to the particular geomechanics problem. The inadequancy of current techniques reflects the long existing gap between descriptive engineering geology and theoretical geomechanics. The satisfactory bridging of this gap should be one of the highest priorities for research in geomechanics. When this is achieved the effects of the construction or development being modelled can be seen in context as part of an overall pattern of stress and strain history.

(4) A formulation to link increments of stress with increments of strain. The main aspects are non-linearity and time dependence. A change in the pattern of stresses induces interrelated strains and fabric changes. The nature and symmetries of the modified fabric will dictate the material response to further changes in stress pattern. The fabric changes accompanying changes in stress pattern take time to develop and this development is affected by the time rate of stress change. Any formulation linking stress and strain for any practical problem should be based on the definition of the magnitudes, sequence and time rates of field stress changes and the interaction of these with the nature, symmetry and time rate of changes of the fabrics of the earthen materials.

(5) A formulation for failure. The development of failure should be traced by relating the symmetry and magnitude of the 'inherent' fabric pattern, to the symmetry and magnitude of the applied stress tensor. This allows the relative effects of 'inherent' fabric and 'induced' fabric to be correctly deduced in relation to the various observed modes of failure. A correct formulation for dilatancy is important from at least two points of view. Firstly, the initiation of dilatancy is often a tell-tale warning of approaching failure and, secondly, arching and wedging can be developed if dilatancy is totally or partially restrained.

(6) An effective stress law indicating the factors involved in fabric reorganization and deformation. It may not be necessary to evaluate the coefficients in the law if all the relevant variables are measured and applied in their correct sequence in stress path tests. The way in which pore pressures develop with changes in stress pattern also needs to be described. Many current formulations ignore the role of shear stresses in this regard.

(7) A flow law incorporating the transition from laminar to turbulent flow and the relationship between the magnitude and anisotropy of the permeability and the dimensions and orientations of the pores. Another important factor is that changes in stress patterns change the pore geometry and hence the permeability.

(8) A description of the physico-chemical reactions that commonly occur in earthen materials. The chief of these is the reaction of clays with water, particularly where there is a change in the electrolyte in the pore liquid.

In conclusion it must be emphasized that the development of mathematical models must be balanced by corresponding developments in the measurement and quantification of the input data and in the monitoring of full-scale structures.

Acknowledgements

The approach adopted in this paper has evolved over several years and was particularly aided by discussions with Dr G. D. Aitchison and the late Dr D. Lafeber. The author recalls with gratitude many discussions with Dr Lafeber dealing with the relationship between geometric and mechanical anisotropies in *natural* earthen materials.

During the preparation of this paper the comments of several of my colleagues have been most useful. These include Dr C. M. Barton, Mrs E. Kriegel, Mr P. Pahl, Mr G. Price and Mr B. G. Richards. The assistance of Mrs G. Gavin, Mr J. Walsh, Mrs. H. Topp and my wife in preparing the final copy of the typescript are gratefully acknowledged.

REFERENCES

Aitchison, G. D. (1973). 'General Report Session 4 (Problems of soil mechanics and construction on soft clays and structurally unstable soils)', *Proc. Eighth Inter. Conf. Soil Mech. Found. Engng*, **3**, 161–190.

Akai, K., Yamanoto, K., and Arioka, M. (1970). 'Experimentelle Forschung über anisotropische Eigenschaften von Kristallinen Schiefern', *Proc. Second Congress Int. Soc. Rock Mech.*, Belgrade, **2**, 181–192.

Alexander, L. G., Worotnicki, G., and Aubrey, K. (1963). 'Stress and deformation in rock and rock support, Tumut 1 and 2 underground power stations', *Proc. Fourth Aust.-New Zealand Conf. Soil Mech. Found. Engng*, 165–178.

Alexandrov, K. S., Ryzhova, T. V., Belikov, B. P., and Shabanova, L. A. (1969). 'Anisotropy of elastic properties of rock', *Inter. Geol. Review*, **11**, 5, 539–547.

Aramburu, J. A. (1974). 'La Angostura Dam Underground Powerhouse: Prediction and measurement of displacements during excavation', *Proc. Third Congress Inter. Soc. Rock Mech.*, *Denver*, **2**, Part B, 1231–1241.

Arthur, J. R. F. and Menzies, B. K. (1972). 'Inherent anisotropy in a sand', *Geotechnique*, **22**, 1, 115–128.

Atkinson, J. H. (1975). 'Anisotropic elastic deformations in laboratory tests on undisturbed London Clay', *Geotechnique*, **25**, 2, 357–374.

Attewell, P. B. (1970). 'Triaxial anisotropy of wave velocity and elastic moduli in slate and their axial concordance with fabric and tectonic symmetry', *Int. J. Rock Mech. Min. Sci.*, **7**, 193–207.

Barden, L. and Khayatt, A. J. (1966). 'Incremental strain rate ratios and strength of sand', *Geotechnique*, **16**, 4, 338.

Barla G. and Goffi, L. (1974). 'Direct tensile testing of anisotropic rocks', *Proc. Third Congress Inter. Soc. Rock Mech.*, *Denver*, **2**, Part A, 93–98.

Barton, C. M. (1973). 'The micromorphological soil investigation work of Dr. D. Lafeber', *Proc. Fourth Inter. Working Meeting on Soil Micromorphology*, *Queens Uni.*, *Ontario* Limestone Press, 1–19.

Barton, C. M. (1975). 'An analysis of rock structure and fabric in the C.S.A. Mine, Cobar, New South Wales', CSIRO, Division of Applied Geomechanics, *Tech. Report*.

Berger, H. (1966). 'Einflüsse der Messmethoden auf die Gültigkeit Statistischer Kluftanalysen', *Proc. First Congress Inter. Soc. Rock Mech.*, *Lisbon*, **1**, 145–151.

Berry, P., Crea, G., Martino, D., and Ribacchi, R. (1974). 'The influence of fabric on the deformability of anisotropic rocks', *Proc. Third Congress Inter. Soc. Rock*, *Mech.*, *Denver*, **2**, Part A, 105–110.

Bhaskaran, R. (1974). 'Strength anisotropy in kaolinite clay', *Geotechnique*, **24**, 4, 674–677.

Bhaskaran, R. (1975). 'Variability in strength and deformation characteristics of anisotropic clays', *Symp. Recent Development Analysis Soil Behaviour and Application to Geotechnical Structures*, *Uni. of N.S.W.*, *Sydney, Australia*, 289.

Biarez, J. (1961). 'Contributions a l'etude des propriétés mécaniques des sols et des matériaux pulvérulents', *Doctoral Thesis*, University of Grenoble, France.

Bishop, A. W. (1966). 'The strength of soils as engineering materials (Sixth Rankine Lecture)', *Geotechnique*, **16**, 2, 91–128.

Bishop, A. W. (1972). 'Shear strength parameters for undisturbed and remoulded soil specimens', *Proc. Roscoe Memorial Symp.*, *Stress-strain Behaviour of Soils*, *Cambridge*, 3–58.

Bishop, A. W., Green, G. E., and Skinner, A. E. (1973). 'Strength and deformation measurements on soils', *Proc. Eighth Inter. Conf. Soil Mech. and Found. Engng*, *Moscow*, **1.1**, 57–64.

Bishop, A. W., Webb, D. L., and Lewin, P. I. (1965). 'Undisturbed samples of London Clay from the Ashford Common Shaft: Strength-effective stress relationships', *Geotechnique*, **15**, 1, 1–31.

Bjerrum, L. (1973). 'Problems of soil mechanics and construction on soft clays and structurally unstable soils (General Report)', *Proc. Eighth Inter. Conf. on Soil Mech. and Found. Engng*, *Moscow*, **3**, 111–159.

Bordia, S. K. (1971). 'The effects of size and stress concentration on the dilatancy and fracture of rock', *Inter. J. Rock Mech. Min. Sci.*, **8**, 629–640.

Boretti-Onyszkiewicz, W. (1966). 'Joints in the flysch sandstones on the ground of strength examinations', *Proc. First Congress Inter. Soc. Rock Mech., Lisbon*, **1**, 153–157.

Borowicka, H. (1973). 'Rearrangement of grains by shear tests with sand', *Proc. Eighth Inter. Conf. Mech. Found. Engng*, **1.1**, 71–78.

Brace, W. F., and Martin, R. J. (1968). 'A test of effective stress law for crystalline rocks of low porosity', *Inter. J. Rock Mech. and Min. Sci.*, **5**, 415.

Brace, W. F., Walsh, J. B., and Frangos, W. T. (1968). 'Permeability of granite under high pressure', *J. Geophys. Res.*, **73**, 2225.

Brace, W. F., Walsh, J. B., and Frangos, W. T. (1968). 'Permeability of granite under high pressure', *J. Geophys. Res.*, **73**, 2225.

Brady, B. T. (1969). 'The non-linear mechanical behaviour of brittle rock, Part I', *Inter J. Rock Mech. Min-Sci.*, **6**, 211–225.

Broadbent, C. D. and Ko, K. C. (1972). 'Rheological aspects of rock slope failures', *Proc. Thirteenth Symp. Roch Mech.*, (*Stability of Rock Slopes*), ASCE, 573–693.

Brooker, E. W. and Ireland, H. C. (1965). 'Earth pressures at rest related to stress history', *Canadian Geotech. J.*, **2**, 1–15.

Brown, E. T. (1974). 'Fracture of rock under uniform biaxial compression', *Proc. Third Congress Int. Soc. Rock Mech., Denver*, **2**, Part A, 111–117.

Busching, H. W., Goetz, W. H., and Harr, M. E. (1967). 'Stress-deformation behaviour of anisotropic bituminous mixtures', *Proc. Assoc. Asphalt Paving Tech.*, **36**, 632–671.

Byerlee, J. D. (1966). 'The frictional characteristics of Westerly granite', *Ph.D. Thesis*, Massachusetts Institute of Technology.

Byrne, J. (1974). 'Physical and numerical models in rock and soil slope stability', *Ph.D. Thesis*, University of North Queensland, Australia.

Campanella, R. G. and Vaid, Y. P. (1973). 'Influence of stress path on the plane strain behaviour of a sensitive clay', *Proc. Eighth Int. Conf. Soil Mech. and Found. Engng, Moscow*, **1.1**, 85–92.

Casagrande, A. and Carrillo, N. (1944). 'Shear failure of anisotropic materials', *J. Boston Soc. Civ. Engrs*, **31**, 4, 122.

Charles, R. J. (1958). 'Static fatigue of glass', *J. Appl. Phys.* **29**, 1549–1560.

Chenevert, M. E. (1969). 'Adsorptive pore pressures on argillaceous rocks', *Proc. Eleventh Symp. Rock Mech.—Theory and Practice*, 599–627.

Chenevert, M. E. and Gatlin, C. (1965). 'Mechanical anisotropies of laminated sedimentary rocks', *J. Soc. Petroleum Engineers*, **5**, 1, 67.

Christensen, N. I. and Ramananantoandro, R. (1971). 'Elastic moduli and anisotropy of dunite to 10 kilobrars', *Journal of Geophysical Research*, **76**, 17, 4003–4010.

Clark, G. B. (1966). 'Deformation moduli of rocks', *ASTM Spec. Tech. Publ. No. 402, Testing Techniques for Rock Mechanics*', 133–174.

Cornet, F. H., and Fairhurst, C. (1972). 'Variations of pore volume in disintegrating rocks', *Symp. Inter. Soc. Rock Mech., Stuttgart*, 'Percolation through fissured rocks', pp. T2-A, 1–8.

Cornet, F. H. and Fairhurst, C. (1974). 'Influence of pore pressure on the deformation behaviour of saturated rocks', *Proc. Third Congress Inter. Soc. Rock Mech., Denver*, **II**, Part A, 638–644.

Cruden, D. M. (1971). 'Single increment creep experiments of rock under uniaxial compression', *Inter. J. Rock Mech. Min. Sci.*, **8**, 127–142.

De Beer, E., Delmer, A. and Wallays, M. (1968). 'Essais de charge en galene et en surface avec plaques de grandes dimensions', *Proc. Inter. Symp. on Rock Mech.*, *Madrid*, 13–33.

De Beer, E. E., Graulich, J. M., and Wallays, M. (1974). 'In-situ testing for determining the modulus of compressibility of a rock mass consisting of shales', *Proc. Third Congress Int. Soc. Rock Mech.*, *Denver*, **IIA**, 645–653.

Diaz-Padilla, J. and Vanmarke, E. H. (1973). 'Settlement Prediction: A Probabilistic Approach', *Research Report R73–40*, Dept. of Civil Engng, MIT.

Dodd, J. S. and Anderson, H. W. (1972). 'Tectonic stresses and rock slope stability', *Proc. Thirteenth Symp. Rock Mech.*, (*Stability of Rock Slopes*), 171–182.

Donath, F. A. (1972). 'Effects of cohesion and granularity on deformational behaviour of anisotropic rock', *Geol. Soc. Am.*, *Memoir* 135, 95–128.

Douglas, P. M. and Voight, B. (1969). 'Anisotropy of granites: A reflection of microscopic fabric', *Geotechnique*, **19**, 3, 376–398.

Dreyer, W. (1972). 'The science of rock mechanics, Part I. (The strength properties of rocks)', *Trans. Tech. Publications*.

Duvall, W. I. (1965). 'Effect of anisotropy on the determination of Dynamic Elastic Constants of Rock', *A.I.M.E. Trans.*, **232**, 4, 309–316.

El-Sohby, M. A. (1964). 'The behaviour of particulate materials under stress', *Ph.D. Thesis*, Uni. of Manchester.

El-Sohby, M. A. and Andrawes, K. Z. (1973). 'Experimental examination of sand anisotropy', *Proc. Eighth Inter. Conf. Soil Mech. Found. Engng*, **1.1**, 103.

Evdokimov, P. D. and Sapegin, D. D. (1964). '*Stability Shear and Sliding Resistance, and Deformation of Rock Foundations*', Translated from Russian by Israel Program for Scientific Translations (1967).

Feda, J., Kamenov, B., and Klablena, P. (1973). 'Investigation of creep and structure of clayey materials', *Proc. Eighth Inter. Conf. on Soil Mech. and Found. Engng*, *Moscow*, **1.1**, 123–128.

Folayan, J. I., Hoeg, K., and Benjamin, J. R. (1970). 'Decision theory applied to settlement predictions', *J. Soil Mech. and Found. Div.*, ASCE, **96**, No. SM4, 1127–1141.

Fookes, P. G. and Denness, B. (1969). 'Fissure patterns in the creaceous sediments', *Geotechnique*, **19**, 4, 453–477.

Franklin, J. A. (1970). 'Observations and tests for engineering description and mapping of rocks', *Proc. Second Congress Inter. Soc. Rock Mech.*, *Belgrade*, **1**, 11–16.

Fraser, R. A. and Wardle, L. J. (1975). 'Raft foundations—case study and sensitivity analysis', Submitted to *Conf. on Application of Statistics and Probability to Soil and Structural Engineering, Aachen*.

Friedman, M. (1964). 'Petrofabric techniques for the determination of principal stress directions in rocks', *Proc. Inter. Conf. on State of Stress in Earth's Crust*, Elsevier, 451–550.

Gerrard, C. M. (1967). 'Some aspects of the stress strain behaviour of a dry sand', *Aust. Rd. Res.*, **3**, 4, 67–90.

Gibson, R. E. (1974). 'The Analytical method in soil mechanics', *Geotechnique*, **24**, 2, 114–140.

Gilkes, R. J. (1968). 'Clay mineral provinces in the tertiary sediments of the Hampshire basis clay', *Minerals*, **7**, 351–361.

Graton, L. C. and Fraser, H. J. (1935). 'Systematic packing of spheres with particular relation to porosity and permeability', *J. of Geology*, **43**, 785–909.

Green, G. E. and Reades, D. W. (1975). 'Boundary conditions, anisotropy and sample shape effects on the stress-strain behaviour of sand in tri-axial compression and plane strain', *Geotechnique*, **25**, 2, 333–356.

Griggs, D. T., Turner, F., Borg, I., and Sosoka, J. (1953). 'Deformation of Yule marble, Part V and VI, *Bull. Geol. Soc. Am.*, **64**, 1323–1352.

Griggs, D. T., Turner, F., and Heard, H. C. (1960). 'Deformation of rocks at 500C and 800C', *Geol. Soc. Am. Mem. (Rock Deformation)*, **79**, 39–104.

Habib, P. (1951). 'Nouvelles récherches en méchanique du sol', *Annales de l'Institut Tech. due Batîment Trav. Pub.*, December, 1.

Hardin, B. C. and Black, W. L. (1966). 'Sand stiffness under various triaxial stresses', *J. Soil Mech. Found. Div.*, *ASCE*, **92**, SM2, 27–42.

Handin, J., Hager, R. V., Friedman, M., and Feather, J. N. (1973). 'Experimental deformation of sedimentary rocks under confining pressure: pore pressure tests', *Amer. Assoc. Petrol. Geol. Bull.*, **47**, 717.

Hardy, H. R., Kim, R. Y., Stefanko, R., and Wang, Y. J. (1970). 'Creep and microseismic activity in geologic materials', *Proc. Eleventh Symp. Rock Mech. (Rock Mech.—Theory and Practice)*, Am. Inst. Min. Metallurg. and Petrol. Engngs, 377–413.

Hasofer, A. M. (1974a). 'Reliability index and failure probability', *J. Struct. Mech.*, **3**, No. 1, 25–27.

Hasofer, A. M. (1974b). 'Exact second moment reliability for sum of products failure equation', *J. Struct. Mech.*, **3**, 1, 97–106.

Hayashi, M. (1966). 'Strength and dilatancy of brittle jointed mass—the extreme value stochastics and anisotropic failure mechanism', *Proc. First Congress Int. Soc. Rock Mech., Lisbon*, **1**, 295–302.

Hoek, E. (1965). 'Rock fracture under static stress conditions', *Natl. Mech. Eng. Res. Inst., CSIR, Pretoria, Report MEG383*.

Holden, J. C. (1967). 'Stresses and strains in a sand mass subjected to a uniform circular load', *Ph.D. Thesis*, University of Melbourne, Australia.

Hoshino, K. and Koide, H. (1970). 'Process of deformation of the sedimentary rocks', *Proc. Second Congress Inter. Soc. Rock Mech., Belgrade*, **1**, 353, 359.

Houpert, R. (1974). 'The role of time in rock failure behaviour (in French)', *Proc. Third Congress Inter. Soc. Rock Mech., Denver*, **2**, Part A, 325–329.

Hughes, J. M. O., Wroth, C. P., and Pender, M. J. (1975). 'A comparison of the results of special pressuremeter tests with conventional tests on a deposit of soft clay at Canvey Island', *Proc. Second Aust.-New Zealand Conf. on Geomechanics, Brisbane*, 292–296.

Jaeger, J. C. (1959). 'The frictional properties of joints in rocks', *Geofis. pura. appl.*, **43**, 148–158.

Jaeger, J. C. (1960). 'Shear failure of anisotropic rocks', *Geol. Mag.*, **97**, 65–72.

Jaeger, J. C. and Cook, N. G. W. (1969). Fundamentals of Rock Mechanics, Methuen.

Johansson, C. E. (1965). 'Structural studies of sedimentary deposits', *Geologiska Föreningens i Stockholm Förhandlingar*, **87**, 3–61.

John, M. (1974). 'Time-dependence of fracture processes of rock materials (in German), *Proc. Third Congress Inter. Soc. Rock Mech., Denver*, **2**, Part A, 330–335.

Kaarsberg, E. A. (1968). 'Elastic studies of isotropic and anisotropic rock samples', *Trans. AIME*, 241, 470–475.

Kallstenius, T. and Bergau, W. (1961). 'Research on the texture of granular masses', *Proc. Fifth Inter. Conf. Soil Mech. Found. Engng*, **1**, 158–165.

Karst, H., Legrand, J., LeTirant, P., Sarda, J. P., and Weber, J. (1965). 'Contribution a l'étude de la mécanique des milieux granulaires', *Proc. Sixth Inter. Conf. Soil Mech. Found. Engng*, **1**, 259–263.

Kawamoto, T. (1970). 'Macroscopic shear failure of jointed and layered brittle media', *Proc. Second Congress Int. Soc. Rock Mech., Belgrade*, **2**, 215–221.

Khalevin, N. I. and Koshkina, T. M. (1966). 'On the quasi-anisotropy of the elastic properties of some rocks of the Urals', *Izv., Earth Physics*, 11, 115–121 (translated by J. Gollob).

King, M. S. (1968). 'Ultrasonic compressional and shear wave velocities of confined rock samples, *Proc. Fifth Canadian Rock Mech. Symp., Toronto*, 127–155.

Kirkpatrick, W. M. and Rennie, I. A. (1972). 'Directional properties of a consolidated kaolin', *Geotechnique*, **22**, 1, 166–169.

Kirkpatrick, W. M. and Rennie, I. A. (1973). 'Clay structure in laboratory prepared samples', *Proc. Inter. Symp. Soil Structure, Gothenburg*, Swedish Geotech. Soc. 103–111.

Knopf, E. B. (1957). 'Petrofabrics in structural geology. Behaviour of materials in the earth's crust, *Quart. Colorado School of Mines*, **52**, No. 3, 101–111.

Ko, H-Y. and Gerstle, K. H. (1972). 'Constitutive relations of coal "New Horizons in Rock Mechanics" ', *Proc. Fourteenth Symp. on Rock Mech.*, ASCE, 157.

Koch, G. S. and Link, R. F. (1971). *Statistical Analysis of Geological Data*, John Wiley and Sons, New York, **1** and **2**.

Ladanyi, B. and Archambault, G. (1969). 'Simulation of shear behaviour of a jointed rock mass', *Proc. Eleventh Symp. Rock Mech., Rock Mech.—Theory and Practice*, 105–125.

Ladd, C. C. (1971). 'Settlement analyses for cohesive soils', *Research Report R71–2*, Dept. Civil Engng, MIT.

Lafeber, D. (1966). 'Soil structural concepts', *Eng. Geol.*, **1**, 4, 261–290.

Lafeber, D. (1969). 'Micromorphometric techniques in engineering soil fabric analysis', *Proc. Third Int. Working Meeting Soil Micromorphology, Wroclaw, Poland*, Zeszyty Problemowe Postepow Nauk Rolniczych 1972, **123**, 669–687.

Lafeber, D. and Willoughby, D. R. (1970). 'Morphological and mechanical anisotropy of a recent beach sand', *Proc. of Symp. on Foundations on Interbedded Sands, CSIRO, Perth*, **1**, 80–86.

Lafeber, D. and Willoughby, D. R. (1971). 'Fabric symmetry and mechanical anisotropy in natural soils', *Proc. Aust.-New Zealand Conf. Geomech., Melbourne*, **1**, 165–174.

Lama, R. D. (1974). 'Concept on the creep of jointed rocks and the status of research', *Jahresbericht 1974, SFB-77*, Institut für Bodenmechanik-u-Felsmechanik, Uni. Karlsruhe.

Lambe, T. W. and Whitman, R. V. (1969). *Soil Mechanics*, John Wiley, New York, 286.

Lauffer, H. and Seeber, G. (1961). 'Design and control of linings of pressure tunnels and shafts based on measurements of the deformability of the rock', *7th Congress on Large Dams, Rome*, Question 25, 679–709.

Lekhnitskii, S. G. (1966). 'Stress distribution close to a horizontal working of elliptical shape in a transversely isotropic mass with inclined planes of isotropy', *Mechanics of Solids*, **1**, 2, 35–41 (*Trans. of Mekhanika Tverdogo Tela*, **1966**, No. 2, 54–62).

Lepper, H. A. (1949). 'Compression tests on oriented specimens of Yule marble', *American J. of Sci.*, **247**, 570–574.

Liam Finn, W. D. and Shead, D. (1973). 'Creep and creep rupture in undisturbed sensitive clay', *Proc. Eighth Inter. Conf. on Soil Mech. and Found. Engng, Moscow*, **1.1**, 135–142.

Lo, K. Y. and Morin, J. P. (1972). 'Strength anisotropy and time effects of two sensitive clays', *Canadian Geotech. J.*, **9**, 261–277.

Lögters, G. and Voort, H. (1974). '*In situ* determination of the deformational behaviour of a cubical rock mass sample under tri-axial load', *Rock Mechanics*, **6**, 65–79.

Louis, C. and Maini, Y. N. (1970). Determination of in situ hydraulic parameters in jointed rocks', *Proc. Second Congress Inter. Soc. Rock Mech., Belgrade*, **1**, 235–245.

Lozinska-Stepien, H. (1966). 'Deformations during compression of the cretaceous clay limestones and marls in an interval of loads from O to the boundary of proportionality in the light of laboratory examinations', *Proc. of the First Congress, ISRM*, **1**, 381–384.

Marshall, T. J. (1958). 'A relation between permeability and size distribution of pores', *J. Soil Sci.*, **9**, 1–8.

Masure, P. (1970). 'Comportement mécanique des roches à anisotropie planaire discontinue', *Proc. Second Congress, ISRM, Belgrade*, **1**, 197–207.

Matsuo, S. I. and Kamon, M. (1973). 'Microscopic research on the consolidated samples of clayey soils', *Proc. Inter. Symp. Soil Structure, Gothenburg*. Swedish Geotech. Soc., 194–199.

Matsuo, M. and Kurada, K. (1974). 'Probabilistic approach to the design of embankments', *Soils and Foundations*, **14**, 2, 1–17.

Maurino, V. E. and Limousin, T. A. (1966). 'Structural conditions of the group "La Tinta" and its relationship with the mechanical behaviour of orthoquartzite rocks', *Proc. First Congress Inter. Soc. Mech., Lisbon*, **1**, 103–108.

Mello-Mendes, F. (1971). 'About the anisotropy of uniaxial compressive strength', *Proc. Inter. Symp. Rock Mech., Rock Fracture, Nancy*, Paper II–13.

Mesri, G. and Gibala, R. (1972). 'Engineering properties of a Pennsylvanian shale', *Proc. Thirteenth Symp. on Rock Mech.* (Stability of Rock Slopes), ASCE, 57–75.

Mitchell, R. J. (1972). 'Some deviations from isotropy in a lightly overconsolidated clay', *Geotechnique*, **22**, 3, 459–467.

Mogi, K. (1962). 'The influence of the dimensions of specimens on the fracture strength of rocks. Comparison between the strength of rock specimens and that of the Earth's crust', *Bull. Earthq. Res. Inst., Tokyo Uni.*, **40**, 175–185.

Morgan, J. R. and Gerrard, C. M. (1973). 'Anisotropy and non-linearity in sand properties', *Proc. Eighth Inter. Conf. Soil Mech. Found. Engng.* **1.2**, 287–292.

Morgenstern, N. R. and Noonan, D. K. J. (1974). 'Fractured coal subjected to direct shear', *Proc. Third Congress Int. Soc. Rock Mech., Denver*, **2**, Part A, 282–287.

Morgenstern, N. R. and Tchalenko, J. S. (1967). 'Microscopic structures in kaolin subjected to direct shear', *Geotechnique*, **27**, 4, 309–328.

Murayama, S. and Matsuoka, H. (1973). 'A microscopic study on shearing mechanism of soils', *Proc. Eighth Inter. Conf. on Soil Mech. and Found. Engng*, **1.2**, 293–298.

Nishimatsu, Y. (1970). 'The torsion test and elastic constants of the orthorhombic rock substance', *Proc. of the Second Congress, ISRM, Belgrade*, **1**, 479–484.

Nur, A. (1974). 'Technophysics: the study of relations between deformation and forces in the earth', *Proc. Third Congress Inter. Soc. Rock Mech.*, *Denver*, **1**, Part A, 243–317.

Nur, A. and Simmons, G. (1969). 'Stress-induced velocity anisotropy in rock: an experimental study', *J. Geophys. Res.*, **74**, 27, 6667–6674.

Obert, L. and Duvall, W. (1967). 'Rock mechanics and the design of structures in rock', Wiley, New York.

Ohnishi, Y. and Goodman, R. E. (1974). 'Results of laboratory tests on water pressure and flow in joints', *Proc. Third Congress Inter. Soc. Rock Mech.*, *Denver*, **II**, Part A, 660–666.

Pahl, P. (1975). 'Use of statistics in engineering design (in preparation), CSIRO Div. of Appl. Geomechanics.

Panov, S. I., Sapegin, D. D., and Khrapko, A. A. (1970). 'Some specific features of deformability of rock masses adjoining a gallery', *Proc. Second Congress Inter. Soc. Rock Mech.*, *Belgrade*, **1**, 485–490.

Parkin, A. K., Gerrard, C. M. and Willoughby, D. R. (1968). 'Discussion on deformation of sand in shear', *J. Soil Mech. and Found. Div.*, *ASCE*, **94**, SM1, 336–340.

Parry, R. H. G. and Nadarajah, V. (1974). 'Anisotropy in a natural soft clayey silt', *Engineering Geology*, **8**, 287–309.

Paulmann, H. G. (1966). 'Messungen der Festigkeits—anisotropie tektonischen Ursprungs an Gesteinproben', *Proc. First Congress Inter. Soc. Rock Mech.*, *Lisbon*, **1**, 125–131.

Peres Rodriques, F. (1966). 'Anisotropy of granites', *Proc. First Cong. Inter. Soc. Rock Mech.*, *Lisbon*, **1**, 721–731.

Peres Rodriques, F. (1970). 'Anisotropy of rocks', *Proc. Second Cong. Inter. Soc. Rock Mech.*, *Belgrade*, **1**, 133.

Pinto, J. L. (1970). 'Deformability of schistous rocks', *Proc. of the Second Congress*, *ISRM, Belgrade*, **1**, 491–496.

Richards, B. G. (1967). 'A review of methods for the determination of the moisture flow properties of unsaturated soils', *CSIRO (Aust)*, Soil Mechanics Section, *Tech. Memo No. 5*.

Richards, B. G. (1971). 'Psychometric techniques for field measurement of negative pore pressure in soils', *Proc. First Aust.-New Zealand Conf. on Geomechanics*, *Melbourne*, **1**, 387–394.

Richards, B. G. (1975). 'The determination of experimentally based load-deformation properties of a mine fill', *Proc. Second Aust.-New Zealand Conf. on Geomechanics*, 56–62.

Richards, B. G. and Gordon, R. (1972). 'Prediction and observation of the performance of a flexible pavement on an expansive clay subgrade', *Proc. Third Inter. Conf. Structural Design of Asphalt Pavements, London*, 113–143.

Ricketts, T. E. and Goldsmith, W. (1972). 'Wave propagation in an anisotropic half-space', *Int. J. Rock Mech. Min. Sci.*, **9**, 493–512.

Robin, P.-Y. F. (1973). 'Note on effective pressure', *J. Geophys. Res.*, **78**, 14, 2434–2437.

Rocha, M. (1972). 'Discussion', *Proc. Symp. Percolation Through Fissured Rock*, *Stuttgart*, D1–11 to D1–15.

Rocha, M. and Silva, J. N. (1970). 'A new method for the determination of deformability in rock masses', *Proc. Second Congress Int. Soc. Rock Mech.*, *Belgrade*, **1**, 423–437.

Rogatkina, Zh. E. (1967). 'Effect of anisotropy of clay soils on their physicomechanical properties', *Soil Mechanics and Foundation Engineering No. 1*, 23–26, (Translated from the Russian, p. 14–15).

Rosengren, K. J. and Jaeger, J. C. (1968). 'The mechanical properties of an interlocked low-porosity aggregate', *Geotechnique*, **18**, 317–326.

Rowe, P. W. (1962). 'The stress-dilatancy relation for static equilibrium of an assembly of particles in contact', *Proc. Roy. Soc. A.*, **269**, 500–527.

Rowe, P. W. (1972). 'The relevance of soil fabric to site investigation practice', *Geotechnique*, **22**, 2, 195–300.

Ruiz, M. D. (1966). 'Anisotropy of rock masses in various underground projects in Brazil', *Proc. First Congress Inter. Soc. Rock Mech., Lisbon*, **1**, 263–267.

Saada, A. S. and Ou, C. (1973). 'Strain-stress relations and failure of anisotropic clays', *J. Soil Mech. Fnds. Div.*, ASCE, **99**, No. SM12, 1091–1111.

Saito, M. (1965). 'Forecasting the time of occurrence of a slope failure', *Proc. Sixth Inter. Conf. Soil Mech. and Found. Engng, Montreal*, **2**, 537–541.

Sangrey, D. A. (1972). 'Naturally cemented sensitive soils', *Geotechnique*, **22**, 1, 139–152.

Scholz, C. H. (1968). 'Mechanisms of creep in brittle rock', *J. Geophys. Res.*, **73**, 3295–3302.

Seeber, G. (1970). '10 Jahre Einsatz der TIWAG–Radialpresse', *Proc. 2nd Congress Inter. Soc. Rock Mech., Belgrade*, **1**, 439–448.

Serafim, J. L. (1963). 'Rock mechanics considerations in the design of concrete dams', *Proc. Inter. Conf. State of Stress in Earth's Crust*, American Elsevier, 611–650.

Sharp, J. C. and Maini, Y. N. T. (1972). 'Fundamental considerations on the hydraulic characteristics of joints in rock', *Proc. Symp. Percolation Through Fissured Rock, Stuttgart*, p. T1–F1 to T1–F15.

Silveira, A. (1966). 'Discussion to Theme 2', *Proc. First Congress Inter. Soc. Rock Mech., Lisbon*, **3**, 237.

Simons, N. E. (1971). 'The stress path method of settlement analysis applied to London clay', *Proc. Roscoe Memorial Symp., Cambridge Uni.*, 241–252.

Singh, R., Henkel, D. J. and Sangrey, D. A. (1973). 'Shear and Ko swelling of an over consolidated clay', *Proc. Eighth Inter. Conf. Soil Mech. and Found. Engng, Moscow*, **12**.

Skempton, A. W. (1961). 'Effective stress in soils concrete and rocks', *Pore Pressure and Suction in Soils*, London, Butterworths, 4–16.

Skempton, A. W. and Henkel, D. J. (1957). 'Tests on London clay from deep borings at Paddington, Victoria and the South Bank', *Proc. Fourth Int. Conf. Soil Mech. & Found. Eng., London*, **1**, 100–106.

Skempton, A. W. and Hutchinson, J. (1969). 'Stability of natural stopes and embankment foundations', *Proc. Seventh Inter. Conf. Soil Mech. and Found. Engng, Mexico*, (**State-of-art**, Volume, 291–340).

Skempton, A. W., Schuster, R. L. and Petley, D. J. (1969). 'Joints and fissures in the London clay at Wraysbury and Edgeware', *Geotechnique*, **19**, 2, 205–217.

Skorikova, M. F. (1965). 'Anisotropy of the elastic properties of rocks of the Sakhalin Islands', *Akad. Nauk. SSSR, Izvestiya Geological Series*, 8, 61–74.

Stepanov, V. and Batugin, S. (1967). 'Assessing the effect of the anisotropy of rocks on the accuracy of stress determination by the relief method', *Soviet Min. Sci.*, **3**, 312–315.

Swanson, S. R. and Brown, W. S. (1971). 'An observation of loading path independence of fracture in rock', *Inter. J. Rock Mech. Min. Sci.*, **8**, 277–281.

Ter-Stepanian, G. (1975). 'Creep of a clay during shear and its rheological model', *Geotechnique*, **25**, 2, 299–320.

Terzaghi, K. (1923). 'Die Berechnung der Durchlassigkeitsziffer des Tones aus dem Verlauf der hydrodynamischen Spannung Ser. Scheinungen', *Sitz. Akad. Wissen, Wien Math-naturw kl. Abt. IIa*, **132**, 105–124.

Thill, R. E., Bur, T. R. and Steckley, R. C. (1973). 'Velocity anisotropy in dry and saturated rock spheres and its relation to rock fabric', *Int. J. Rock Mech. Min. Sci.*, **10**, 535–557.

Thill, R. E., Willard, R. J. and Bur, T. R. (1969). 'Correlation of longitudinal velocity variation with rock fabric', *Journal of Geophysical Res.*, **74**, 20, 4897–4909.

Todd, T., Simmons, G. and Scott-Baldridge, W. (1973). 'Acoustic double refraction in low-porosity rocks', *Bull. Ser. Soc. Am.*, **63**, 6, 2007–2020.

Tremmel, E. and Widmann, R. (1970). 'Das Verformungsverhalten von Gneis', *Proc. Second Congress Inter. Soc. Rock Mech., Belgrade*, **1**, 567–575.

Truesdell, C. and Noll, W. (1965). 'The non-linear field theories of mechanics', *Handbuch der Physik*, Springer Verlag, **III/3**.

Tsytovich, N. A. (1975). 'On the scope of geomechanics', *Proc. Second Aust.-New Zealand Conf. on Geomechanics, Brisbane*, 1–3.

Turner, F. J. and Weiss, L. E. (1963). *Structural Analysis of Metamorphic Tectonites*, McGraw-Hill.

Voight, B. (1968). 'On the functional classification of rocks for engineering purposes', *Proc. Inter. Symp. Rock Mech., Madrid*, 131–135.

Vyalov, S. S. (1969). 'Discussion at Main Session 2', *Proc. Seventh Inter. Conf. Soil Mech. and Found. Engng, Mexico*, **3**, 255–258.

Vyalov, S. S., Zaretsky, Yu. K., Maximyak, R. V., and Pekarskaya, N. K. (1973). 'Kinetics of structural deformations and failure of clays', *Proc. Eighth Inter. Conf. Soil. Mech. and Found. Engng, Moscow*, **1.2**, 459–464.

Walsh, J. B. (1965a). 'The effect of cracks on the uniaxial elastic compression of rocks', *J. Geophys. Res.*, **70**, 2, 399–411.

Walsh, J. B. (1965b). 'The effect of cracks in rocks on Poisson's ratio', *J. Geophys. Res.*, **70**, 20, 5249–5257.

Ward, W. H., Marsland, A., and Samuels, S. G. (1965). 'Properties of the London clay at the Ashford Common Shaft', *Geotechnique*, **15**, 4, 321–344.

Ward, W. H., Samuels, S. G. and Butler, M. E. (1959). 'Further studies of the properties of London clay', *Geotechnique*, **9**, 2, 33–58.

Wardle, L. J. and Fraser, R. A. (1975). 'FOCALS—Foundation on cross-anisotropic layered system', *User Manual, CSIRO*, Div. of Appl. Geomechanics, Melbourne, Australia.

Wawersik, W. K. (1974). 'Time dependent behaviour of rock in compression', *Proc. Third Congress Inter. Soc. Rock Mech., Denver*, **2**, Part A, 357–363.

Wiebenga, W. A., Mann, P. E. and Dooley, J. C. (1964). 'Meadowbanks dam site, seismic determination of rock constants', Bureau of Mineral Resources (Australia), *Record No. 1964/114*.

Worotnicki, G. (1969). 'Effect of topography on ground stress', *Proc. Rock Mech. Symp., Sydney*, I.E. Aust. and Aus. I.M.M., 71–86.

Worotnicki, G., Alexander, L. G., Ashcroft, J. F., and Willoughby, D. R. (1975). 'Deformation and behaviour of high rise filled stopes at CSA Mine, Cobar, NSW', *Proc. Second Aust.-New Zealand Conf. on Geomechanics, Brisbane*, 48–55.

Wroth, C. P. (1972). 'Some aspects of the elastic behaviour of over consolidated clay', *Proc. Roscoe Mem. Symp., Stress-strain behaviour of soils, Cambridge*, 347–361.

Wu, T. H., Lo, A. K., and Malvern, L. E. (1963). 'Study of failure envelope of soils', *J. Soil Mech. Found. Div.*, *ASCE*, **89**, SM1, 145–181.
Yong, R. N. and McKeys, E. (1971). 'Yield and failure of a clay under triaxial stresses', *J. Soil Mech. Found. Div.*, *ASCE*, **97**, SM1, 159–176.

Chapter 3

Mechanical Properties of Sand and Clay and Numerical Integration Methods: Some Sources of Errors and Bounds of Accuracy

G. Gudehus, M. Goldscheider and H. Winter

3.1 INTRODUCTION

The main factor influencing the reliability of numerical calculations of soil deformations is the implemented stress–strain law. This can be demonstrated by some recent findings about sand and clay worked out in Karlsruhe.

Dry sand is dealt with as a rate-independent simple material with memory. A special memory property was discovered by cuboidal deformation tests: for proportional strain paths from arbitrary initial states straight-line stress paths are reached asymptotically. The states reached in such a manner are the simplest ones possible for sand. With such states as a starting point the behaviour for more complicated strain paths is explained and discussed.

The representation of stress–strain behaviour by an incremental law is dealt with in Section 3.3, as this form of constitutive equation is specially useful for finite element methods. The frequently used method of *superposition* for the evaluation of the incremental material matrix is discussed in detail. The superposition can lead to serious errors, however. Because of the complicated memory effects in sand, the discussion of superposition is by no means simple.

In Section 3.4 some consequences of errors in the incremental constitutive matrix for finite element methods are outlined. It turns out that reliable results of numerical calculations with sand can only be expected for a few well-defined special cases.

The behaviour of *saturated clay* as determined in biaxial tests is briefly described in Section 3.5. For purposes of calculation, clay can be looked upon as a non-linear Bingham material with strain-hardening. The behaviour over the plastic portion, which is only defined for a certain

121

reference strain rate, is similar to the behaviour of sand. The viscous portion obeys a logarithmic law.

Finally, in Section 3.6 some consequences of this behaviour are outlined for *creep* problems. Because of the strong non-linearity results of finite element calculations cannot yet be presented. However, analytical solutions in closed form are at hand to check future numerical calculations. These analytical solutions are also extended to some more general creep problems to obtain approximate formulae.

3.2 STRESSES IN DRY SAND UNDER PROPORTIONAL DEFORMATION

Sections 3.2 and 3.3 which follow rest upon results of a current research programme (Goldscheider, 1975) which have only been partly published.

We consider cuboidal deformations as introduced by Goldscheider and Gudehus (1973), with three (effective) principal stresses σ_i $(i = 1, 2, 3)$, logarithmic principal strains ε_i, and their time derivatives $\dot{\sigma}_i$ and $\dot{\varepsilon}_i$ respectively. Derivatives with respect of an arbitrary parameter l, which is monotonously increasing with time t are denoted by σ_i' and ε_i'. Tensors are also sometimes symbolized by $\boldsymbol{\sigma}$, $\boldsymbol{\varepsilon}$, etc. Pressure and compression obtain negative signs as in the convention of general continuum mechanics.

Using the invariants

$$I_\sigma := \sigma_1 + \sigma_2 + \sigma_3 \qquad I_\varepsilon := \varepsilon_1 + \varepsilon_2 + \varepsilon_3 \qquad (3.1)$$

one can introduce the deviatoric components

$$s_i := \sigma_i - I_\sigma/3 \qquad e_i := \varepsilon_i - I_\varepsilon/3 \qquad (3.2)$$

of principal stress and strain. The following invariant notations will also be used:

amount

$$|\boldsymbol{\sigma}| = \sigma := \sqrt{[\sigma_1^2 + \sigma_2^2 + \sigma_3^2]}, \qquad |\boldsymbol{\varepsilon}| = \varepsilon := \sqrt{[\varepsilon_1^2 + \varepsilon_2^2 + \varepsilon_3^2]} \qquad (3.3)$$

amount of deviator

$$|\mathbf{s}| = s := \sqrt{[s_1^2 + s_2^2 + s_3^2]} \qquad |\mathbf{e}| = e := \sqrt{[e_1^2 + e_2^2 + e_3^2]} \qquad (3.4)$$

$s/\sqrt{3}$ is usually called octahedral shear stress, and e may be called distortion. We introduce path lengths in the principal component spaces between two states *a* and *b* by

$$l_\sigma := \int_a^b |\mathrm{d}\boldsymbol{\sigma}| = \int_a^b (\mathrm{d}\sigma_1^2 + \mathrm{d}\sigma_2^2 + \mathrm{d}\sigma_3^2)^{1/2};$$

$$l_\varepsilon := \int_a^b |\mathrm{d}\boldsymbol{\varepsilon}| = \int_a^b (\mathrm{d}\varepsilon_1^2 + \mathrm{d}\varepsilon_2^2 + \mathrm{d}\varepsilon_3^2)^{1/2} \tag{3.5}$$

Two non-dimensional invariants depend on angles in principal component space (Figure 3.1), viz.

$$\cot \psi_\sigma := \frac{I_\sigma}{s\sqrt{3}} \qquad \cot \psi_\varepsilon := \frac{I_\varepsilon}{e\sqrt{3}}. \tag{3.6}$$

The angle ψ is measured in a plane containing the space diagonal, whereas another angle α is measured in a deviatoric plane:

$$\cos 3\alpha_\sigma := \sqrt{6} \frac{s_1^3 + s_2^3 + s_3^3}{s^{3/2}}; \qquad \cos 3\alpha_\varepsilon := \frac{e_1^3 + e_2^3 + e_3^3}{e^{3/2}}. \tag{3.7}$$

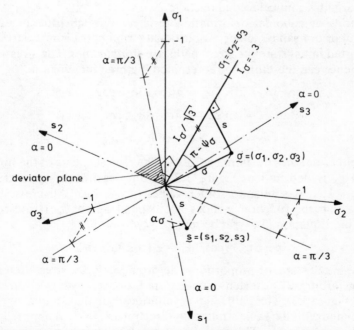

Figure 3.1 Principal component space and the geometrical meaning of the invariants (compression negative)

Analogous invariants can be formulated for $\dot{\sigma}_i$, $\dot{\varepsilon}_i$, σ'_i, and ε'_i. $\alpha_{\varepsilon'}$ is called the angle of distortion, and $\cos 3\alpha_{\varepsilon'}$ is called the direction of distortion. Volume increase is characterized by $\cot \psi_{\varepsilon'} > 0$.

In the sense of continuum mechanics dry sand can be denoted as a rate-independent, isotropic simple material with memory (Goldscheider, 1972). The remembrance of deformation history must not be overlooked in any soil mechanics problem influenced by material properties of sand. Because of the isotropy of the constitutive functional, stress and strain tensors are always coaxial for cuboidal deformation and can therefore be represented in the same principal component space. Rate independence implies that the derivatives $\dot{\sigma}_i$ and $\dot{\varepsilon}_i$ can be replaced by σ'_i and ε'_i, taken with respect to the path lengths as defined in Equation (3.5).

From the aspect of memory, *proportional strain paths* ($\varepsilon'_1/\varepsilon'_2/\varepsilon'_3 =$ constant) from a stress-free initial state are distinguished among all other strain histories for dry sand: the total strain history, as far as it is decisive for the stress and, therefore, the actual state, is fully determined by the actual strain. It is only provided that the stress-free initial state is undistorted in the sense of functional isotropy. It can be shown that the constitutive behaviour for such strain paths is fully represented by three scalar equations connecting the invariants as introduced above.

A series of cuboidal deformation tests has brought out an essential property of dry sands: under proportional strain paths from a stress-free, undistorted initial state the stress paths are *straight lines*. The stress-strain-dependence can therefore be represented by three functions

$$\cos 3\alpha_\sigma = \cos 3\alpha_{\sigma'} = g_1(\cos 3\alpha_{\varepsilon'}, \cot \psi_{\varepsilon'}, n_0) \tag{3.8}$$

$$\tan \psi_\sigma = \tan \psi_{\sigma'} = g_2(\cos 3\alpha_{\varepsilon'}, \cot \psi_{\varepsilon'}, n_0) \tag{3.9}$$

$$\sigma = g_3(\cos 3\alpha_{\varepsilon'}, \cot \psi_{\varepsilon'}, \varepsilon, n_0) \tag{3.10}$$

Herein n_0 denotes the initial porosity. The typical course of the functions g_2 and g_3 is depicted in Figure 3.2 for the case of triaxial extension, $\cos 3\alpha_{\varepsilon'} = 1$; it is similar for other values of $\cos 3\alpha_{\varepsilon'}$. All previous tests indicate that the function g_1 does not depend on $\cot \psi_{\varepsilon'}$ (Goldscheider, 1976), i.e. Equation (3.8) can be replaced by

$$\cos 3\alpha_\sigma = \cos 3\alpha_{\sigma'} = g_1(\cos 3\alpha_{\varepsilon'}, n_0). \tag{3.8a}$$

If the initial state for proportional deformation is not stress-free and, in addition, arbitrarily distorted or undistorted, a generally-curved stress path results (Figure 3.3). This path tends asymptotically to that straight line which is associated with the same strain path direction ($\varepsilon'_1/\varepsilon'_2/\varepsilon'_3$) imposed from a stress-free initial state. This experimental finding expresses a special memory of dry sand: independent of any time-scale, the effect of previous

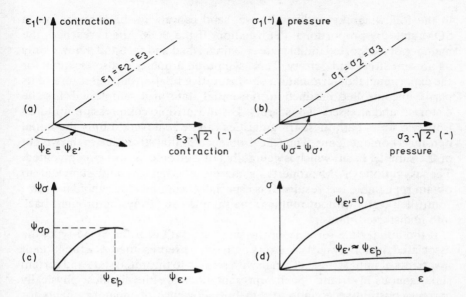

Figure 3.2 Stresses in sand for proportional deformation from a stress-free initial state (axi-symmetric case). (a) Proportional deformation. (b) Corresponding proportional stress path. (c) Relationship for path directions. (d) Relationship for path lengths

distortion histories is forgotten in the course of a sufficiently long proportional-strain path. The memory is, therefore, not fading (Truesdell and Noll, 1965), but it can be *swept out* up to a certain minimal content.

Evidently, states occurring during proportional deformations from stress-free initial states are the simplest states possible for sand. They are called 'states of minimum memory' or 'swept-out-memory', abbreviated by SOM

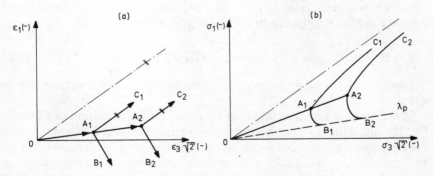

Figure 3.3 Stresses in sand for two subsequent straight strain paths OA, AB or OA, AC (axi-symmetric case). (a) Strain paths. (b) Corresponding stress paths

in the following. As outlined above, sand can always be brought into a SOM-state by proportional deformation. If the SOM line is reached, the memory of a distorted initial state is extinguished and the sand 'knows' only its present stress and density. This asymptotic property is also essential for the experimental determination of constitutive relationships. Because of its partly uncontrolled production, the initial state of a sample will first be distorted and stressed haphazardly. By an isotropic compression up to an isotropic stress path these irregularities can be removed, if only the initial density is homogeneous. Thus the problem of initial stress due to the weight of the sample, itself, which is generally not isotropic, is also circumvented. The asymptotic SOM-property is therefore necessary and sufficient to obtain repeatable test results. It is especially economic for cuboidal strain-controlled tests: without refilling, the sample can always be brought back into undistorted states.

If the initial state for a proportional strain path is of the SOM-type, the associated, generally curved, stress path can be represented as a function of invariants of initial stress, of strain with respect to the initial state and certain simultaneous invariants. Such representations are the simplest physically correct constitutive equations with full allowance of memory effects for sands.

For the numerical solution of such boundary value problems, for which the approximation by a SOM-path with stress-free initial state, Equations (3.8) to (3.10), is not sufficiently exact one can approximate the real strain path, curved in general, by a sequence of proportional strain paths with distorted initial SOM-states. A more detailed allowance for memory effects is not advisable and appropriate at present.

One can interpret these results in terms of plasticity, although a separation into elastic and plastic strains is not made. Equations (3.8) and (3.9) are analogous to *flow rules*. For each actual prorosity n there is a *limiting condition*, which is certainly not a flow condition. Because of the observed isotropy the limiting condition can be represented by

$$\text{f}(\cos 3\alpha_\sigma, \cot \psi_\sigma, n) = 0 \tag{3.11}$$

Equation (3.11) represents a three-fold-symmetric cone in principal stress space.

In the *limiting state* the stress satisfies the limiting condition of Equation (3.11), and with $\alpha_{\varepsilon'}$ kept constant the variable $\cot \psi_{\varepsilon'}$ has such a value $\cot \psi_{\varepsilon'p}$, for which σ does not change any more (Goldscheider, 1975). In other words, in a limiting state, a sample does not change its stress when the strain path is continued proportionally in the corresponding direction. Note that this property can only hold for small deformations as the porosity n is also influencing the limiting condition and as $\cot \psi_{\varepsilon'p} \neq 0$, in general. In the limiting state $|\cot \psi_\sigma|$ reaches its minimum value for $\alpha_\sigma = $ constant.

Therefore, in the limiting state the condition $\partial g_2 / \partial(\cot \psi_{\varepsilon'}) = 0$ should be satisfied by the representation of g_2 for given values of $\cos 3\alpha_{\varepsilon'}$ or $\cos 3\alpha_\sigma$ and n. Starting in the stress-free initial state in a direction $(\cos 3\alpha_{\varepsilon'}, \cot \psi_{\varepsilon'p})$, the stress remains $\sigma = 0$.

The value of $\tan \psi_\sigma$ in a limiting state is a measure of *internal friction*, dependent on porosity n. The value of $\tan \psi_\sigma$ depends on $\cos 3\alpha_\sigma$ by way of Equation (3.11). The cone in principal stress space can be approximated by a hexagonal pyramid similar but not equivalent to the Mohr–Coulomb condition (Goldscheider, 1976). It is noted that this cone cannot be used as a plastic potential in a deviatoric flow rule [instead of Equation (3.8)] as proposed by Gudehus (1973).

A measure of *dilatancy* can be introduced: $\cot \psi_{\varepsilon'd}$ is that value of $\cot \psi_{\varepsilon'}$ which is associated with a purely deviatoric stress path continuation $\cot \psi_{\sigma'} = 0$; $\cot \psi_{\varepsilon'd}$ is dependent on $\cot \psi_\sigma$, $\cos 3\alpha_\sigma$ and n. In the limiting state $\cot \psi_{\varepsilon'd} = \cot \psi_{\varepsilon'p}$ holds by definition. In other words, there are proportional strain path directions characterized by certain volume change-distortion ratios $\cot \psi_{\varepsilon'd}$ for which the hydrostatic pressure remains constant.

Conversely, a certain amount of hydrostatic *stressing* $\cot \psi_{\sigma's}$ occurs if an isochoric strain path, i.e. one with $\cot \psi_{\varepsilon'} = 0$, is imposed. The value of $\cot \psi_{\sigma's}$ depends on $\cot \psi_\sigma$, $\cos 3\alpha_\sigma$ and n. In the language of plasticity, this stressing effect is caused by the balance of plastic (say dilatant) and elastic volumetric strain rates.

Therefore an elastic modulus of compressibility is a minimum requirement of an elastic–plastic model for sand. On the other hand, an elastic shear modulus can hardly be identified: For strain path continuations from initial SOM-states, and without changes of stress level I_σ, the material seems to be completely plastic. It is noted that these elastic properties are also included in the Cam-clay theory.

The dependence of $\cot \psi_{\varepsilon'd}$ (measure of dilatancy) and $\cot \psi_{\sigma's}$ (measure of stressing) on the stress level I_σ is weak and can be neglected here. However, both parameters are strikingly dependent on the deviatoric direction of strain path $\cos 3\alpha_{\varepsilon'}$. It is well known that sand is usually dilatant when distorted in the vicinity of a limiting state, or stressing if the deviatoric direction of the strain path is in accordance with the deviatoric direction of stress corresponding to Equation (3.8). In the cuboidal deformation tests it was found that the signs of $\cot \psi_{\varepsilon'd}$ and $\cot \psi_{\sigma's}$ are reversed if, in a SOM-state close to the limiting condition, the deviatoric direction $\cos 3\alpha_{\varepsilon'}$ of the strain path was reversed into $\cos 3\alpha_{\varepsilon'*} = -\cos 3\alpha_{\varepsilon'}$. In other words, the previously dilatant material is *contractant* or unstressing in the same density after a suitable reversal of strain path.

It was observed that the amounts of contractancy or unstressing were always, independent of porosity, bigger than the ones of dilatancy or stressing.

During the continuation of the strain path in the direction $\cos 3\alpha_{\varepsilon'*}$, the value of $\cot \psi_{\sigma'}$ will change and finally reach the value associated with the new asymptotic SOM-state. Sand may therefore be called a *contractant–dilatant material*. This material property is of special importance for boundary value problems with stress or strain reversals.

This consideration is leading over to strain paths *not* starting from initial SOM-states. Although the asymptotic behaviour is regular due to the SOM-property of sands, the initial behaviour can be very complicated, and almost completely irregular. The memory of the previous history is not as well-defined as for initial SOM-states and can rarely be represented by constitutive equations. This complicated *general memory* can make sand mechanics very difficult.

We only briefly consider another type of special initial states. As noted above, the behaviour with initial SOM-states is mainly plastic. The plasticity can be proved experimentally by measuring the dissipated work in closed strain paths or stress paths, neglecting thermal effects. To this, initial states causing a *minimally plastic* subsequent behaviour can be defined as follows. An incremental stiffness $M = \Delta\sigma/\Delta l_\varepsilon$ is introduced to characterize the increment $\Delta\sigma$ of amount of stress with increment of strain path length Δl_ε defined by Equations (3.3) and (3.5) respectively. Certainly M will depend on the directional invariants, $\cot \psi_{\varepsilon'}$ and $\cos 3\alpha_{\varepsilon'}$, of the strain path in question. If the initial state is of the SOM-category, M in every direction has the lowest possible value. Now imagine a previous history such that in a certain deviatoric direction M is maximal as compared with its value for all other possible histories. To exclude the stress-level dependence in this comparison, only initial states with the same value of I_σ are considered. The behaviour with maximal stiffness may be called elastic, although it is not purely elastic. Such a behaviour can be reached after a large number of cyclic deformations.

In all other directions the behaviour is, in general, mainly plastic.

3.3 INCREMENTAL CONSTITUTIVE MATRIX

The incremental constitutive tensor M_{ijkl} of a rate-independent simple material is defined by

$$\sigma'_{ij} = M_{ijkl}\varepsilon'_{kl} \tag{3.12}$$

In this equation, the dash denotes the derivative with respect to the arc-length of strain path. The matrix is only defined for a continuously differentiable strain path and continuous constitutive behaviour. For simplicity's sake we restrict ourselves to cuboidal deformations of isotropic materials; in this case, due to the co-axiality of σ_{ij} and ε_{kl}, Equation (3.12) reads in principal components

$$\sigma_i' = M_{ij}\varepsilon_j' \qquad (3.13)$$

The representations are used in the finite element methods with variable stiffness. For (at least approximately) proportional strain paths the actual value of M_{ij} is obtained by differentiation of constitutive equations for the strain paths in question. Representations for M_{ij} are frequently used on the basis of the following simplifying assumptions: *hypo-elasticity, superposition, symmetry*. As these assumptions essentially influence the course and outcome of finite element calculations they will be discussed in the following.

3.3.1 Hypo-elasticity

Apart from the trivial case $M_{ij} = $ constant, the simplest state-dependence that can be assumed for M_{ij} is hypo-elasticity, i.e. it depends on the actual stress σ. This assumption is only valid for sand with a special class of deformation paths, which are free from sharp bends (for instance all proportional paths from the stress-free state). Note that for other types of smooth paths M_{ij} must have another dependence on σ, which is in opposition to the hypo-elastic concept. For, whereas with a hypo-elastic material only tensor variables of the instantaneous configuration are relevant (Truesdell and Noll, 1965), the stress rate σ_i' of sand for a given strain rate ε_j' is also markedly dependent on the previous history. Take a proportional deformation path from a distorted reference configuration as the simplest example: clearly σ_i' will depend on ε_j' in a non-linear manner. The non-linearity is specially due to the different behaviour for reversed and non-reversed paths, i.e. the dependence of M_{ij} on ε_j' implies

$$\left. \begin{array}{l} M_{ij}(\varepsilon_e') \neq M_{ij}(-\varepsilon_e') \\ M_{ij}(\varepsilon_e') \neq -M_{ij}(-\varepsilon_e') \end{array} \right\} \qquad (3.14)$$

For this reason, various authors (Darve, 1974; Meissner and Wiebel, 1974) have proposed different representations of M_{ij} for 'loading' and 'unloading'. If this assumption is applied for isochoric plane (($\alpha_\sigma = $ constant with $\cot \psi_{\varepsilon'} = 0$) or axisymmetric deformations ($\alpha_\sigma = $ constant for arbitrary $\cot \psi_\varepsilon$), the hypo-elastic representation is formally correct for sand.

3.3.2 Superposition

In the application of the incremental matrix a superposition method is usually applied. It is rather difficult to define precisely the content of this superposition method and far more difficult to judge the possible errors caused by using it. Although the subsequent discussion is restricted to a few special cases of superposition, it is not easily understandable. It is essential, to the practical value of finite element calculations for sand bodies, that the problems accompanying superposition are attended to.

Superposition can be defined as follows: in an actual state κ^0, the strain and stress values may be $\boldsymbol{\varepsilon}^0 = (\varepsilon_1^0, \varepsilon_2^0, \varepsilon_3^0)$ and $\boldsymbol{\sigma}^0 = (\sigma_1^0, \sigma_2^0, \sigma_3^0)$. With a deformation increment $\Delta\boldsymbol{\varepsilon}$, a state κ^1 with strain $\boldsymbol{\varepsilon}^1$ and stress $\boldsymbol{\sigma}^1$ may be reached; the stress increment is $\Delta\boldsymbol{\sigma} = \boldsymbol{\sigma}^1 - \boldsymbol{\sigma}^0$. To determine $\boldsymbol{\sigma}^1$ the constitutive equation for the strain path $\Delta\boldsymbol{\varepsilon} = \boldsymbol{\varepsilon}^1 - \boldsymbol{\varepsilon}^0$ and the suitable initial state (not necessarily coinciding with κ^0) is needed. Now, the direct path $\Delta\boldsymbol{\varepsilon}$ is decomposed into at least two paths $\Delta\boldsymbol{\varepsilon}^\alpha$ and $\Delta\boldsymbol{\varepsilon}^\beta$, with $\Delta\boldsymbol{\varepsilon} = \Delta\boldsymbol{\varepsilon}^\alpha + \Delta\boldsymbol{\varepsilon}^\beta$. For example, a plane strain increment $\Delta\boldsymbol{\varepsilon} = (\Delta\boldsymbol{\varepsilon}_1, 0, \Delta\varepsilon_3)$ can be decomposed into

$$\left.\begin{aligned}\Delta\boldsymbol{\varepsilon}^\alpha &= (\Delta\varepsilon_1, 0, 0)\\ \Delta\boldsymbol{\varepsilon}^\beta &= (0, 0, \Delta\varepsilon_3)\end{aligned}\right\} \tag{3.15}$$

As well as this decomposition into principal components, another one into deviatoric and isotropic portions is usual. The stress increments $\Delta\boldsymbol{\sigma}^\alpha$ and $\Delta\boldsymbol{\sigma}^\beta$ are first determined from the experimentally observed response for the components $\Delta\boldsymbol{\varepsilon}^\alpha$ and $\Delta\boldsymbol{\varepsilon}^\beta$ respectively. These values of $\Delta\boldsymbol{\sigma}^\alpha$ and $\Delta\boldsymbol{\sigma}^\beta$ are decisively dependent on the choice of the initial state κ for the path increments $\Delta\boldsymbol{\varepsilon}^\alpha$ and $\Delta\boldsymbol{\varepsilon}^\beta$. Different choices of κ are possible, for instance:

(1) the actual, distorted instantaneous state κ^0;
(2) an undistorted state with isotropic stress, of the same value for I_σ as in the state κ^0, or with $\sigma_1 = \sigma_3$ in a plane strain problem;
(3) the undistorted and (at least approximately) stress-free state.

As a rule, the initial state is chosen according to experimental considerations and not to analytical requirements. With a force-controlled apparatus the choice (2) is the simplest.

With this definition of stress increments $\Delta\boldsymbol{\sigma}^\alpha$ and $\Delta\boldsymbol{\sigma}^\beta$, the assumption of superposition can be written as

$$\Delta\boldsymbol{\varepsilon} = \Delta\boldsymbol{\varepsilon}^\alpha + \Delta\boldsymbol{\varepsilon}^\beta \Rightarrow \Delta\boldsymbol{\sigma}^* \doteq \Delta\boldsymbol{\sigma}^\alpha + \Delta\boldsymbol{\sigma}^\beta = \Delta\boldsymbol{\sigma} \tag{3.16}$$

This equation is strictly correct only for purely elastic behaviour, as M_{ij} is trivially independent of ε_i' in this case.

The superposition is sometimes justified by the argument, that with absolutely small $\Delta\boldsymbol{\varepsilon}$ the absolute error of $\Delta\boldsymbol{\sigma}^*$ will also be small. This argument is certainly erroneous as the error can only be judged from the ratios of stress and strain increments and not from their absolute magnitudes.

The superposition is also carried out with stress as independent variable (e.g. Darve, 1974). The above definition applies analogously.

To judge the assumption of superposition one must compare actual stress increments with those predicted by superposition. This comparison is made in the following on the basis of Section 3.2. For simplicity's sake we restrict ourselves to axi-symmetric deformations, $\cos 3\alpha_{\varepsilon'} = \pm 1$ (for plane strain $\cos 3\alpha_{\varepsilon'}$ is variable with $\cot \psi_{\varepsilon'}$). A reversal of the distortional direction is not excluded by this restriction. We choose strains as independent variables and apply the usual decomposition into isotropic and deviatoric parts. On the other hand, a decomposition into two axi-symmetric parts is applied, *viz.*

$$\left. \begin{aligned} \Delta\boldsymbol{\varepsilon}^{\alpha} &:= (\Delta\varepsilon_1, 0, 0) \\ \Delta\boldsymbol{\varepsilon}^{\beta} &:= (0, \Delta\varepsilon_3, \Delta\varepsilon_3) \end{aligned} \right\} \tag{3.17}$$

These parts are called axi-symmetric principal components. This type of decomposition is as arbitrary as the one into two one-dimensional parts in plane strain.

With a decomposition into one-dimensional parts the only experimental paths needed are uni-axial compression and extension; the so-called compression test is started from a stress-free state and corresponds to a proportional strain path. For the decomposition as defined by Equation (3.17) we therefore take, according to the choice (3), for loading a stress-free undistorted initial state. Because of experimental difficulties it is not usual to choose $\boldsymbol{\kappa} = \boldsymbol{\kappa}^0$, although this could generally yield the best approximation of stress increments; neither are suitable constitutive equations for the option (1) yet at hand.

For decomposition into deviatoric and isotropic parts tri-axial tests with a non-zero initial isotropic stress were always used; for determining the deviatoric part the hydrostatic pressure is usually kept constant. We therefore choose an undistorted state with the same isotropic stress as for $\boldsymbol{\kappa}^0$ as initial state $\boldsymbol{\kappa}$ in the sense of (2).

In Figures 3.4 and 3.5 the following typical cases are represented ($\Delta\boldsymbol{\varepsilon}$: given strain increment; $\Delta\boldsymbol{\sigma}$: associated actual stress increment; $\Delta\boldsymbol{\varepsilon}^{\alpha}$, $\Delta\boldsymbol{\varepsilon}^{\beta}$: components from decomposition of $\Delta\boldsymbol{\varepsilon}$; $\Delta\boldsymbol{\sigma}^{\alpha}$, $\Delta\boldsymbol{\sigma}^{\beta}$: associated stress increments; $\Delta\boldsymbol{\sigma}^* = \Delta\boldsymbol{\sigma}^{\alpha} + \Delta\boldsymbol{\sigma}^{\beta}$: stress increment as predicted by the method of superposition; $\boldsymbol{\sigma}^0$: stress in the initial state $\boldsymbol{\kappa}^0$):

(1) The initial state $\boldsymbol{\kappa}^0$ is of the SOM-type, proportional continuation (Figures 3.4).

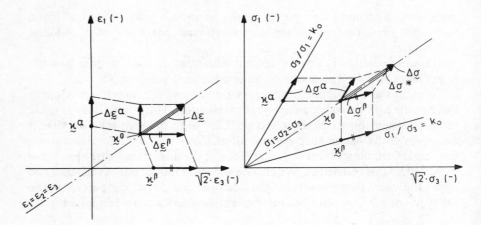

Figure 3.4.1   Initial state $\mathbf{K}^0$ SOM and isotropic, proportional continuation; decomposition of $\Delta\varepsilon$ into axi-symmetric principal components $\Delta\varepsilon^\alpha$ and $\Delta\varepsilon^\beta$

(1a) $\boldsymbol{\kappa}^0$ is undistorted, isotropic stress: for a decomposition into axi-symmetric principal components (Figure 3.4.1) due to isotropy of the material both $\Delta\boldsymbol{\sigma}$ and $\Delta\boldsymbol{\sigma}^*$ result as isotropic increments, however $|\Delta\boldsymbol{\sigma}^*| < |\Delta\boldsymbol{\sigma}|$ holds. The error is not large, as for isotropic and one-dimensional deformation from a stress-free initial state the portion of dissipated energy is comparatively small. Decomposition into isotropic and deviatoric parts will trivially lead to the same stress as the real strain path.

(1b) $\boldsymbol{\kappa}^0$ is an at-rest-state with an earth-pressure coefficient K_0: from a decomposition into isotropic and deviatoric parts (Figure 3.4.2) increments $\Delta\boldsymbol{\sigma}$ and $\Delta\boldsymbol{\sigma}^*$ result which are different by direction and amount. $\boldsymbol{\sigma}^* = \boldsymbol{\sigma}^0 + \Delta\boldsymbol{\sigma}^*$ must always be an allowable stress in the sense of the limiting condition. The decomposition into axi-symmetric principal components is trivially identical with the real path in this case.

(1c) $\boldsymbol{\kappa}^0$ is approximately a limiting state ($\sigma_3/\sigma_1 \approx K_P$; $\psi_{\varepsilon'} \approx \psi_{\varepsilon'p}$): decomposition into isotropic and deviatoric parts of $\Delta\varepsilon$ (Figure 3.4.3) must always yield such increments $\Delta\boldsymbol{\sigma}^\alpha$ and $\Delta\boldsymbol{\sigma}^\beta$, that ($\boldsymbol{\sigma}^0 + \Delta\boldsymbol{\sigma}^\alpha + \Delta\boldsymbol{\sigma}^\beta$) is a non-allowable stress. The new stress as calculated by the method of superposition therefore must be corrected by a condition of consistency to allow for the limiting condition. For boundary value problems this correction will generally require stress redistributions for reasons of equilibrium. In Figure 3.4.3 this correction is consequently made in such a manner that the isotropic stress remains constant. If the sand is dilatant in the limiting state this correction will yield a wrong sign for $\Delta\boldsymbol{\sigma}^*$; the reason for this error is the very high stiffness of sand under isotropic deformation.

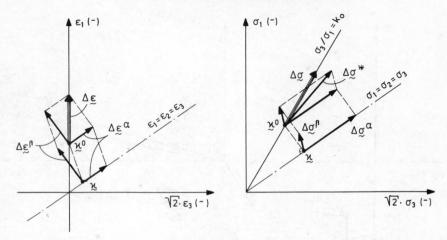

Figure 3.4.2 Initial state κ^0 SOM and at-rest state, proportional continuation; decomposition of $\Delta\varepsilon$ into isotropic and deviatoric part

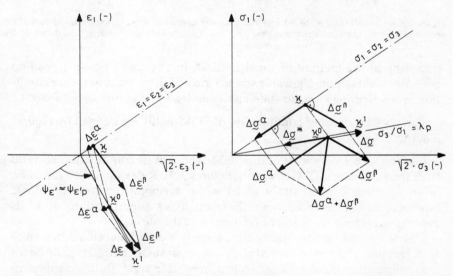

Figure 3.4.3 Initial state κ^0 SOM and limiting state approximately, proportional continuation; decomposition of $\Delta\varepsilon$ into isotropic and deviatoric part; use of the consistency condition.

For a decomposition into axi-symmetric principal components (Figure 3.4.4) one of the two components is always an extension ($\Delta\varepsilon^\alpha$ in Figure 3.4.4); this component can formally yield traction, if traction is not excluded by a consistency condition, which is not necessary for the components

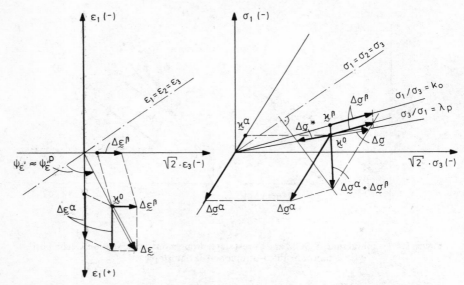

Figure 3.4.4 Initial state κ^0 SOM and limiting state approximately, proportional continuation; decomposition of $\Delta\varepsilon$ into axi-symmetric principal components $\Delta\varepsilon^\alpha$ and $\Delta\varepsilon^\beta$ and use of the consistency condition

occurring in the method of superposition. In any case, the superposition $\sigma^0 + \Delta\sigma^*$ yields a non-allowable stress. Correction by the consistency condition into a limiting stressed state can again lead to a wrong sign for $\Delta\sigma^*$.

The possible cases of continuation of SOM-paths are defined by Figures 3.4.1 to 3.4.4.

(2) The initial state κ^0 is of the SOM-type, but its continuation deviates from the associated SOM-direction (Figures 3.5). Relevant for the direction of σ' for such bended strain paths is the asymptotic behaviour which, however, is not considered in the method of superposition, as κ^0 is generally replaced by different fictitious initial states.

(2a) κ^0 is undistorted, the continuation is a one-dimensional deformation. Because of the asymptotic behaviour, $\psi_{\sigma'}$ is smaller than it would be for a one-dimensional deformation from a stress-free state. Both for a decomposition into isotropic and deviatoric parts (Figure 3.5.1) and into axi-symmetric principal components (Figure 3.5.2) the method of superposition yields $\psi_{\sigma'^*} > \psi_{\sigma'}$. The decomposition into axi-symmetric principal components is not identical to the real path because of $\kappa \neq \kappa^0$.

(2b) κ^0 is undistorted, the further deformation is isochoric: decomposition into isotropic and deviatoric parts according to the method of superposition yields $\Delta\sigma^* = \Delta\sigma$, as $\kappa = \kappa^0$ was stipulated for this case. On the other

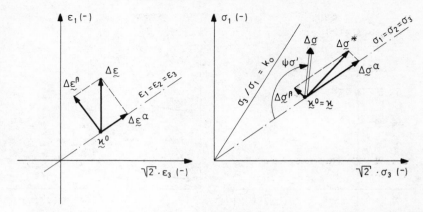

Figure 3.5.1· Initial state κ^0 SOM and isotropic, subsequent one-dimensional deformation; decomposition of $\Delta\varepsilon$ into isotropic $\Delta\varepsilon^\alpha$ and deviatoric $\Delta\varepsilon^\beta$ part

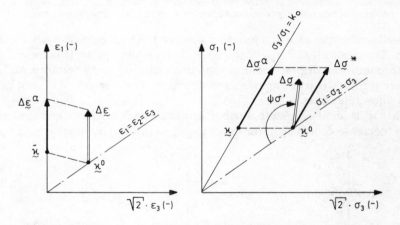

Figure 3.5.2 Initial state κ^0 SOM and isotropic, subsequent one-dimensional deformation; decomposition of $\Delta\varepsilon$ into axi-symmetric principal components $\Delta\varepsilon^\alpha = 0, \Delta\varepsilon^\beta$

hand, decomposition into axi-symmetric principal components again yields $\psi_{\sigma'*} > \psi_{\sigma'}$ due to neglection of the asymptotic behaviour.

(2c) κ^0 is an at-rest-state, further deformation is isochoric and stressing (increase of $|\tan \psi_\sigma|$) for decomposition into axi-symmetric principal components (Figure 3.5.3) one component, $\Delta\varepsilon^\alpha$, is obtained as a SOM-continuation from κ^0, the other component, $\Delta\varepsilon^\beta$, is an unloading path which is different from the loading path except for purely isotropic deformation. $\Delta\sigma^*$ has another direction than $\Delta\sigma$. The value $\sigma^0 + \Delta\sigma^*$ can result as a

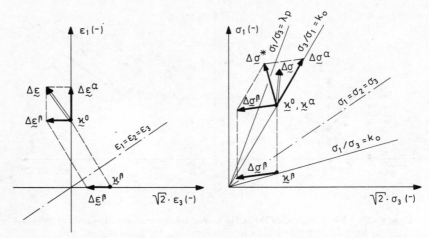

Figure 3.5.3 Initial state κ^0 SOM and at-rest-state, subsequent 'stressing', isochoric deformation $\Delta\varepsilon$; decomposition of $\Delta\varepsilon$ into axi-symmetric principal components.

non-allowable stress, which requires a correction by the consistency condition. Decomposition into isotropic and deviatoric parts (Figure 3.5.4) corresponds to a displacement of the initial state $\kappa^0 \to \kappa$. Therefore $\Delta\sigma^*$ is different from $\Delta\sigma$ by its amount and direction. The sum $\sigma^0 + \Delta\sigma^*$ can be a non-allowable stress.

(2d) κ^0 is an at-rest-state, further deformation is isochoric and unstressing (decrease of $|\tan\psi_\sigma|$): for decomposition into axi-symmetric principal

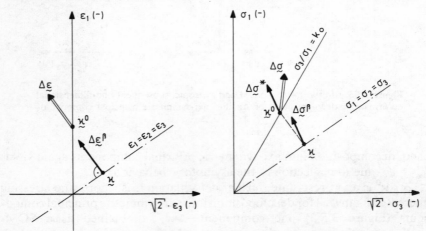

Figure 3.5.4 Initial state κ^0 SOM and at-rest-state, subsequent 'stressing', isochoric deformation $\Delta\varepsilon$; decomposition of $\Delta\varepsilon$ into isotropic and deviatoric part with isotropic initial state κ

components (Figure 3.5.5) one component $\Delta\varepsilon^\alpha$ is the reverse of the proportional path leading to κ^0; for this reason $\Delta\sigma^\alpha$ deviates from a SOM-line both in Figure 3.5.5 and Figure 3.5.3. Here $\Delta\sigma^*$ is different from $\Delta\sigma$ by its amount and direction. The decomposition into isotropic and deviatoric parts

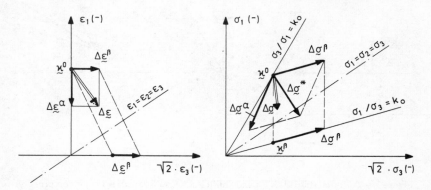

Figure 3.5.5 Initial state κ^0 SOM and at-rest-state, subsequent 'unstressing' isochoric deformation $\Delta\varepsilon$; decomposition of $\Delta\varepsilon$ into axi-symmetric principal components $\Delta\varepsilon^\alpha$, $\Delta\varepsilon^\beta$

is identical with the real path if the effect of the reversal is allowed for, that is to say, if $\kappa = \kappa^0$. If, however, κ is chosen as an isotropic state (as in Figure 3.5.6) $\Delta\sigma^*$ and $\Delta\sigma$ are essentially different.

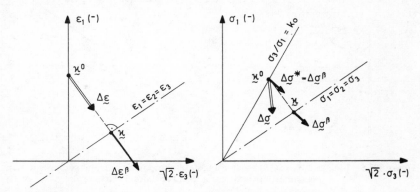

Figure 3.5.6 Initial state κ^0 SOM and at-rest-state, subsequent 'unstressing' isochoric deformation $\Delta\varepsilon$; decomposition of $\Delta\varepsilon$ into isotropic ($\Delta\varepsilon^\alpha = 0$) and deviatoric ($\Delta\varepsilon^\beta$) parts neglecting the effects of reversal

(2e) κ^0 is a limiting state, followed by an isotropic compression (Figures 3.5.7 and 3.5.8): with both types of decompositions $|\Delta\sigma^*| > |\Delta\sigma|$ results, and

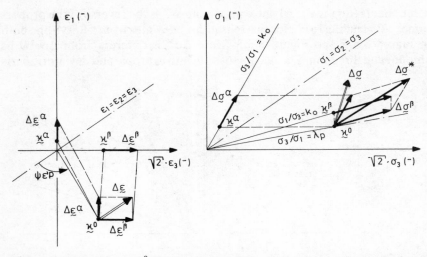

Figure 3.5.7   Initial state $\boldsymbol{\kappa}^0$ SOM and limiting state; subsequent isotropic compression $\Delta\boldsymbol{\varepsilon}$; decomposition of $\Delta\boldsymbol{\varepsilon}$ into axi-symmetric principal components $\Delta\boldsymbol{\varepsilon}^\alpha$, $\Delta\boldsymbol{\varepsilon}^\beta$

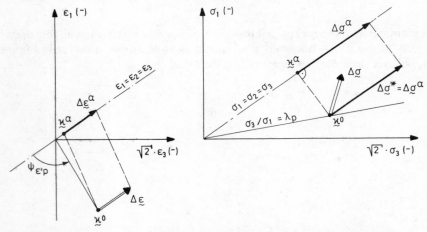

Figure 3.5.8   Initial state $\boldsymbol{\kappa}^0$ SOM and limiting state; subsequent isotropic compression $\Delta\boldsymbol{\varepsilon}$; decomposition into isotropic and deviatoric parts.

the directions of $\Delta\boldsymbol{\sigma}^*$ and $\Delta\boldsymbol{\sigma}$ are indicating the influence of anisotropy with respect to $\boldsymbol{\kappa}^0$ as reference state.

(2f) $\boldsymbol{\kappa}^0$ is a limiting state, followed by an unloading or loading isochoric deformation: differences between $\Delta\boldsymbol{\sigma}^*$ and $\Delta\boldsymbol{\sigma}$ by amount and direction have the same signs, but higher amounts, as in Figures 3.5.3 through 3.5.6.

(3) The initial state κ^0 is not of a SOM-type. No precise statements can be made for an arbitrary continuation; such paths must be approximated by proportional paths with initial SOM-states, assuming that the errors caused by superposition are similar as in case (2). If it is known that the response for a certain direction of $\Delta\boldsymbol{\varepsilon}$ is elastic (cf. Section 3.2), the method of superposition yields $\Delta\boldsymbol{\sigma}^* = \Delta\boldsymbol{\sigma}$, if the same elastic constants are used for the directions of $\Delta\boldsymbol{\varepsilon}^\alpha$ and $\Delta\boldsymbol{\varepsilon}^\beta$ as for the direction of $\Delta\boldsymbol{\varepsilon}$; note that the real soil cannot be elastic simultaneously for all the three directions. This special case of an elastic continuation is of interest only for cyclic processes.

We can summarize as follows: The error caused by the method of superposition increases with the proximity of the initial state to a limiting state. If the direction of deformation is not a SOM-continuation considerable errors can result from the neglection of directional effects. By the method of superimposition a fictitious incremental matrix M_{ij}^* is obtained instead of the real one M_{ij}. For an estimation to be carried out in the following section it is assumed that for a certain load increment the principal axes of $\boldsymbol{\varepsilon}$ and $\boldsymbol{\sigma}$ are not rotating, yielding

$$M_{ij} = \lambda Q_{il}M_{lj^*}. \tag{3.18}$$

This equation means that the stress increment $\Delta\boldsymbol{\sigma}^*$ as determined by the method of superposition is rotated by a matrix Q_{ij} and stretched by a scalar factor λ in principal component space with respect to the real stress increment $\Delta\boldsymbol{\sigma}$. It is difficult to determine bounds for λ and Q_{ij}; roughly $0.5 < |\lambda| < 2$.

The *non-symmetry* of M_{ij} is sufficiently proven by the non-associated plastic behaviour of sand. The non-symmetry can easily be examplified with a conventional elastic-plastic representation for rectangular stretch for plain strain (Vardoulakis, 1977).

The flow condition can be written as

$$(\sigma_1 - \sigma_2)/(\sigma_1 + \sigma_2) = \sin \phi_m \tag{3.19}$$

Herein $\sin \phi_m$ is the mobilized friction, corresponding to $\tan \psi_\sigma$ and obeying the hardening law

$$\sin \phi_m = \sin \phi_{\max} f(\varepsilon_1 - \varepsilon_2) \tag{3.20}$$

with the hardening function $f(\varepsilon_1 - \varepsilon_2)$. The flow rule may read

$$(\varepsilon_1' + \varepsilon_2')/(\varepsilon_1' - \varepsilon_2') = \sin \nu \tag{3.21}$$

with $\sin \nu$ as a measure of dilatancy, corresponding to $\cot \psi_{\varepsilon'p}$. The law of elasticity may read

$$\sigma_1' + \sigma_2' = K(\varepsilon_1'^e + \varepsilon_2'^e) = K\{(\varepsilon_1' + \varepsilon_2') - \sin \nu(\varepsilon_1' - \varepsilon_2')\} \tag{3.22}$$

for volumetric strains, whereas elastic shear strains may be neglected. Combining Equations (3.19) to (3.22), the incremental matrix is obtained as

$$\left.\begin{aligned}
M_{11} &= K\left\{(1-\sin \nu)(1-\sin \phi_m)-\frac{\sigma_1+\sigma_2}{K}\sin \phi_{max}f'\right\} \\[2mm]
M_{12} &= K\left\{(1+\sin \nu)(1-\sin \phi_m)+\frac{\sigma_1+\sigma_2}{K}\sin \phi_{max}f'\right\} \\[2mm]
M_{21} &= K\left\{(1-\sin \nu)(1+\sin \phi_m)+\frac{\sigma_1+\sigma_2}{K}\sin \phi_{max}f'\right\} \\[2mm]
M_{22} &= K\left\{(1+\sin \nu)(1+\sin \phi_m)-\frac{\sigma_1+\sigma_2}{K}\sin \phi_{max}f'\right\}
\end{aligned}\right\} \quad (3.23)$$

Evidently $M_{12}=M_{21}$ is only valid for $\sin \nu = \sin \phi_m$, which condition is never satisfied for sand. For the typical dependence of dilatancy on mobilized friction the deviation from symmetry is maximal in the limiting state.

3.4 ERROR ESTIMATES FOR BOUNDARY VALUE PROBLEMS WITH SAND

We consider the effects of possible errors in the incremental law [Equation (3.13)] on the results of a boundary value problem which is numerically investigated by means of the finite element (FE) method. An upper bound for the relative error resulting from 'exact' and approximate constitutive laws is obtained. Discretization errors are neglected. This means that the numerical solution as obtained by using the 'exact' constitutive law [Equation (3.13)] is called 'exact'. The relationship [Equation (3.18)] between 'exact' and approximate incremental matrices is assumed to hold.

The following assumptions are made:

(a) $\boldsymbol{\varepsilon}$ and $\boldsymbol{\sigma}$ are coaxial in the exact and the approximate problem.
(b) the transformation law for principal axes does not vary within a spatial element and is the same in the exact and the approximate problem.
(c) Q_{ij} and λ from Equation (3.18) are constants in each element.
(d) The problem is one of plane strain.
(e) The approximate constitutive matrix M_{ij} is formally a Hookean matrix with appropriate 'elastic' constants.
(f) The FE-discretization is performed with the displacement approach and linear trial functions.

Assumption (e) implies the symmetry of the approximate constitutive matrix which is assumed for simplicity.

Assumption (f) is no restriction because of (b). From (d) we find

$$[Q] = \begin{bmatrix} \cos \varphi & \sin \varphi \\ -\sin \varphi & \cos \varphi \end{bmatrix}. \tag{3.24}$$

φ is an angular error parameter in principal component space. The element stiffness matrices for principal components are formed with the constitutive laws [cf. Equation (3.13), (3.18) and (3.24)]

$$\{\sigma^*\} = [M^*]\{\varepsilon\} \tag{3.25a}$$

$$\{\sigma\} = \lambda \, (\cos \varphi [M^*] + \sin \varphi [T][M^*])\{\varepsilon\} \tag{3.25b}$$

with

$$[T] = \begin{bmatrix} 0 & 1 \\ -1 & 0 \end{bmatrix} \tag{3.25c}$$

The asterisk indicates the approximate values as determined by a method of superposition, say.

Following the standard procedure we formulate the element stiffnesses, and omitting the element-identification index, we get

$$[k^*] = [B]^T[M^*][B] \cdot \text{volume} \tag{3.26a}$$

$$[k] = \lambda [B]^T (\cos \varphi [M^*] + \sin \varphi [T][M^*])[B] \cdot \text{volume} \tag{3.26b}$$

In Equation (3.26) $[B]$ is the usual strain-displacement matrix. Equation (3.26b) can be written in component form referred to the co-ordinate system of principal axes as follows.

$$k_{\alpha\beta} = \lambda \, \cos \varphi k_{\alpha\beta}^* - \lambda \, \sin \varphi \hat{k}_{\alpha\beta}; \qquad \alpha, \beta = 1, 2 \tag{3.27a}$$

A simple matrix analysis shows that the quotient $\hat{k}_{\alpha\beta}/k_{\alpha\beta}^*$ (no sum) contains only material parameters but no geometric terms. Therefore Equation (3.27a) yields

$$k_{\alpha\beta} = \lambda \, \cos \varphi k_{\alpha\beta}^* - \lambda \, \sin \varphi \Omega_{\alpha\beta} k_{\alpha\beta}^* \qquad \text{(no sum)} \tag{3.27b}$$

with a factor $\Omega_{\alpha\beta}$ which is independent of geometry.

Before summing up the element stiffnesses they must be transformed into a global co-ordinate system.

Some algebraic manipulations result in

$$\hat{k}_{il} = \Omega_{il} k_{il}^*; \qquad i, l = 1, 2 \qquad \text{(no sum)} \tag{3.28}$$

with

$$|\Omega_{il}| \leq \Omega_2 := \frac{(M_{11}^*)^2 + (M_{12}^*)^2}{M_{11}^* \cdot M_{12}^*}; \qquad i, l = 1, 2 \tag{3.29}$$

The indices i, l are now referring to a global co-ordinate system. For Poisson's ratios between 0.25 and 0.33 we find Ω_2 between 2.5 and 3.4.

By way of Equations (3.27) and (3.28) we obtain

$$\Delta k_{il} := k_{il} - k_{il}^* = c_{il} k_{il}^*; \qquad i, l = 1, 2 \qquad \text{(no sum)} \qquad (3.30)$$

with

$$c_{il} := \lambda \cos \varphi - \lambda \sin \varphi \Omega_{il} - 1; \qquad i, l = 1, 2 \qquad (3.31)$$

The global stiffness matrix is formed by summing up all local stiffnesses over the element identification index e

$$\Delta K_{il} := \sum_e c_{il}^e (k_{il}^*)^e \qquad (3.32a)$$

$$K_{il}^* := \sum_e (k_{il}^*)^e \qquad (3.32b)$$

In order to measure the error Δu of the approximate solution we introduce the well-known maximum norm

$$\|\{u\}\|_m = \|\{u_1, \ldots, u_n\}^T\|_m := \max_{i=1}^{n} |u_i| \qquad (3.33)$$

The corresponding matrix norm reads

$$\|[K]\|_m := \max_{i=1}^{n} \left(\sum_{l=1}^{n} |K_{il}| \right) \qquad (3.34)$$

With these definitions the inequality

$$\|[\Delta K]\|_m \leq \|[K^*]\|_m \cdot \Omega_1 \max_{i,k,e} |c_{ik}^e| \qquad (3.35a)$$

is obtained with

$$\Omega_1 := \max_i \left[\left(\sum_{k,e} |k_{ik}^{*e}| \right) \Big/ \left(\sum_k \sum_e k_{ik}^{*e} \right) \right] \qquad (3.35b)$$

It can easily be seen that

$$\max_{i,k,e} |c_{ik}^e| \leq \max_e (|\lambda^e \cos \varphi^e - 1| + \Omega_2 |\lambda^e \sin \varphi^e|) \qquad (3.36)$$

As a preliminary result we have

$$\|[\Delta K]\|_m \leq \|[K^*]\|_m \Omega_1 \max_e (|\lambda^e \cos \varphi^e - 1| + \Omega_2 |\lambda^e \sin \varphi^e|) \qquad (3.37)$$

We now use the fundamental inequality

$$\frac{\|\{\Delta u\}\|_m}{\|\{u^* + \Delta u\}\|_m} \leq \text{cond}_m([K^*]) \frac{\|[\Delta K]\|_m}{\|[K^*]\|_m} \tag{3.38}$$

which is obtained from the pair of linear systems of equations

$$[K^*]\{u^*\} = \{f\} \tag{3.39a}$$

$$[K^* + \Delta K]\{u^* + \Delta u\} = \{f\} \tag{3.39b}$$

with the notation

$$\text{cond}_m([K^*]) := \|[K^*]\|_m \cdot \|[K^*]^{-1}\|_m \tag{3.39c}$$

Equation (3.38) is valid for any norm and therefore generalizations are possible. Considering Equation (3.39a) as the resulting system of a FE-discretization with an approximate constitutive law we get, from Equations (3.37) and (3.38), an upper bound for the relative error of the approximate solution with respect to the exact solution (exact in the above-mentioned sense)

$$\frac{\|\{\Delta u\}\|_m}{\|\{u^* + \Delta u\}\|_m} \leq \text{cond}_m([K^*]) \cdot \Omega_1 \cdot \max_e (|\lambda^e \cos \varphi^e - 1| + \Omega_2 |\lambda^e \sin \varphi^e|)$$

$$\tag{3.40}$$

This inequality is analytically exact and is applicable to all, even extremely bad, cases. We note that the right-hand side of Equation (3.40) consists of terms which depend on the approximate stiffness matrix $[K^*]$ only.

In typical technical applications values of 2 and 25 for Ω_1 and $\text{cond}_m([K^*])$ respectively are rarely exceeded.

It is well known that $\text{cond}_m([K^*])$ makes Equation (3.38) very conservative in most cases. Therefore the inequality [Equation (3.40)] is conservative, too. However, examples exist for which equality in Equation (3.38) is reached.

We further remark that the left-hand side of Equation (3.40) is not to be evaluated at any arbitrary node of the system but at such nodes where displacements are comparatively large. Only there large errors can occur, the largest of which is used to form $\|\{\Delta u\}\|_m$.

From the above consideration we can conclude that not the actual value of the bound in Equation (3.40) need to be discussed, but the construction of this bound. It consists of two parts, namely

$$\Omega_s := \text{cond}_m([K^*]) \cdot \Omega_1 \tag{3.41a}$$

and

$$\Omega_M := \max_e (|\lambda^e \cos \varphi^e - 1| + \Omega_2 |\lambda^e \sin \varphi^e|) \tag{3.41b}$$

Ω_s contains terms of the approximate stiffness matrix only and Ω_M depends on the approximation of the material behaviour. The magnitude of $\text{cond}_m\,([K^*])$ usually makes Ω_s dominant.

We subsequently try to find a less conservative and empirical value for Ω_s. It should be kept in mind, however, that in general Ω_s has to be chosen according to Equation (3.41a).

With the definitions of Equation (3.41) the inequality [Equation (3.40)] reads

$$\Delta := \frac{\|\{\Delta u\}\|_m}{\|\{u^* + \Delta u\}\|_m} \le \Omega_s \cdot \Omega_M \tag{3.42}$$

or

$$\Delta \cdot \Omega_M^{-1} \le \Omega_s \tag{3.43}$$

Equation (3.43) suggests the following interpretation: Ω_s is an upper bound for the relative error Δ divided by a material factor Ω_M.

Considering a certain boundary value problem and its FE-results, which we call reference results henceforth, we assume to know an upper bound Δ_P for Δ and a lower bound $\Omega_{M,P}$ for Ω_M by comparison of computer results with in-situ measurements *and* laboratory tests respectively.

As $\Delta \cdot \Omega_M^{-1}$ depends on Ω_M continuously (note that Δ also is a function of Ω_M) we assume

$$\Delta \le \Delta_P \Omega_{M,P}^{-1} \Omega_M \tag{3.44}$$

to hold within a reasonable range of Ω_M. This means that Ω_s of (3.43) is replaced by the empirically determined factor $\Delta_P \cdot \Omega_{M,P}$. Mostly one finds $\Delta_P \cdot \Omega_{M,P} \ll \Omega_s$. Therefore Equation (3.44) is much more realistic than Equation (3.40) for the problem at hand.

Without further computation inequality [Equation (3.44)] readily yields manageable error bounds for the given problem with respect to variation of the actual material behaviour. Geometry and boundary conditions of the problem must remain the same, however.

In the following example we refer to certain classes of similar problems which differ in the material behaviour only.

Comparison of a reference FE-computation with reality may lead to 20 per cent error in displacement maximally and a lower bound for $\Omega_{M,P}$ at $\lambda = 1 \cdot 3$, $\varphi = 20°$. Assuming $\Omega_2 = 3 \cdot 4$ we get

$$\Delta_P \cdot \Omega_{M,P}^{-1} = 0 \cdot 12$$

For a similar problem in which Ω_M is obtained for $\lambda = 1 \cdot 7$ and $\varphi = 60°$ inequality (3.44) yields under the above assumptions

$$\Delta \le 5 \cdot 16 \times 0 \cdot 12 \le 0 \cdot 63$$

i.e. the reference results contain up to 63 per cent error in displacement for this similar problem.

We conclude this example with two remarks: First, Ω_M is not necessarily maximal when λ and φ are maximal; second, error estimates only refer to magnitudes and not to directions of resulting displacements.

What conclusions can be drawn now from this situation? Obviously the implemented material behaviour essentially influences the results of any numerical manipulation of a boundary value problem. The behaviour of sand-like materials is only partly investigated and even well-known material laws must be approximated before any numerical treatment is possible.

In the above consideration we have seen the effects of approximation in the material behaviour. Essentially the condition number of the global stiffness matrix has been shown to be the amplifier between material inaccuracies and errors in the results. We conclude this section in giving some recommendations for an appropriate choice of constitutive laws.

One should only use initial SOM-states as these can readily be reproduced in the laboratory and as they are sufficiently well-defined. Assuming such an initial state an FE-computation based on a rather simple hypo-elastic or elastic–plastic constitutive law can be very helpful as a first approximation. Spatial discretization is of minor importance as the major part of error mostly results from the incorrect material law.

If a higher accuracy for displacements and forces is required the stress and deformation paths of the first compution can be traced in the laboratory to obtain better information for a new computer run with updated M_{ij}^*-values. In view of high costs and rather poor results no further step seems to be reasonable. Until now this procedure has not been thoroughly investigated and it is not known to be convergent—in some sense—to the true solution.

3.5 VISCOUS BEHAVIOUR OF SATURATED UNDRAINED CLAY

Macroscopically, undrained saturated clay can be considered as a non-linear viscous strain-hardening material. For numerical purposes one can write down a non-linear Bingham law with a 'plastic' and a viscous portion

$$s = s_p(\varepsilon, \dot{\varepsilon}_0) + s_v(\dot{\varepsilon}/\dot{\varepsilon}_0) \tag{3.45}$$

This representation is based on an experimental study by Leinenkugel (1976) with biaxial deformations. Using the strain invariants of Section 3.2, Equation (3.45) can also be looked upon as an invariant constitutive equation for deviators.

The viscous portion $s_v(\dot{\varepsilon}/\dot{\varepsilon}_0)$ was empirically determined by a jump-technique as

$$s_v(\dot{\varepsilon}/\dot{\varepsilon}_0) = p_e \theta \log (\dot{\varepsilon}/\dot{\varepsilon}_0) \qquad (3.46)$$

Herein θ is a material constant characteristic of viscosity; $\dot{\varepsilon}_0$ is an arbitrary reference strain rate; p_e is the so-called 'equivalent' isotropic stress, $I_\sigma/3$, associated with the actual void ratio e in virgin consolidation. The void ratio e and equivalent stress p_e are empirically connected by

$$p_e = p_0 \exp [B(e_0 - e)] \qquad (3.47)$$

with a pair of reference values (p_0, e_0) and a material constant B which is apparently independent on the direction of virgin consolidation path (at least, B has the same value for isotropic and one-dimensional consolidation, Roscoe *et al.*, 1968). For very low strain rates $\dot{\varepsilon}$ Equation (3.46) is over-simplified; a more precise representation can be obtained from a physical argument (Leinenkugel, 1976).

The 'plastic' portion $s_p(\varepsilon, \dot{\varepsilon}_0)$ is only defined for an arbitrary but fixed reference strain rate $\dot{\varepsilon}_0$. The experiments have shown that this portion is decreasing with decreasing reference strain rate. For technical applications it is useful to work with a reference strain rate appropriate for laboratory tests. The strain-dependence of s_p is rather similar to the one of sand: s_p increases monotonously with ε up to a maximum-(peak). It can be concluded from cuboidal deformation tests (Palmer and Pearce, 1973), that a deviatoric flow rule similar to the one for sand, Equation (3.8), holds. The asymptotic behaviour for straight deviatoric paths from distorted initial states is also similar to that of sand (Wood, 1975). Therefore it should be possible to extend the concept of SOM-paths to clay. We do not go into further details of the history-dependence of s_p here, however.

A finite stress-strain law for s_p can be used for monotonous paths from undistorted initial states, see Figure 3.6. The representation

$$s_p(\varepsilon, \dot{\varepsilon}_0) = c_u(\dot{\varepsilon}_0)\sqrt{(\varepsilon/\varepsilon_0)} \qquad (3.48)$$

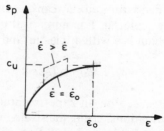

Figure 3.6 Working diagram of 'visco-plastic' clay

for this condition has turned out to be useful for approximate calculations (Gudehus, 1975). The peak value $c_u(\dot\varepsilon_0)$ corresponds to the undrained cohesion; it must, however, be kept in mind that this value is dependent on the reference strain rate $\dot\varepsilon_0$. For distorted initial states (at-rest state after one-dimensional consolidation, for example) the representation of Equation (3.48) is only a crude approximation for arbitrary directions of strain paths; more precise calculations would require representations with further invariants as additional independent variables, as was outlined for sand in Section 3.2.

3.6 UNDRAINED CREEP IN SATURATED CLAY

Before introducing a new type of constitutive law (like the one of Section 3.5) into existing numerical procedures or before developing new numerical methods it is useful to investigate some simple cases analytically. Such solutions can be very helpful to check numerical results.

For some typical boundary value problems with statical boundary conditions analytical solutions in closed form were worked out by Gudehus (1975). In all cases the creep law has been found to have the general form

$$\log{(t\dot\varepsilon_0)} = \log{[a\sqrt{(u_0/\tau_0\varepsilon_0)} - 1]} + a\sqrt{(u_0/\tau_0\varepsilon_0)} - b \qquad (3.49)$$

Herein, t is the time and u_0 the displacement at some characteristic point of the boundary. The parameters a and b are determined by the formulae of Figure 3.7 with the material constants as introduced in the preceding section.

The resulting type of creep law is mainly caused by the additive character of the constitutive law Equation (3.45), the exponential in Equation (3.46) and the square root in Equation (3.48). This creep law cannot only serve to control numerical results but can also be useful for design practice and parametric studies (Gudehus, 1975).

The above creep law was obtained for such geometrical cases which are essentially one-dimensional. Under certain reasonable assumptions this creep law can also be extended to truly two-dimensional cases.

Let (x_0, z_0) be an arbitrary point in the region under consideration. The displacement u in the x-direction (and w in the z-direction analogously) is expanded into a Taylor series in a neighbourhood of (x_0, z_0)

$$u(x, z; t) = u(x_0, z_0; t) + O(\|(x, z) - (x_0, z_0)\|) \qquad (3.50)$$

for $(x, z) \to (x_0, z_0)$, O being the Landau-symbol.

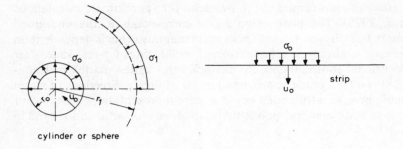

	a	b
cylinder	$\dfrac{c_u(1 - r_o/r_1)}{s_e\,\theta\,\ln(r_1/r_o)}$	$\dfrac{\sigma_1 - \sigma_o}{2\,s_e\theta\,\ln(r_1/r_o)} + \ln\dfrac{a^2 r_1}{2\varepsilon_o r_o}$
sphere	$\dfrac{\sqrt{2/3}\,c_u\left(1 - \sqrt{r_o^3/r_1^3}\right)}{s_e\,\theta\,\ln(r_1/r_o)}$	$\dfrac{\sigma_1 - \sigma_o}{4\,s_e\,\theta\,\ln(r_1/r_o)} + \ln\dfrac{a^2}{3\varepsilon_o}$
strip	$\dfrac{c_u}{s_e\,\theta}$	$\dfrac{\sigma_o}{(2+\pi)s_e\theta} + \ln\dfrac{a^2}{2\varepsilon_o}$

Figure 3.7 Meaning of constants in analytical creep formula

Assuming that the time-dependence of quotients of gradients of u and $u(x_0, z_0; t)$ is negligible we can write

$$u(x, z; t) = u_0(t)f_0(x, z) \tag{3.51a}$$

with

$$u_0(t) := u(x_0, z_0; t) \tag{3.51b}$$

and a function $f_0(x, z)$ describing the influence of the neighbourhood of (x_0, z_0). From Equation (3.50) we find

$$f_0(x, z) = 1 + O(\|(x, z) - (x_0, z_0)\|) \tag{3.52}$$

for

$$(x, z) \to (x_0, z_0)$$

which means that $f_0(x, z)$ approaches to unity at least of order 1 as (x, z) approaches to (x_0, z_0).

For brevity we write the constitutive law Equation (3.45) in an abstract form

$$s = f_1(\varepsilon) + f_2(\dot{\varepsilon}) \tag{3.53}$$

Assuming volume-constancy we are able to express the amount of distortional strain in terms of the displacement u only,

$$\varepsilon = -(\partial u/\partial x)/\cos 2\mu \qquad (3.54)$$

The angle μ describes the rotation of principal axes which is assumed to be the same for ε and σ as usual. The value of $\dot{\varepsilon}$ is obtained by simple differentiation with respect to time, leading via Equation (3.53) to

$$s = f_1\left(-\frac{\partial u/\partial x}{\cos 2\mu}\right) + f_2\left(-\frac{\partial\dot{u}/\partial x + 2\dot{\mu}\,\partial u/\partial x \tan 2\mu}{\cos 2\mu}\right) \qquad (3.55)$$

Equation (3.51a), inserted into Equation (3.55), yields a relationship with s, μ, u_0 and f_0 as unknowns.

If (x_0, z_0) is chosen as fixed the contribution of f_0 to Equation (3.55) degenerates to $[(x_0, z_0)$-dependent] constants. At a free boundary, for example, μ is known and remains the same for all times and $s = s_0$ can at least approximately be determined by conventional earth statics. This statical determinacy is typical for creep problems. Consequently, Equation (3.55) yields an ordinary differential equation for u_0

$$\dot{u}_0 = F_2^{-1}[s_0 - F_1(u_0)] \qquad (3.56)$$

wherein F_1 and F_2 are equal to f_1 and f_2 multiplied by certain constants respectively. The inversion F_2^{-1} of F_2 is well defined as the viscous behaviour of all known materials—especially that of clay—is monotonic. If we choose f_1 and f_2 appropriately, for example according to Equations (3.46) and (3.48), Equation (3.56) can be integrated explicitly, leading to the same type of creep law as Equation (3.49).

Three statements can be made now: Obviously the general form of the creep law is given by the material law implemented. Second, a closed form of the creep law can at best be obtained at selected points of the geometry. Third, the coefficients in Equation (3.56) are point-dependent. Therefore only a local creep law can be expected in the two-dimensional case. However, the type of the creep law remains the same at all points for which μ, s and f_0 can be determined.

The main open problem is to find f_0 with reasonable accuracy. It is supposed that this could be done in model tests at selected boundary points once for each boundary-value problem. The advantage of the resulting creep formulae for design practice is obvious and should not be disregarded in view of the various numerical methods.

REFERENCES

Darve, F. (1974), 'Contribution à la détermination de la loi rhéologique incrémentale des sols,' *Dissertation*. Univ. Grénoble.

Goldscheider, M. (1972). 'Spannungen in Sand bei räumlicher monotoner Verformung', *Dissertation*. Univ. Karlsruhe.

Goldscheider, M. and Gudehus, G. (1973). 'Rectilinear Extension of dry sand: Testing apparatus and experimental results', *Proc. 8th Int. Conf. on Soil Mech. and Found. Engng.*; *Moscow*.

Goldscheider, M. (1975). 'Dilatanzverhalten von Sand bei geknickten Verformungswegen', *Mechanics Research Communications*, **2**, 143–148.

Goldscheider, M. (1976). 'Grenzbedingung und Fließregel von Sand', Pergamon. *Mechanics Research Communications*, **2**, 463–468.

Gudehus, G. (1973). 'Elastoplastische Stoffgleichungen für trockenen Sand', *Ing. Arch.*, **42**.

Gudehus, G. (1975). 'Näherungsformeln für einige Kriechvorgänge in tonigem Untergrund', In: *Festschrift Prof. Lorenz*. Verlag Ernst u. Sohn.

Leinenkugel, H.-J. (1976). 'Deformations- und Festigkeitsverhalten bindiger Erdstoffe—experimentelle Ergebnisse und ihre physikalische Deutung', *Dissertation*. Univ. Karlsruhe.

Meißner, H. und Wibel, A. (1974). 'Sandverformungen und Spannungsverteilungen in der Umgebung von Bohrpfählen', *Vortrag der Baugrundtagung Frankfurt/Main*.

Palmer, C. C. and Pearce, J. A. (1973). 'Plasticity theory without yield surfaces', *Symposium on Plasticity and Soil Mechanics, Cambridge*. 188–201.

Roscoe, K. H. and Burland, J. B. (1968). 'On the generalised stress–strain behaviour of "wet" clay', *Engineering Plasticity*. Ed. J. Heyman and F. A. Leckie, Cambridge University Press. 535–609.

Truesdell, C. and Noll, W. (1965). 'The Non-linear Field-Theories of Mechanics', *Handbuch d. Phys.* **III/3**, Ed. S. Flügge, Springer.

Vardoulakis, I., Goldscheider, M., and Gudehus, G. (1977). 'Formation of shear bands in sand bodies as a bifurcation problem', Submitted for publication in *Int. J. Numerical Meth. Geomechanics*.

Wood, D. M. (1975). 'Explorations of principal stress space with kaolin in a true triaxial apparatus', *Géotechnique*, **25**, 4, 783–797.

Chapter 4

A Unified Approach to Soil Mechanics Problems (Including Plasticity and Visco-plasticity)

O. C. Zienkiewicz, C. Humpheson and R. W. Lewis

4.1 INTRODUCTION

The objects of the present Chapter are twofold; in the first place we shall show how a comprehensive and rational numerical formulation may be made to problems of saturated soil or rock mechanics based on the two-phase nature of the material. In the second place we shall investigate some specific forms of constitutive relationships and show by means of examples the dependence of total behaviour on the constitutive laws assumed. The paper thus divides itself naturally into two parts. One of general applicability and with almost unlimited validity—the other specific to the physical characteristic of the drained (or skeletal) material. Here various forms of plastic or viscoplastic relations will be invoked and discussed in some detail.

PART I
SOIL (OR ROCK) AS A TWO-PHASE MATERIAL

4.2 COUPLED BEHAVIOUR EQUATIONS

The main characteristics of soil under saturated conditions is its two-phase nature in which the skeleton of cemented (or loose) particles is surrounded by a fluid in which shear stresses are small and which exerts a pressure p on the solid phase. Biot (1941, 1955, 1956a, 1956b), Terzaghi (1943), Schiffman, Chen, *et al.* (1969), and Gibson and McNamee (1963) have formulated the essential behaviour relationship of such materials with a linear elastic skeleton. Here we shall extend such a formulation to a general non-linear case introducing simultaneously the finite element discretization process (Schiffman, Chen, *et al.*, 1969).

4.2(a) EFFECTIVE STRESS—CONSTITUTIVE RELATIONSHIP

Defining the total stress vector $\boldsymbol{\sigma}$ as

151

$$\boldsymbol{\sigma} = [\sigma_{xx}, \sigma_{yy}, \phi_{zz}, \sigma_{xy}, \sigma_{yz}, \sigma_{zx}]. \tag{4.1}$$

(with tensions as positive in the normal convention of mechanics) we can decompose this into a hydrostatic component $\mathbf{m}p$ and an *effective* stress $\boldsymbol{\sigma}'$

$$\boldsymbol{\sigma} = \boldsymbol{\sigma}' - \mathbf{m}p \tag{4.2}$$

(bold face letters in the text represent matrix or vector quantities, scalars being printed in italic.)

While such a static decomposition (shown in Figure 4.1), is always permissible, we shall now make the assumption that the *effects* of the two stress-phases can be superimposed. As the latter part of the total stresses together with the pressures within the pores places all the solid phase in a purely hydrostatic stress state (assuming on the average homogeneous and isotropic properties) its effect is merely to introduce a general volumetric strain

$$\varepsilon_v^p = -\frac{p}{k_s} \text{ or increments } d\varepsilon_v^p = -\frac{dp}{k_s} \tag{4.3a}$$

or a general strain

$$\boldsymbol{\varepsilon}^p = -\mathbf{m}\frac{p}{3k_s} \text{ or increments } d\boldsymbol{\varepsilon}^p = -\mathbf{m}\frac{dp}{3k_s} \tag{4.3b}$$

in which k_s is the average bulk modulus of the solid phase.

In soil mechanics this strain is generally considered negligible but as its importance in rocks is significant we shall retain it here.

By the above argument we can conclude that it is the effective stress $\boldsymbol{\sigma}'$ which is responsible for all major deformations—linear or non-linear— and indeed that the failure states can only be adequately expressed in terms of such effective stresses. With this generally agreed assumption we can write the constitutive skeletal relations. Whatever the instantaneous or time based response such relations can be written in the incremental form

$$d\boldsymbol{\sigma}' = \mathbf{D}_T(d\boldsymbol{\varepsilon} - d\boldsymbol{\varepsilon}^c - d\boldsymbol{\varepsilon}^p) \tag{4.4}$$

in which $\mathbf{D}_T$ is the tangent modulus matrix, $d\boldsymbol{\varepsilon}^p$ is the strain due to pressure changes and $d\boldsymbol{\varepsilon}^c$ are creep strains which with some generality can be written as

$$d\boldsymbol{\varepsilon}^c = \mathbf{g}(\boldsymbol{\sigma}') \, dt \tag{4.5}$$

where $\mathbf{g}(\boldsymbol{\sigma}')$ is a stress dependent vector defining the strain rate.

Both $\mathbf{D}_T$ and $\mathbf{g}$ are obtained from appropriate tests of the *drained* material.

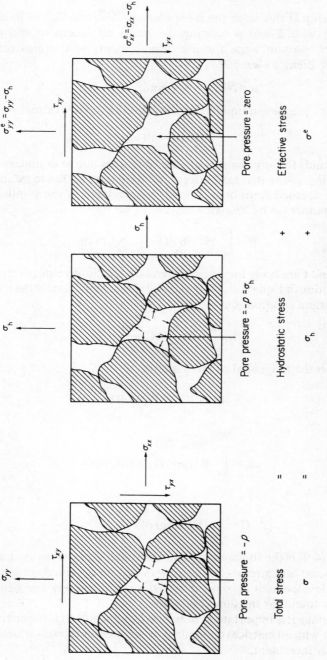

Figure 4.1 Total and effective stresses in a porous material

Introducing at this stage the finite element discretisation in its *displace-ment form* with $\bar{\mathbf{u}}$ and $\bar{\mathbf{p}}$ defining the nodal displacement and pressure parameters, we can write for the displacements and strains (using the notation of Zienkiewicz, 1971)

$$\mathbf{u} = \mathbf{N}\bar{\mathbf{u}}; \qquad \boldsymbol{\varepsilon} = \mathbf{B}\mathbf{u}; \qquad p = \bar{\mathbf{N}}\bar{\mathbf{p}} \qquad (4.6)$$

and for the *incremental* equilibrium equation in the total stress state

$$\int \mathbf{B}^T \, d\boldsymbol{\sigma} - d\mathbf{f} = 0. \qquad (4.7)$$

Here d**f** stands for any *changes* of external forces due to boundary or body force loading. (Note that *total* stress boundary traction has to be specified.) Again the detailed form of such loads is calculated in the standard finite element manner (as by Zienkiewicz, 1971), i.e.

$$d\mathbf{f} = \int_{\Omega} \mathbf{N}^T \, d\mathbf{b} \, d\Omega + \int_{\Gamma} \mathbf{N}^T \, d\mathbf{t} \, d\Gamma \qquad (4.8)$$

where **b** and **t** are body forces and boundary tractions respectively.

Substitution of Equations (4.4) and (4.2) gives immediately the incremental equilibrium conditions as

$$\mathbf{k}_T \frac{d\bar{\mathbf{u}}}{dt} - \mathbf{L}\frac{d\bar{\mathbf{p}}}{dt} - \mathbf{C} - \frac{d\mathbf{f}}{dt} = 0 \qquad (4.9)$$

where $\mathbf{k}_T$ is the tangential stiffness matrix

$$\mathbf{k}_T = \int_{\Omega} \mathbf{B}^T \mathbf{D}_T \mathbf{B} \, d\Omega \qquad (4.10a)$$

and

$$\mathbf{L} = \int_{\Omega} \mathbf{B}^T (\mathbf{m} - \mathbf{D}_T \mathbf{m}/3k_s) \, d\Omega \qquad (4.10b)$$

$$\mathbf{C} = \int_{\Omega} (\mathbf{B}^T \mathbf{D}_T \mathbf{g}) \, d\Omega \qquad (4.10c)$$

Equation (4.9) is the fundamental one for which if pressures are known the displacements and stresses in the system can be obtained. In general the pressure development is coupled with the strain changes and hence these have to be found for the flow conditions.

At this stage it is important to note that Equation (4.9) is in general highly non-linear with all matrices dependent on stresses and strains which occur at a particular increment.

4.2(b) THE FLOW CONTINUITY RELATIONSHIP

With the hydraulic head h defined as

$$\gamma h = \gamma z + p \qquad (4.11)$$

where γ is the fluid density and z the vertical co-ordinate, flow velocities can be obtained by Darcy's law as

$$\mathbf{v} = -\mathbf{k}\nabla(\gamma h) = -\mathbf{k}\nabla(\gamma z + p) \qquad (4.12)$$

In above, $\mathbf{k}$ is the permeability matrix (which in isotropic situations can be replaced by a simple scalar value p). The permeability will in general be a quantity strongly dependent on ε_v the total volumetric strain reached.

The basic statement of continuity of flow requires that the divergence of the flow velocity vector be equal to the rate of fluid accumulation per unit volume of space, i.e.

$$\nabla^T \mathbf{v} = \text{rate of fluid accumulation} \qquad (4.13\text{a})$$

Now, various factors contribute to the R.H.S. term

(1) Change of total strain resulting in a rate of accumulation

$$\frac{\partial \varepsilon_v}{\partial t} = \mathbf{m}^T \frac{\partial \boldsymbol{\varepsilon}}{\partial t} \qquad (4.13\text{b})$$

(2) The changes of grain volume due to pressure changes yielding

$$(1-n)\frac{1}{k_s}\frac{\partial p}{\partial t} \qquad (4.13\text{c})$$

where n is the porosity.

(3) Fluid compressibility defined by a bulk modulus β contributes

$$n \cdot \frac{1}{\beta} \cdot \frac{\partial p}{\partial t} \qquad (4.13\text{d})$$

and finally:

(4) Compression of solid grains due to effective stress changes $\partial \boldsymbol{\sigma}'/\partial t$. Although this strain is small its importance in rock flow associated with oil technology is such that it should not be neglected. As the arguments for its derivation are not well expounded elsewhere these are presented here. Thus, due to above change of effective stress an *average* hydrostatic compression of magnitude $-\frac{1}{3}\mathbf{m}^T(\partial \boldsymbol{\sigma}'/\partial t)1/(1-n)$ is developed. This acting on a total volume of solid $(1-n)$ produces a volume accumulation.

$$-\frac{1}{3k_s}\mathbf{m}^T\frac{\partial \boldsymbol{\sigma}'}{\partial t}$$

Finally, substituting Equations (4.4) and (4.2) into this we obtain for the rate of accumulation due to these changes

$$-\frac{1}{3k_s}\mathbf{m}^T\mathbf{D}_T\left(\frac{\partial\mathbf{\epsilon}}{\partial t}-\frac{1}{3k_s}\mathbf{m}\frac{\partial\mathbf{p}}{\partial t}-\mathbf{g}\right)\tag{4.13e}$$

The combined differential equation governing the flow becomes on substitution of (Equation 4.12) (with no source terms)

$$\nabla^T\mathbf{k}\nabla(\gamma z+p)\left(\mathbf{m}^T-\frac{\mathbf{m}^T\mathbf{D}_T}{3k_s}\right)\frac{\partial\mathbf{\epsilon}}{\partial t}$$

$$+\left[(1-n)/k_s+n/\beta+\frac{1}{(3k_s)^2}\mathbf{m}^T\mathbf{D}_T\mathbf{m}\right]\frac{\partial\mathbf{p}}{\partial t}=0\tag{4.14}$$

Again a finite element discretization of the above can be performed by using the Galerkin procedure in a standard way incorporating any prescribed flow boundary conditions (4.19) (Sandhu and Wilson, 1969). Details of such discretizations are standard (see Zienkiewicz, 1971) and will result, using the trial expansion (4.6)), in

$$\mathbf{H}\bar{\mathbf{p}}-s\frac{d\bar{\mathbf{p}}}{dt}-\mathbf{L}^T\frac{d\bar{\mathbf{u}}}{dt}-\bar{\mathbf{f}}=0\tag{4.15}$$

with

$$\mathbf{H}=\int_\Omega[(\nabla\bar{\mathbf{N}})^T\mathbf{k}\nabla\bar{\mathbf{N}}]\,d\Omega\tag{4.16a}$$

$$\mathbf{S}=\int_\Omega\bar{\mathbf{N}}^Ts\bar{\mathbf{N}}\,d\Omega\qquad s=\left[\frac{(1-n)}{k_s}+\frac{n}{\beta}+\frac{1}{(3k_s)^2}\mathbf{m}^T\mathbf{D}_T\mathbf{m}\right]\tag{4.16b}$$

$$\mathbf{L}=\int_\Omega\bar{\mathbf{N}}^T\left(\mathbf{m}^T-\mathbf{m}^T\frac{\mathbf{D}_T^T}{3k_s}\right)\mathbf{B}\,d\Omega\tag{4.16c}$$

$$\bar{\mathbf{f}}=\int_\Gamma\bar{\mathbf{N}}^T\mathbf{g}\,d\Gamma-\int_\Omega\frac{1}{3k_s}\mathbf{m}^T\mathbf{D}_T\mathbf{g}\,d\Omega+\int\nabla\bar{\mathbf{N}}^T\mathbf{k}\nabla\gamma\bar{z};\tag{4.16d}$$

in above s denotes the compressibility terms contained in the square brackets terms of Equation (4.14). Although the last term is generally insignificant no computational advantage accrues if it is omitted.

Summarizing, the complete *coupled behaviour* of the two phase skeleton-fluid state is governed by a system of ordinary differential equations which we can write concisely as

$$\begin{bmatrix}0&0\\0&\mathbf{H}\end{bmatrix}\begin{Bmatrix}\bar{\mathbf{u}}\\\bar{\mathbf{p}}\end{Bmatrix}+\begin{bmatrix}\mathbf{K}_T&-\mathbf{L}\\-\mathbf{L}^T&-\mathbf{S}\end{bmatrix}\frac{d}{dt}\begin{Bmatrix}\bar{\mathbf{u}}\\\bar{\mathbf{p}}\end{Bmatrix}=\begin{Bmatrix}d\mathbf{f}/dt+\mathbf{c}\\\bar{\mathbf{f}}\end{Bmatrix}\tag{4.17}$$

The symmetry of this general equation is assured providing k_T is symmetric (as in the case in associated plasticity) and general solution can be obtained providing initial conditions of $\boldsymbol{\sigma}_0$, $\mathbf{p}_o$, etc. are known. Solution of such transient equations can be accomplished by various processes of time stepping and provide a complete consolidation history. With linear elastic assumptions such solutions have been obtained by Sandhu and Wilson 1969), Ghaboussi and Wilson (1973), Hwang, Morgenstern, *et al.* (1971) and many others. More recently a full non-linear set of such equations has been solved by Lewis, Norris, *et al.* (to be published). Here we shall be concerned with either long-term fully drained behaviour or alternatively with instantaneous, undrained conditions. Both these conditions are special cases of above discretization and can be derived from Equation (4.17).

4.3 FULLY DRAINED—STEADY STATE CONDITIONS

If the second term of Equation (4.17) or Equation (4.15) is examined we note that providing pressures and displacements reach constant values, it reduces to

$$\mathbf{H}\bar{\mathbf{p}} = \bar{\mathbf{f}} \tag{4.18}$$

and the pressures can be independently determined assuming of course that the permeability is known and independent of strain.

The first term of Equation (4.17) or Equation (4.18) results in

$$\mathbf{k}_T \, d\bar{u} = d\mathbf{f} + \mathbf{L} \, d\bar{\mathbf{p}} + [\mathbf{c} \, dt] \tag{4.19}$$

with time intervening only in the creep term which is assumed to tend to zero as steady state is approached. (Indeed the time here can be considered in a fictitious manner as shown later.) Equation (4.19) represents essentially an incremental form of a non-linear mechanics problem with forces $\mathbf{L}\bar{\mathbf{p}}$ due to pore pressures added in and standard programs and methods used in such solutions can be directly applied once the constitutive relations are known. For plastic or viscoplastic constitutive laws such analyses are devised by Zienkiewicz (1971 and other authors; Zienkiewicz, Valliappan, *et al.*, 1969; Zienkiewicz, 1974a). For a simple elastic medium we have on integration

$$\mathbf{k}_T \bar{u} = \mathbf{f} + \mathbf{L}\bar{\mathbf{p}} \tag{4.20}$$

showing the 'forces' due to pore pressure.(This formulation is a slight variant on that derived by Zienkiewicz (1971), where forces due to pressure are computed in a different way. The equivalence of both forms has been proved elsewhere (Zienkiewicz, 1974a).)

4.4 INSTANTANEOUS LOAD (UNDRAINED CONDITION)

If Equations (4.17) are multiplied by dt and $dt \to 0$ we note that all finite terms disappear. Reforming, however, a creep term which may appear in a different time scale we reduce the general equation to a system

$$\begin{bmatrix} \mathbf{K}_T & -\mathbf{L} \\ -\mathbf{L}^T & -\mathbf{S} \end{bmatrix} \begin{Bmatrix} d\bar{\mathbf{u}} \\ d\bar{\mathbf{p}} \end{Bmatrix} = \begin{Bmatrix} d\mathbf{f} + [\mathbf{c}\,dt] \\ 0 \end{Bmatrix} \tag{4.21}$$

Again this is an incremental form of the well known nearly incompressible (or if $S = 0$, incompressible) solid formulation and once again for an elastic linear behaviour on integration will yield

$$\begin{bmatrix} \mathbf{K}_T & -\mathbf{L} \\ -\mathbf{L}^T & -\mathbf{S} \end{bmatrix} \begin{Bmatrix} \bar{\mathbf{u}} \\ \bar{\mathbf{p}} \end{Bmatrix} = \begin{Bmatrix} \mathbf{f} \\ 0 \end{Bmatrix} \tag{4.22}$$

a form developed originally by Herrmann (1965) and used subsequently by others (Christian, 1968) for solution of incompressible elastic solids.

4.5 AN ALTERNATIVE FORM OF INSTANTANEOUS LOAD SOLUTION (UNDRAINED CONDITIONS)

Equations (4.24) or (4.22) represent the classical approach to the study of incompressible or nearly incompressible solids. In the former case S is zero and $\bar{\mathbf{p}}$ is in effect the Langrangian multiplier inserted to ensure incompressibility. When $S \neq 0$ other possible approaches exist. As the pressure can, in such a case, be determined from the strains (or displacements) it is possible to eliminate these from the equations and deal solely with displacement as the basic unknown.

For instance, by inversion of matrix S the value of $\bar{\mathbf{p}}$ can be found from the second of Equation (4.21) explicitly and elimination from the first set of equations results in

$$[\mathbf{k}_T + \mathbf{L}\mathbf{S}^{-1}\mathbf{L}^T]\,d\mathbf{u} = d\mathbf{f} + [\mathbf{c}\,dt] \tag{4.23}$$

Here a new 'stiffness matrix' replaces the original one based on skeletal (effective stress) properties.

Clearly the procedure implied by Equation (4.23) is inconvenient involving the inversion of a substantial matrix S and it is more convenient to return directly to the constitutive relations and reformulate the problems. We shall now find that a direct non-singular relationship can now be written between the *total stresses* and *strains*. This total stress relation is generally one of near-imcompressibility and corresponds precisely to the type of formulation used in solid mechanics when a Poisson's ratio with a value approach but not equal to 0·5 is inserted in an ordinary displacement formulation. Naylor (1974) has shown that such a formulation can be very effectively used.

To derive the direct relationship we examine the differential form of the continuity Equation (4.14) and note that if no flow occurs

$$(\mathbf{m}^T - \mathbf{m}^T \mathbf{D}_T / 3k_s) \, d\varepsilon = -s \, d\mathbf{p} \tag{4.24}$$

Inserting the above in Equations (4.2) or (4.4) we obtain

$$d\boldsymbol{\sigma} = d\boldsymbol{\sigma}' - \mathbf{m} \, d\mathbf{p} = \mathbf{D}_T (d\varepsilon - d\varepsilon^c) - \mathbf{m} \left(1 + \frac{1}{3k_s} \right) d\mathbf{p}$$

$$= \left[\mathbf{D}_T + \left(\mathbf{m} - \frac{\mathbf{D}_T m}{3k_s} \right) \left(\mathbf{m}^T - \mathbf{m}^T \frac{\mathbf{D}_T}{3k_s} \right) \frac{1}{s} \right] d\varepsilon - \mathbf{D}_T \, d\varepsilon^c$$

$$= \bar{\mathbf{D}}_T \, d\varepsilon - \mathbf{D}_T \, d\varepsilon^c \tag{4.25}$$

The above relationship gives essentially a constitutive relationship in terms of total stress which in the absence of creep is entirely determined by tests on the undrained material as

$$d\boldsymbol{\sigma} = \bar{\mathbf{D}}_T \, d\varepsilon \tag{4.26}$$

It is common to establish such laws and deal with the analysis explicitly in total stress terms. We note that the skeletal matrix $\mathbf{D}_T$ is related to the total matrix $\bar{\mathbf{D}}_T$ by 'penalty' terms which incorporate approximate incompressibility (Zienkiewicz, 1974b).

In terms of the total stress the analysis procedure follows from Equation (4.7) yielding

$$\left(\int \mathbf{B}^T \bar{\mathbf{D}}_T \mathbf{B} \, d\Omega \right) d\bar{\mathbf{u}} - d\mathbf{f} - \int \mathbf{B}^T \mathbf{D}_T \, d\varepsilon^c \, dt = 0 \tag{4.27}$$

PART II

CONSTITUTIVE LAWS OF SOIL AND ROCK. EXAMPLES OF BEHAVIOUR UNDER DRAINED OR UNDRAINED CONDITIONS

4.6 PLASTICITY IN TERMS OF EFFECTIVE STRESS

4.6.1 Ideal elasto-plastic models

Whilst a large part of soil stress–strain relations shows irreversible (plastic) behaviour undoubtedly the major part of such irreversibility is associated with the failure condition when under conditions of almost constant stresses unlimited deformations occur. It is therefore natural to attempt to model soil behaviour as an ideally plastic-elastic solid. If the combination of stresses $\boldsymbol{\sigma}'$ which causes failures is denoted by

$$F(\boldsymbol{\sigma}') = 0 \qquad (4.28)$$

then we assume that deformation will continue in a plastic manner, but if

$$F(\boldsymbol{\sigma}') < 0 \qquad (4.29)$$

only linear elasticity can occur.

Further, as a stress higher than the failure condition is not permissible, condition

$$F(\boldsymbol{\sigma}') > 0 \qquad (4.30)$$

is not permitted.

The failure surface is thus equated to the yield condition of a material which is not strain dependent.

To define the manner in which the material can strain during plastic flow it is essential to introduce the notion of a plastic potential

$$Q = Q(\boldsymbol{\sigma}') \qquad (4.31)$$

This potential defines the direction (but not the magnitude) of strain increments by its 'gradients'

$$d\boldsymbol{\epsilon}^{pl} = \lambda \frac{\partial Q}{\partial \boldsymbol{\sigma}} \qquad (4.32)$$

in which λ is a proportionality constant. In other words if components $d\boldsymbol{\epsilon}^{pl}$ are associated with components of stress in the stress space the direction of straining is *normal* to the plastic potential Q.

In classical plasticity theory, following Druckers postulation (Drucker, 1951), so-called associative behaviour is invoked with

$$Q \equiv F \qquad (4.33)$$

but in general soil mechanics we have no need to call for this restriction.

Some typical failure–yield surfaces are shown in Figure 4.2. The one best capable of describing the behaviour of soil and rock material is the Mohr-Coulomb surface, shown in its classical angular form in Figure 4.2a and Figure 4.2b. Circular approximation for these surfaces are shown in Figures 4.2c and 4.2d. In Chapter 5 the authors show that a very general form of a yield surface approximating better to the Mohr-Coulomb one but without corners can be described by a form

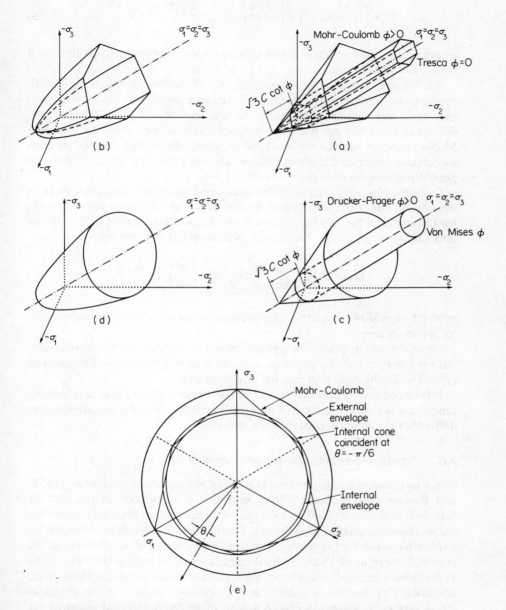

Figure 4.2 General and linearized yield surfaces in principal stress space

$$F = \alpha I_\sigma^2 + \beta I_\sigma + \gamma + \left[\left(\frac{(1+k)-(1-k)\sin 3\theta}{2k} \right) II_\sigma \right]^2 = 0 \qquad (4.34)$$

where I_σ, II_σ and θ are three stress invariants denoting respectively the mean stress, deviatoric invariant and the Lode angle.

All the yield surfaces shown will indicate, if used as the plastic potential, appreciable volume changes. Only Q surfaces parallel to the $\sigma_1 = \sigma_2 = \sigma_3$ axis show no change in volume. As changes in volume during plastic deformation of soil are not as pronounced as would be indicated by say a Mohr-Coulomb surface we shall use in what follows the concept of non-associated material for flows where Q takes on the special form not permitting volume changes.

Once the plasticity laws are determined and the linear elastic matrix $\mathbf{D}_e$ is introduced it is possible to determine the incremenetal tangential matrix $\mathbf{D}_T$ for the material by well established procedures (Zienkiewicz, 1971; Nayak and Zienkiewicz, 1972). This elasto-plastic matrix is given by

$$\mathbf{D}_T = \mathbf{D}_e \left[\mathbf{I} + \frac{\partial Q}{\partial \boldsymbol{\sigma}} \cdot \frac{\partial F}{\partial \boldsymbol{\sigma}} \mathbf{D}_e \Big/ A + \cdot \left(\frac{\partial F}{\partial \boldsymbol{\sigma}} \right)^T \mathbf{D}_e \frac{\partial Q}{\partial \boldsymbol{\sigma}} \right] \qquad (4.35)$$

in which $A = \partial F / \partial k$ is a strain-dependent parameter which for ideal plasticity is simply zero.

Once the elasto-plastic tangential matrix is determined the procedures outlined in Part I of this paper permit—at least in principle—us to solve all typical soil behaviour patterns for any structures.

It is important to observe that if non-associated plasticity is invoked the tangential material matrix will be non-symmetric introducing appreciable difficulties in the numerical solution processes.

4.6.2 Strain-dependent elasto-plastic models

The now classical and fundamental work of Roscoe, Schofield, *et al.* (1958) and Roscoe and Burland (1968), excellently introduced in the text by Schofield and Wroth (1968) allows for the occurrence of plasticity in stresses below those associated with failure. Further, by supposing that the strain-hardening parameter is simply a volumetric strain state (or density) of the material, it can model well the final continuing deformation state occurring at the failure (critical) conditions. Such yield surface can be described quite adequately by a series of ellipses in a 'meridional section' of the principal stress surface as shown in Figure 4.3(a). Here the horizontal tangents are made to coincide with the Mohr-Coulomb failure surface as shown.

Depending on the original state of the material (over or under-

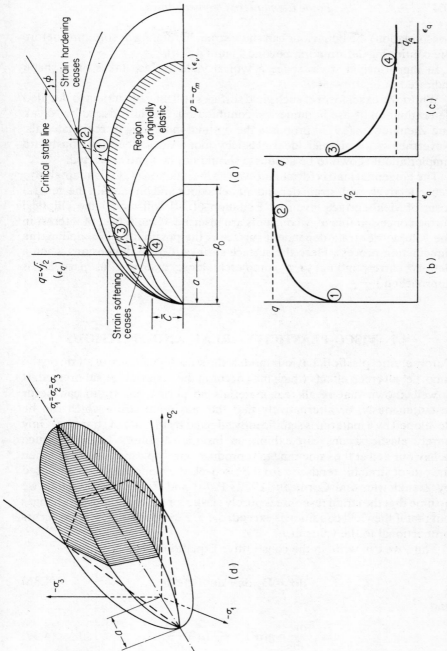

Figure 4.3 Critical state strain hardening/softening yield surface: (a) Graphical representation of yield surface in space of the two stress invariants p and q; (b) Strain hardening behaviour; (c) Strain softening behaviour; (d) Generalization corresponding to Mohr–Coulomb critical surface

consolidation) the behaviour can show strain hardening or softening before the continuing deformation beyond Figure 4.3(b).

In the principal stress space a typical yield surface takes on a shape indicated in Figure 4.3(c).

Whilst the exact form of such yield surfaces still may be subject to detailed determination its use in numerical computation, first introduced by Nayak and Zienkiewicz (1973) promises the optimal modelling of real materials. Nevertheless the simpler ideal plasticity models described previously are simpler and if shown to be adequate should not be lightly rejected.

The tangential matrix formulation given in Equation (4.35) is adaptable to deal effectively with strain dependent behaviour and once again the general form of yield surface given by Equation (4.34) will model the elliptical surface once suitable $\alpha-\gamma$ constants are inserted. (One aspect of interest in the volumetric strain dependent surface is the possibility of modelling the liquefaction process. Here the surface shrinks to zero dimensions when a density corresponding to a completely loose assembly of particles is approached.)

4.7 VISCO-PLASTICITY—REAL AND FICTITIOUS

Purely elastic–plastic behaviour models show no dependence of strain on the time, i.e. all creep effects which may occur in the material are suppressed. It is well known that in all real materials no permanent strain can occur instantaneously, or alternatively that the maximum stress which can be developed by a material is significantly affected by the rate of straining. Only purely elastic strains can exhibit an instant response. To model such behaviour and at the same time to reproduce purely plastic conditions when the rate of straining tends to zero the visco-plastic model has been proposed by Zienkiewicz and Cormeau (1972, 1974) and Zarka (1973). Here we assume that the strain response is purely elastic for any instant stress changes but that if the yield condition is exceeded, i.e. $F > 0$, a new creep rate occurs proportional to the value of F.

Thus, we can write in the constitutive Equation 4.4

$$d\boldsymbol{\sigma}' = \mathbf{D}_2(d\boldsymbol{\varepsilon} - d\boldsymbol{\varepsilon}^c - d\boldsymbol{\varepsilon}^P) \tag{4.36}$$

and

$$\frac{d\boldsymbol{\varepsilon}^c}{dt} = \mathbf{g}(\boldsymbol{\sigma}') = \gamma \langle F(\boldsymbol{\sigma}') \rangle \frac{\partial Q}{\partial \boldsymbol{\sigma}'} \tag{4.37}$$

with

$$\langle F \rangle = 0 \text{ if } F < 0$$

$$\langle F \rangle = F \text{ if } F \geqslant 0$$

F is once again a set of potential surfaces and γ a flow (viscosity) constant.

It is clear that the 'creep' ceases when $F \leqslant 0$ and that these purely plastic conditions are arrived at.

The authors believe that models of a visco-plastic kind are a reality and describe truly the phenomena encountered. *However they also provide an exceedingly convenient means of solving plasticity problems as a limiting condition when all creep rates have ceased.*

If the constitutive relationships (4.36) and (4.37) are inserted in the general formulations previously obtained the reader will observe that at all stages of computation

$$\mathbf{k}_T = \mathbf{k}$$

where $\mathbf{k}$ is the simple constant elastic stiffness matrix. The non-linear plasticity effects are now on the right hand side of the numerical equation and the time stepping process can be considered as an auxiliary iteration. The process is not dissimilar from an earlier 'initial stress' method introduced by the senior author (Zienkiewicz, Valliappan, *et al.*, 1969) but now adjustable time-steps can provide a more speedy convergence. Such fictitious use of visco-plasticity was used in the examples to be cited later and permits non-associated and associated materials to be dealt with in equal ease.

4.8 PLASTICITY IN TERMS OF TOTAL STRESS

As shown in Section 5 the constitutive relationship and tangential matrix $\bar{\mathbf{D}}_T$, see Equation (4.25), in terms of the total stress–strain relationship can be deduced once the skeletal behaviour pattern is known. Thus, for any one of the elasto-plastic models discussed we could find an appropriate stress–strain behaviour. However, it is of interest to discuss the problem qualitatively noting that in general the compressibility of both the fluid and skeleton particles is very low. Thus during any total stress change $\Delta \boldsymbol{\sigma}$ almost the whole of the component $\Delta \sigma_m$ the mean stress increase, is supported by a pressure increase $-\Delta p$. Further if elastic behaviour is assumed the deviatoric component of $\Delta \boldsymbol{\sigma}$ will produce no volume changes and no further changes in pore pressure will be generated. If a purely elastic behaviour is thus assumed to exist up to the yield surface (which is equated with the failure condition), then yield will *commence* at the same *effective stress* as that corresponding to the original effective mean stress in the material before application of any total stress changes.

In Figure 4.4 we show, for instance, the typical (meridional) section of the Mohr–Coulomb relationship in terms of effective stresses. Consider now the effect of imposing a change $\Delta\sigma_m$ and $\Delta\bar{\sigma}$ in terms of total stress on a material which has an initial effective mean stress σ'_m. As long as purely elastic behaviour is assumed the effective stress changes will occur along a vertical line AB and yield will commence when $\Delta\bar{\sigma}$ reaches a magnitude **AB**.

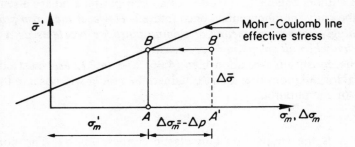

Figure 4.4 Effect of undrained total stress changes on a material with an initial mean effective stress σ'_m

This value of deviatoric stress change is constant irrespective of any mean total stress changes and with respect to these changes the materials obey a Tresca or von Mises criteria up to initiation of yield. Once yield has commenced however, and volumetric changes are associated with it, changes of skeleton volume may occur and it would appear that the behaviour could be appreciably affected by the amount of strain. Experiments apparently do not indicate such a strain dependence and one could conclude that the effective strain flow rule of failure must be such that constant volume is preserved favouring thus the non-associated or Roscoe type plasticity models.

The same experiment confirms that the strength or yield stress does in *fact vary with the initial effective stress in the material and can not be considered as an intrinsic material property* (see Chapter 28 of Zienkiewicz and Naylor, 1972).

While the above arguments are largely based on the assumption of purely elastic skeleton behaviour up to yield they are approximately valid also for the small strain associated with strain dependent (Roscoe) plasticity models.

One conclusion that is apparent from the above arguments is that in any analysis of clay or silt foundations which are *fully saturated* the total stress yield strength increases (usually linearly) with depth below the surface of the material—and when the drained (effective stress) cohesion is negligible as is the case in most clays and silts—a zero strength of the surface exists.

4.9 LOAD-DEFORMATION-BEHAVIOUR OF A SUBMERGED FOUNDATION, 'DRAINED' AND 'UNDRAINED' BEHAVIOUR

4.9.1 The test example

The test sample is illustrated in Figure 4.5 and is a typical submerged structure resting at the bottom of the sea. Before any loads are placed an initial pressure distribution in pores corresponds to hydrostatic conditions p_0 and the effective stresses are simply hydrostatic

$$\sigma'_{x0} = \sigma'_{y0} = \sigma'_{z0} = \sigma'_{m0} = \gamma_s y$$

where γ_s is the weight of the submerged material.

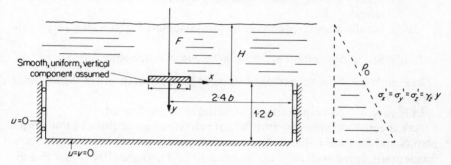

Figure 4.5 Typical submerged structure. Plane strain conditions

In terms of effective stress the failure condition for the material is taken to be given by a Mohr–Coulomb surface with $c = 10$ lbf/in^2 and $\phi = 20°$.

As initial pore pressures and stresses are fully balanced and calculation starts from this point it will be observed that the depth of submergence H is immaterial and need not be specified. For simplicity in this example we will show results here for a weightless foundation. Similar calculations can of course be carried out allowing for gravity, which in practical situations is obviously of fundamental importance.

The initial elastic properties of the drained soil are taken to be given by $E = 30 \times 10^4$ lbf/in^2, $\nu = 0.3$. Compressibility of solid phase particle $1/k_s$ is ignored and $\beta = 10^6$ lbf/in^2 is assumed (value for water).

For the Roscoe type model the strain plasticity behaviour is characterized by a constant χ which is dependent upon the initial voids ratio, the compression index and the swelling index. These properties are normally determined from oedometer tests but in this example fictitious values are chosen so as to give similar deformation properties to those obtained using a Mohr–Coulomb material. The soil is also assumed to be slightly overconsolidated so giving an initial elastic range which again will be similar to that obtained previously.

The footing itself is assumed to have a smooth base and to be flexible.

4.9.1 Application of foundation load under drained conditions

The application of foundation load under drained conditions represents the long-term behaviour of the foundation. The pore pressure forces remain unchanged and the foundation is analysed in the same manner as if it were dry with the specified *initial effective stresses*.

Three behaviour patterns are postulated for the material.

I(d) Ideally elastic–plastic with fully associated behaviour (large dilatancy).

II(d) Ideally elastic–plastic with non-associated behaviour (zero dilatancy).

III(d) Strain dependent elastic-plastic associated behaviour.

In Figure 4.6 the results of displacement load calculation are shown for all three cases.

In Figure 4.7 corresponding flow patterns are indicated.

As expected all three widely different behaviour assumptions show similar results and indicate collapse loads in close agreement to each other. These incidentally agree well with the prediction of Terzaghi (1943) and Prandtl (1920).

The independence of such results of the flow rule assumed has been demonstrated elsewhere by the present authors (1975) and appears to be fairly general in situations where the confinement of displacements does not exist. In the case of *undrained* behaviour where such confinement (by the near incompressibility of the fluid) exists we shall expect and find much wider differences.

4.9.2 Application of foundation load under undrained conditions

In this case we assume the loads to be applied so rapidly that all drainage is prevented. Now pressure changes Δp will be superposed on the initial pressures p_0 and these will affect pronouncedly the behaviour.

Now four cases will be studied; the first three in terms of assumed effective stress properties and the fourth in terms of total stresses.

Cases I(u), II(u) and III(u) correspond precisely to the material properties assumed in the corresponding drained case. Case IV(t) assumes a von Mises type behaviour in terms of total stress changes. The yield stress is proportional to the depth y (or to σ'_{m0}) and is given by

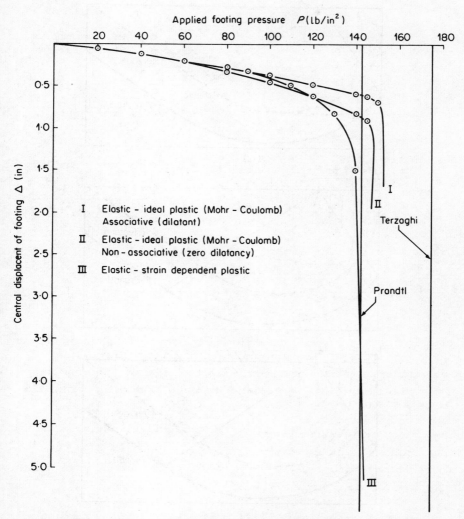

Figure 4.6 Load deformation characteristics for drained behaviour; plane footing

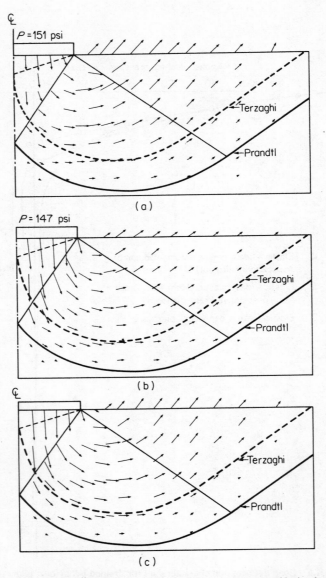

Figure 4.7 Relative plastic velocities at collapse (drained behaviour). (a) Associated Mohr-Coulomb (dilatant). (b) Non-associated Mohr-Coulomb (zero dilatancy). (c) Strain dependent critical state

$$\bar{\sigma}_y = c + \sigma'_{m0} \tan \phi$$

but since in this example $\sigma'_{m0} = 0$ the yield strength is simply equal to the cohesion c.

Once again the load-deformation curves are shown in Figure 4.8. Figure 4.9 shows corresponding pore pressure changes for cases I(u) to III(u).

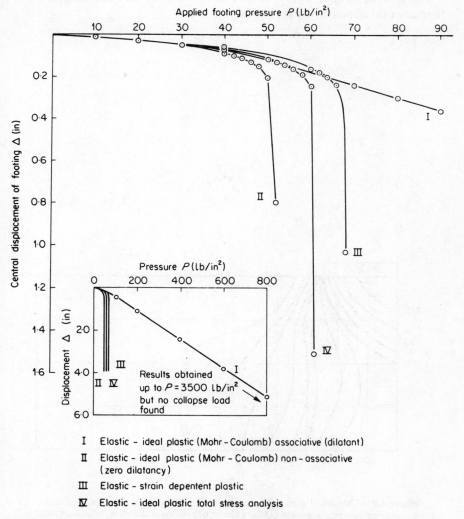

I   Elastic – ideal plastic (Mohr – Coulomb) associative (dilatant)

II   Elastic – ideal plastic (Mohr – Coulomb) non – associative (zero dilatancy)

III   Elastic – strain depentent plastic

IV   Elastic – ideal plastic total stress analysis

Figure 4.8   Load deformation characteristics (undrained conditions) for plane footing. Note: For total stress analysis we use $\mathbf{D}_T$ calculated by Equation 4.25

This close agreement between results of the simple non-associative ideal plasticity and that of the Roscoe strain dependent plasticity is to be remarked. The fact that now the associated ideal plasticity indicates no collapse is at first surprising. The obvious explanation for it is contained in the development of very large negative pressures due to dilatancy movement.

The total stress analysis results are in reasonable agreement with the more fundamental effective stress studies.

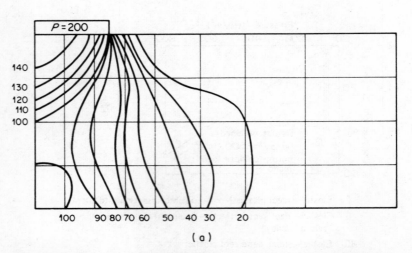

Figure 4.9 Changes of pore pressures (Δp) due to application of load and effective deviatoric strain rate contours. (a) Pure elastic behaviour of skeleton. (b) Associative (dilatant) Mohr–Coulomb plasticity. (c) Non-associative (zero-dilatancy) Mohr–Coulomb plasticity. (d) Strain dependent plasticity (critical state)

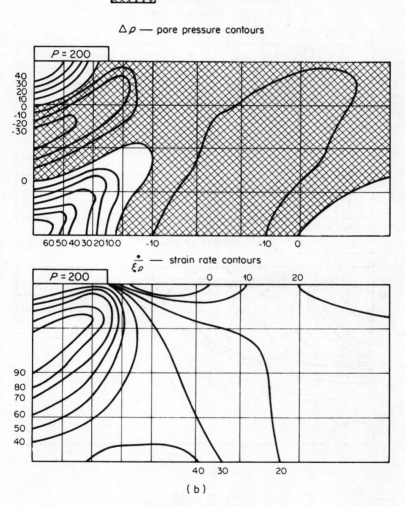

(b)

Figure 4.9—*continued*

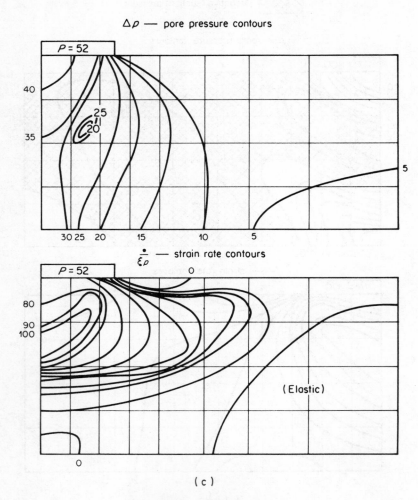

Figure 4.9—*continued*

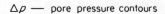

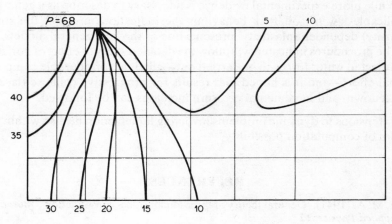

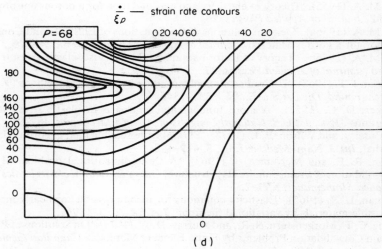

Figure 4.9—*continued*

4.10 CONCLUDING REMARKS

The general procedures developed in this paper and some of the results shown indicate how it is possible to derive practical results for deformation, pore pressure development and collapse behaviour of structures from the assumption of fundamental skeletal properties only.

While more experimental evidence is necessary to describe as a generally applicable law of soil/rock behaviour the indications are that the strain (density) dependent plasticity, presents one of the best general models.

The procedures indicated will allow the detailed study of effect of horizontal rejected water forces to be carried out—albeit at considerable computational effort—and it is hoped that results for progressive collapse (lack of shakedown) and incremental pressure increases can be followed.

Extensions to dynamic problems involving liquefaction lie also within the realm of computation possibility.

REFERENCES

Biot, M. A. (1941). 'General theory of three-dimensional consolidation', *Journal of Applied Physics*, **12**.

Biot, M. A. (1955). 'Theory of elasticity and consolidation for a porous anisotropic solid', *Journal of Applied Physics*, **26**.

Biot, M. A. (1956a). 'General Solutions of the Equations of Elasticity and Consolidation for a Porous Material', *Journal of Applied Mechanics, Proc. ASME*.

Biot, M. A. (1956b). 'Theory of Deformation of a Porous Viscoelastic Anisotropic Solid', *Journal of Applied Physics*, **27**.

Christian J. T. (1968). 'Undrained stress distribution by numerical methods', *J. Soil Mech. Found. Div., A.S.C.E.*, **94**, 1333–1345.

Drucker, D. C. (1951). 'A more fundamental approach to plastic stress–strain solutions', *Proc. 1st U.S. National Congress of Applied Mechanics*, 487–91.

Ghaboussi, J. and Wilson, E. L. (1973). 'Flow of compressible fluid in porous elastic media', *Int. J. Num. Meth. in Eng.*, **5**, 419–442.

Gibson, R. E. and McNamee, J. (1963). 'A three-dimensional problem of the consolidation of a semi-infinite clay structure, *Quarterly Journal of Mechanics and Applied Mathematics*, **XVI**, 2.

Herrman, L. R. (1965). 'Elasticity equations for incompressible, or nearly incompressible materials by variational theorem', *J.A.I.A.A.*, 3, 1896.

Hwang, C. T., Morgenstern, N. R., and Murray, D. W. (1971). 'On Solutions of Plane Strain Consolidation Problems by Finite Element Methods', *Canadian Geotechnical Journal*, **8**, 109–118.

Lambe, T. W. and Whitman, R. V. (1969). *Soil Mechanics*. J. Wiley & Sons.

Lewis, R. W., Norris, V. A., and Zienkiewicz, O. C. (to be published). 'Non-linear consolidation problems', submitted to *ASCE Soil Mechanics Division*.

Nayak, G. C. and Zienkiewicz, O. C. (1972). 'Elasto-plastic stress analysis. A generalization for various constitutive relations including strain softening', *Int. J. Num. Meth. in Eng.* **5**, 113–135.

Nayak, G. C. and Zienkiewicz, O. C. (1972). 'A convenient form of invariants and its application in plasticity', *Proc. A.S.C.E.* **98**, 949–954.

Naylor, D. J. (1974). 'Stresses in nearly incompressible materials by finite elements with applications to the calculation of excess pore pressures', *Int. J.N.M.E.* **8**, 443–460.

Prandtl, L. (1920). 'Uber die Härte plastischer Körper', *Nachr. kgl. Ges. Wiss. Göttingen. Math. phys. Klasse.*

Roscoe, K. H., Schofield, A. N., and Wroth, C. P. (1958). 'On the yielding of soils', *Geotechnique* **8**, 22–53.

Roscoe, K. H. and Burland, J. B. (1968). 'On the generalised stress strain behaviour of "wet" clay'. In *Engineering Plasticity* (Ed. J. Heyman and F. A. Leckie), 535–609. Cambridge: University Press.

Sandhu, R. S. and Wilson, E. L. (1969). 'Finite element analysis of flow in saturated porous media', *Proc. Am. Soc. Civ. Engs.*, **95**, EM. 641–652.

Schiffmann, R. L.,. Chen, A. T. F., and Jordan, J. C. (1969). 'An analysis of consolidation theories', *Journal of Soil Mechanics and Foundation Div. ASCE*, **95** SM1.

Schofield, A. N. and Wroth, C. P. (1968). *Critical State Soil Mechanics*, London: McGraw-Hill.

Terzaghi, K. (1943). *Theoretical Soil Mechanics*, Wiley: New York.

Zarka, J. (1973). 'Constitutive laws of metals in plasticity and visco-plasticity', *Lecture* presented at the Royal Institute of Technology, Stockholm.

Zienkiewicz, O. C., Valliappan, S., and King, I. P. (1969). 'Elasto-plastic solutions of engineering problems. Initial stress finite element approach, *Int. J. Num. Meth. in Eng.*, **1**, 75–100.

Zienkiewicz, O. C. (1971). 'The Finite Element Method in Engineering Science', London/New York: McGraw-Hill.

Zienkiewicz, O. C. and Cormeau, I. C. (1972). 'Visco-plasticity solution by the finite element process', *Arch. Mech.*, **24**, 873–888.

Zienkiewicz, O. C. and Naylor, D. J. (1972). 'The adoption of critical state soil mechanics for use in finite elements', *Proc. Roscoe Memorial Symposium*, 537–547, Cambridge: Foulis.

Zienkiewicz, O. C. (1974a). *Lecture Notes*. Springer.

Zienkiewicz, O. C. (1974b). 'Constrained variational principles and penalty function methods in the finite element analysis', *Lecture Notes in Mathematics*, Springer-Verlag, New York, 207–214.

Zienkiewicz, O. C. and Cormeau, I. C. (1974). 'Visco-plasticity—plasticity and creep in elastic solids. A unified numerical solution approach', *Int. J. Num. Meth. Eng.*, **8**, 821–845.

Zienkiewicz, O. C., Humpheson, C., and Lewis, E. W. (1975). 'Associated and non-associated visco-plasticity and plasticity in soil mechanics', (C/R/249/75), *Geotechnique.*

Chapter 5

Some Useful Forms of Isotropic Yield Surfaces for Soil and Rock Mechanics

O. C. Zienkiewicz and G. N. Pande

5.1 INTRODUCTION

Various forms of yield surface are currently used in soil mechanics and similar applications. In the simplest ideal plasticity form this yield surface is made to coincide with the well known Mohr–Coulomb criterion. The form of the Mohr–Coulomb surface is angular in the π-plane and in addition has a singular vertex point as shown in Figure 5.1 in the principal stress space. To avoid such angularity Drucker and Prager (1952) have introduced an inscribed cone which still possesses a vertex but in which the 'ridge' corners have been smoothed. Unfortunately this gives a very poor approximation to the real failure conditions (Humpheson and Nyalor, 1975).

In more complex strain dependant plasticity it is common to assume elliptical sections in the meridional plane thus avoiding the vertex singularity

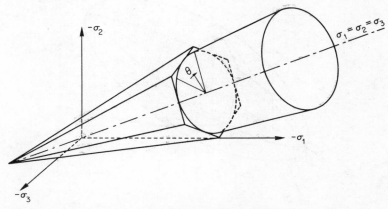

Figure 5.1 A Mohr–Coulomb surface and the Drucker–Prager approximation

but if the critical failure state of Mohr–Coulomb is to be modelled we shall need to introduce ridges (Zienkiewicz, Humpheson, *et al.*, 1975) as shown in Figure 5.2.

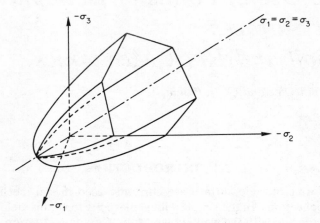

Figure 5.2   A meridionally curved Mohr–Coulomb surface

In yet other applications (such as rock or concrete) it is evident that the Mohr–Coulomb envelope is not straight in the meridional planes and some curvature of the type shown in Figure 5.3 needs to be introduced (Meek, 1973).

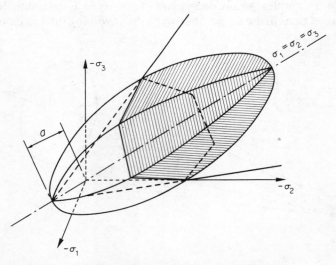

Figure 5.3   Strain hardening closed surfaces of elliptic form

We shall show that a single smooth surface can be developed to approximate to all the above types of yield conditions—the choice of the best surface being still in the hands of the analyst who has to model the soil behaviour in the best possible manner.

The elimination of the vertex singularity is useful in speeding the convergence of numerical computation when large friction angles ϕ and small cohesion conditions exist. Further, if viscoplastic algorithms are being used for the solution, the curved nature of the yield surface is of considerable computational advantage (Meek, 1973).

5.2 INVARIANT REPRESENTATION

Any isotropic yield surface can be represented in a unique manner by the three stress invariants σ_m, $\bar{\sigma}$ and III_σ

$$\sigma_m = I_\sigma = \tfrac{1}{3}\sigma_{ii}$$
$$\bar{\sigma} = II_\sigma = \sqrt{(\tfrac{1}{2}s_{ij}s_{ij})}; \qquad s_{ij} = \sigma_{ij} - \delta_{ij}\sigma_m \tag{5.1}$$
$$III_\sigma = \tfrac{1}{3}s_{ij}s_{jk}s_{ki}$$

However, for a convenient interpretation of such yield surfaces in the principal stress space it is useful to introduce an alternative set of invariants which include the 'Lode' angle θ (Nayak and Zienkiewicz, 1972). We thus replace the third invariant with

$$-\frac{\pi}{6} < \theta = \frac{1}{3}\sin^{-1}\left(\frac{-3\sqrt{3}}{2}\frac{III_\sigma}{\bar{\sigma}^3}\right) < \frac{\pi}{6} \tag{5.2}$$

and use this quantity as the third invariant.

The angle θ has a distinct physical meaning as it represents the angle in a plane perpendicular to the $\sigma_1 = \sigma_2 = \sigma_3$ axis (Figure 5.4). Indeed in this plane the magnitude of the vector represents the second stress invariant $\bar{\sigma}$ while on all points of the π-plane σ_m (the first stress invariant) is constant. Figure 5.4 shows a typical π-plane section of the Mohr–Coulomb surface and of the inscribed Drucker cone. For isotropy the figure shows that a six-fold symmetry has always to exist.

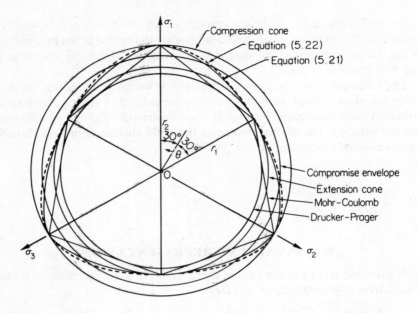

Figure 5.4 The π-plane section of Mohr–Coulomb surface with $\phi = 20°$ and various smooth approximations

As the three principal stresses can be written now in descending order of magnitude as (tensile stresses are taken positive)

$$\begin{Bmatrix} \sigma_1 \\ \sigma_2 \\ \sigma_3 \end{Bmatrix} = \frac{2}{\sqrt{3}} \bar{\sigma} \begin{Bmatrix} \sin\left(\theta + \dfrac{2\pi}{3}\right) \\ \sin\theta \\ \sin\left(\theta + \dfrac{4\pi}{3}\right) \end{Bmatrix} + \sigma_m \qquad (5.3)$$

it is easy to write the Mohr–Coulomb criterion as

$$F = \sigma_m \sin\phi + \bar{\sigma}\left(\cos\theta - \sin\theta \sin\frac{\phi}{\sqrt{3}}\right) - c\cos\phi = 0. \qquad (5.4)$$

Substitution of σ_m = constant gives from above the relationship between $\bar{\sigma}$ and θ in the π-plane (Figure 5.4) whereas substitution of θ = const. gives the 'meridional' section relating σ_m and $\bar{\sigma}$.

We note immediately that the sections in the π-plane are always geometrically similar while those in the meridional planes show only a scale distortion dependent on the value of θ.

Generally it is clear that a set of surfaces written as

$$F = f(\sigma_m) + h(\bar{\sigma}/g(\theta)) = 0 \tag{5.5}$$

will possess similar characteristics and that the Mohr–Coulomb relationship is but one of such forms. We shall now seek to write expressions of the above from which will eliminate the angularity of the π-plane and the vertices in the meridional planes.

5.3 GENERAL MERIDIONAL SECTIONS

As in a π-plane

$$\bar{\sigma}/g(\theta) = \text{constant} \tag{5.6}$$

we can choose to describe $\bar{\sigma}$ by a meridional value of $\bar{\sigma}$ in an arbitrary section. Taking for instance the value of $\bar{\sigma}$ as $\bar{\sigma}_+$ at $\theta = \pi/6$ we can write

$$\bar{\sigma} = \bar{\sigma}_+ g(\theta) \tag{5.7}$$

with $g(\theta)$ so defined as to make $g(\pi/6) = 1$.

In that meridional plane the Equation (5.5) will take the form of

$$F = f(\sigma_m) + h(\bar{\sigma}_+) = 0 \tag{5.8}$$

We shall now seek useful forms of such meridional sections.

A very general form of such surfaces can be written in a quadratic form

$$F = \alpha\sigma_m^2 + \beta\sigma_m + \gamma + \bar{\sigma}_+^2 = 0 \tag{5.9}$$

and generalized to

$$F = \alpha\sigma_m^2 + \beta\sigma_m + \gamma + (\bar{\sigma}/g(\theta))^2 = 0 \tag{5.10}$$

5.3.1 An approximation to Mohr–Coulomb without vertex corner

Here it is seen from Figure 5.5 that a hyperbola can give as close an approximation as desired to the two straight Mohr–Coulomb lines as desired. The equation of the hyperbola

$$\left(\frac{\sigma_m - d}{a}\right)^2 - \frac{\bar{\sigma}_+^2}{b^2} = 1 \tag{5.11}$$

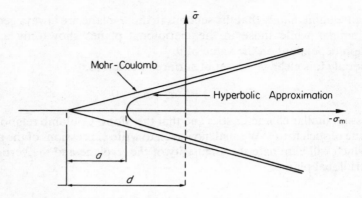

Figure 5.5   A hyperbolic approximation of Mohr–Coulomb

gives immediately the forms (5.9) or (5.10) with

$$\alpha = -\frac{b^2}{a^2}$$

$$\beta = +2\frac{b^2}{a^2} \cdot d \qquad\qquad (5.12)$$

$$\gamma = b^2 - \frac{b^2}{a^2} \cdot d^2$$

with a, b and d taking the meaning of the symbols shown in Figure 5.5. In terms of the $c - \phi$ parameters it is simple to show that

$$\alpha = -\sin^2 \phi$$

$$\beta = 2c \sin \phi \cos \phi \qquad\qquad (5.13a)$$

$$\gamma = a^2 \sin^2 \phi - c^2 \cos^2 \phi$$

in which a is chosen suitably to round off the vertex corner. As $a \to 0$ approximation to the classical Mohr–Coulomb surface can be made as close as desired.

As Equation (5.11) gives in fact two branches of hyperbolae and we are interested in a single yield surface Equation (5.11) should be used in the form

$$\frac{\sigma_m - d}{a} + \sqrt{\left(\frac{\bar{\sigma}_+}{b^2} + 1\right)} = 0 \qquad\qquad (5.13b)$$

where only a single sign of the square root is taken.

In terms of the general Equation (5.10) the form becomes

$$F = \sqrt{} - \alpha(\sigma_m + \beta/2\alpha) + \sqrt{[\bar{\sigma}_+^2 + \gamma - \beta^2/4\alpha]} = 0 \qquad (5.13c)$$

5.3.2 Parabolic Mohr–Coulomb type relations

A parabolic relationship of the type

$$(\sigma_m - d) + a\bar{\sigma}_+^2 = 0 \qquad (5.14)$$

is useful in modelling the behaviour of rock material and concrete (Figure 5.6). Again this is of the general form of Equation (5.9) or (5.10) with

$$\alpha = 0$$

$$\beta = +\frac{1}{a} \qquad (5.15)$$

$$\gamma = -\frac{d}{a}$$

and appropriate values can be inserted from tests.

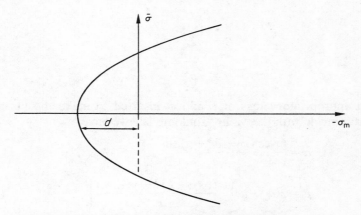

Figure 5.6 Parabolic form of Mohr–Coulomb relationship

5.1.3 Strain dependent—elliptical surfaces

One of the most reliable plasticity descriptions of yield surfaces is one involving elliptical surfaces with horizontal tangent on the Mohr–Coulomb critical surface. Such ellipses can be written as (Figure 5.7).

$$\left(\frac{\sigma_m - d}{a}\right)^2 + \frac{\bar{\sigma}_+^2}{b^2} = 1 \qquad (5.16)$$

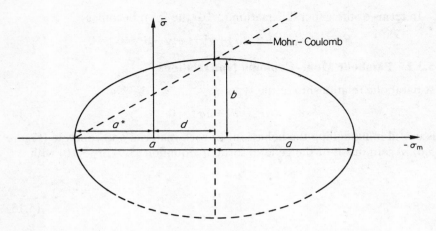

Figure 5.7   An elliptic form of strain (density) dependent yield surface

or in the standard form of Equations (5.9) and (5.10) with

$$\alpha = \frac{b^2}{a^2}$$

$$\beta = -2\frac{b^2}{a^2} \cdot d \qquad (5.17)$$

$$\gamma = -b^2 + \frac{b^2}{a^2} \cdot d^2$$

With appropriate values of c and ϕ inserted to make the horizontal tangent coincide with the Mohr–Coulomb law we have

$$\alpha = \left[\frac{c \cos \phi - (a^* - a) \sin \phi}{a}\right]^2$$

$$\beta = 2(a^* - a)\left[\frac{c \cos \phi - (a^* - a) \sin \phi}{a}\right]^2 \qquad (5.18)$$

$$\gamma = [c \cos \phi - (a^* - a) \sin \phi]^2 \left[\left(\frac{a - a^*}{a}\right)^2 - 1\right]$$

This form was used by Zienkiewicz, Humpheson, *et al.* (1975) for compu tation of some soil mechanics problems.

5.4   GENERAL π-SECTION

The general form of the yield surface is now determined by Equation (5.8) if a suitable function is known.

The function $g(\theta)$ is such that $g(\pi/6) = 1$ and this function determines the shape of the π-section. For instance the Mohr–Coulomb relation, Equation (5.4), gives

$$g(\theta) = \frac{[(\cos \pi/6 - \sin \pi/6)\sin \phi]/\sqrt{3}}{(\cos \theta - \sin \theta \sin \phi)/\sqrt{3}} \tag{5.19}$$

This is an expression defining a straight line with corners occurring at $\theta = \pm \pi/6$ as shown in Figure 5.4. To avoid such corners we seek continuous convex functions such that

$$\frac{dg(\theta)}{d\theta} = 0 \qquad \text{at} \qquad \theta = \pm \pi/6$$

Such functions can be written in a polynomial or trigonometric form. Taking generally

$$g(\pi/6) = 1 \quad \text{and} \quad g(-\pi/6) = K \tag{5.20}$$

Williams and Warnke suggest an elliptic expression of the form

$$g(\theta) = \\ \frac{(1 - K^2)(\sqrt{3} \cos \theta - \sin \theta) + (2K - 1) \\ \quad [(2 + \cos 2\theta - \sqrt{3} \sin 2\theta)(1 - K^2) + 5k^2 - 4K]^{1/2}}{(1 - K^2)(2 + \cos 2\theta - \sqrt{3} \sin 2\theta) + (1 - 2K)^2} \tag{5.21}$$

An alternative simpler expression is due to Gudehus (1973) and Argyris, (Faust, *et al.*, 1973) giving

$$g(\theta) = \frac{2K}{(1 + K) - (1 - K) \sin 3\theta} \tag{5.22}$$

As both expressions give almost identical answers as shown in Figure 5.4, the simpler one is preferable and Equation (5.22) together with Equation (5.10) defines completely a very general form of yield surfaces.

The value of K can be made to coincide with the Mohr–Coulomb relation in terms of the friction angle

$$K = \frac{3 - \sin \phi}{3 + \sin \phi} \tag{5.23}$$

But in general other ratios can be determined *from experiment*. Indeed as the ratio must remain constant on some occasions a difficulty may arise in determining the mean angle ϕ for which the ratio is to be specified.

Finally it is of interest to observe that if $K = 1$, Equation (5.22) degenerates to $g(\theta) = 1$.

This leads to the simple circular section of the yield surface as assumed in the Drucker–Prager forms and signifies no dependence of the yield surface on the third stress invariant.

In visco-plastic algorithms it is of interest to observe the shape of yield-plastic potential surfaces with $F \neq 0$. In Figure 5.8 we show a set of such surfaces in the meridional plane defined by the Equations (5.10) and (5.13).

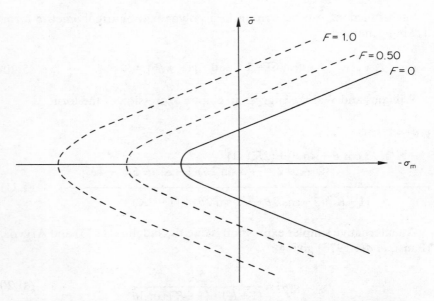

Figure 5.8   A set of $F \neq 0$ for an approximation by Equations (5.10) and (5.13) to a Mohr–Coulomb surface

In Figure 5.9 we show some differences between results obtained for a plane strain flexible footing on a weightless material (see Humpheson and Naylor, 1975) in which, successively, Mohr–Coulomb, various circular approximations and interpolations of Equations (5.21) and (5.22) have been used.

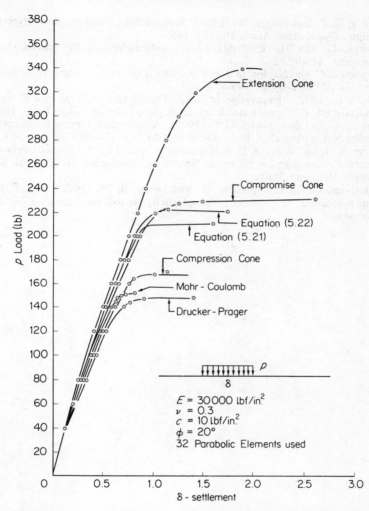

Figure 5.9 Influence of different forms of yield surface on bearing capacity (weightless soil). A plane strain strip load

REFERENCES

Argyris, J. H., Faust, G., Szimmat, J., Warnke, E. P., and William, K. J. (1973). 'Recent developments in the finite element analysis of PCRV', *2nd Int. Conf. SMIRT*, Berlin.

Drucker, D. C. (1953). 'Limit analysis of two and three dimensional soil mechanics problems', *J. Mech. Phys. Solids* **1**, 217–226.

Drucker, D. C. and Prager, W. (1952). 'Soil mechanics and plastic analysis in limit design', *Quart. Appl. Math.* **10**, 157–165.

Gudehus, G. (1973). 'Elastoplastische Stoffgleichungen für trockenen Sand', *Ingenieur-Archiv*, 42.

Humpheson, C. and Naylor, D. J. (1975). 'The importance of the form of the failure criterion', *C/R/243/75*, Swansea.

Meek, J. L. (1973). 'Excavation in Rock. Theory and practice' in *F.E. Structural Analysis*, ed. Y. Yamada and R. H. Gallagher, Univ. of Tokyo Press, 195–214.

Nayak, G. C. and Zienkiewicz, O. C. (1972). 'A convenient form of invariants and its application in plasticity', *Proc. ASCE 98* EM. No. ST4 949-54.

William, K. J. and Warnke, E. P. 'Constitutive model for the tri-axial behaviour of concrete', Seminar on Concrete Structures Subjected to Tri-axial Stresses, *ISMES*, Bergamo, Italy.

Zienkiewicz, O. C., Humpheson, C., and Lewis, R. W. (1975). 'Associated and Non-associated viscoplasticity and plasticity in soil mechanics', *C/R/249/75*, Swansea.

Chapter 6

The Predicted Performance of Soft Clay Under a Trial Embankment Loading based on the Cam-Clay Model

C. P. Wroth

6.1 INTRODUCTION

The soil mechanics Group at Cambridge University has had as its long-term objective the development of fundamental and consistent stress-strain laws for soils and, it is hoped, the establishment of a proper understanding of their mechanical behaviour.

The stage in this continuing program has been reached where sophisticated elasto-plastic models of soil behaviour have been developed, and these models have been used in finite element computations to obtain complete solutions to boundary value problems in foundation engineering.

The Foundation Deformation Prediction symposium held at M.I.T. in November 1974 provided an ideal opportunity for the relevance and use of these novel models to be assessed in a real engineering situation. The basic model adopted is the plane strain version of modified Cam-clay within a purpose-made computer program, both of which were developed by Simpson (1973). The salient features of the mathematical model and of the computer program are described in this paper, after a brief outline of the Prediction symposium.

6.2 M.I.T. PREDICTION SYMPOSIUM

In August 1967 construction of a major road embankment across the tidal marshes at Saugus, just north of Boston, was commenced. This embankment was designed to carry the interstate thruway, I-95, and in order to accelerate the substantial settlements to be expected, the embankment was surcharged. Because of the engineering problems associated with such a high embankment on relatively weak ground, the performance of the embankment was

191

carefully monitored by means of hydraulic piezometers, settlement gauges and slope indicators (inclinometers). The interpretation of the field data has been reported by D'Appolonia *et al.* (1971), Lambe *et al.* (1972) and Lambe (1973).

A cross-section of the embankment at Station 263 is given in Figure 6.1, showing approximately the positions of the various instruments and the ground conditions. Full details of the soil properties are given by D'Appolonia, *et al.* 1971.

The filling of the embankment to the surcharge level of elevation +40 ft (12·2 m) was completed by July 1969. Subsequently the alignment of the road was completely changed, so that the embankment was never finished and put into use. As a result, a full-scale field trial was planned, in which a length of approximately 300 ft (100 m) of the embankment was to be filled rapidly until failure occurred.

The field trial provided an opportunity for a special symposium to be held at which the results of genuine Class A predictions (Lambe, 1973) of the performance of the embankment could be compared with its observed behaviour. Ten groups accepted invitations to make predictions, and submit them to an independent referee before the field trial began. The required predictions were as follows:

(1) Additional height of fill necessary to cause a stability failure (differential settlement of the crest of the embankment of 0·5 m constituted failure).

(2) When 6 ft (1·83 m) of fill had been added:
    (a) additional horizontal movement of SI-3 and SI-4 at elevations −30ft (9·14 m) and −70 ft (21·34 m)
    (b) additional settlement of SP-1
    (c) additional pore pressures at P-3, P-4 and P-6
    (d) heave at H-1 and H-2.

(3) Additional pore pressures at P-3, P-4 and P-6 at failure.

Information about the field trial and results of field and laboratory tests were transmitted to the predictors in a series of Bulletins. The field data consisted of records of settlement, horizontal movements and pore pressures observed during the five years that the embankment had remained at its full surcharge height, and profiles of vane shear strengths. The laboratory data consisted of (constant rate of strain) one-dimensional consolidation tests, unconfined compression tests and various tri-axial tests.

6.3 THE CAM-CLAY MODEL OF SOIL BEHAVIOUR

6.3.1 Basic definitions

The parameters adopted are:

mean normal effective stress:

$$s' = \tfrac{1}{2}(\sigma_1' + \sigma_3')$$

shear stress:

$$t = \tfrac{1}{2}(\sigma_1' - \sigma_3')$$

volumetric strain:

$$-\delta V/V = (\delta\varepsilon_1 + \delta\varepsilon_3)$$

shear strain:

$$\delta\gamma = 2\delta\varepsilon = (\delta\varepsilon_1 - \delta\varepsilon_3)$$

where (σ_1', σ_3') and $(\delta\varepsilon_1, \delta\varepsilon_3)$ are respectively the major and minor principal effective stresses and strain-increments. Conditions of plane strain have been assumed to apply throughout the computations, so that $\delta\varepsilon_2 \equiv 0$, and the effect of the intermediate principal effective stress is ignored. Compressive stresses and strains have been taken as positive.

In the development of the concepts incorporated in the models, use has been made of the ideas and terminology of classical plasticity and in particular of terms such as plastic strain, yield, normality, etc. These terms will be defined briefly where first introduced.

The typical behaviour of a soil specimen in a shear test can be characterized by the curve of Figure 6.2a. If the specimen is loaded along the path OA and then unloaded along ABC, the path ABC can be approximated as elastic behaviour, with the strain represented by OC being a permanent, irrecoverable *plastic* strain denoted by ε^p. On reloading the specimen behaves essentially elastically along CDE (displaying a small amount of hysteresis) until at point E it experiences the previous *maximum shear stress*; it *yields* and undergoes further plastic strain. Point F denotes *failure* (a unique condition for this particular test); failure must be distinguished from yield which is a progressive phenomenon and which may occur at any point along the primary loading curve OAEF depending on the exact loading sequence in the shear test.

Analogous behaviour will be displayed by a soil specimen if tested in consolidation, as shown in Figure 6.2b which is an unconventional plot of effective pressure against volume change. If this diagram is rotated clockwise through 90° to give Figure 6.2c, the more usual plot of consolidation is obtained.

It should be realized that for a specimen that is in the overconsolidated state represented by point C in Figure 6.2c its preconsolidation pressure p_c' given by point E is the current *yield stress* for further consolidation; it is the pressure at which further plastic volumetric strains begin to occur.

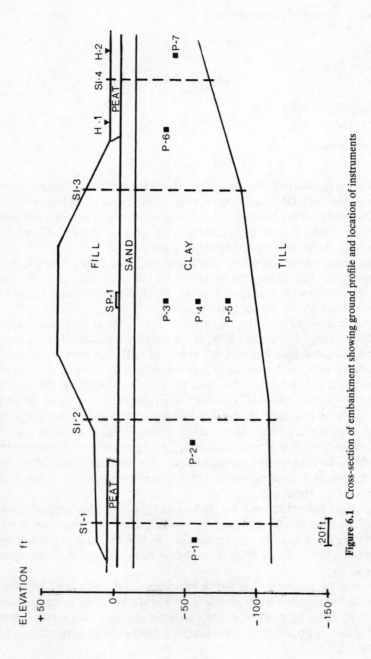

Figure 6.1 Cross-section of embankment showing ground profile and location of instruments

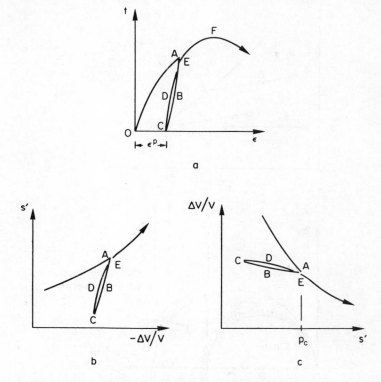

Figure 6.2   Typical behaviour of soil specimen in consolidation and shear
tests

6.3.1.1   *Yield curves.*

Consider a soil specimen that has been isotropically normally consolidated (with $\sigma'_1 = \sigma'_3$) to point A in Figure 6.3a, and then been allowed to swell to some state along the unloading curve ABC. If the specimen were subjected to a variety of effective stress paths, it is assumed that there is a well defined region of stress states (s', t) for which the specimen would remain elastic. This region is bounded by a *yield curve*. If the stresses applied to the specimen take its state outside the current yield curve, it will yield and experience both plastic volumetric and plastic shear strains.

Consider a second specimen that has been normally consolidated to G, and then been allowed to swell to some point on the unloading curve GHI. Associated with this specimen is a larger yield curve, but one of the same shape as that for the first specimen.

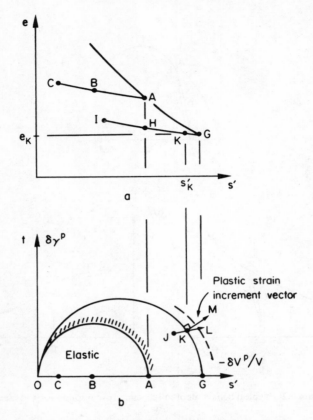

Figure 6.3 Yield curves for specimens with different consolidation histories

6.3.2 Parameters for describing the yield curve

The *sizes* of the yield curves are dicated by the points A and G, which lie on the normal isotropic consolidation curve. The choice of yield curve appropriate for any specimen depends on the maximum consolidation pressure (i.e. the preconsolidation pressure, p'_c).

The *shape* of the yield curve, Figure 6.4a, is assumed to be *elliptical*; this choice is based on considerations of energy dissipated plastically within the specimen, and on proposals put forward by Burland (1967), details of which are not considered here.

The major axis of the ellipse, OA is fixed by the consolidation history relevant to the specimen. The minor axis BX_1 is given by the assumption that the point X_1 is on the line of critical states, or failure states of normally

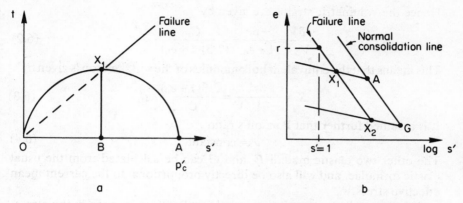

Figure 6.4 Shape of yield curve

consolidated specimens. This line is parallel to the normal consolidation line in the semi-logarithmic plot of Figure 6.4b.

For a given specimen with known voids ratio e, and effective pressure s' (knowledge of both σ_1' and σ_3' is required, i.e. for a field specimen the lateral effective stress must be known or estimated), the relevant yield curve is given by the four parameters

C_c the compression index
C_s the swelling or recompression index
ϕ' the angle of internal friction
and Γ.

The last parameter Γ is required to locate either the failure line or the normal consolidation line in Figure 6.4b; it is the voids ratio for which s' has unit value. It is in some ways analogous to the liquid limit (see Schofield and Wroth, 1968, pp. 151–161) and increases markedly with the plasticity index of the clay being considered.

6.3.3 Elastic behaviour

The elastic behaviour of the specimen for stress states within the current yield curve is assumed to be isotropic, but with the elastic moduli directly dependent on the current mean stress, s'. This latter feature is a consequence of the volumetric strains associated with the swelling and recompression lines AX_1 and GX_2 in Figure 6.4b. If the initial state of the specimen is given by (e_0, s_0') the equation of AX_1 is

$$e - e_0 = C_s \log_{10}(s_0'/s') = \frac{C_s}{2 \cdot 3} \log_e(s_0'/s') \tag{6.1}$$

Hence the volumetric strains are given by

$$\frac{-\delta V}{V_0} = \frac{-\delta e}{1 + e_0} = \frac{C_s}{(2 \cdot 3)(1 + e_0)} \cdot \frac{\delta s'}{s'_0} \tag{6.2}$$

This means that the equivalent bulk modulus of the soil skeleton is given by

$$K = \frac{\delta s'}{-\delta V/V} = \frac{2 \cdot 3(1 + e_0)}{C_s} \cdot s'_0 \tag{6.3}$$

It is assumed further that Poisson's ratio

$$\nu' = \text{constant} \tag{6.4}$$

The other two elastic moduli E' and G can be calculated from the usual elastic formulae, and will also be directly proportional to the current mean effective stress, s'_0.

Only two soil parameters are required therefore to specify the stress-dependent isotropic elastic behaviour, and these are C_s and ν'.

6.3.4 Plastic behaviour

Suppose that the state of stress experienced by the specimen is at point J in Figure 6.3b close to the relevant yield curve. If the stress increment JKL is applied to the specimen, the increment JK will cause elastic strain increments only, whereas the increment KL will cause *both* elastic and plastic strain increments. As the specimen yields at K the yield curve is expanded as the specimen undergoes consolidation. The plastic volumetric strain $\delta V^p/V$ that occurs from K to L is given by a *hardening law*, which is derived from the normal consolidation line

$$e - e_k = C_c \log_{10}(s'_k/s') \tag{6.5}$$

The details of this derivation are not given here, but can be found in Schofield and Wroth (1968). The important point is that only one further soil parameter, the compression index C_c, is required.

The *flow rule* governing the ratio of the plastic strain increments is given by the condition of *normality*. This condition stipulates that if the associated plastic strain increments $-\delta V^p/V$ and $\delta \gamma^p$ are plotted on the same axes as the stresses in Figure 6.3b, the vector KM of plastic strain increment is normal to the yield curve at K. The gradient of the curve at K is known from its elliptical shape, so that the ratio $(\delta V^p/V)/\delta \gamma^p$ can be calculated and since $\delta V^p/V$ is already established (from the hardening law), $\delta \gamma^p$ can be evaluated.

6.4   SELECTION OF SOIL PARAMETERS

The selection of parameters to use in the Cam-clay model of the Boston Blue clay was made from the data of laboratory tests reported in the Bulletins.

Values of C_c, C_s and Γ were taken from one one-dimensional consolidation test, a value of ϕ' from one drained tri-axial test and a value of ν' was guessed (on the basis of previous experience). The one-dimensional consolidation test and the drained tri-axial test were carefully selected to be representative of the complete series of tests; in effect they provided average values for the soil parameters. The values used in the computations were $C_c = 0 \cdot 338$, $C_s = 0 \cdot 138$, $\Gamma = 2 \cdot 15$, $\phi' = 26 \cdot 5°$ and $\nu' = 0 \cdot 35$.

Figure 6.5 gives the results produced by the computer for (imaginary) plane strain tests carried out on the Boston Blue clay. It is included to demonstrate that the model gives a specification of the behaviour of the clay which is in itself complete, and also realistic. The curves ABF_u in each of the four inter-related diagrams are the results of an undrained compression test on a specimen initially at state A, which represents a typical element in the ground at a depth of 50 ft (15·24 m) with $K_0 = 0 \cdot 8$ before construction of the existing embankment. Yield of the specimen starts at B.

The curves ACF_d are the results of a fully drained compression test for which σ_3' has been kept constant. Yield in this case starts at C.

Figure 6.6 provides a direct comparison between the results of a one-dimensional consolidation test and those produced by the computer. Not only does the model reproduce qualitatively the main features of the consolidation behaviour, but it also accurately reproduces the ratio K_0 of lateral to vertical effective stresses observed during one-dimensional unloading in a specially instrumented consolidometer. In the lower diagram the value of K_0 is plotted against the overconsolidation ratio, OCR. (N.B. 1 kip/ft^2 = 1000 lbf/ft^2 = 47·85 kN/m^2). This relationship allows a value of K_0 to be estimated for any element of soil from the value of its overconsolidation ratio deduced from conventional laboratory consolidation tests.

6.5 MODEL OF SAND BEHAVIOUR

The model for the behaviour of sand used in the computations is based on one developed by Simpson (1973). It has been used for the successful matching of computed stress and strain fields within a sand mass with those obtained from model experiments on retaining walls, reported by Simpson and Wroth (1972).

The model is based on the concepts developed at Cambridge and it is very similar in character to that of Cam-clay. Its main features are its ability to model both the strain-softening that occurs after peak strength is reached in a shear test, and the dilatation that occurs; neither of these is reproducible by an elastic model, however complicated.

Typical results produced by the computer for plane-strain tests on both loose and dense samples of sand are displayed in Figure 6.7. Both tests start

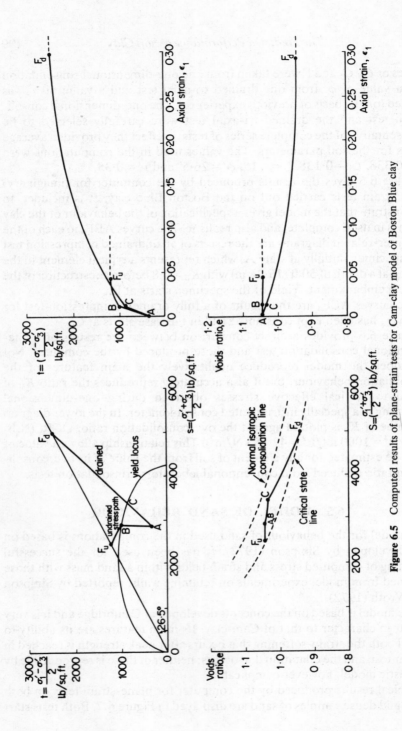

Figure 6.5 Computed results of plane-strain tests for Cam-clay model of Boston Blue clay

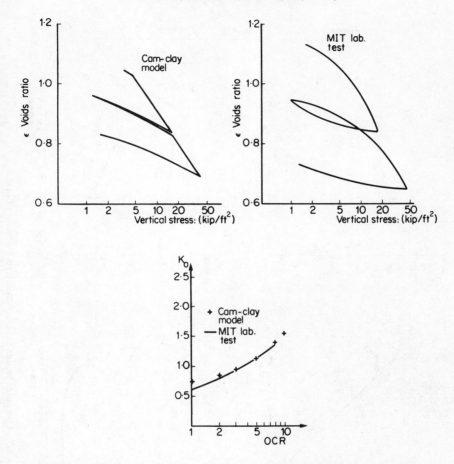

Figure 6.6 Comparison of computed and experimental results for one-dimensional consolidation

at the same stress state but at different void ratios; and both are drained compression tests in which σ_3' has been kept constant. The computed stress–strain curves and volumetric strains are of the form to be expected for a real sand.

Because there was insufficient information available on the sand at the site of the I-95 embankment, and because its influence on the overall performance of the trial embankment was considered to be small, the existing model with parameters chosen to match Leighton Buzzard sand was used without modification.

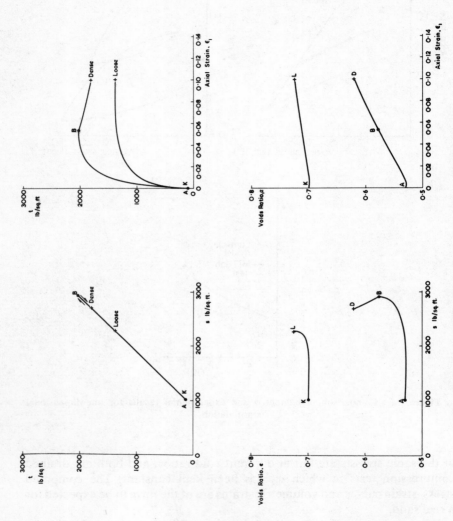

Figure 6.7 Computed results of plane-strain tests for model of sand

6.6 FINITE ELEMENT PROGRAM

The finite element program used for the predictions was one developed by Simpson (1973) as part of his research work. It has many special features, the most notable being:

(1) The plane strain elements used are simple three-noded constant strain triangles (the program has since been extended to use six-noded linear strain triangles).

(2) The program can handle strain-softening and dilatation (as already indicated by the results of Figure 6.7).

(3) The program treats soil as a *two-phase* material; the behaviour of the soil is always controlled by the effective stresses, and equilibrium by total stresses. To the pore water is ascribed an appropriately large (but finite) bulk modulus, so that for the so-called undrained condition there has to be compatibility between the small volume change of the water and that of the soil skeleton. The program keeps track of total *and* effective stresses for every element. For example, Figure 6.8 shows the effective (ESP) and total stress paths (TSP) for the indicated element positioned under the centre line of the embankment; the stage at which this element yielded is clearly shown by the abrupt change in the direction of the effective stress path at Y. At Z the element has reached failure and is being held in equilibrium by the surrounding elements but is unable to sustain any greater shear stress. The first part XY of the effective stress path is the partly drained simulation of the combined effects of the initial construction and subsequent five years of partial consolidation; the method is described below.

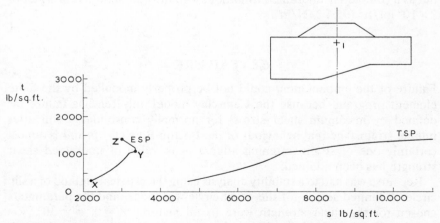

Figure 6.8   Total and effective stress paths for element 1 under centre line of embankment

(4) The program allows for the effect of independent rotation of the principal axes of stress, stress-increment and strain-increment. Coincidence of principal axes of stress with those of plastic strain increment, and between those of stress increment and elastic strain increment was assumed.

(5) The program includes a facility for refining the mesh of elements during a computation, so that progressive failure and growth of failure zones may be modelled.

6.7 MATCHING FIELD CONSOLIDATION

The predictions are based on two separate computations. The first computation was modelling the construction of the initial embankment up to the level of $+40$ ft $(12 \cdot 2\text{m})$ as a partially drained situation, for which a bulk modulus for the water K_w of 1×10^5 lbf/ft^2 ($4 \cdot 785$ MN/m^2) was adopted; this gave a reasonable match to the field data available. The criterion for acceptability was when adequate agreement had been obtained for the computed horizontal movements with the field data from the inclinometers after 600 days (August 1969). The computed profiles are given in Figure 6.9.

The field data for the changes that occurred between 600 days (August 1969) and five years (August 1974) showed relatively small changes in excess pore pressures but substantial settlements which were attributed mainly to undrained creep. Because the *in situ* effective stresses had not altered significantly during this period it was believed that the computation represented as well as it could the existing stresses in the ground at the start of the test. The final stage was to model the filling of the embankment up to the predicted failure height of elevation $+61$ ft $(18 \cdot 6$ m). This was carried out as a completely undrained condition, with the bulk modulus of water of 2×10^6 lbf/ft^2 ($95 \cdot 7$ MN/m^2).

6.8 FAILURE

Failure of the embankment could not be properly modelled by the finite element program, because the Cam-clay model only reaches failure (as defined by maximum shear stress) for normally consolidated soil after infinite strain. The real behaviour of the Boston Blue clay *in situ* is almost certainly one of strain-softening after a peak value of undrained shear strength has been attained.

Recourse was had to a stability analysis using the classical method of a slip circle. A limited search for the worst circle was made, and the parameters chosen for the shear strength were (i) fill material $c' = 0$, $\phi' = 30°$, $\gamma = 120$ lbf/ft^3 ($18 \cdot 86$ kN/m^3); (ii) sand layer in the existing ground $c' = 0$,

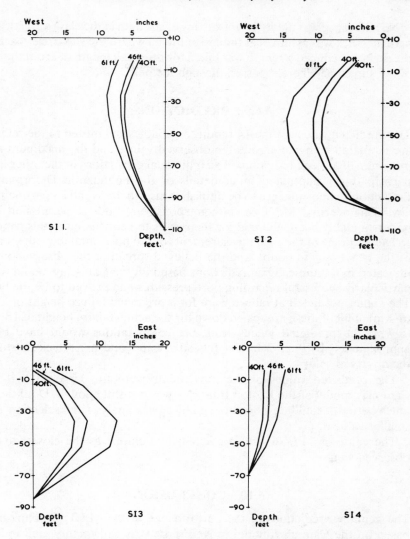

Figure 6.9 Computed horizontal movements of inclinometer tubes

$\phi' = 35°$, $\gamma = 120 \text{ lbf/ft}^3$ (18·86 kN/m³); (ii) Boston Blue clay $c_u = 8·8 \text{ lbf/in}^2$ (60 kN/m²). The last figure was chosen partly on the quoted, *in situ* vane shear strengths, and partly on the results of undrained pressuremeter tests carried out at the site by Hughes using the Camkometer (self-boring pressuremeter) developed at Cambridge by Wroth and Hughes (1973).

No allowance was made for anisotropy of strength in the clay; a 10 ft (3 m) vertical crack was assumed at the top of the fill where the slip circle reached the surface; reduced strength was taken for the small length of arc at the toe of the slip circle where it passed through the peat.

6.9 PREDICTIONS

The predicted values of the 14 required variables, submitted to the referee are tabulated below alongside the observed values and the maximum and minimum of all ten predictions. The individual predictions of the other nine participating groups, and fuller details of the Foundation Deformation Prediction symposium, are to be published elsewhere by the Department of Civil Engineering, M.I.T. and their sponsoring bodies; permission has understandably been withheld for the results to be included in this paper.

The accuracy of the field measurements of the horizontal movement and of the heave was in doubt, and the believed spread of the observations is indicated in the table. The predictions based on the Cam-clay model were particularly successful regarding pore pressures and proved to be the best. The values predicted at failure were for a predicted failure height of 21 ft (6·4 m) of fill; if these are scaled down for the actual failure height of 18·7 ft (5·7 m) the predicted values from the computations would have been approximately 24·0, 25·2 and 7·0 ft head of water, and, as a set, closer still to the observed values.

The predicted values of the movements were too large so that the Cam-clay model of the Boston Blue clay was not stiff enough. Doubtless a much better fit could now be obtained by a back analysis and selection of a smaller value of C_s.

The value of 21 ft (6·4 m) predicted for failure was the closest to the observed value.

6.10 CONCLUSIONS

The genuine predictions of the performance of the M.I.T. Embankment based on the Cam-clay model proved to be very satisfactory, and indeed were as close, if not closer, to the field behaviour than the other predictions presented at the symposium. The majority of the other predictions were based on elastic models of the Boston Blue clay, some linear, some non-linear. All of these elastic computations were carried out in terms of total stresses, so that no direct information is available from the computations regarding values of excess pore pressures; these have to be estimated subsequently by using some assumption of the undrained behaviour of the clay, such as selection of suitable pore pressure parameters.

Table 6.1 Predicted and observed values
Column A: Prediction by Cambridge Group
Column B: Observed value
Column C: Largest prediction
Column D: Smallest prediction

Item predicted	**A**	**B**	**C**	**D**
Additional horizontal movement due to				
6 ft of fill: (inches) at				
SI-3, Elev. −30 ft	1·6	0·5±0·3	8·6	0·17
SI-3, Elev. −70 ft	0·6	0·3±0·2	8·6	0·016
SI-4, Elev. −30 ft	0·7	0·0±0·2	5·3	0·25
SI-4, Elev. −70 ft	0	0	2·25	0
Additional settlement of SP-1				
due to 6 ft of fill:				
(inches)	2·6	0·66	13·7	0·76
Additional pore pressure due to				
6 ft of fill: (feet				
head of water) at				
P-3	9·0	9·4	26·0	6·0
P-4	9·6	6·4	22·0	7·2
P-6	5·8	5·7	13·0	2·5
Additional heave due to 6 ft of				
fill: (inches) at				
H-1	0	−0·12±0·2	4·8	0
H-2	0	−0·15±0·2	6·2	0
Additional height of fill				
at failure: (feet)	21·0	18·7	27·0	8·0
Additional pore-pressure at failure:				
(feet head of water) at				
P-3	27·0	21·9	38·0	12·8
P-4	28·3	21·8	42·0	12·5
P-6	7·9	10·9	26·0	4·0

In contrast, the finite element computations based on the Cam-clay model are carried out in terms of total *and* effective stresses, and the excess pore pressures are automatically calculated.

The Cam-clay model also has the major advantage that it only requires five basic soil parameters for a complete description of the behaviour of *all* elements in a particular stratum; the model does not require the engineer to exercise judgement about how the stiffness of the soil may vary with depth or with level of effective stress. Moreover the five basic soil parameters can be obtained from one good quality consolidation test and one good quality triaxial drained compression test, (so long as these are representative of the behaviour of the clay and lead to appropriate average values for the parameters).

Although the Cam-clay model is believed to be particularly appropriate for describing the behaviour of soft clay when the ground is being loaded—such as the case of the M.I.T. Embankment—it must be emphasised that it would not be appropriate for modelling other soils in other boundary value problems. For example it would be inappropriate for predicting the deformations around a large excavation in heavily over-consolidated clay.

6.11 ACKNOWLEDGEMENTS

The Author acknowledges the major part played in the development of the computer program and the Cam-clay model by Dr B. Simpson, the continuing development of these and the computations carried out by Dr S. A. Thompson and the stability calculation carried out by Dr J. M. O. Hughes.

He is also very grateful to the Department of Civil Engineering, M.I.T., the Commonwealth of Massachusetts Department of Public works and to the U.S. Department of Transportation Federal Highway Administration, who jointly sponsored the Prediction symposium, for the invitation and opportunity to take part.

REFERENCES

Burland, J. B. (1967). 'Deformation of soft clay', *Ph.D. Thesis*, University of Cambridge.

D'Appolonia, D. J., Lambe, T. W., and Poulos, H. G. (1971). 'Evaluation of pore-pressures beneath an embankment', *Journ. Soil Mech. & Found. Div., ASCE* **97**, SM 6.

Lambe, T. W. (1973). 'Predictions in soil engineering', *Géotechnique* **23**, 149–202.

Lambe, T. W., D'Appolonia, D. J., Karlsrud, K., and Kirby, R. C. (1972). 'The performance of the foundation under a high embankment', *Journ. Boston Soc. of Civil Eng.*, **59**.

Schofield, A. N. and Wroth, C. P. (1968). *Critical State Soil Mechanics*, McGraw-Hill, London.

Simpson, B. (1973). 'Finite elements applied to problems of plane strain deformation in soils', *Ph.D. Thesis*, University of Cambridge.

Simpson, B. and Wroth, C. P. (1972). 'Finite element computations for a model retaining wall in sand', *Proc. 5th European Conf. Soil Mech. and Found. Engr.*, *Madrid*, **1**, 85–93.

Wroth, C. P. and Hughes, J. M. O. (1973). 'An instrument for the *in situ* measurement of the properties of soft clays', *Proc. 8th Int. Conf. Soil Mech. and Found. Engr.*, *Moscow* **1**, 487–494.

Chapter 7

Soil–Structure Interaction and Simulation Problems

C. S. Desai

7.1 INTRODUCTION

Coupling between behaviour of soils and structures needs to be considered in the analysis and design of structures founded on and in soils. It is recognized that numerical methods can provide realistic and satisfactory solutions for many static and dynamic problems involving coupling or interaction between soils and structures. Among the numerical methods, the Finite Element (FE) has been a prominent procedure that has been used successfully for solution of a wide range of problems (Desai, 1972a); some of these problems are footings, piles, retaining structures, locks, underground structures, buildings and dams.

Closely associated with the topic of interaction is the problem of the simulation of various natural and artificial sequences of construction. Such sequences influence the history of stresses and deformations that the soil and structure undergo. A number of procedures have been proposed for simulation of the sequences of constructuion in conjunction with the FE method.

7.1.1 Numerical procedure

The common procedure used is based on the displacement method of analysis. Here the displacements u, v, w, in the three co-ordinate directions x, y, z, respectively are assumed as unknowns and the FE equations are usually derived from the principle of minimum potential energy.

7.1.2 Soil and structural elements

The stiffness of elements of soil and structure is defined by using their constitutive or stress–strain laws. Very often, the structural materials, whose strength is usually much higher than that of the surrounding soils, are assumed to be linearly elastic. The soils are generally non-linear and should be treated as such. Two common approaches are to treat the soil as piecewise linear and to consider it as elastic–plastic. The former approach has been widely used (Clough and Duncan, 1969; Clough and Duncan, 1971; Clough, Weber *et al.*, 1972; Clough and Woodward, 1967; Desai, 1971; Desai, 1974a; Desai, 1974b; Desai, 1975; Desai, not published a, b, c; Desai and Holloway, 1972; Desai, Johnson, *et al.*, 1974; Duncan and Chang, 1970; Ellison, D'Appolonia, *et al.*, 1971; Tsui and Clough, 1974) and can be suitable for problems involving static and monotonic loads. For a general analysis, the elastic–plastic approach can be more suitable (Baker, Sandhu, *et al.*, 1969; Chang, Nair *et al.*, 1972; Chung and Lee, 1972; Desai, 1972a; Desai, 1974b; Desai, to be published; DiMaggio and Sandler, 1971; Gudehus, 1973; Hoëg, 1972; Isenberg and Bagge, 1972; Isenberg, Lee, *et al.*, 1973; Meissner and Wibel, 1974; Nayak and Zienkiewicz, 1974; Pariseau, Voight, *et al.*, 1970; Reyes and Deere, 1966; Sandler, Wu, *et al.*, 1971; Schofield and Wroth, 1968; Simpson and Wroth, 1972; Smith, 1970; Smith and Kay, 1971; Traughber, 1974; Wittke, 1974; Wittke, to be published; Zienkiewicz, Valliappan, *et al.*, 1970; Zienkiewicz, Valliappan *et al.*, 1968). Approaches based on higher order elasticity and hypo-elasticity have also been proposed (Desai, 1972b; Ko, 1976). The constitutive laws for soils are derived from uni-axial, conventional, tri-axial, truly tri-axial (in cubical device), consolidation, hydrostatic and direct shear tests. One-dimensional line, quadrilateral and hexahedral elements are used to represent soils and structures.

7.1.3 Interface behaviour

If the loading is such that significant amount of relative slip does not occur between the soil and structure, it may be admissible to assume compatibility between the two. However, in many cases it is necessary to consider relative slip, debonding and cycles of closing and opening of the interfaces. To account for this behaviour, special finite elements have been proposed. The stiffness properties of such interface elements are derived from tests that can simulate the transfer of shear stresses. The direct shear test, consisting of the structural material in the bottom half and the soil in the upper half, is often used. This test suffers from certain limitations, and modified and improved tests have been recently proposed.

7.1.4 Scope

The scope of this paper includes a review and discussion of the foregoing topics. In the first section, a number of factors relevant to the formulation of the FE method and constitutive laws for soils and interfaces are reviewed and discussed. The discussion is tied in with numerical solutions of a number of problems. Available procedures for simulation of various sequences of construction are reviewed and discussed in the second section. Possible schemes for improvement in the existing procedures are also discussed.

7.2 SOIL–STRUCTURE INTERACTION PROBLEMS

If the loading conditions do not require inclusion of slip and debonding, points on soil and corresponding points on structure can be assumed to remain in contact (Cooke and Price, 1973). Thus the necessity of interface elements can be avoided. It is also possible to solve for deformations in the soil and in the structure separately and then perform analysis such that slip is or is not permitted (Balam, Poulos, *et al.*, 1974). For general analysis, special interface elements are necessary (Chang, Nair, *et al.*, 1972; Clough and Duncan, 1969; Desai, 1974a; Desai, 1975; Desai and Holloway, 1972; Desai, Johnson, *et al.*, 1974; Ghaboussi, Wilson, *et al.*, 1973; Goodman, Taylor, *et al.*, 1968; Isenberg, Lee *et al.*, 1973; Mahtals and Goodman, 1970; Tsui and Clough, 1974; Wittke, to be published).

7.2.1 Finite element procedure

In the displacement method (Desai and Abel, 1972), the formulation is obtained by minimizing the potential energy of the system in which energy is contributed both by the solid and interface elements. The energy in solid elements is based on strain energy expressed by using the following relation:

$$\{\varepsilon\} = [B]\{q\} \tag{7.1}$$

where $\{\varepsilon\}$ is the matrix of strains, $[B]$ is the strain transformation matrix and $\{q\}$ is the vector of nodal displacements.

The energy in the interface element is expressed through relative displacements (Goodman, Taylor, *et al.*, 1968) as,

$$\{u_r\} = [B_r]\{q_r\} \tag{7.2}$$

$\{u_r\}$ is the vector of relative displacements at nodes, $[B_r]$ is the transformation matrix, and $\{q_r\}$ is the vector of relative nodal displacements. A modified interface element has been proposed recently (Ghaboussi, Wilson, *et al.*, 1973) and is briefly described subsequently; further details can also be found in Chapter 10.

In the following we describe a few practical problems solved by using the FE method. These problems will act as references for a number of factors that are discussed in this chapter.

7.2.2 Piles in sands

Figure 7.1 shows details of piles that were investigated by using the procedure described by Desai (1974a). In Figure 7.2 are shown typical

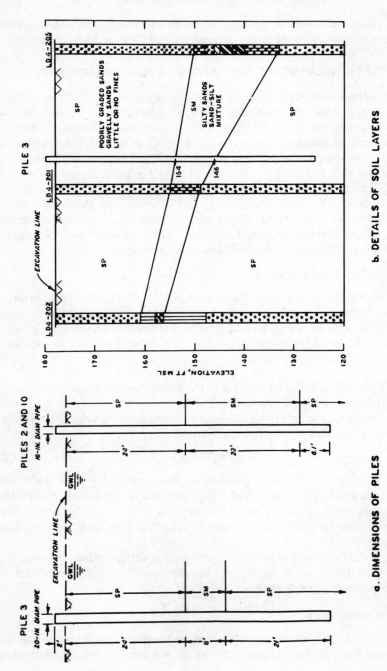

Figure 7.1   Piles in sands

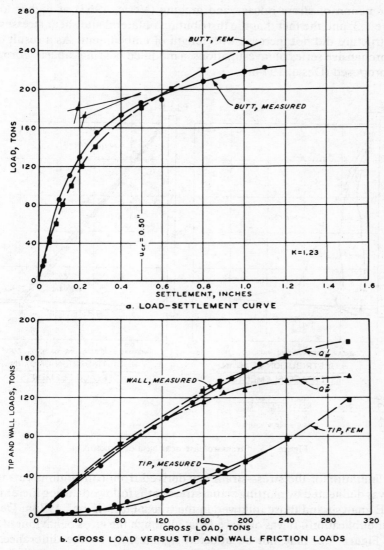

Figure 7.2   Comparisons of load-displacement curves—piles in sand

results in comparison with observations in the field (Fruco and Associates, 1964). The non-linear behaviour of sands and interfaces were derived from conventional tri-axial and direct shear tests respectively (Desai, under preparation). They were simulated by using a hyperbolic function (Desai 1971; Duncan and Chang, 1970). It was possible to observe the phenomenon of stress release and arching (Vesic, 1967) at higher load, Figure 7.3, and the fact that the distribution of lateral and shear stresses on the structure did not increase with length of embedment. As a result of a comprehensive series of investigations, a modified bearing capacity formula was proposed (Desai, 1974a).

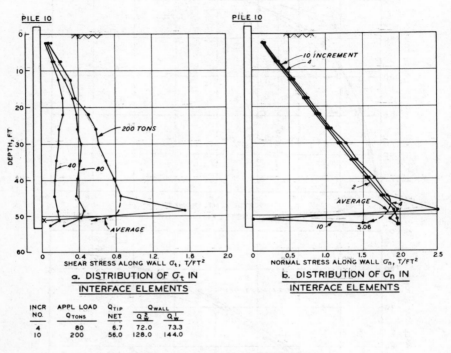

INCR NO.	APPL LOAD Q_{TONS}	Q_{TIP} NET	Q_{WALL} $Q\frac{2}{W}$	$Q\frac{\perp}{W}$
4	80	6.7	72.0	73.3
10	200	56.0	128.0	144.0

Figure 7.3 Stress–release near base of structure

A limitation of the stress-strain law derived from conventional tri-axial test was delineated by plotting actual stress paths followed during incremental FE analysis and those followed in the triaxial test (Desai, 1974a; Desai, under publication). It was observed that although the gross behaviour of the pile, Figure 7.2, may not be affected significantly by the differences in stress-paths, it is believed that local distribution of stresses can be influenced significantly. A discussion on the topic of stress-paths is given subsequently.

7.2.3 Piles in stiff clay

The main difficulty in deriving stress–strain behaviour for stiff clays is the sample disturbance. A FE analysis (Desai, under preparation) for piles in

Beamont Clay (O'Neill and Reese, 1970), showed that the initial modulus E_i from laboratory triaxial tests was too small, and the undrained strength, c_u, may be overestimated. It was found necessary to multiply the value of undrained strength c_u in the equation $E_i = \lambda c_u$ by a factor of $\lambda \simeq 800 - 1600$ (Desai, under publication) to obtain satisfactory correlation with the initial portion of the load-settlement curve, Figure 7.4. The clay and the interfaces exhibit strain-softening behaviour. If such behaviour is not included in the analysis, the correlation between computed and observed load taken by wall friction was poor. Further details on incorporation of softening behaviour are given later.

7.2.4 Pile groups—gravity lock foundation

It is relatively difficult to perform a three-dimensional (3-D) FE analysis in which interface elements are introduced. Indeed for some problems it is necessary to perform 3-D analysis (Desai, 1975). As an intermediate step, an approach based on replacement of a 3-D system by a structurally equivalent 2-D system was used. Here the Columbia-lock-pile foundation, Figure 7.5 (Desai, Johnson, *et al.*, 1974; Worth *et al.*, 1966), system was idealized as a 2-D plane strain problem, Figure 7.6, by assigning proportional stiffnesses to the piles. Figure 7.7 shows the FE mesh.

A number of sequences of construction—dewatering, excavation, build-up, back-filling, filling water in the lock and uplift pressure—were simulated. These sequences were preceded by an analysis in which initial stresses were introduced.

Figures 7.8 and 7.9 show comparisons between computed and observed displacements and distribution of loads in piles. Figure 7.9 also shows distribution of loads as computed by using Hrennikoff's method. In view of the assumptions made, the gross computed behaviour is considered to be satisfactory. A number of factors related to FE analysis and simulation of construction will be discussed subsequently.

2.3 FACTORS

The foregoing FE analysis including the interface elements gave satisfactory answers from the viewpoint of practical accuracy for a number of problems. The gross load-settlement behaviour can be computed to a good degree of accuracy, at least for monotonically increasing loads. However, a number of difficulties and irregularities can be observed if detailed distributions of stresses and deformations at specific locations are desired. A number of factors that can influence the behaviour of interaction problems are discussed below.

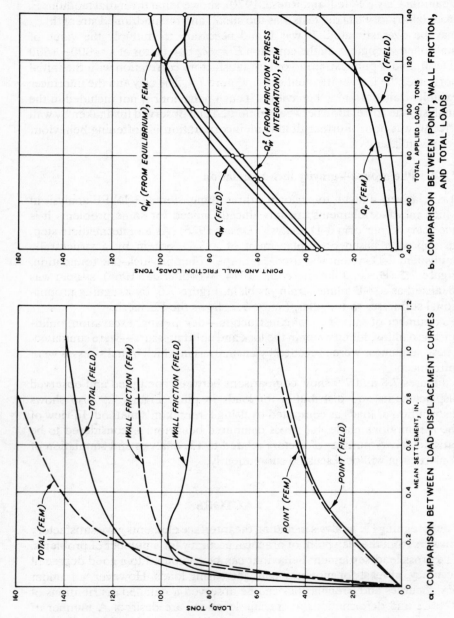

Figure 7.4 Comparison of load–displacement curves—pile in clay

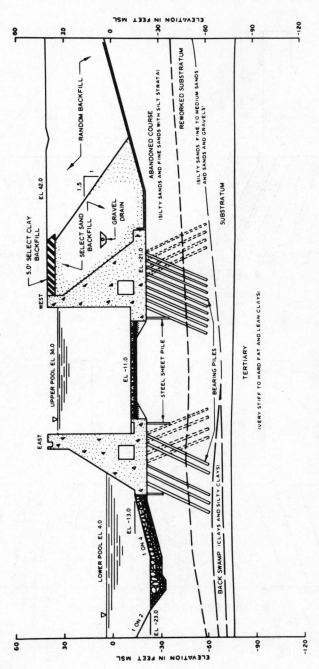

Figure 7.5 Columbia Lock and pile foundations

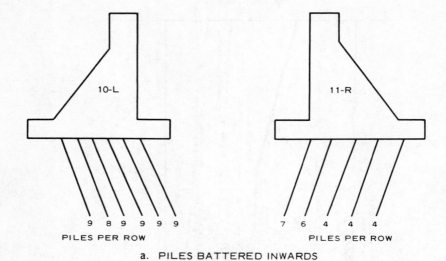

a.　PILES BATTERED INWARDS

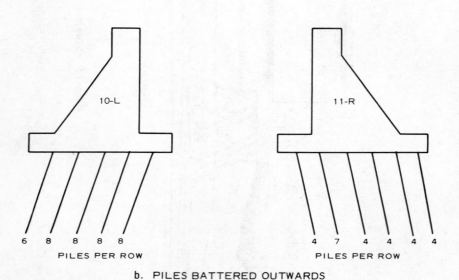

b.　PILES BATTERED OUTWARDS

Figure 7.6　Two-dimensional idealization

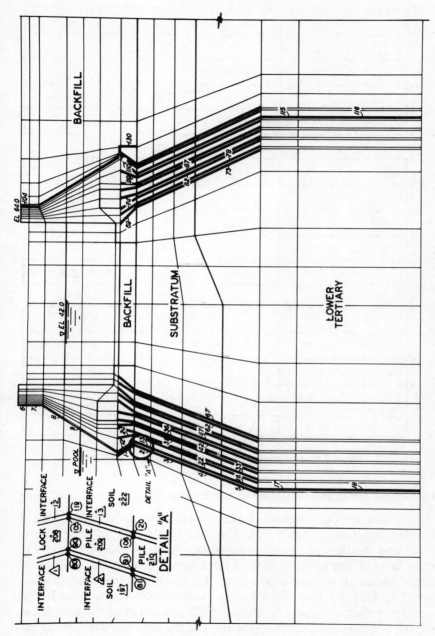

Figure 7.7 Finite element mesh

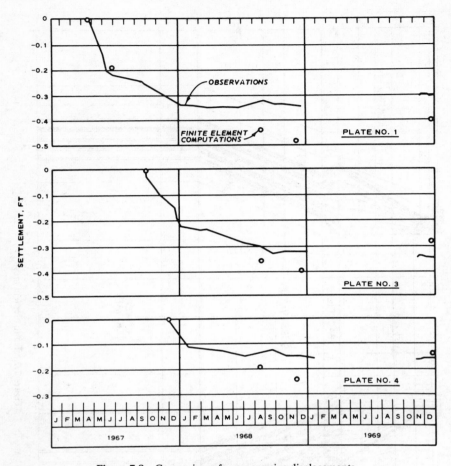

Figure 7.8 Comparisons for progressive displacements

7.3.1 Stress-relief and tensile stress conditions

At higher loadings, the material in the soil and the interfaces near the base of the (pile) foundation, Figure 7.3, may experience release of confining stresses and tensile stress conditions. Subsequently, separation or cracks may occur near that location. Since a formulation based on assumption of material continuity cannot account for this condition, irregular stresses, Figure 7.3, can occur. One of the ways to overcome this situation can be the use of stress transfer approach (Desai, 1977b; Zienkiewicz, Valliappan, *et al.*, 1968) which permits relieving the soil and the interface elements of the tensile stresses in excess of what the material can carry.

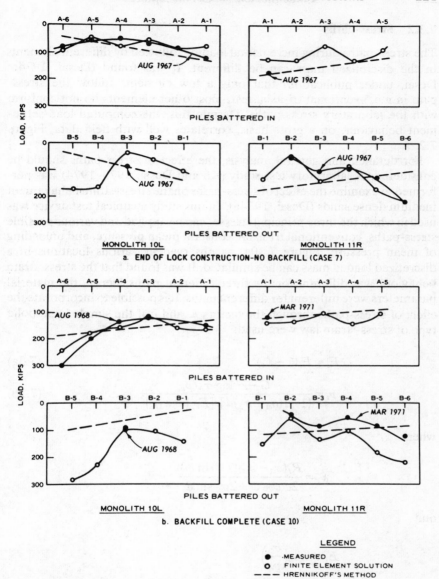

Figure 7.9 Comparisons for loads in piles

The stresses in the interface elements near the geometrical discontinuity at the tip can cause irregular stresses. Modifications in the formulation of interface element will be required to overcome this difficulty. This aspect will be discussed subsequently.

7.3.2 Stress-paths

The stress-paths during incremental loading followed by different elements in the discretized mass can be different. It was found (Desai, 1974a; Desai, under publication) that only a few elements follow the stress-path in a conventional tri-axial test; most other elements do not conform with the laboratory stress-paths. Despite this, the computed load-settlement behaviour, on a gross basis, correlates well with field data, Figure 7.2.

For detailed and general analysis, the effect of stress-paths should be considered. A laboratory test study (Ko and Desai, 1973–1974) was performed to examine the effect of stress-paths on the stress-strain behaviour of medium dense sands (Desai, 1974a). In this study a cubical test device was used in which the three principal stresses can be applied and various possible stress-paths, conventional tri-axial, constant mean pressure, and unloading of mean pressure, Figure 7.10a, as observed at various locations in a discretized loaded mass can be simulated. It was found that the stress-strain behaviour was different for the three different paths; hence, the material parameters were different for different paths. It is possible to incorporate the effect of stress-paths through the factors K and n if the simple hyperbolic type of stress-strain law were used:

$$E_t = E_i(1-\lambda_1)^2 \tag{7.3a}$$

$$\nu_t = \frac{G - F \log \sigma_3/p_a}{\{1 - [(\sigma_1 - \sigma_3)d]/[E_i(1-\lambda_1)]\}^2} \tag{7.3b}$$

where

$$\lambda_1 = \frac{R_f(\sigma_1 - \sigma_3)(1 - \sin \phi)}{2c \cos \phi + 2\sigma_3 \sin \phi}$$

and

$$E_i = Kp_a\left(\frac{\sigma_3}{p_a}\right)^n$$

and the material parameter K, n, R_f, c, ϕ are discussed in various publications (Desai, 1974a).

Variations of K and n for different gradients of stress-path $g = [d(\sigma_1 - \sigma_3)]/dp$ are shown in Figure 7.10b. It is thus possible to make E_t and ν_t functions of g. A similar procedure for clayey soils was recently proposed

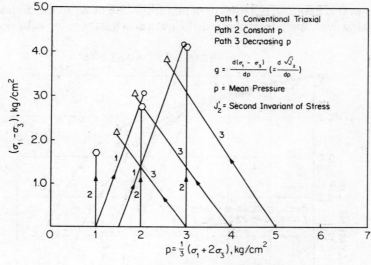

a. LABORATORY LOADING PATHS

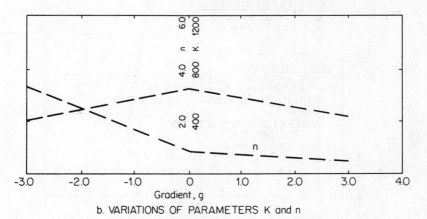

b. VARIATIONS OF PARAMETERS K and n

Figure 7.10 Cubical tri-axial tests on sands

(Yudhbir and Varadarjan, 1975). Indeed, a general constitutive law would be ideal since it will be valid for any stress-path.

7.3.3 Variation of coefficient of lateral earth pressure K_0

As shown in Figure 7.11, the magnitudes of the co-efficient of lateral earth pressure, K_0, has significant influence on load-deformation behaviour. The results in this figure were based on a uniform value of K_0 in the discretized mass. However, spatial distribution of K_0 can also influence the behaviour.

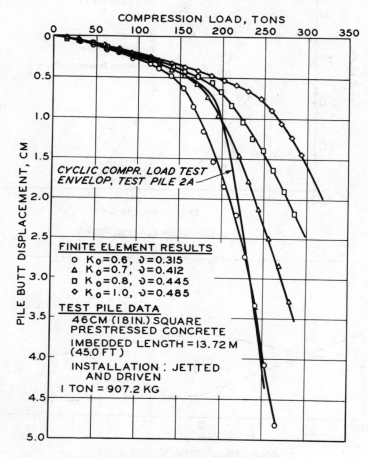

Figure 7.11   Influence of magnitudes of K_0

Figure 7.12a shows assumed variation of K_0 as suggested by Broms (1966), and Figure 7.12b shows computed results for the variations. It appears that if the variation of K_0 is included in zones near the structure, the computed behaviour would be satisfactory. In other words, uniform values of K_0 can be assumed beyond a certain distance around and below the pile. The subject of precise determination of K_0 is still in the active stage and would require significant amount of field laboratory and analytical research.

7.3.4 Size of load increment

The magnitude of load increment can influence the load–deformation behaviour, particularly in the higher loading zones. Figure 7.13 shows the effects of size of loads on load–deformation behaviour. Such effect is consistent with the incremental load procedure with displacement method of analysis (Desai and Abel, 1972). Hence, it will be advisable to use smaller load increments, particularly at higher loadings.

7.3.5 Driving stresses

In the case of a driven pile, the process of driving will induce stresses that remain in the pile before external load is applied. These stresses can influence the load–deformation behaviour (Desai, 1974a; Fruco and Associates, 1964), particularly the distribution of load in the structure. It can be possible to distribute such stresses in the soil-structure system before external loads are applied (Desai, under publication). Here the driving

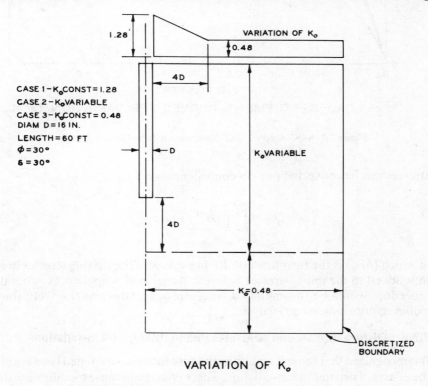

Figure 7.12a   Spatial variation of K_0 (Broms, 1966)

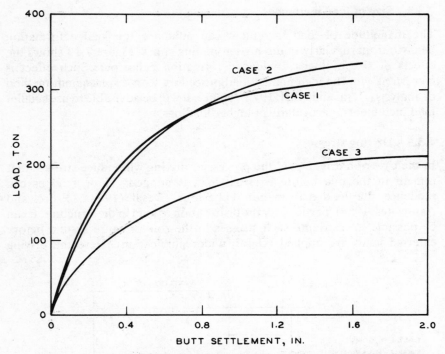

c. **LOAD-SETTLEMENT CURVES FOR VARIATION OF K_o**

Figure 7.12b Computed load–displacement curves for varying K_0

stresses can be converted into an equivalent load $\{Q_0\}$.

$$\{Q_0\} = \iiint\limits_{V} [B]^T \{\Delta\sigma_d\} \, dV \qquad (7.4)$$

in which $\{\Delta\sigma_d\}$ is the increment of driving stresses. The driving stresses are thus added to the initial stresses before external load is applied. A general procedure would be to simulate driving stresses as the pile is driven; this would require a dynamic analysis.

7.3.6 Disturbance around structures due to driving and installation

It is recognized that the soil around a structure (pile) is remoulded because of the effects of driving and installation. These effects can cause modification in strength and in stress–strain behaviour of the disturbed soils. The amount of

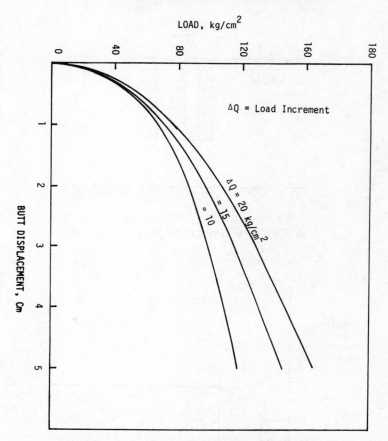

Figure 7.13 Influence of magnitudes of load increment

remoulding may be about 100 per cent at the interface and may be negligible beyond a distance of about twice the diameter of the pile. In the case of clayey soils, driving can cause an increase in pore-water pressures around the pile, which then dissipates with time and thus modifies the behaviour of soils.

Balam, Poulos *et al.*, (1974), performed an FE analysis to study effects of installation. Figures 7.14 and 7.15 show a typical set of properties and results from their work. Figure 7.14 shows assumed variation of modulus E_s and shear strength. The disturbed zone extends upon a distance of r_1 below and around the pile. The value of elastic modulus varies linearly from a value E_r at interface to a value of E_s for undisturbed soil. The adhesion c_a at interface is assumed equal to c_u, and $c_a = 500\ c_u$. The shear strength in the

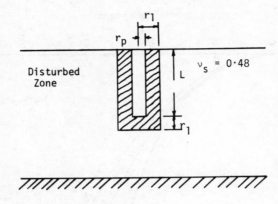

A. PILE IN CLAY-EXTENT OF DISTURBED ZONE

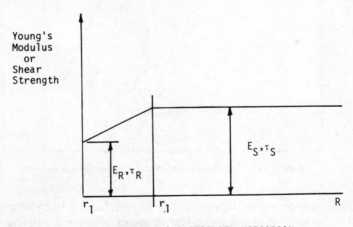

B. ASSUMED MODULUS AND STRENGTH VARIATION

Figure 7.14 Zones affected by installation (Balam, Poulous *et al.*, 1974)

disturbed zone varies from $c_r = E_r/500$ to $c_u = E_s/500$. FE results were obtained for various values of r_1/r_p. Figure 7.15 shows settlement factor I_{RR} for pile plotted against r/r_p. It can be seen that settlements are influenced until a distance of about $r/r_p = 2$ and beyond that value no significant difference is observed. These results seem to be in agreement with the influence of spatial variation of K_0, Figure 7.12; because driving can increase K_0 in the vicinity of the pile.

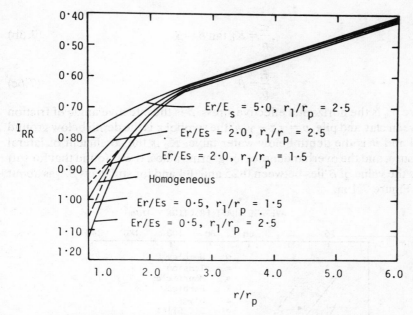

Figure 7.15 Finite element results (Balam, Poulos, *et al.*, 1974)

7.3.7 Adhesion

Usually the adhesion c_a at interface is expressed as,

$$c_a = \alpha c_u \tag{7.5}$$

where c_u is the undrained strength of clay. If failure takes place in the soil below the base, if the disturbance due to installation is not significant, and since the soil may gain strength with time, use of Equation (7.5) may be justified (Burland, 1973). The value of α may vary from $0\cdot3$ to $1\cdot5$, and it is often difficult to choose a value of α. Burland (1973) noted that relating adhesion to undrained strength may not be justified. Some of the reasons are (1) the major shear deformation is confined to a narrow zone around the pile, (2) installation disturbs and causes remoulding in the adjacent zones, and (3) no simple relationship is possible between undrained and drained strengths. Consequently Equation (7.5) may not be of general applicability.

An alternative concept based on effective stress was proposed by Burland (1973). Under the assumption that the soil has no effective cohesion due to remoulding, the shaft friction τ_s at any point is expressed as

$$\tau_s = \sigma_h' \tan \delta = p K_0 \tan \delta \tag{7.6a}$$

or

$$\frac{\bar{\tau}_s}{p} = K_0 \tan \delta = \beta \qquad (7.6b)$$

or

$$\frac{\bar{\tau}_s}{\bar{p}} = \bar{\beta} \qquad (7.6c)$$

where σ_h' is the horizontal effective stress, δ is the effective angle of friction between clay and pile, $p = \gamma_s z - \gamma_w h$, the symbol z is the depth below ground level and h is the depth below water table, K_0 is the coefficient of lateral pressure, and the overbar denotes long term values. It was found that for soft clays the value of $\bar{\beta}$ lies between 0·25 and 0·4 and for stiff clays $\bar{\beta}$ was about 0·8, Figure 7.16a.

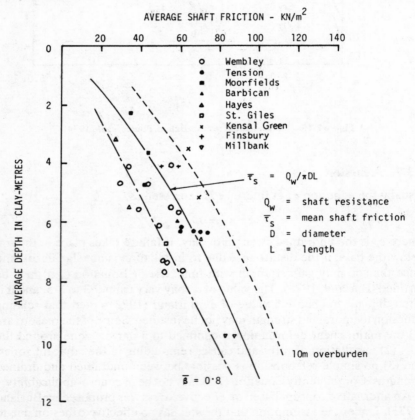

a. VARIATION OF AVERAGE SHAFT FRICTION (FROM BURLAND, 1973)

Figure 7.16 Variation of factor β (Burland, 1973)

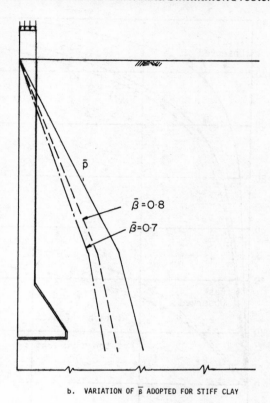

b. VARIATION OF $\bar{\beta}$ ADOPTED FOR STIFF CLAY

Figure 7.16 (continued)

An FE analysis was performed by using various values of $\bar{\beta}$, (Figure 7.16b) and $E_i = 400 \, c_u$ for the stiff clay. Results are shown in Figure 6.17. It seems that values of $\bar{\beta}$ greater than 0·8 would be required for the clay considered. The question of the value of factor λ still needs to be considered, and a higher value of λ will be required for satisfactory correlation with observations.

7.3.8 Magnitudes of cohesion and adhesion

The magnitudes of c_a and c_u can have significant influence on behaviour of structures in stiff clays. Figure 7.18 shows results for $\alpha = 0·40$ and $0·42$ and full value of c_u ($= 1·08 \, \text{tonf/ft}^2 = 10\,530 \, \text{kgf/m}^2$) and 75 per cent of c_u. For the clay considered, average values of c_u used are shown in Figure 7.19; a

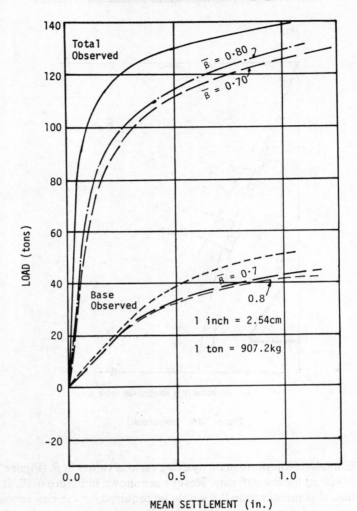

Figure 7.17   Results for different β

value of $\lambda = 400$ was used for results in Figure 7.18. Figure 7.20 shows results for the pile for various values of $\alpha = 0.25$, 0.59, 1.0 and 1.1 and values of $c_u = 100$ and 75 per cent of those in Figure 7.25. It can be seen that small changes in α can cause significant changes in the behaviour.

7.3.9   Constitutive laws

The importance of adequate determination of constitutive laws to define the behaviour of soils is recognized. As noted previously, a number of publica-

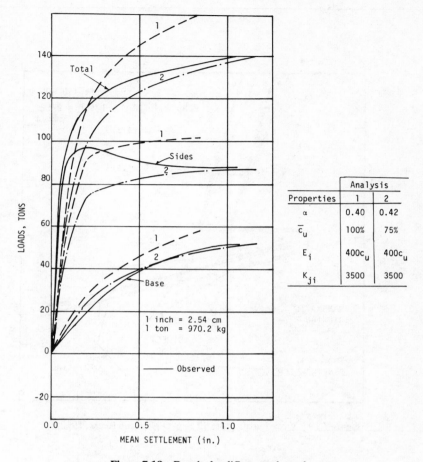

Figure 7.18 Results for different values of α

tions have covered details of nonlinear elastic and elastic–plastic constitutive laws for soils. Hence, it is intended to cover herein some aspects of constitutive laws only for interfaces for both static and dynamic analysis.

7.3.10 Interface behaviour

A number of schemes have been used and are possible. In the simple procedure, only the shear and normal stiffness of the interface element are defined as

$$[k] = \begin{bmatrix} k_{nn} & 0 \\ 0 & k_{ss} \end{bmatrix} \quad (7.7)$$

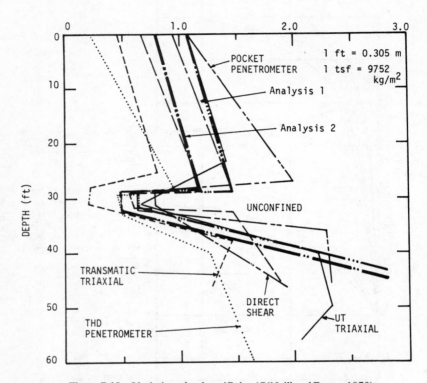

Figure 7.19   Variation of c_u for stiff clay (O'Neill and Reese, 1970)

where k_{nn} and k_{ss} are the normal and shear stiffness of the joint element (Goodman, Taylor, *et al.*, 1968). This assumes that the shear and normal nodes are uncoupled. A simple bilinear relationship can be assumed where critical values of σ_c and σ_{nc} are defined, Figure 7.21; the former can be defined on the basis of Mohr–Coulomb criterion:

$$\tau = c_{a_i} + \sigma_n \tan \delta \tag{7.8}$$

Beyond the critical values of stress, the stiffnesses can be assigned arbitrary small values. Apparently, this definition of $[k]$ ignores such effects as dilatancy and softening.

The non-linear stress-displacement relation can be simulated by using a hyperbolic relationship (Clough and Duncan, 1969; Desai, 1974a) where

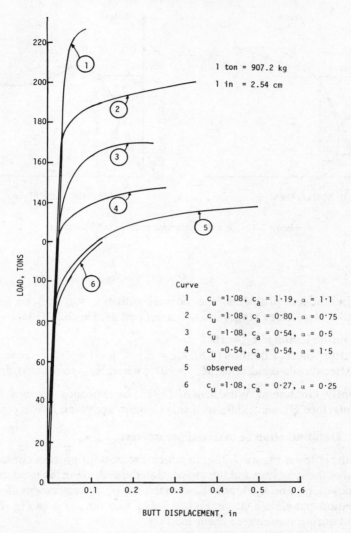

Figure 7.20   Results for different values of α and strengths

tangent shear stiffness, k_{sst}, is defined as

$$k_{sst} = (1 - \lambda_2)^2 k_i \qquad (7.9)$$

where

$$k_i = K_j \gamma_w (\sigma_n / p_a)^2$$

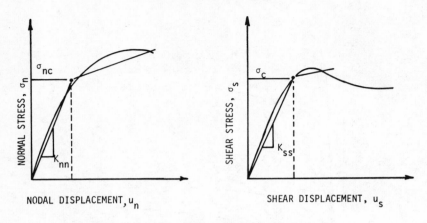

Figure 7.21   Stress–displacement curves of interfaces

and

$$\lambda_2 = R_f \tau / (c_a + \sigma_n \tan \delta)$$

For interaction problems, the normal stiffness, k_{nn}, can be assigned arbitrarily. Here three stages are often defined as (Desai, 1974a)

(1) During loading, $k_{nn} = 10^{10}$
(2) After failure, Equation (7.8), $k_{nn} = k_r$ (7.10)
(3) After tensile conditions, $K_{nn} = 10^{-3}$; where k_r = residual stiffness.

Recently, Ghaboussi, Wilson, *et al.* (1973) have proposed a modification in the interface element; details of this element are given in Chapter 10.

7.3.11   Determination of material parameters, k_{ss}, k_{nn}

Direct shear tests, Figure 7.22a, in which the bottom portion contains the material of the structure and the top portion the soil, are often used to derive the values of k_{nn} and k_{ss}. Under a normal load, σ_n, measurement of vertical deformation can yield a curve. Figure 7.21a, and the curve in Fig. 7.21b is obtained during subsequent shear loading.

7.3.12   Limitations of direct shear test

In the direct shear test, the direction of critical stress can be inclined to the direction of shearing and the maximum shear stress can be greater than the measured shear stress parallel to the axis of shear box (Huck, *et al.*, 1974). Moreover, the distribution of shear stresses may not be uniform.

A number of factors can contribute to the complexity of interface behaviour. These factors can include modification in soil properties due to migration of moisture and remoulding, uncertainty in actual normal stresses and the possibility of failure occurring at zones other than at the junction.

Modified test devices have been proposed by Brumund and Leonards (1973). Figure 7.22b shows a schematic diagram of the apparatus. Interface is introduced as the circumference of a circular rod which is inserted co-axially into a cylinder of soil (sand). The sand is surrounded by a light membrane. Shearing stress, static or dynamic, is applied through an axial load to the rod. Values of coefficients of friction, δ, are obtained for both static and dynamic conditions for smooth and rough concrete interfaces.

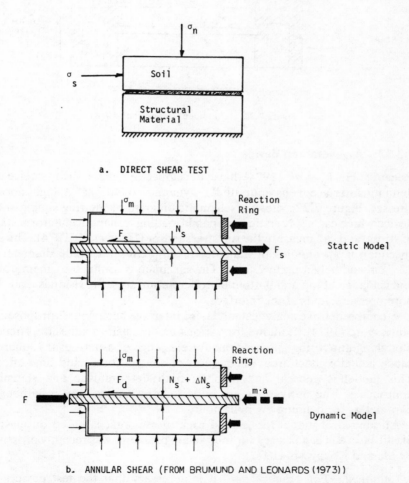

a. DIRECT SHEAR TEST

b. ANNULAR SHEAR (FROM BRUMUND AND LEONARDS (1973))

Figure 7.22 Laboratory tests for determination of interface behaviour

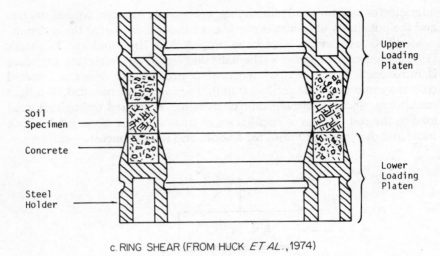

c. RING SHEAR (FROM HUCK *ET AL.*, 1974)

Figure 7.22   (continued) (Huck *et al.* 1974)

7.3.13   A general test device

Recently Huck *et al.* (1974) have developed a simple shear device for defining interface behaviour under dynamic conditions at high normal stresses. Figure 7.22c shows a schematic diagram of the ring simple-shear device which can apply static or dynamic loading, can induce uniform states of stress, and can measure the full stress tensor (Huck *et al.*, 1974). The soil specimen is an annulus of diameter of 17·7 cm with inside diameter of 12·7 cm and height up to 2·5 cm. The specimen is confined by membranes and is loaded at top and bottom by concrete surfaces. Provision is made for pore pressure vents at the interface.

A comprehensive analytical model for interface behaviour is proposed by Huck *et al.* (1974). It allows for various modes such as adhesion, friction, ploughing and lifting and accounts for existence of asperities (as spherical caps), actual contact area, obliquences of contact forces and time effects. This model is general and involves both deterministic and statistical approaches. The derivations are quite lengthy and require a number of parameters for defining the behaviour.

An analytical model for jointed rock masses that is based on elastic-plastic laws and can be used for interaction problems was recently proposed by Ida and Kobayashi (1972).

Comment.   For practical use, it is necessary that the test devices be simple and the material parameters as few as possible consistent with required accuracy. It appears that further research will be required to achieve this aim.

7.3.14   Flexibility of structures

Most FE formulations for interaction problems have used four node quadrilateral elements for two-dimensional analysis. This element with the following interpolation function

$$\begin{Bmatrix} u \\ v \end{Bmatrix} = \begin{bmatrix} N_1 & 0 & N_2 & 0 & N_3 & 0 & N_4 & 0 \\ 0 & N_1 & 0 & N_2 & 0 & N_3 & 0 & N_4 \end{bmatrix} \{q\} \qquad (7.11)$$

where $\{q\}^T = [u_1 v_1 u_2 v_2 u_3 v_3 u_4 v_4]$. This function yields a kind of bilinear variation of displacements and is relevant essentially for 'plane' deformations. Its capability to account for bending mode can, however, be limited. Consequently, use of the element for the structure, particularly when the structure is highly flexible and can undergo bending deformations, may not be strictly valid. In such a case, it may be necessary to use a higher order element for structural element such that bending modes are properly allowed for. It may be that when the higher order element for the structure is combined with a lower order element, Equation (7.11) for soils, some degrees of freeedom at the junction may not participate in the assembly procedure. Even with this situation, the results with higher order element for the structure can give improved accuracy as compared with the accuracy obtained by using the lower order element for both the soil and structure (Smith, 1971).

7.3.15   Strain-softening

This phenomenon can occur in both soils and at interfaces. A number of approaches based on nonlinear elastic and plastic approaches have been proposed (Desai, 1972b; Desai, 1974b; Hoeg, 1972; Lo and Lee, 1973; Nayak and Zienckiewicz, 1974; Traughber, 1974). Applications of various approaches for solution of practical problems have yet not been accomplished fully. An approximate approach proposed by Desai (1974b) and an application will be covered briefly.

The approach is based on a combination of incremental, iterative and stress transfer schemes. The procedure allows approximate satisfaction of compatibility of stress and strain at each stage including pre- and post-softening behaviour. Details are given by Desai (1974b).

A rather new hypothesis is proposed in which the response can be divided into two or more portions. The material parameters after softening has initiated can be defined as function of a number of significant factors to be

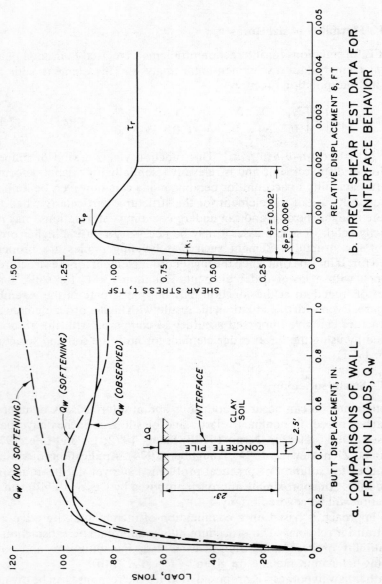

Figure 7.23 Finite element results for softening behaviour

determined from laboratory tests. The general form is expressed as

$$G = F(G_i, \sigma_p, \sigma_r, \varepsilon_p, \varepsilon_r, \phi_p, \phi_r, A_j, \alpha_k) \tag{7.12}$$

where G is a material parameter, G_i is the initial value of G, the terms σ_p, σ_r are the stress at peak and in residual conditions, ε_p, ε_r are the strain at peak and in residual condition, ϕ_p, ϕ_r are the angles of friction at peak and in residual condition, A_j is the area under stress–strain curve and α_k is a parameter dependent on such factors as moisture content and relative density.

A preliminary example was solved by using this approach. Figure 7.23b shows shear stress-displacement relation from a direct shear test on a stiff fissured clay (O'Neill and Reese, 1970). A special form of Equation (7.12) which considers some of the parameters for this behaviour is

$$k_{sst} = \alpha_p k_i - \frac{\alpha_p k_i - \alpha_r k_i}{\delta_r - \delta_p}(\delta - \delta_p) \tag{7.13}$$

where $\alpha_p = 0\cdot01$ and $\alpha_r = 0\cdot005$; δ are displacements and subscripts r and p denote residual and peak conditions, respectively.

In Figure 7.23a are shown comparisons between load-settlement curve for wall friction load computed from a FE analysis, from observations and from computations without accounting for softening.

7.3.16 Three-dimensional analysis

Most applications have involved 2-D idealizations of practical problems. A few analyses have considered three-dimensional situations (Wittke, 1974; Wittke, under publication). A 3-D formulation including an interface element has been developed and its application for analysis of such 3-D problems as laterally loaded (pile) structures has been in progress (Desai, 1975). Figure 7.24 shows the elements for soils (Figure 7.24a) and interfaces (Figure 7.24b). The interface element (Desai, 1975; Mahtab and Goodman, 1970) used is obtained by combining contributions of two tetrahedron elements. Non-linear interface properties are introduced for two shear stiffnesses in the plane of the element and a stiffness normal to the element.

7.3.17 Formulation procedure

Almost all previous formulations have used displacement method for formulating the FE equations. Here stresses are derived from computed displacements. For problems involving tensile stress conditions, separation of interfaces and cracking, the displacement approach may not be ideal. In this case, it may be more appropriate to use a hybrid or mixed approach (Pian, 1971; Pian, 1973), in which stresses in the element can also be

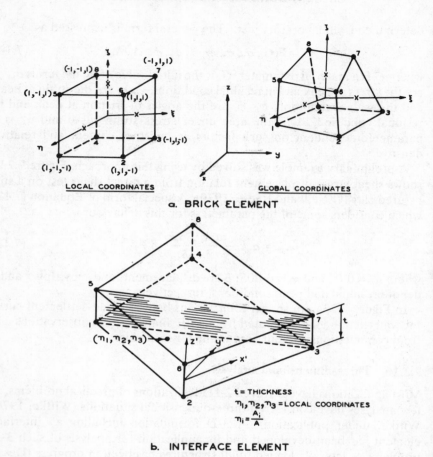

a. BRICK ELEMENT

b. INTERFACE ELEMENT

Figure 7.24 Three-dimensional elements

assumed as unknown. It may be possible to redefine elements depending upon the stage of loading and consequent separation and cracking.

7.4 SIMULATION OF CONSTRUCTION SEQUENCES

Before construction of a structure, the first step generally constitutes introducing the initial stresses. Estimation of initial stresses due to geologic history undergone by a soil mass is a difficult problem, and as noted earlier, will require further research and investigations. Subsequent steps in construction are essentially man-made and can be simulated in a numerical scheme. A brief review of the simulation procedures with a discussion of their capabilities, limitations and need for improvements will be covered in what follows.

7.4.1 Dewatering

This step is simulated by computing the change in state of stress in an element due to a change in hydrostatic pressure caused by dewatering. The change is then added to the initial stresses. Often, the change is computed on the basis of load caused by such a change; the load is computed by multiplying the change in pressure by relevant projected areas (Clough and Duncan, 1969).

An alternative procedure would be to evaluate an equivalent load vector $\{Q_0\}$ as (Desai, unpublished; Desai, under publication).

$$\{Q_0\} = \iiint_V [B]^T \{\sigma_d\} \, dV \qquad (7.14)$$

where $[B]$ is strain transformation matrix and $\{\sigma_d\} = [\Delta p \ \Delta p \ \Delta p \ 0 \ 0 \ 0]$ is the vector of change in hydrostatic pressure, p. Then a FE analysis with $\{Q_0\}$ gives the necessary stresses to be added (subtracted) from the initial stresses.

7.4.2 Influence of shape of water table

Often stages of dewatering are simulated by assuming the ground water level as a horizontal plane through the level of water in the pumping well. This assumption may be valid if the soil is pervious and the wells are spaced closely. In clayey soils, the water-table during dewatering may not be horizontal but can represent a cone of depression. In such an event the first assumption is not realistic. Details of the influence of different assumptions of the level and shape of water table on FE computations are given by Desai (under publication).

The foregoing analyses are done as if the material is undrained whereas in subsequent sequences, the material may be assumed as drained. This anomaly can be avoided by simulating dewatering by using a general consolidation procedure wherein both deformation during dewatering and drainage are accounted for (Desai, 1975; Sandhu and Wilson, 1969).

7.4.3 Excavation

Excavation is simulated by dividing the total excavation into a number of sequences. It is assumed that after each sequence, Figure 7.25, the exposed surface can be treated as 'stress free'. In other words, stresses normal, σ_n, to

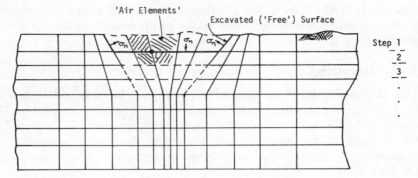

Figure 7.25   Simulation of excavation sequences

the exposed surface are zero. This concept is similar to free-surface-flow problems in seepage where the flow normal to the free surface is zero.

The idea proposed by Goodman and Brown (1963) and Brown and King (1966) has been used to simulate excavation. Usually, the correction loads, $\{Q_0\}$, required to create a 'stress free' surface are obtained by multiplying the computed stresses at the nodes on the free surface by the projected areas on which they act (Clough and Duncan, 1969). Then a cycle of FE analyses is performed to find the change in stresses due to the correction loads, and the change is added to the stresses computed in the previous stage; the first stage consists of stresses due to initial conditions modified for dewatering. Often, the stresses for computing correction loads are found by interpolation of stresses at the centroids of surroundig elements (Clough and Duncan, 1969).

The foregoing procedures can cause computational difficulties for some problems. For linear elastic analysis, it has been shown by Christian and Wong (1973) that the number of steps can influence the computed stresses and deformations. It was shown that for excavation in elastic soils, the foregoing procedure yielded different results for different number of steps. Moreover, it becomes necessary to modify the procedure if there exist structures exposed to such surface as sheet piles and lining at the excavated surface. The discrepancies are often reduced by using least-square polynomial extrapolation of stresses for computing correction loads.

An alternative to the foregoing procedure of computing correction loads to create the stress free surface would be to make use of the displacements computed during the previous stage of excavation (Desai, unpublished; Desai, under publication). It is believed that this scheme would be more direct since it can take advantage of the computed stresses that are consistent with assumed orders of the displacement approximation. It does not require use of an auxiliary interpolation model which is based on the computed stresses. For instance, the stresses at the node on the excavated surface (Figure 7.25) can be evaluated as

$$\{\sigma_i\} = [C][B(s_i, t_i)]\{q_m\} \qquad (7.15)$$

where $\{\sigma_i\}$ is the vector of stresses at point i, the term $[C]$ is the stress-strain matrix, $[B]$ is the strain-transformation matrix, s_i, t_i are the local co-ordinates of point i and $\{q_m\}$ is the vector of computed nodal displacements in element m. If required, stresses at node i can be obtained as an average of stresses at node i contributed by two or four, of the elements surrounding the node.

The correction load vector then can be computed as

$$\{Q_{0,i}\} = \iiint_{v} [B(s_i, t_i]\{\sigma_i\} \, dv \qquad (7.16)$$

An FE analysis is then performed by applying the correction load, Equation (7.16), to all points on the excavated surface. The resulting changes in the stresses are accumulated as

$$\{\sigma_j\} = \{\sigma_0\} + \sum_{j=1}^{n} \{\Delta\sigma_i\}_j \qquad (7.17)$$

where j is the number of steps of excavation.

An approach based on computation of correction load on the similar basis was recently suggested (Chandrasekaran and King, 1974). In this approach, the increments of correction load are computed and then added to the correction loads computed for each step from initial conditions.

7.4.4 Excavated elements

In the existing procedures the space of elements that are removed is replaced by the so-called 'air' elements. The strength of the air elements, Figure 7.25, is assumed to be very small and a small value of E is assigned to them. Existence of such elements can be a factor in the computational difficulties, because they can render the assemblage stiffness matrix $[K]$ in

$$[K]\{r\} = \{R\} \qquad (7.18)$$

to be ill-conditioned. It was found (Desai, unpublished) that the nodes in the air elements and in their vicinity (in the adjacent soil media) can experience unusually large deformations as compared with the deformations in the unexcavated mass. Although, it may be possible to devise a way to remove such large deformations, their occurrence can leave irregularities and ill-effects in the subsequent behaviour.

The foregoing difficulty may be avoided by redefining the mesh at each step of excavation or embankment or backfilling (Desai, unpublished). In such a scheme, the meshes can be redefined such that consistent relationship is established between numbers of nodes and elements of the original and previous meshes. That is, when the results are printed, the printout should consist of current numbers of nodes and elements, and their relation with the numbers in a reference mesh layout. This would facilitate easy interpretation of results. A procedure for mesh generation for highway cuts has been developed by Kalkani (1974).

Necessity of using adequate (non-linear) constitutive laws that allows properly for the unloading is important in simulation of excavation. Stress paths followed by various zones can significantly influence the deformation behaviour and should be included in the definition of the constitutive law. Moreover, it is believed that use of mixed or hybrid (Desai and Abel, 1972; Pian, 1971; Pian, 1973) schemes instead of the displacement approach commonly used, can provide more general procedures for the excavation problem.

Consolidation can occur with both embankment and excavation. It is possible to incorporate such effects in the simulation procedures; however, provision should be made for both consolidation and swelling.

7.5 SUMMARY

Use of the FE methods for solution of soil-structure interaction problem is reviewed and discussed. A number of solutions of practical problems are described and various factors that can influence the problem are critically examined. The associated question of simulation of sequences of construction is reviewed, difficulties and limitations are discussed and possible improvements are proposed.

ACKNOWLEDGEMENT

A portion of the results described herein is a review of the work done by the author while employed with Waterways Experiment Station, Vicksburg, Mississippi.

REFERENCES

Baker, L. E., Sandhu, R. S., and Shieh, W. Y. J. (1969). 'Application of elasto-plastic analysis in rock mechanics by FE method', *Proceedings, 11th Symp. on Rock Mech., Berkeley.*

Balam, N. P., Poulos, H. G., and Booker, J. R. (1974). 'Finite element analysis of the effects of installation on pile load-settlement behaviors', *Res. Report*, No. R246, Civil Engg. Lab. Univ. of Sydney.

Broms, B. B. (1966). 'Methods of calculating the ultimate bearing capacity of piles', *Sols. Soils*, Swedish Geotech. Inst., **18–19**, 21–31.

Brown, C. B. and King, I. P. (1966). 'Automatic embankment analysis', *Geotechnique*, **XVI**, 3.

Brumund, W. E. and Leonards, G. A. (1973). 'Experimental study of static and dynamic friction between sand and typical construction materials', *J. of Testing and Evaluation*, ASTM, **1**, 2, 162–165.

Burland, J. B. (1973). 'Shaft friction of piles in clay', *Ground Engineering*, **6**, 3.

Chandrasekaran, V. S. and King, J. W. (1974). 'Simulation of excavation using finite elements', *Tech. Note, J. of SMFD*, ASCE, **100**, No. GT9.

Chang, C. Y., Nair, K., and Karwoski, W. J. (1972). 'Finite element analysis of excavations in rock', *Proceedings, Symp. on Appl. of FE Method in Geotech. Engg., Vicksburg*.

Christian, J. T. and Wong, I. H. (1973). 'Errors in simulating excavation in elastic media by finite elements', *Soils and Foundations*, Jap. Soc. of Sm & FE, **13**, 1.

Chung, T. J. and Lee, J. K. (1972). 'Incremental plasticity theory applied to boundary value problems in soil', *Proceedings, Symp. on Appl. of FEM in Geotech. Engg., Vicksburg, Mississippi*.

Clough, G. W. and Duncan, J. M. (1969). 'Finite element analysis of port Allen and Old River locks', *Report No. S-69-3*, Waterways Expt. Sta., Vicksburg, Mississippi.

Clough, G. W. and Duncan, J. J. (1971). 'Finite element analysis of retaining wall behaviour', *J. SMFD, ASCE*, **97**, Sm12.

Clough, G. W., Weber, P. B., and Lamont, J. (1972). 'Design and observation of a tied-back wall', *Proceedings, ASCE Sp. Conf. on Performance of Earth and Earth Supported Structures*, Purdue Univ., **2**, Part 2.

Clough, R. W. and Woodward, R. J. (1967). 'Analysis of embankment stresses and deformations', *J. SMFD, ASCE*, **93**, No. SM4.

Cooke, R. W. and Price, G. (1973). 'Strains and displacements around friction piles', *Proceedings, 8th Intl. Conf. Soil Mech. and Found. Eng.*, Moscow, **2**.

Desai, C. S. (1971). 'Nonlinear analyses using spline functions', *J. SMFD ASCE*, **97**, No. SM10.

Desai, C. S. (ed.) (1972a). *Proceedings, Symp. on Applications of Finite Element Method in Geotechnical Engineering, Vicksburg*.

Desai, C. S. (1972b). 'Overview, trends and projections', *Proceedings, Symp. on Appl. of FEM in Geotech. Engg., Vicksburg, Mississippi*.

Desai, C. S. (1974a). 'Numerical design analysis of piles in sands', *J. of Geotech. Engg. Div., ASCE*, **100**, No. GT6.

Desai, C. S. (1974b). 'A consistent finite element technique for work-softening behavior', *Proceedings, Intl. Conf. on Computational Methods in Nonlinear Mech.*, J. T. Oden *et al.* (eds.), Univ. of Texas, Austin.

Desai, C. S. (1975). 'Finite element procedure and code for three-dimensional soil-structure interaction', *Report*, Dept. of Civil Engg., Viriginia Polytech. Inst. and State Univ., Blacksburg.

Desai, C. S. (unpublished). *Analysis and Evaluation of Simulation Procedures*.

Desai, C. S. (under preparation). *Finite Element Method for Design-Analysis of Pile Foundations in Sands and Clays*.

Desai, C. S. (under publication). 'Deep foundations', Chap. 7 in *Numerical Methods in Geotechnical Engineering*, Desai, C. S., and Christian J. T. (eds.), McGraw-Hill Book Co., New York.

Desai, C. S. (1975). 'Analysis of consolidation by numerical methods', *Symp. on Recent Advances and Developments in Analysis of Soil Behavior and Application to Geotech. Structures, Univ. of NSW, Australia.*

Desai, C. S. and Abel, J. F. (1972). *Introduction to the Finite Element Method*, Van Nostrand Reinhold Co., N.Y.

Desai, C. S. and Holloway, D. M. (1972). 'Load-deformation analysis of deep pile foundations', *Proceedings, Symp. on Appl. of FE Method in Geotech. Engg., Viscksburg, Mississippi.*

Desai, C. S., Johnson, L. D., and Hargett, C. M. (1974). 'Analysis of pile-supported gravity lock', *J. of Geotech. Engg. Div., ASCE*, **100**, No. GT9.

DiMaggio, F. L. and Sandler, I. S. (1971). 'Material model for granular soils', *J. of Engg. Mech. Div., ASCE*, **97**, No. EM3.

Duncan, J. M. and Chang, C. Y. (1970). 'Nonlinear analysis of stress and strain in soils', *J. of SMFD, ASCE*, **96**, No. SM5.

Ellison, R. D., D'Appolonia, E., and Thiers, G. R. (1971). 'Load-deformation mechanism for bored piles', *J. SMFD, ASCE*, **97**, No. SM4.

Fruco and Associates (1964). 'Pile driving and loading tests; Lock and Dam No. 4', U.S. Army Engr. Dist., CE, Little Rock, Ark.

Ghaboussi, J., Wilson, E. L., and Isenberg, J. (1973). 'Finite element for rock joints and interfaces', *J. of SMFD, ASCE*, **99**, No. SM10.

Goodman, L. E. and Brown, C. B. (1963). 'Dead load stresses and the instability of slopes', *J. SMFD, ASCE*, **89**, No. SM3.

Goodman, R. E., Taylor, R. L., and Brekke, T. (1968). 'A model for the mechanics of jointed rock', *J. SMFD, ASCE*, **94**, No. SM3, Mar. 1968.

Gudehus, G. (1973). 'Ebene und achsensymmetrische formänderungen in Sand: Grundgleichungen', *Die Bautechnik*, **50**.

Hoëg, K. (1972). 'Finite element analysis of strain-softening clay', *J. SMFD, ASCE*, 98, No. SM1.

Huck, P. J., *et al.* (1974). 'Dynamic response of soil/concrete interfaces at high pressure', *Report AFWL-TR-73-264*, IIT Research Institute, Chicago.

Iida, R. and Kobayashi, S. (1972). 'Theoretical study on the nonelastic behaviors of jointed rock masses', *J. of Research, Public Works Research Inst., Tokyo*, Japan.

Isenberg, J. and Bagge, L. F. (1972). 'Analysis of steel-lined penetration shafts for deeply buried structures', *Proceedings, Symp. on Appl. of FEM in Geotech. Engg., Vicksburg.*

Isenberg, J., Lee, L. C., and Agbabian, M. S. (1973). 'Response of structures to combined blast effects', *J. of Transp., ASCE*, **99**, No. TE4.

Kalkani, E. C. (1974). 'Mesh generation program for highway excavation cuts', *Int. J. Num. Meths. in Engg.*, **8**, 369–394.

Ko, H. Y. (1976). 'Nonlinear characterization and analysis of granular soils', *Proc., 2nd Intl. Conf. on Numerical Methods in Geomechanics*, Blacksburg, Va.

Ko, H. Y. and Desai, C. S. (1973–74). 'Effect of stress paths on behavior of sands at Jonesville Lock site'. to be published.

Lo, K. Y. and Lee, C. F. (1973). 'Stress analysis and slope stability in strain-softening materials', *Geotechnique*, **XXIII**, No. 3.

Mahtab, M. A. and Goodman, R. E. (1970). 'Three-dimensional finite element analysis of jointed rock slopes', *Proceedings, 2nd Cong. Int. Soc. for Rock Mech., Belgrade.*

Meissner, H. and Wibel, A. (1974). 'Parameter eines elasto-plastischen Stoffansatzes für körnige Erdstoffe', *Die Bautechnik*, **8**, 263–269.

Nayak, G. C. and Zienkiewicz, O. C. (1974). 'Elasto-plastic stress analysis: A generalization of various constitutive relations including strain-softening', *Int. J. Num. Meth. in Engg.*, **5**, No. 1.

'Navigation Lock, Lock and Dam No. 5, Arkansas River', (1964). *Report, Corps of Engineers, Arkansas Dist. Little Rock Ark.*

O'Neill, M. W. and Reese, L. C. (1970). 'Behavior of axially loaded drilled shafts in Beamont clay', *Res. Repts. 87–90*, Univ. of Texas, Austin.

Pariseau, W. G., Voight, B., and Dahl, H. D. (1970). 'Finite element analyses of elastic-plastic problems in mechanics of geologic media: An overview', *Proceedings, 2nd Intl. Congress, Soc. for Rock Mech.*, Belgrade.

Pian, T. H. H. (1971). 'Formulations of finite element methods for solid continua', in *Recent Advances in Matrix Methods of Structural Analysis and Design*, Gallagher, R. H. *et al.* (eds.), Univ. of Alabama Press, Huntsville, Ala.

Pian, T. H. H. (1973). 'Hybrid models', in *Numerical and Computer Methods in Structural Mechanics*, Fenves, S. J., *et al.* (eds.), Academic Press, New York.

Reyes, S. F. and Deere, D. V. (1968). 'Elastic-plastic analysis of underground openings by the finite element method', *Proceedings, 1st Congress of Intl. Soc. for Rock Mech.*, **2**, Lisbon.

Sandhu, R. S. and Wilson, E. L. (1969). 'Finite element analysis of seepage in elastic media', *J. of Engg. Mech. Div.*, ASCE, **95**.

Sandhu, R. S., Wu, T. H., and Hoopson, R. J. (1971). *Stresses, deformations and progressive failure of nonhomogeneous fissured rock*', O.S.U.R.F. 3177-1, Ohio State Univ.

Schofield, A. and Wroth, P. (1968). *Critical State Soil Mechanics*, McGraw-Hill Book Co., N.Y.

Simpson, B. and Wroth, C. P. (1972). 'Finite elements computations for a model retaining wall in sand', *Proceedings, 5th European Conf. on Soil Mech. and Found. Engg.*, Madrid.

Smith, I. M. (1970). 'A finite element approach to elastic soil-structure interaction', *Canadian Geotech. J.*, **7**, No. 2.

Smith, I. M. and Kay S. (1971). 'Stress analysis of contractive or dilative soil', *J. SMFD, ASCE*, **97**, No. SM7.

Smith, I. M., Personal discussions.

Tsui, Y. and Clough, G. W. (1974). 'Plane strain approximations in FE analyses of temporary walls', *Proceedings, ASCE Sp. Conf. on Analysis and Design in Geotech. Engg.*, Austin, Texas, **1**.

Yudhbir and Varadarajan, A. (1975). 'Stress-path dependent deformation moduli of clay', *J. of Geotech. Engg. Div.*, ASCE, **101**, No. GT3.

Traughber, E. B. (1974). 'Analysis of strain-softening behavior of soils', *Ph.D. Dissertation*, Stanford Univ., Stanford, Calif.

Vesič, A. S. (1967). 'Study of bearing capacity of deep foundations', *Report B-189*, Georgia Inst. of Tech., Atlanta, Ga.

Wittke, W. (1974). 'Bemessung von horizontal belasteten Grossbohrpfählen nach der methode finiter Elemente', *Der Bauingenieur*, **449**.

Wittke, W. (under publication). 'Static analysis for underground openings in jointed rock', Chap. 18 in *Numerical Methods in Geotechnical Engineering*, Desai, C. S. and Christian, J. T. (eds.), McGraw-Hill Book Co., New York.

Worth, N. L. *et al.* (1966). 'Pile tests, Columbia Lock and Dam', *Tech. Rept.* No. 3-741, Corps of Engineers, Vicksburg, Miss.

Zienkiewicz, O. C., Valliappan, S., Dullage, C., and Stagg, K. G. (1970). 'Analysis of nonlinear problems in rock mechanics with particular reference to jointed rock systems', *Proceedings, 2nd Congress, Intl. Soc.for Rock Mech., Belgrade,* **3**.

Zienkiewicz, O. C., Valliappan, S., and King, I. P. (1968). 'Stress analysis of rock as "no tension" material', *Geotechnique,* **18**.

Chapter 8

Some Time-dependent Soil–Structure Interaction Problems

I. M. Smith

8.1 INTRODUCTION

In many practical situations, the rate at which pore-fluid flows through a soil is slow in relation to the rate at which loads are imposed on that soil. The response of the soil to the applied load is therefore time-dependent. This is equally true for the response of a clay foundation when an embankment is constructed on it over a period of years and for a fine-grained silty sand underlying an offshore oil-production platform when it is subject to some thousands of wave load applications every hour.

In addition to this 'primary' time-dependent behaviour due to drainage of pore-fluid, there is sometimes a 'secondary' time-dependent response due to viscous deformation or creep at constant effective stress. This is widely believed to be of minor importance for most soils. The present contribution is concerned wholly with primary time-dependent phenomena in soil mechanics, which can be explained in terms of the concept of effective stress.

Although the ultimate aim of the contribution is to present a unified approach to the solution of all time-dependent problems of this nature it proves to be convenient, especially when discussing previous work, to define two separate types of problem: first-order or dissipation problems and second-order or oscillation problems. First-order problems, typified by the previously mentioned dissipation of excess pore-water pressure beneath an embankment, may be described by a differential equation of the form

$$\mathbf{A}\frac{d\mathbf{u}}{dt} + \mathbf{B}\mathbf{u} = \mathbf{P}(t) \qquad (8.1)$$

where $\mathbf{u}$ is a vector of excess pore-water pressures or displacements, $\mathbf{P}(t)$ is the loading and $\mathbf{A}$ and $\mathbf{B}$ are matrices arising from the spatial discretization of the problem.

The method of spatial discretization used herein will be the finite element method.

251

Second-order problems, typified by the previously mentioned offshore platform oscillation, may be described by a differential equation of the form

$$\mathbf{M}\frac{d^2\mathbf{x}}{dt^2} + \mathbf{c}\frac{d\mathbf{x}}{dt} + \mathbf{K}\mathbf{x} = \mathbf{P}(t) \tag{8.2}$$

where $\mathbf{x}$ is a vector of displacements, $\mathbf{P}(t)$ is the loading and $\mathbf{M}$, $\mathbf{C}$ and $\mathbf{K}$ are the mass, damping and stiffness matrices of the finite element discretization.

Appropriate finitizations in time for first and second-order problems will now be discussed.

8.2 FIRST ORDER PROBLEMS

8.2.1 Uncoupled analyses

The simplest approach to structure–soil interaction problems, and the one most commonly adopted in practice, involves the uncoupling of structure and soil and of the solid and fluid components in the soil. Thus, the load transmitted by the structure to the fluid phase of the soil is assumed to be calculable *a priori*, and the problem reduces to the computation of the rate of dissipation of this excess porepressure with time. The process has been termed 'pseudo-consolidation theory' by Schiffman, Chen, *et al.* (1969).

The differential equation to be solved is of the form:

$$\mathbf{A}\frac{d\mathbf{u}}{dt} + \mathbf{B}\mathbf{u} = \mathbf{P}(t) \tag{8.1}$$

where $\mathbf{u}$ is a vector of excess pore-water pressures. The spatial discretization by the finite element method which leads to the formation of matrices $\mathbf{A}$ and $\mathbf{B}$ is now well known, e.g. Zienkiewicz (1971). It is only necessary here to note that these matrices have, in most applications, a sparse, banded form, and that the system of equations is 'stiff' in the mathematical sense.

There is a considerable volume of mathematical literature devoted to the study of the solution of stiff systems of ordinary differential equations having the form of Equation (8.1). Before proceeding with an examination of some of the more promising new methods, the nature and properties of the methods in current use in most engineers' computer programs will be described.

8.2.2 Finite differences in time

Most algorithms for the solution of Equation (8.1) make use of linear interpolation or finite differencing between successive instants in time (Zienkiewicz, 1971, Sandhu and Wilson, 1969). In general, depending on the positioning of the differences and their weighting over the interval, this leads to the discretized equation in time (Mitchell, 1971):

$$\mathbf{A}\left[\alpha\left(\frac{d\mathbf{u}}{dt}\right)_{n+1}+(1-\alpha)\left(\frac{d\mathbf{u}}{dt}\right)_{n}\right]$$
$$+\mathbf{B}[\alpha\mathbf{u}_{n+1}+(1-\alpha)\mathbf{u}_{n}]=\alpha\mathbf{P}_{n+1}+(1-\alpha)\mathbf{P}_{n} \qquad (8.3)$$

where α is a parameter varying between 0 and 1 and n and $n+1$ are successive instants in time. The most popular choices for α are:

$$\alpha=0 \qquad \text{(explicit method)}$$
$$\mathbf{u}_{n+1}=\mathbf{u}_{n}-\Delta t\mathbf{A}^{-\prime}\mathbf{B}\mathbf{u}_{n}+\Delta t\mathbf{A}^{-\prime}\mathbf{P}_{n} \qquad (8.4)$$

$$\alpha=\tfrac{1}{2} \qquad \text{(Crank–Nicolson method)}$$
$$\mathbf{u}_{n+1}=(\mathbf{I}+\tfrac{1}{2}\Delta t\mathbf{A}^{-\prime}\mathbf{B})^{-1}(\mathbf{I}-\tfrac{1}{2}\Delta t\mathbf{A}^{-\prime}\mathbf{B})\mathbf{u}_{n}$$
$$+\tfrac{1}{2}\Delta t(\mathbf{I}+\tfrac{1}{2}\Delta t\mathbf{A}^{-\prime}\mathbf{B})^{-\prime}\mathbf{A}^{-\prime}(\mathbf{P}_{n+1}+\mathbf{P}_{n}) \qquad (8.5)$$

$$\alpha=1 \qquad \text{(fully implicit method)}$$
$$\mathbf{u}_{n+1}=(\mathbf{I}+\Delta t\mathbf{A}^{-\prime}\mathbf{B})^{-\prime}\mathbf{u}_{n}+\Delta t(\mathbf{I}+\Delta t\mathbf{A}^{-\prime}\mathbf{B})^{-\prime}\mathbf{A}^{-\prime}\mathbf{P}_{n+1} \qquad (8.6)$$

where Δt is the time increment between instants n and $n+1$ and $\mathbf{I}$ is the unit matrix.

It can be seen from Equations (8.4), (8.5) and (8.6) that all methods involve the inversion of a matrix (in practice the reduction of equation coefficients). If a finite difference discretisation in space is used, $\mathbf{A}$ becomes the unit matrix $\mathbf{I}$ so that the explicit method requires much less work. This is not the case when finite element spatial discretizations are used. In order to avoid reducing the equation coefficients more than once for $\alpha>0$, the term Δt is usually kept constant, but Hwang, Morgenstern, *et al.* (1971) describe a method in which $\alpha\Delta t$ is varied logarithmically.

The results obtained when these methods are applied to a typical consolidation problem in soil mechanics are shown in Figure 8.1. To this simple problem an analytical solution exists and it can be seen that for the time-step Δt chosen in the computations:

(1) The explicit method fails to yield any solution at all (i.e. the calculation is unstable).

(2) The Crank–Nicolson method results in predicted pore-pressures which oscillate violently about the true curve.

(3) The implicit method results in a serious underprediction of the rate of pore-pressure dissipation with time.

While it is always possible, by reducing the time-step, to obtain accurate answers by all of these methods (Desai and Johnson, 1973) the engineer's

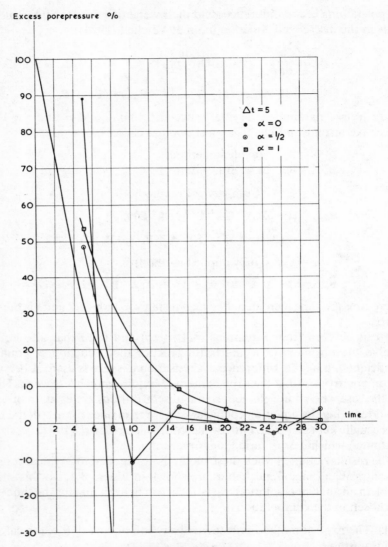

Figure 8.1 Two-dimensional pseudo-consolidation problem analysed by linear differencing in time

job is to use a method which combines reasonable accuracy with minimum cost. Methods will be described later in this paper by which acceptably accurate results can be obtained to the problem shown in Figure 8.1, without altering the time-step, and at the expense of a little extra work compared with that involved in the finite difference methods with $\alpha > 0$. It is first necessary to understand why the difference methods are inaccurate in their respective ways.

8.2.3 Continuous time, discrete space equations

In order to simplify the algebra, consider Equation (8.1) when the load is a constant:

$$\mathbf{A}\frac{d\mathbf{u}}{dt} + \mathbf{B}\mathbf{u} = \mathbf{P} \tag{8.7}$$

subject to the initial conditions:

$$\mathbf{u}(t = 0) = \mathbf{u}_0 \tag{8.8}$$

The solution of the equation is:

$$\mathbf{u}(t) = \exp{(-t\mathbf{A}^{-\prime}\mathbf{B})}(\mathbf{u}_0 - \mathbf{B}^{-\prime}\mathbf{P}) + \mathbf{B}^{-\prime}\mathbf{P} \tag{8.9}$$

or, in incremental form:

$$\mathbf{u}(t + \Delta t) = \exp{(-\Delta t\mathbf{A}^{-\prime}\mathbf{B})}[\mathbf{u}(t) - \mathbf{B}^{-\prime}\mathbf{P}] + \mathbf{B}^{-\prime}\mathbf{P} \tag{8.10}$$

If $\mathbf{C} = \Delta t\,\mathbf{A}^{-\prime}\mathbf{B}$, the matrix $\exp{(-\mathbf{C})}$ is defined by the convergent series:

$$\exp{(-\mathbf{C})} = \mathbf{I} - \mathbf{C} + \tfrac{1}{2}\mathbf{C}^2 - \cdots \tag{8.11}$$

The expense of matrix multiplications in practice renders direct determinations of $\exp{(-\mathbf{C})}$ impossible, but now that the exponential form of the solution is recognised, it is possible to seek approximations to $\exp{(-\mathbf{C})}$ which have the desired exponential properties. These approximations are usually called 'rational approximations' and can be designed to be as close a fit to $\exp{(-\mathbf{C})}$ as is necessary. In selecting methods based on rational approximations the aim will be to combine maximum accuracy with minimum work.

8.2.4 A simple rational approximation

Consider the rational approximation ($\mathbf{C}$ is in general a complex quantity):

$$\exp{(-Z)} \simeq \frac{1 - (1 - \alpha)Z}{1 + \alpha Z} \tag{8.12}$$

Since in first-order problems $\mathbf{C}$ is real, the approximations can be plotted on the real axis and compared with the exponential as shown in Figure 8.2 for various values of α in the range 0 to 1.

The matrix equivalent is:

$$\exp(-\mathbf{C}) \simeq \frac{\mathbf{I} - (1-\alpha)\Delta t\ \mathbf{A}^{-\prime}\mathbf{B}}{\mathbf{I} + \alpha\Delta t\ \mathbf{A}^{-\prime}\mathbf{B}}$$

$$= [\mathbf{I} + \alpha\,\Delta t\ \mathbf{A}^{-\prime}\mathbf{B}]^{-\prime}[\mathbf{I} - (1-\alpha)\,\Delta t\mathbf{A}^{-\prime}\mathbf{B}] \qquad (8.13)$$

Inserting the approximation in Equation (8.10) we have:

$$\mathbf{u}_{n+1} = [\mathbf{I} + \alpha\,\Delta t\ \mathbf{A}^{-\prime}\mathbf{B}]^{-\prime}[\mathbf{I} - (1-\alpha)\,\Delta t\ \mathbf{A}^{-\prime}\mathbf{B}](\mathbf{u}_n - \mathbf{B}^{-\prime}\mathbf{P}) + \mathbf{B}^{-\prime}\mathbf{P} \qquad (8.14)$$

which the reader may verify leads to Equation (4) when $\alpha = 0$, to Equation (8.5) when $\alpha = \frac{1}{2}$ and to Equation (8.6) when $\alpha = 1$. Thus it has been possible to recover the well-known difference methods from their equivalent rational approximations. By studying the graphs drawn in Figure 8.2 it can be seen that for $\alpha < \frac{1}{2}$, the rational approximation does not have a finite asymptote.

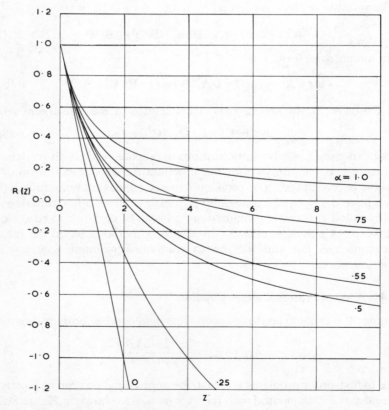

Figure 8.2 Rational approximations for linear difference formulae

This is the graphical explanation of the well known fact that $\alpha = \frac{1}{2}$, the Crank–Nicolson method, is at the limit of stable methods. In addition, the fully implicit rational approximation lies always above $\exp(-Z)$ while the Crank–Nicolson approximation crosses the Z-axis and asymptotes to -1. Since the solution methods are iterative methods, whenever a negative solution is found, the solution, propagating with a factor $(-1)^r$ for r steps, will tend to oscillate between positive and negative values. This explains the oscillatory behaviour of the Crank–Nicolson solution in Figure 8.1 compared with the excessively 'damped' behaviour of the fully implicit solution.

8.2.5 Padé approximations

The rational approximation used in the previous section is a member of a family of such approximations called Padé approximations (Donnelly, 1965, Graves-Morris, 1973). If $f(Z)$ is analytic in the region of the complex plane containing the origin $Z = 0$, a Padé approximation to the function $f(Z)$ is defined by:

$$f(Z) \simeq P_{m,n}(Z) = \frac{S_{m,n}(Z)}{t_{m,n}(Z)} \tag{8.15}$$

where $S_{m,n}(Z)$ and $t_{m,n}(Z)$ are polynomials respectively of degree n and m in Z with leading coefficients of unity. For each pair of non-negative integers m and n, those polynomials $S_{m,n}(Z)$ and $t_{m,n}(Z)$ can be selected for which the Taylor series expansion of $P_{m,n}(Z)$ about the origin agrees with the Taylor series expansion of $f(Z)$ for as many leading terms as possible.

The details of the derivation of $S_{m,n}(Z)$ and $t_{m,n}(Z)$ are given elsewhere (Siemieniuch and Gladwell, 1974) and the first few entries of the Padé table for $f(Z) = \exp(-Z)$ are reproduced in Table 8.1.

Table 8.1 Padé table for $\exp(-2)$

$\exp(-Z)$	$n = 0$	$n = 1$	$n = 2$
$m = 0$	1	$1 - Z$ (A)	$1 - Z + (Z^2/2)$
$m = 1$	$\dfrac{1}{1+Z}$ (B)	$\dfrac{1 - (Z/2)}{1 + (Z/2)}$ (C)	$\dfrac{1 - (2Z/3) + (Z^2/6)}{1 + (Z/3)}$
$m = 2$	$\dfrac{1}{1 + Z + (Z^2/2)}$	$\dfrac{1 - (Z/3)}{1 + (2Z/3) + (Z^2/6)}$	$\dfrac{1 - (Z/2) + (Z^2/12)}{1 + (Z/2) + (Z^2/12)}$

Notes (A): Explicit method.
(B): Fully implicit method.
(C): Crank–Nicolson method.

The following observations can be made from a study of the table:

(1) The first-order Padé approximations recover the familiar difference methods.

(2) Approximations lying above the diagonal will lead to unstable algorithms.

(3) Approximations lying on the diagonal will lead to algorithms at the limit of stability.

(4) The accuracy of the approximations can be judged from their series expansions:

$$\left.\begin{array}{l} \exp(-Z) = 1 - Z + \tfrac{1}{2}Z^2 - \tfrac{1}{6}Z^3 + \tfrac{1}{24}Z^4 - \tfrac{1}{120}Z^5 + \cdots \\[4pt] P_{1,0} = 1 - Z + Z^2 - Z^3 + Z^4 - \cdots \\[4pt] P_{1,1} = 1 - Z + \tfrac{1}{2}Z^2 - \tfrac{1}{4}Z^3 + \tfrac{1}{8}Z^4 - \cdots \\[4pt] P_{2,2} = 1 - Z + \tfrac{1}{2}Z^2 - \tfrac{1}{6}Z^3 + \tfrac{1}{24}Z^4 - \tfrac{1}{144}Z^5 + \cdots \end{array}\right\} \tag{8.16}$$

Thus the $P_{2,2}$ method has error $O(Z^5)$ compared with the $P_{1,1}$ method which has error $O(Z^3)$. However this improvement in accuracy can only be purchased at the cost of considerably more computation. On substitution into Equation (8.10) it can be shown that the algorithm for the $P_{2,2}$ method is

$$[\mathbf{A} + \tfrac{1}{2}\Delta t \mathbf{B} + \tfrac{1}{12}\Delta t^2 \, \mathbf{BA}^{-'}\mathbf{B}]\mathbf{u}_{n+1}$$
$$= [\mathbf{A} - \tfrac{1}{2}\Delta t \, \mathbf{B} + \tfrac{1}{12}\Delta t^2 \mathbf{BA}^{-'}\mathbf{B}]\mathbf{u}_n + \Delta t \, \mathbf{P} \tag{8.17}$$

If the algorithm is implemented in this form, $\mathbf{A}^{-'}$ becomes in general fully populated and the cost of forming $\mathbf{A}^{-'}$, computing the products $\mathbf{BA}^{-'}\mathbf{B}$ and solving the resulting equations with augmented bandwidth makes the method, in the author's experience, uncompetitive with simply taking more steps in a lower-order method, such as Crank–Nicolson.

An alternative algorithm for solving Equation (8.17) can be devised by factorizing the matrix on the left-hand side of the equation, and introducing a number of dummy solution steps. This circumvents the need to form any matrix inverses or products but, in the case of Equation (8.17), results in complex factors (Siemieniuch and Gladwell, 1974). Since complex arithmetic is roughly twice as expensive in store and time on the computer, methods involving it have not been pursued by the present author. Argyris and his co-workers have recently proposed the use of this method in second order problems (Argyris, Dunne, *et al.*, 1973a, b) and it will be re-considered below in that context. In the meantime, higher order methods which result in real arithmetic only will be further investigated.

8.2.6 Nørsett approximations

It is possible to construct rational approximations

$$r_{m;n}(Z) = \frac{c_{m,n}(Z)}{d_{m,n}(Z)} \tag{8.18}$$

to $\exp(-Z)$ such that $d_{m,n}(Z)$ factorizes into real linear factors and such that $c_{m,n}(Z)$ and $d_{m,n}(Z)$ are chosen to approximate $\exp(-Z)$ to maximal order in Z. The factors of $d_{m,n}(Z)$ may be distinct, such that

$$d_{m,n}(Z) = \prod_{i=1}^{m} (1 + \alpha_i Z) \tag{8.19}$$

and α_i are real. When using this approximation a sequence of m equations:

$$[\mathbf{A} + \alpha_i \, \Delta t \, \mathbf{B}]\mathbf{w}_{i+1} = \mathbf{w}_i, \qquad i = 1, 2, 3, \ldots m \tag{8.20}$$

must be solved at each time-step. To minimize computer storage, only methods in which α_i is constant will be considered.

The construction of such a class of approximations to $\exp(-Z)$ with denominators of the form $(1 + \alpha Z)^n$ is given by Nørsett (1974) and Makinson (1968).

These approximations are given explicitly by:

$$f_n(\alpha, Z) = (-1)^n \sum_{k=0}^{n} (-1)^k L_n^{(n-k)}\left(\frac{1}{\alpha}\right) \frac{(\alpha Z)^k}{(1 + \alpha Z)^n} \tag{8.21}$$

where L_m is the Laguerre polynomial of degree m, and α is a parameter which can be chosen to suit particular requirements.

For example, on the basis of L-acceptability (Siemieniuch and Gladwell, 1974) an $\bar{\alpha}$, nth-order method can be devised which leads to the algorithm:

$$[\mathbf{A} + \bar{\alpha} \, \Delta t \, \mathbf{B}]\mathbf{w}_1 = \bar{\alpha} \, \Delta t \, (\mathbf{B}\mathbf{u}_n - \mathbf{P})$$

$$[\mathbf{A} + \bar{\alpha} \, \Delta t \, \mathbf{B}]\mathbf{w}_{i+1} = \bar{\alpha} \, \Delta t \, \mathbf{B}\mathbf{w}_i, \qquad i = 1, 2, \ldots n-2 \tag{8.22}$$

$$[\mathbf{A} + \bar{\alpha} \, \Delta t \, \mathbf{B}]\mathbf{u}_{n+1} = \mathbf{A}\left[\mathbf{u}_n + \sum_{j=1}^{n-1} L_j\left(\frac{1}{\bar{\alpha}}\right)\mathbf{w}_j\right] + \bar{\alpha} \, \Delta t \, \mathbf{P}$$

Second-order members of this family are plotted on the real axis in Figure 8.3, where they are compared with $\exp(-Z)$. The approximation with $\bar{\alpha} = 1 + \frac{1}{2}\sqrt{2}$ lies always above $\exp(-Z)$ so that its behaviour would be expected to be of the implicit type, whereas the approximation with $\bar{\alpha} = 1 - \frac{1}{2}\sqrt{2}$ crosses the axis so that oscillatory results would be anticipated for

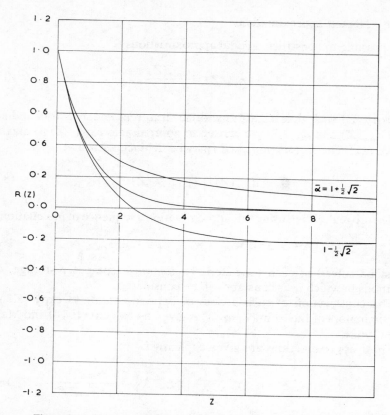

Figure 8.3   Rational approximations for second order Nørsett formulae

large time-steps. This prediction is confirmed in Figure 8.4 when the methods are applied to the previous consolidation problem. In this case the second-order methods involve about 10 per cent more work than the first-order methods.

A third-order member of the $\bar{\alpha}$ family is plotted on the real axis in Figure 8.5 and compared with $\exp(-Z)$. On the same graph is plotted a third-order approximation produced by a different α assumption, say $\hat{\alpha}$. This is in fact Calahan's method (Gear, 1971, Zlamal, 1973). Both of the third-order methods cross the Z-axis so that oscillatory behaviour can be anticipated for large time-steps. This is confirmed in Figure 8.6, although the order of the methods has now greatly improved the accuracy of the solutions and the oscillations are mild. Again the increase in computational effort by raising the order of approximation by one is about 10% in this case.

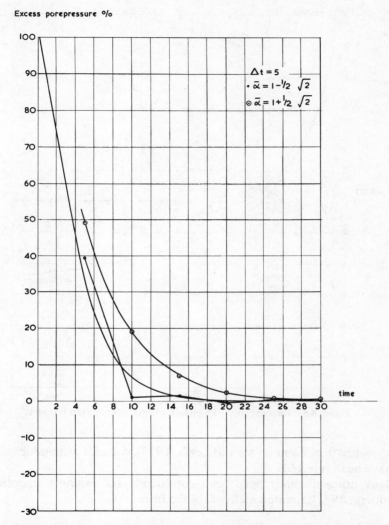

Figure 8.4 Two-dimensional pseudo-consolidation problem analysed by second-order Nørsett methods

8.2.7 Further remarks

The aim in the previous sections has been to produce considerable gains in accuracy of time discretizations at modest extra cost. Methods which would cost substantially more due to extra matrix multiplications, augmented

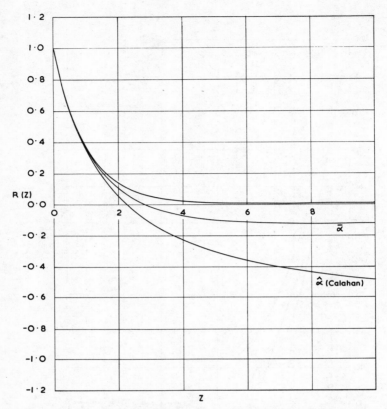

Figure 8.5 Rational approximations for third order Nørsett formulae

band-widths (e.g. Zienkiewicz and Lewis, 1973), complex arithmetic and so on have been rejected.

Many other methods have been considered, for example smoothing (Lindberg, 1971), iterated methods of the form:

$$\exp(-Z) \simeq \frac{1}{(1+Z/n)^n} \tag{8.23}$$

and Chebyshev approximations (Varga, 1961), but the Nørsett methods previously described have proved to be the best methods tested to date.

8.2.8 Coupled analyses

If the solid soil skeleton and the pore-fluid are coupled together as in Biot's theory, the following coupled first-order equations in time arise (Sandhu and

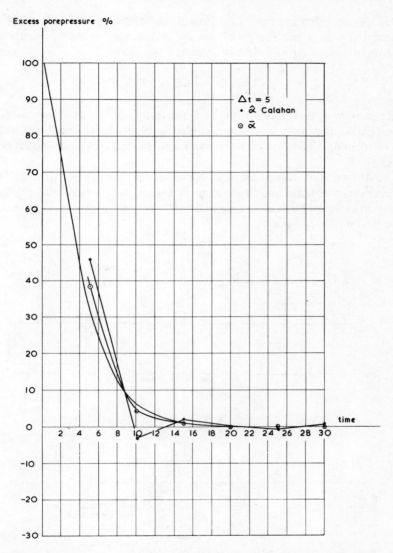

Figure 8.6 Two-dimensional pseudo-consolidation problem analysed by third order Nørsett methods

Wilson, 1969)

$$\mathbf{K}_1\mathbf{v} + \mathbf{C}\mathbf{u} = \mathbf{P}$$

$$\mathbf{C}^T\frac{\mathrm{d}\mathbf{v}}{\mathrm{d}t} - \mathbf{K}_2\mathbf{u} = 0$$

$$(8.24)$$

where K_1 and K_2 are the solid and fluid 'stiffness matrices', C is the connection matrix and v, u and P are the displacement, pore-pressure and load vectors respectively. By eliminating u we have

$$CK_2^{-\prime}C^T\frac{dv}{dt} + K_1 v = P \qquad (8.25)$$

which has now the same form as Equation (8.9) so that the methods developed in the previous sections can again be used. However, the necessity of forming $CK_2^{-\prime}C^T$ now adds considerably to the computational complexity.

The benefits of using coupled consolidation theory in structure-soil interaction problems are illustrated in Figure 8.7, where the effect of variation in the stiffness of an embankment on the pore-pressures generated in its foundation are plain.

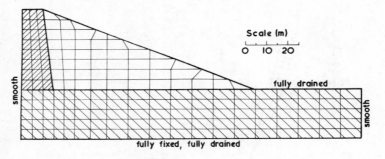

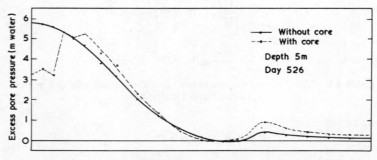

Figure 8.7 Effect of embankment inhomogeneity on foundation pore-pressures computed by Biot theory (linear differencing in time, $\alpha = \frac{1}{2}$)

8.3 SECOND-ORDER-PROBLEMS

Much more has been written in the engineering literature about time discretization methods for second-order problems than for the first-order problems considered above. The most widely used methods are the 'Newmark methods' (Newmark, 1959) and the 'Wilson θ methods' (Wilson, 1968; Bathe and Wilson, 1973a, b). Higher-order methods (Argyris, Dunne, *et al.*, 1973a, b) based on Hermitian polynomial interpolations have also been proposed.

It is the purpose in the present section to develop methods of time discretization for second-order problems based again on the concept of rational approximations to the governing differential equations in time. Before proceeding, the results obtained by the use of the Newmark and Wilson methods in typical problems are discussed.

Figure 8.8 shows the computed free-vibration response of a structure having a small number of degrees of freedom (12) and a moderate range in natural periods ($2 \cdot 33 \times 10^{-2}$ to $4 \cdot 6 \times 10^{-4}$). For a time step of about one-tenth of the smallest natural period the Newmark $\beta = \frac{1}{4}$ method gives an undamped picture of the response of the structure (displacement and acceleration) while the Wilson averaging method with $\theta = 1 \cdot 4$ gives a rather damped response.

Figure 8.9 shows the computed free-vibration response of a structure having a larger number of degrees of freedom (180) and a larger range in natural periods ($3 \cdot 74 \times 10^{-1}$ to $1 \cdot 9 \times 10^{-3}$). For a time-step of about one-quarter of the smallest natural period, the Newmark $\beta = 1/4$ method suffers from spurious oscillations which render the displacement results fairly erroneous and the accelerations quite unacceptable. In this problem, however, the Wilson $\theta = 1 \cdot 4$ method leads to rather good results, although with slight damping.

In the light of these results, it is difficult to support the many papers which have sought to prove that Newmark's method is unconditionally superior to that of Wilson, e.g. Finn and Miller (1973). Apparently, any comparison depends on the problem being analyzed. The study of rational approximations in the time domain can assist in resolving this difficulty.

8.3.1 Equivalent first order equation

The relevant differential equation is

$$\mathbf{M}\frac{d^2\mathbf{x}}{dt^2} + \mathbf{C}\frac{d\mathbf{x}}{dt} + \mathbf{K}\mathbf{x} = \mathbf{P}(t) \tag{8.2}$$

or

$$\mathbf{M}\ddot{\mathbf{x}} + \mathbf{C}\dot{\mathbf{x}} + \mathbf{K}\mathbf{x} = \mathbf{P}(t)$$

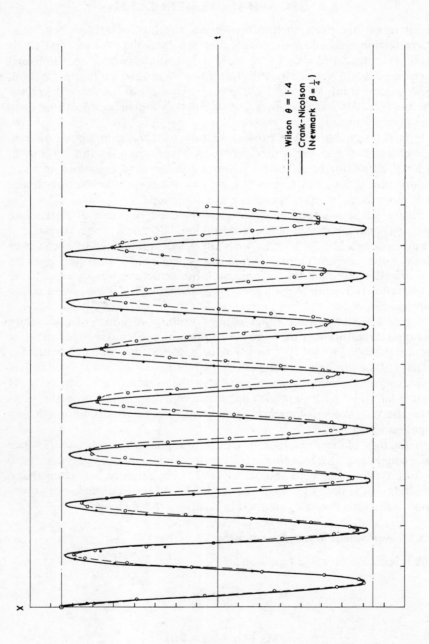

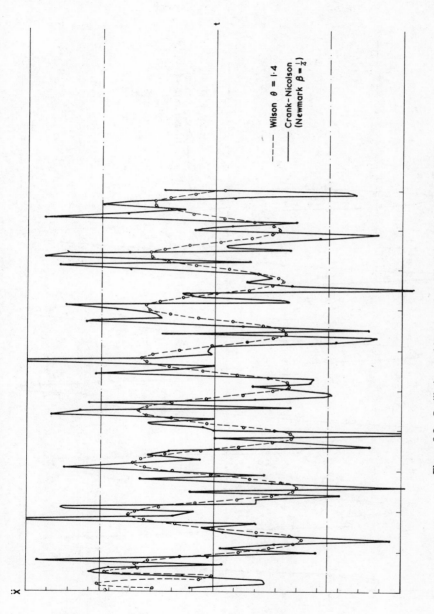

Figure 8.8 Oscillation problem 1 analysed by linear interpolation in time

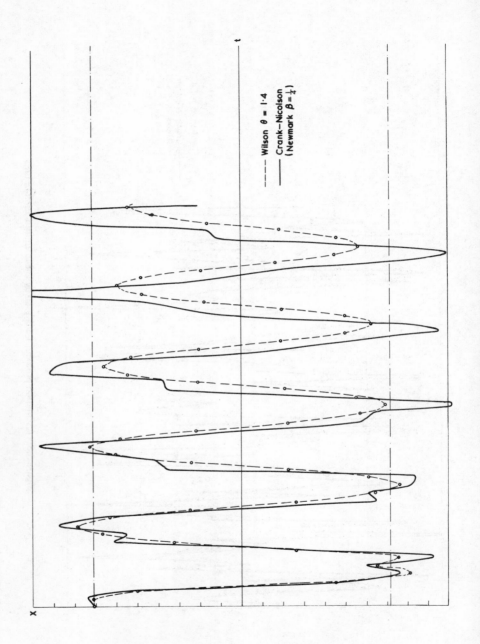

Wilson $\theta = 1\cdot4$
Crank–Nicolson
(Newmark $\beta = \frac{1}{4}$)

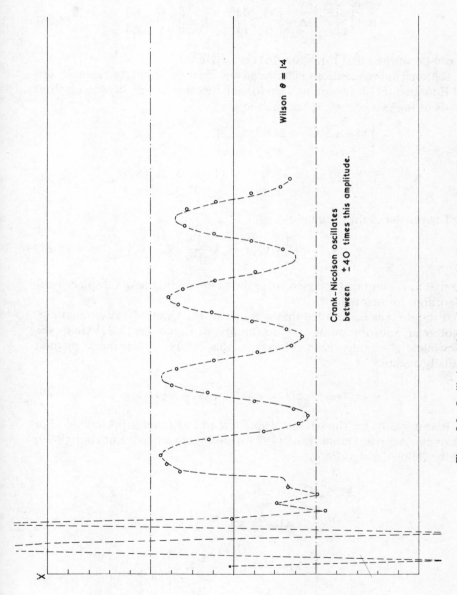

Wilson $\theta = 1.4$

Crank–Nicolson oscillates
between ± 40 times this amplitude.

Figure 8.9 Oscillation problem 2 analysed by linear interpolation in time

and by making the substitutions

$$\mathbf{u} = \begin{Bmatrix} \dot{\mathbf{x}} \\ \mathbf{x} \end{Bmatrix} \qquad \mathbf{A} = \begin{bmatrix} \mathbf{M} & \mathbf{0} \\ \mathbf{0} & \mathbf{I} \end{bmatrix} \qquad \mathbf{B} = \begin{bmatrix} \mathbf{C} & \mathbf{K} \\ -\mathbf{I} & \mathbf{0} \end{bmatrix} \qquad (8.26)$$

it can be verified that Equation (8.1) is recovered.

Rational approximations in time can now be used again; for example, use of Equation (8.14) (assuming zero forcing function to simplify the algebra) leads to the pair of recurrence equations:

$$\begin{bmatrix} \mathbf{M} + \alpha \Delta t \mathbf{C} & \alpha \Delta t \mathbf{K} \\ -\alpha \Delta t \mathbf{I} & \mathbf{I} \end{bmatrix} \begin{Bmatrix} \dot{\mathbf{x}}_{n+1} \\ \mathbf{x}_{n+1} \end{Bmatrix}$$
$$= \begin{bmatrix} \mathbf{M} - (1-\alpha) \Delta t \, \mathbf{C} & -(1-\alpha) \Delta t \, \mathbf{K} \\ (1-\alpha) \Delta t \, \mathbf{I} & \mathbf{I} \end{bmatrix} \begin{Bmatrix} \dot{\mathbf{x}}_n \\ \mathbf{x}_n \end{Bmatrix} \qquad (8.27)$$

The second of these equations is

$$\dot{\mathbf{x}}_{n+1} = \frac{1}{\alpha \Delta t} (\mathbf{x}_{n+1} - \mathbf{x}_n) - \frac{1-\alpha}{\alpha} \dot{\mathbf{x}}_n \qquad (8.28)$$

so that $\dot{\mathbf{x}}_{n+1}$ can be eliminated from the first equation and a displacement algorithm formulated.

It should now be recalled that $\alpha = \frac{1}{2}$ yields the Crank–Nicolson method. Moreover, substitution of $\alpha = \frac{1}{2}$ in the first of Equations (8.27) yields the Newmark $\beta = \frac{1}{4}$ algorithm. However, the complete Newmark method usually assumes

$$\dot{\mathbf{x}}_{n+1} = \frac{1}{\Delta t} (\mathbf{x}_{n+1} - \mathbf{x}_n) - \frac{\Delta t}{4} (\ddot{\mathbf{x}}_{n+1} + \ddot{\mathbf{x}}_n) \qquad (8.29)$$

It can easily be shown that Equation (8.29) is over-prescribed. For example, Argyris, Dunne, *et al.* (1973b) attempt to enforce Equation (8.29) in the following algorithm:

$$\begin{bmatrix} \mathbf{M} + \dfrac{\Delta t}{2} \mathbf{C} & \dfrac{\Delta t}{2} \mathbf{K} \\ \dfrac{\Delta t}{4} \mathbf{C} & \mathbf{M} + \dfrac{\Delta t^2}{4} \mathbf{K} \end{bmatrix} \begin{Bmatrix} \dot{\mathbf{x}}_{n+1} \\ \mathbf{x}_{n+1} \end{Bmatrix}$$
$$= \begin{bmatrix} \mathbf{M} - \dfrac{\Delta t}{2} \mathbf{C} & -\dfrac{\Delta t}{2} \mathbf{K} \\ \Delta t \mathbf{M} - \dfrac{\Delta t^2}{4} \mathbf{C} & \mathbf{M} - \dfrac{\Delta t^2}{4} \mathbf{K} \end{bmatrix} \begin{Bmatrix} \dot{\mathbf{x}}_n \\ \mathbf{x}_n \end{Bmatrix} \qquad (8.30)$$

Substitution of the second of these equations in the first leads to

$$\dot{\mathbf{x}}_{n+1} = \frac{2}{\Delta t}(\mathbf{x}_{n+1} - \mathbf{x}_n) - \dot{\mathbf{x}}_n \qquad (8.31)$$

which is Equation (8.28) with $\alpha = \frac{1}{2}$. Therefore Equations (8.27) are the only consistent description of the Crank–Nicolson method for second-order problems, and this method is identical with the usual way of implementing Newmark's $\beta = \frac{1}{4}$ algorithm in terms of N unknown displacements only. It is at the least misleading for Argyris, Dunne, *et al.* (1973b) to write a Newmark algorithm in terms of $2N$ unknowns (N displacements and N velocities) and to refer (Argyris, Dunne, *et al.*, 1973a) to 'direct solution of a $2N$ by $2N$ set of linear equations'. If problems were indeed solved in this way it would be extraordinarily wasteful of computer time.

Whereas solutions of first-order problems took the form

$$\mathbf{u} = \exp(-\mathbf{A}^{-\prime}\mathbf{B}t) \qquad (8.32)$$

where $\mathbf{A}^{-\prime}\mathbf{B}$ is real, solutions of second-order problems take the form (for zero damping)

$$\mathbf{x} = \exp\left[i - \sqrt{\left(\frac{\mathbf{K}}{\mathbf{M}}\right)}t \right] \qquad (8.33)$$

and the adequacy of rational approximations must be judged by their ability to approximate the complex exponential. This has a constant modulus of one and an argument varying linearly with time at a slope of 45° to the time axis.

The nature of the linear approximations in Equation (8.12) may be judged from Figures 8.10 and 8.11, for modulus and argument respectively. Figure 8.10 demonstrates the well-known fact that the Crank–Nicolson (or Newmark $\beta = \frac{1}{4}$) method has no damping at all. However a very small reduction in α below $\frac{1}{2}$ produces a violently unstable method and conversely a small increase in α above $\frac{1}{2}$ produces a method with severe damping. Figure 8.11 demonstrates that none of these methods has desirable argument (phase) properties. For moderate time-steps all will lead to serious divergences in the computed phases compared with the true ones. The reasons for the spurious oscillations found in Figure 8.9 are now clear. The complete absence of damping allows the out-of-phase high frequencies to augment the fundamental mode amplitudes.

8.3.2 Padé approximations

Of the linear approximations discussed in the previous section $\alpha = 1$ yields the stable implicit member of the Padé family and $\alpha = \frac{1}{2}$ yields the just stable Crank–Nicolson method. The use of second-order Padé methods and in

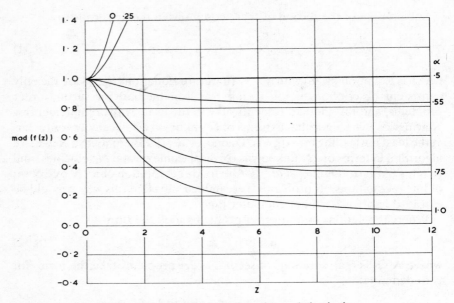

Figure 8.10 Modulus plot: linear interpolation in time

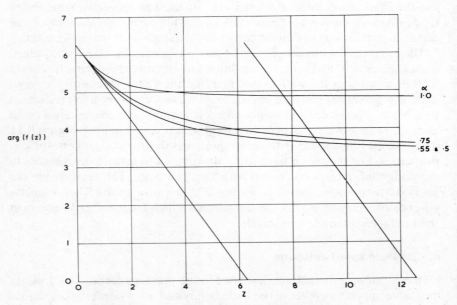

Figure 8.11 Argument plot: linear interpolation in time

particular the $P_{2,2}$ method has been advocated by Argyris, Dunne *et al.* (1973a, b). By substitution in Equation (8.17) for $P = 0$, the method is seen to be

$$
\begin{bmatrix}
\mathbf{M} + \dfrac{\Delta t}{2}\mathbf{C} + \dfrac{\Delta t^2}{12}(\mathbf{CM}^{-1}\mathbf{C} - \mathbf{K}) & \dfrac{\Delta t}{2}\mathbf{K} + \dfrac{\Delta t^2}{12}\mathbf{CM}^{-1}\mathbf{K} \\[2ex]
-\dfrac{\Delta t}{2} - \dfrac{\Delta t^2}{12}\mathbf{M}^{-1}\mathbf{C} & \mathbf{I} - \dfrac{\Delta t^2}{12}\mathbf{M}^{-1}\mathbf{K}
\end{bmatrix}
\begin{Bmatrix} \dot{\mathbf{x}}_{n+1} \\ \mathbf{x}_{n+1} \end{Bmatrix}
$$

$$
=
\begin{bmatrix}
\mathbf{M} - \dfrac{\Delta t}{2}\mathbf{C} + \dfrac{\Delta t^2}{12}(\mathbf{CM}^{-1}\mathbf{C} - \mathbf{K}) & -\dfrac{\Delta t}{2}\mathbf{K} + \dfrac{\Delta t^2}{12}\mathbf{CM}^{-1}\mathbf{K} \\[2ex]
\dfrac{\Delta t}{2} - \dfrac{\Delta t^2}{12}\mathbf{M}^{-1}\mathbf{C} & \mathbf{I} - \dfrac{\Delta t^2}{12}\mathbf{M}^{-1}\mathbf{K}
\end{bmatrix}
\begin{Bmatrix} \dot{\mathbf{x}}_n \\ \mathbf{x}_n \end{Bmatrix}
\qquad (8.34)
$$

The second of these equations is not the same as that given by Argyris, Dunne, *et al.* (1973b) but is more consistent. In this algorithm it is now indeed necessary to solve the $2N$ equations in velocities and displacements in every time-step. This fact, together with the need to form $\mathbf{M}^{-1}$ and the various matrix products led the present author to reject the method in favour of the Nørsett methods described below. However its properties, and those of the other second-order Padé methods may be inferred from Figures 8.12 and 8.13. The $P_{2,0}$ and $P_{2,1}$ methods are seen to be of no practical use. The $P_{2,2}$ method has zero damping and better phase properties than the $P_{1,1}$

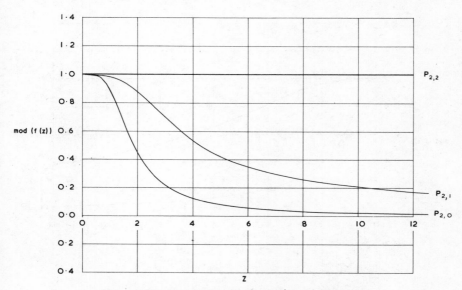

Figure 8.12 Modulus plot: second-order Padé methods

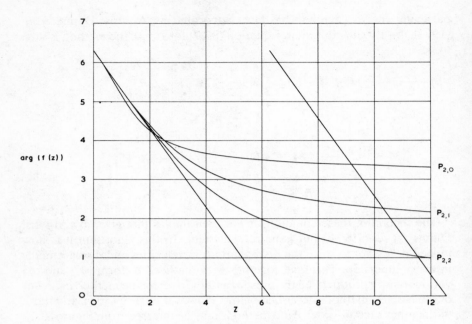

Figure 8.13 Argument plot: second-order Padé methods

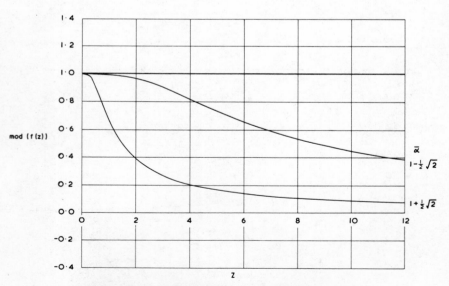

Figure 8.14 Modulus plot: second-order Nørsett methods

method (Crank–Nicolson). However, it can be expected to suffer from the same spurious oscillation difficulties when there is a wide band of natural frequencies in an analysis.

8.3.3 Nørsett approximations

Of the many Nørsett-type methods available, only the real factorizable methods have been considered for the same reasons of computational efficiency as before. The algorithms are obtained by appropriate substitution in Equations (8.2.2) and involve only one matrix reduction per time-step and no matrix inversions or multiplications.

The modulus and argument of two second-order members of the family are plotted against $\exp(-Z)$ in Figures 8.14 and 8.15. The approximation with $\bar{\alpha} = 1 + \frac{1}{2}\sqrt{2}$ has quite unacceptable damping and phase-shift properties but the method with $\bar{\alpha} = 1 - \frac{1}{2}\sqrt{2}$ is very promising. For relatively small time-steps it has small damping, but this increases with time-step. The effect of this ought to be a selective damping of higher modes in an analysis involving a wide range of natural frequencies. The phase-shift of the method lies between that of the Crank-Nicolson and $P_{2,2}$ methods.

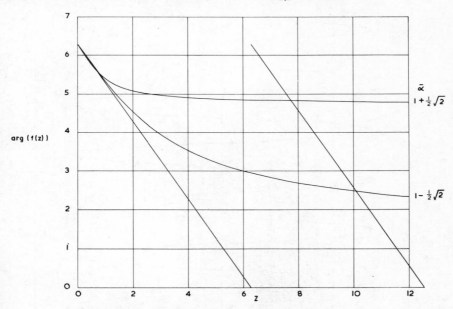

Figure 8.15 Argument plot: second-order Nørsett methods

The results obtained from analyses using the better second-order algorithm are shown in Figures 8.16 and 8.17. In the problem with the small

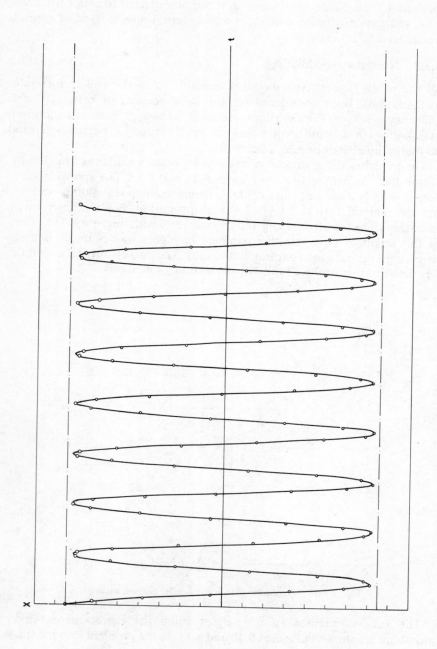

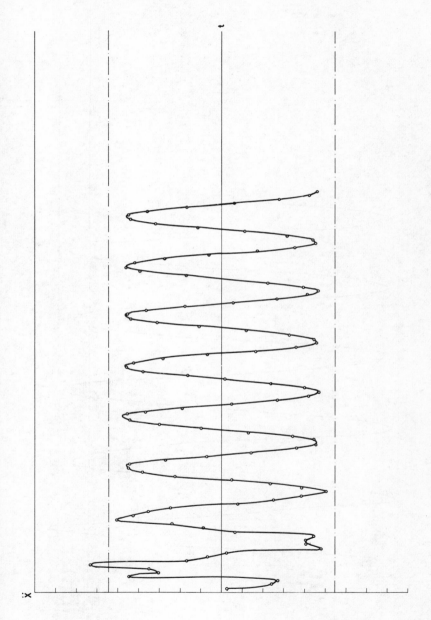

Figure 8.16   Oscillation problem 1 analysed by second-order Nørsett method

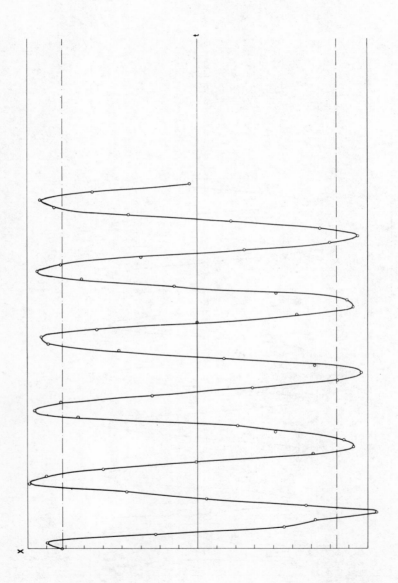

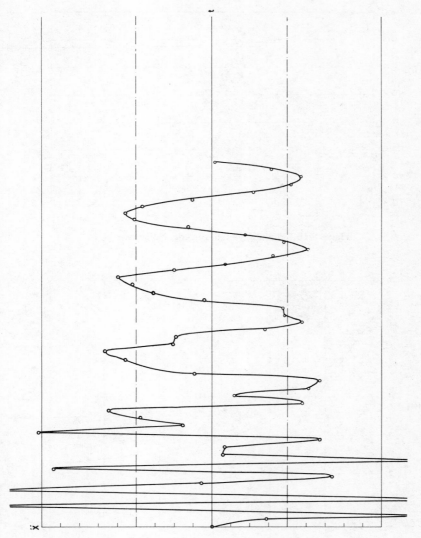

Figure 8.17   Oscillation problem 2 analysed by second-order Nørsett method

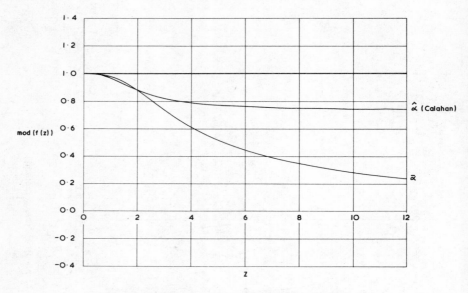

Figure 8.18   Modulus plot: third-order Nørsett methods

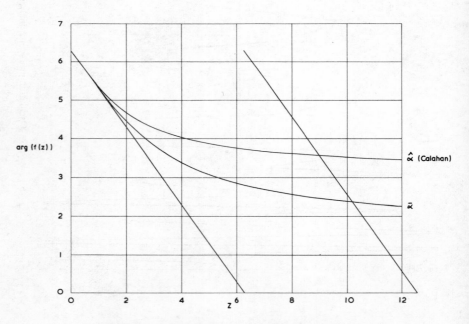

Figure 8.19   Argument plot: third-order Nørsett methods

range of natural periods the performance of the method is excellent. When the range of natural periods is large the method produces some amplification of the fundamental mode in the manner of the Crank–Nicolson method, but to a far less serious extent. The results are acceptable for many purposes. There is a 5 per cent elongation of the fundamental phase.

The third-order $\bar{\alpha}$ and $\hat{\alpha}$ methods previously examined in first-order problems are compared in Figures 8.18 and 8.19. The $\bar{\alpha}$ method has desirable properties, being somewhat similar to the better second-order method but with rather more damping. The $\hat{\alpha}$ Calahan method has considerable damping which was found to be unacceptable in practical analyses.

The results obtained using the third-order $\bar{\alpha}$ method are shown in Figures 8.20 and 8.21. In the problem with the small range of natural periods the mild damping of the method is clear, although the percentage amplitude decay is only half of that produced by the Wilson method with $\theta = 1\cdot4$. When the range of natural periods is large the mild damping associated with the method is again apparent. There is no perceptible elongation of the fundamental phase in this case.

8.3.4 Further remarks

In the above examples, the increased accuracy of the higher-order methods has again been purchased at a cost of some 10% increase in computation for each increase in order of method (Wilson's method is essentially a first-order method although it does involve slightly more work than the Crank–Nicolson method). The telling conclusion has been the quite dramatic effect of apparently minor damping in second-order problems. Methods like the Calahan method, or a linear rational approximation with $\alpha = 0\cdot55$, which work well in first-order problems, are quite useless in second-order problems. In this context, although there appears to be no simple rational approximation to the Wilson method, it is not surprising that small variations in θ have a considerable influence on the results obtained.

Two good Nørsett methods have been identified, namely the second-order $\bar{\alpha} = 1 - \frac{1}{2}\sqrt{2}$ method and a third-order $\bar{\alpha}$ method. Since these methods have different but predictable properties, analysing a problem by both of them may be a good way of determining probable bounds on the behaviour of a structure–soil system.

Most of the methods which have been subjected to numerical evaluation in this paper have been previously suggested in the mathematical literature. However, the present work shows that conventional stability and acceptability criteria do not necessarily lead to good engineering methods. Some suggested methods would be expensive, such as the Padé off-diagonal

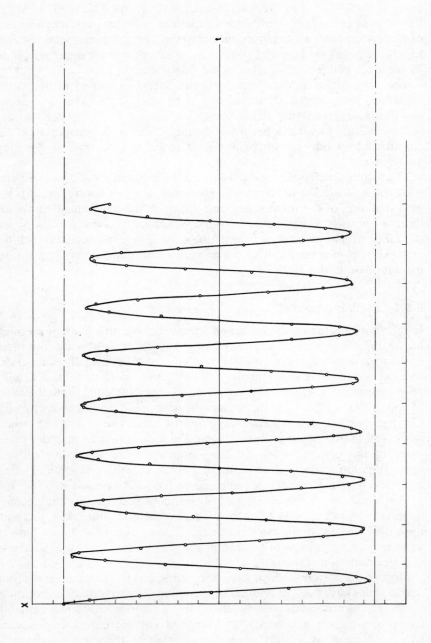

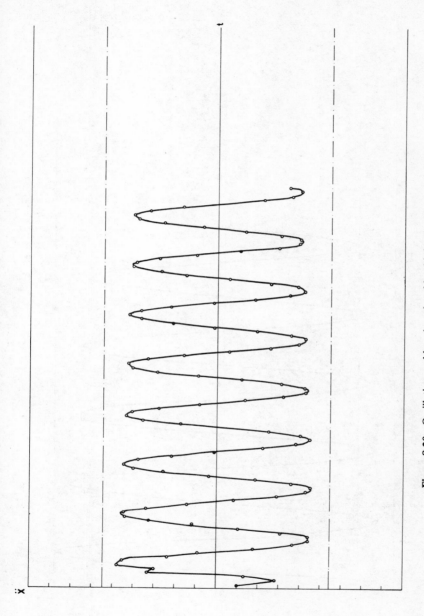

Figure 8.20 Oscillation problem 1 analysed by third-order Nørsett method

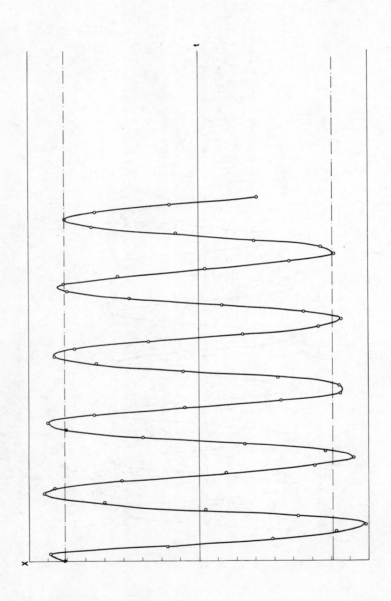

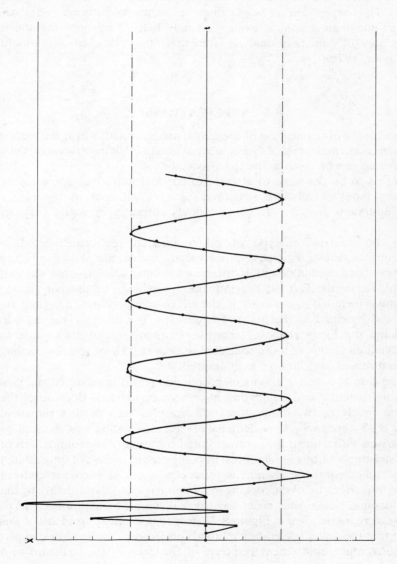

Figure 8.21 Oscillation problem 2 analysed by third-order Nørsett method

methods (Nassif, 1975), and have undesirable properties. Blue and Gummel (1970) have already pointed to the dangers of using Padé$_{N,N}$ methods when the eigenvalues are widely spaced in magnitude, but these methods have nevertheless been subsequently proposed (Trujillo, 1975). The expression of algorithms in terms of rational approximations and their graphical evaluation may help to advance the status of this area of numerical analysis from that of a 'black art' (Goudreau and Taylor, 1972).

8.3 APPLICATIONS

The main area of application of the above methods with which the author has been concerned is that of dynamic behaviour of offshore structures. Only brief details can be given in the space available.

It seems to be desirable to attempt to conduct finite element analyses of many types of offshore structures as a supplement to the rather crude minimum-degree-of-freedom models currently in vogue (Taylor, 1974).

For the steel-jacket type of oil production platform located in earthquake-sensitive regions, response spectra such as that shown in Figure 8.22 have been used in design. In this case the input accelerogram was that obtained during the Taft 1952 earthquake. It can be seen that when viscous damping is included in the analysis, the effects of algorithmic damping are slight and confined to the higher frequencies. The analysis was used to determine the likely range of sensitive frequencies and as a guide to potential liquefaction of loose cohesionless deposits. However, no coupling of structure and foundation was attempted.

In the case of concrete gravity oil production platforms coupled analyses involving structure and foundation have been conducted. Because of the expense involved, two-dimensional idealizations such as that shown in Figure 8.23 were used. The adequacy of the idealization was checked by comparison with a linear three-dimensional couterpart. The foundations of many structures of this kind at present being placed consist of intercalated beds of stiff clay and dense sand, but softer clay layers are encountered from time to time. Because of the rocking motion imparted to the structure by the wave loading, yielding can occur in weaker materials beneath the edges of the structure, as detailed in Figure 8.23. It is to non-linear problems of this nature that the direct integration methods previously described best apply. The horizontal displacement response of the deck of the structure to a typical parcel of waves for representative damping and added mass is shown in Figure 8.24.

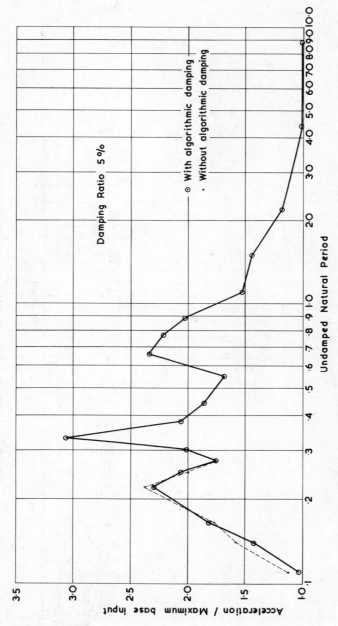

Figure 8.22 Acceleration response spectrum for steel offshore oil production platform

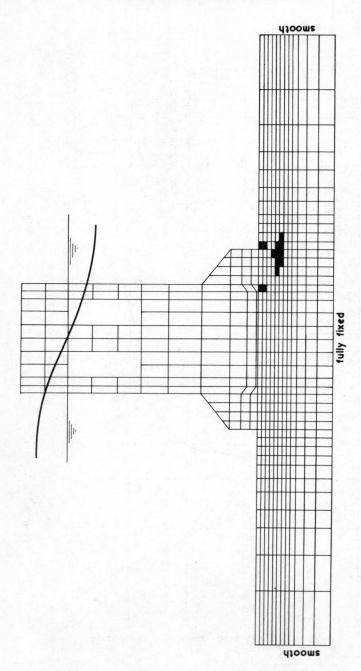

Figure 8.23 Idealization of concrete gravity platform/foundation system

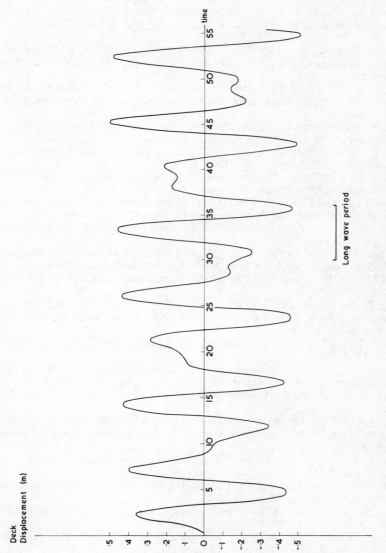

Figure 8.24 Horizontal deck displacement response of gravity platform subject to wave loading

REFERENCES

Argyris, J. H., Dunne, P. C., and Agelopoulos, T. (1973a). 'Non-linear oscillations using the finite element method', *Comp. Meth. Appl. Mech. Eng.*, **2**, 203–250.

Argyris, J. H., Dunne, P. C., and Agelopolous, T. (1973b). 'Dynamic response by large step integration', *Earthquake Engineering and Structural Dynamics*, **2**, 185–203.

Bathe, K. J. and Wilson, E. L. (1973a). 'Linear and non-linear earthquake analysis of complex structures', *Proc. 5th World Conf. on Earthquake Engineering, Rome*, Session 5B.

Bathe, K. J. and Wilson, E. L. (1973b). 'Stability and accuracy analysis of direct integration methods', *Earthquake Engineering and structural Dynamics*, **1**, 283–291.

Blue, J. L. and Gummel, K. (1970). 'Rational approximations to matrix exponential for systems of stiff differential equations', *J. Comp. Physics*, **5**, 70–83.

Desai, C. S. and Johnson, L. D. (1973). 'Evaluation of some numerical schemes for consolidation', *Int. J. Num. Meth. Eng.*, **7**, 243–254.

Donnelly, J. O. P. (1965). 'The Padé table in *Methods of numerical approximation*', Handscomb (ed.). Pergamon.

Finn, W. D. L. and Miller, R. I. S. (1973). 'Dynamic analysis of plane non-linear earth structures, *Proc. 5th World Conf. on Earthquake Engineering, Rome*.

Gear, C. W. (1971). *Numerical initial value problems in ordinary differential equations*, Prentice-Hall.

Goudreau, G. L. and Taylor, R. L. (1972). 'Evaluation of numerical integration methods in elastodynamics', *Comp. Meth. App. Mech. Eng.*, **2**, 65–98.

Graves-Morris, P. R. (ed.) (1973). *Padé Approximants and their Applications*, Academic Press.

Hwang, C. T., Morgenstern, N. R., *et al.* (1971). 'On solutions of plane strain consolidation problems by finite element methods', *Canadian Geotechnical Journal*, **8**, 109–118.

Lindberg, B. (1971). 'On smoothing and extrapolation for the trapezoidal rule', *B.I.T.*, **11**, 29–52.

Makinson, G. J. (1968), 'Stable high order implicit methods for the numerical solution of systems of differential equations', *The Computer Journal*, **2**, 3.

Mitchell, A. R. (1971). *Computational Methods in Partial Differential Equations*, Wiley.

Nassif, N. R. (1975). 'On the discretisation of the time variable in parabolic partial differential equations', *Conference on Finite Element Methods, Brunel University, England*.

Newmark, N. (1959). A method of computation for structural dynamics, *Proc. A.S.C.E.*, **85**, EM3.

Nørsett, S. P. (1974). 'One-step methods of Hermite type for numerical integration of stiff systems', *B.I.T.*, **14**.

Sandhu, R. S., and Wilson, E. L. (1969). Finite element analysis of seepage in elastic media, *Proc. A.S.C.E.*, **95**, EM3, 641–652.

Schiffman, R. L., Chen, A. T. F., and Jordan, J. G. (1969). 'An analysis of consolidation theories', *Proc. A.S.C.E.*, **95**, SM1, 285–312.

Siemientuch, J. L. and Gladwell, T. (1974). 'On time discretisations for linear time-dependent partial differential equations', *Numerical Analysis Report* No. 5, Dept. of Mathematics, University of Manchester.

Taylor, R. E. (1974). 'Structural dynamics of off-shore platforms', *Proc. I.C.E. Conference on Off-Shore Structures, London.*

Trujillo, D. M. (1975). 'The direct numerical integration of linear matrix differential equations using Padé approximations', *Int. J. Num. Meth. Eng*, **9**, 259–270.

Varga, R. S. (1961). *Matrix iterative analysis.* Prentice-Hall.

Wilson, E. L. (1968). 'A computer program for dynamic stress analysis of underground structures', *Structural Engineering Laboratory Report No. 68-1*, University of California, Berkeley.

Zienkiewicz, O. C. (1971). *The Finite Element Method in Engineering Science*, McGraw-Hill.

Zienkiewicz, O. C. and Lewis, R. W. (1973). 'An analysis of various time-stepping schemes for initial value problems', *Earthquake Engineering and Structural Dynamics*, **1**, 407–408.

Zlamal, M. (1973). 'Finite element methods for parabolic equations', *Proc. Conf. Numerical Solution of Differential Equations, Dundee*, 215–221.

Chapter 9

Generation and Dissipation of Pore-Water Pressures

A. Verruijt

9.1 INTRODUCTION

In this paper the application of the finite element method to determine stresses and deformations in a saturated soil is discussed. The starting point for such an analysis usually is the theory of linear consolidation (Biot, 1941; de Josselin de Jong, 1963). Non-linear soil behaviour will be discussed briefly, emphasizing dilatancy; that is a volume change due to a deviatoric stress.

9.2 LINEAR CONSOLIDATION

The phenomenon of deformation of a porous medium, accompanied by flow of the fluid in the pores through the medium, is called consolidation. The theory of linear consolidation is based on five basic concepts: conservation of mass of the pore fluid, Darcy's law for the flow of the fluid, equilibrium of the porous medium as a whole, Hooke's law for the deformation of the solid skeleton, and Terzaghi's principle of effective stress.

9.2.1 The pore fluid

For rather loose soils, such as sand or clay, it can be assumed that all deformations of the soil are due to a re-arrangement of the particles, and that these particles themselves are completely incompressible. If the pores are completely saturated with pore fluid, a decrease in volume of the soil must be accompanied by either a compression of the pore fluid or a net outflow of the fluid. It is usually sufficiently accurate to assume that the pore fluid is linearly compressible. Under the conditions formulated above the principle of conservation of mass of the pore fluid leads to the following basic equation (the so-called storage equation, de Josselin de Jong, 1963; Verruijt, 1969)

$$\frac{\partial e}{\partial t} = n\beta \frac{\partial \sigma}{\partial t} - q_{i,i} \tag{9.1}$$

293

Here e is the volume strain of the porous medium, n is the porosity, β is the compressibility of the pore fluid (for pure water the value of β is approximately $0\cdot5 \times 10^{-9}$ m^2/N), σ is the stress in the pore fluid, and q_i is the specific discharge vector of the pore fluid, with respect to the porous medium. The expression $q_{i,i}$ is the divergence of the specific discharge vector, the comma denoting partial differentiation, and summation over the three indices $i = 1, 2, 3$ being implied by the repetition of the index i.

The equation of motion of the pore fluid is Darcy's law,

$$q_i = \frac{\kappa}{\mu}\sigma_{,i} \tag{9.2}$$

where κ is the permeability of the porous medium (varying between 10^{-10} m^2 for a coarse sand and 10^{-16} m^2 for a dense clay), and μ is the dynamic viscosity of the pore fluid (for water at 20°C the value of μ is approximately 10^{-3} kg/ms). The pore stress σ in Equations (9.1) and (9.2) is considered to be the excess pore stress, with reference to an initial state in which the stresses are in equilibrium with gravity and possibly some other existing set of forces.

Substitution of Equation (9.2) into Equation (9.1) leads to the following differential equation

$$\frac{\partial}{\partial t}(u_{i,i}) - n\beta\frac{\partial\sigma}{\partial t} + \left(\frac{\kappa}{\mu}\sigma_{,i}\right)_{,i} = 0 \tag{9.3}$$

Here the volume strain e has been written as the divergence $(u_{i,i})$ of the displacement vector of the porous medium.

It may be mentioned that for civil engineering purposes Equation (9.3) can be considered to give a very accurate description of the real behaviour of a fluid in a deformable porous medium. The description of the mechanical behaviour of the porous medium, to be presented below, involves much larger errors.

9.2.2 The porous medium

For the description of the mechanical behaviour of the porous medium a linear stress–strain relationship will be used as a first approximation.

Equilibrium of the soil as a whole requires that

$$\sigma_{ij,i} + f_j = 0, \qquad (j = 1, 2, 3) \tag{9.4}$$

where σ_{ij} is the stress tensor, and f_j is the volume force. The stresses in the soil consist of the pore stress σ and the so-called effective stresses. These effective stresses are a measure for the concentrated forces in the contact points of the particles. The basic idea behind Terzaghi's concept of effective stress is that the deformations of a soil are determined by these contact forces. A certain stress in the pore fluid generates an equal stress in the particles (because they are surrounded by fluid), but this stress does not affect the deformations. The mathematical formulation of the principle of effective stress is

$$\sigma_{ij} = \sigma'_{ij} + \sigma\delta_{ij} \tag{9.5}$$

where σ'_{ij} is the effective stress tensor and δ_{ij} is Kronecker's delta.

The porous medium is now assumed to be an isotropic linear elastic material (this is the essential approximation in the theory). The relationship between the effective stresses and the displacement vector then is, assuming small deformations,

$$\sigma'_{ij} = G(u_{i,j} + u_{j,i}) + (K - \tfrac{2}{3}G)u_{k,k}\delta_{ij} \tag{9.6}$$

Here K and G are the compression modulus and the shear modulus of the porous medium (for engineering soils the values of these may be somewhere between $5 \times 10^6 \, \text{N/m}^2$ and $10^8 \, \text{N/m}^2$).

From Equations (9.5) and (9.6) the following expression for the total stresses can be deduced

$$\sigma_{ij} = G(u_{i,j} + u_{j,i}) + (K - \tfrac{2}{3}G)u_{k,k}\delta_{ij} + \sigma\delta_{ij} \tag{9.7}$$

Substitution of this expression into Equation (9.4) gives the equations of equilibrium expressed in terms of the displacements and the pore stress,

$$[G(u_{i,j} + u_{j,i})]_{,i} + [(K - \tfrac{2}{3}G)u_{k,k}]_{,j} + \sigma_{,j} + f_j = 0 \tag{9.8}$$

The Equations (9.3) and (9.8) together constitute the basic differential equations of the theory of linear consolidation. To these equations a set of initial conditions and boundary conditions has to be added. The initial condition is that at a certain instant of time (say at time $t = 0$) all variables are equal to zero. The differential equations describe the phenomena occurring due to a certain loading, applied after $t = 0$.

The boundary conditions are twofold: one for the porous medium, and one for the pore fluid. In many cases the boundary conditions for the porous medium are that on a certain part of the boundary (say S_1) the total stress vector is prescribed, and that on the remaining part of the boundary (say S_2) the displacement is prescribed. These boundary conditions can be formulated as follows,

$$\text{on} \quad S_1: \quad \sigma_{ij}n_i = t_j \tag{9.9}$$

$$\text{on} \quad S_2: \quad u_i = a_i \tag{9.10}$$

Here the vectors t_j and a_i are supposed to be given along the respective parts of the boundary.

The boundary conditions for the pore fluid that occur most frequently are that on a certain part of the boundary (say S_3) the pore stress is prescribed, and that on the remaining part of the boundary (say S_4) the flux is prescribed. The mathematical formulation of these boundary conditions is

$$\text{on} \quad S_3: \quad \sigma = g \tag{9.11}$$

$$\text{on} \quad S_4: \quad q_i n_i = h \tag{9.12}$$

where g is supposed to be given on S_3, and h is supposed to be given on S_4.

Equations (9.3) and (9.8), together with the initial condition and the boundary conditions (9.9) and (9.12), constitute a complete formulation of the phenomenon of linear consolidation. Under certain regularity conditions existence and uniqueness of the solution is ensured.

9.3 TIME STEP

The independent variables in the system of equations are the spatial coordinates (x_1, x_2, x_3) and the time t. An approximation to the spatial variations will be sought by finite elements. In order to approximate the variations with time the differential equations are integrated over a time step (from t_0 to $t_+ = t_0 + \Delta t$). The average value of a quantity, for instance the pore stress σ, is defined as follows

$$\bar{\sigma} = \frac{1}{\Delta t} \int_{t_0}^{t_+} \sigma \, \mathrm{d}t = \varepsilon \sigma^0 + (1 - \varepsilon)\sigma^+ \tag{9.13}$$

where $\sigma^0 = \sigma(t = t_0)$ and $\sigma^+ = \sigma(t = t_+)$. The parameter $\varepsilon \, (0 \le \varepsilon \le 1)$ is a constant depending upon the type of interpolation used. Linear interpolation corresponds to $\varepsilon = \frac{1}{2}$. Taking a value $\varepsilon = 1$ corresponds to the use of a forward difference, and $\varepsilon = 0$ corresponds to the use of a backward difference in a finite difference approximation. It has been shown that a sufficient condition for numerical stability is $\varepsilon \le \frac{1}{2}$ (Booker and Small, 1974).

The differential Equations (9.3) and (9.8) can now be transformed into

$$\bar{u}_{i,i} - u_{i,i}^0 - n\beta\bar{\sigma} + b\beta\sigma^0 + (1 - \varepsilon)\Delta t \left(\frac{\kappa}{\mu}\bar{\sigma}_{,i}\right)_{,i} = 0 \tag{9.14}$$

$$[G(\bar{u}_{i,j} + \bar{u}_{j,i})]_{,i} + [(K - \tfrac{2}{3}G)\bar{u}_{i,i}]_{,j} + \bar{\sigma}_{,j} + f_j = 0 \tag{9.15}$$

where the bar denotes the average of a quantity, as defined in Equation (9.13).

The boundary conditions [Equations (9.9) to (9.12)] can also be averaged over the time step. This does not change the form of these conditions, except that the quantities in the left and right hand members are transformed into averages.

The procedure for the elimination of the time derivatives described above (Verruijt, 1972) is practically identical to the procedure used by Sandhu and Wilson (1969), in which the approximation of the time derivative is introduced after the finite element approximation in space. The method used by Christian and Boehmer (1970) is essentially different in the treatment of the storage equation.

9.4 VARIATIONAL PRINCIPLE

The mathematical problem defined by the differential Equations (9.14) and (9.15) and the boundary conditions can be replaced by a variational principle. It can be shown that the solution of the problem is identical to the value of the variables v_i and τ for which the following quantity U has a stationary value,

$$U = \frac{1}{2} \int_V \left(\left(K - \frac{2}{3} G \right) v_{i,i} v_{j,j} + G(v_{i,j} + v_{j,i}) v_{i,j} - 2 f_i v_i \right.$$

$$\left. + 2\tau(v_{i,i} - u_{i,i}^0) - (1 - \varepsilon) \Delta t \frac{\kappa}{\mu} \tau_{,i} \tau_{,i} - n\beta\tau^2 + 2n\beta\tau\sigma^0 \right) dV$$

$$- \int_{S_1} t_i v_i \, dS + \int_{S_4} (1 - \varepsilon) \Delta t \, h \, dS \qquad (9.16)$$

Here v_i and τ are arbitrary functions throughout the volume V with the constraints

$$\text{on} \quad S_2: \quad v_i = a_i \qquad (9.17)$$

$$\text{on} \quad S_3: \quad \tau = g \qquad (9.18)$$

The proof that a stationary value of U occurs if $v_i = \bar{u}_i$ and $\tau = \bar{\sigma}$ can be given in the usual way (see any text on variational methods, for instance Courant and Hilbert, 1937).

9.5 FINITE ELEMENTS

Approximate solutions of the variational problem can be found with the aid of finite elements (see for instance Zienkiewicz, 1971). For two-dimensional problems of plane-strain consolidation a linear interpolation over triangular elements is appropriate. The displacement components and the pore stress are defined in the nodes. The effective stresses are constant in each element. The displacements and the pore stresses can be determined by solving a system of linear equations.

A computer program, in FORTRAN-IV, for the solution of plane strain consolidation is reproduced in the appendix. The main characteristics of the program are the following,

(1) All soil properties $(K, G, \kappa/\mu$ and $n\beta)$ are constants for each element.
(2) Body forces are exluded $(f_i = 0)$.
(3) The external loads are applied simultaneously, and they vary proportionally with time.
(4) The linear equations are solved by a method of frontal elimination (Verruijt, 1975).

Further characteristics are given in the Appendix.

In Figure (9.1) some results obtained with the program are represented. The example refers to the classical case of one-dimensional consolidation.

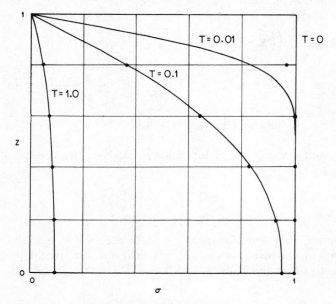

Figure 9.1 Isochrones for one-dimensional consolidation; numerical and analytical solution

The isochrones obtained by a finite element calculation, using 24 elements, are indicated by dots. The exact results, which can be found in most soil mechanics textbooks, are indicated by the fully-drawn lines. The quantity T is the dimensionless time parameter.

Results for a second example are shown in Figure 9.2. This example refers to a massive cylinder, drained along its circumference, and loaded by a radial

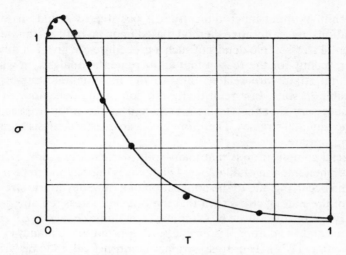

Figure 9.2 Consolidation of a massive cylinder; numerical and analytical solution

stress applied at time $t = 0$. The pore stress in the centre of the cylinder has been calculated using a network consisting of 88 elements and 55 nodal points. It appeared that time-steps can be taken progressively greater as consolidation proceeds. A computation using 14 time-steps took about 20 seconds for compilation on an IBM 360/65 computer, and 140 seconds for the actual computation. In Figure 9.2 the numerical results are compared with analytical results obtained by de Leeuw (1964).

The examples show that the numerical results are reasonably accurate. It should be mentioned, however, that in more complicated cases the accuracy may not be too good, depending upon the configuration and the magnitude of the time-step, especially in case of a sudden loading on a small part of the boundary.

9.6   DILATANCY

As mentioned above, the weakest link in the system of equations is the stress–strain relationship of the porous medium. It is well-known that soils do not behave as a linear elastic material. Usually in compression soils become gradually stiffer. In shear soils become gradually weaker, eventually failing when the ratio between deviatoric stress and isotropic stress approaches some critical value. Such a behaviour can be taken into account by a modification of the stress–strain relationship. More refined calculations can then be made by stepwise linear approximation of the stress–strain relationship. Without much difficulty it is possible to include irreversible deformations, by an iterative method, based upon an initial estimate for the incremental stresses. No details of such a procedure are given in this paper, however, mainly for the reason that an incremental analysis, in which the incremental strains are related only to the incremental stresses, seems inapplicable to soils. In a realistic description of the behaviour of soils it seems necessary that the strains are related to the total stresses as well as the incremental stresses. Therefore an elasto-plastic analysis seems to be more appropriate.

A special complication is that many soils, particularly sands, exhibit the so-called phenomenon of dilatancy. Dilatancy is understood to be a change of volume occurring due to the application of a pure deviatoric stress, i.e. a change of the state of stress such that the isotropic stress remains constant. Dilatancy can be introduced by assuming the volume change to consist of an elastic part and an additional isotropic part representing dilatancy (Verruijt, 1971; Kenter, 1974). The stress–strain relationship can then be written as

$$\sigma'_{ij} = G(u_{i,j} + u_{j,i}) + (K - \tfrac{2}{3}G)u_{k,k}\delta_{ij} - Ke^*\delta_{ij} \qquad (9.19)$$

where e^* is the additional volume change due to dilatancy. The stresses and the displacements in Equation (9.19) are considered to be incremental qualities occurring in a certain time-step. The dilatancy e^* depends on the absolute stresses and the shear deformation, for instance in the following way

$$e^* = |\Delta\gamma| \frac{\sin\psi - \sin\phi'}{1 - \sin\psi \sin\phi'} \qquad (9.20)$$

where ϕ' is a friction angle, and ψ is the mobilized angle of friction. The quantity $\Delta\gamma$ is an incremental shear strain invariant in the time· step considered. Equation (9.20) corresponds to Rowe's stress dilatancy equation (Rowe, 1962).

The introduction of the additional volume change due to dilatancy in the stress–strain relationship entails a modification of the variational principle. If it is assumed that e^* is a constant during a certain time step the modification of the functional U, as defined in Equation (9.16), consists of the addition of a term ΔU defined as follows (Kenter, 1974),

$$\Delta U = -\int Ke^* v_{i,i}\, dV \qquad (9.21)$$

Of course the volume change due to dilatancy e^* in a certain step is not known beforehand. Therefore this volume change has to be estimated, and the calculations have to be performed in an iterative way. The procedure followed in each iteration is sometimes called the initial strain method (Zienkiewicz, 1971). At present studies are being performed at the Delft Soil Mechanics Laboratory (L.G.M.) and at the Geotechnical Laboratory of the Delft University of Technology to investigate the validity and the convergence of the non-linear computations. The results of these investigations will be presented elsewhere.

APPENDIX

A computer program for linear plane strain consolidation

In this Appendix a computer program for the analysis of linear problems of plane-strain consolidation is reproduced. The program is based upon a sub-division of the field into triangular elements, with the displacement components and the pore stress defined in each node, and linear interpolation in the elements. This means that the effective stresses are constant in each element. It is assumed that all loads are applied in the same mutual ratio as functions of time. These loads can consist of combinations of horizontal and vertical displacements or forces. Thus, for instance, the two force components in a node may be given (in a free node these forces are zero), or the vertical force component and the horizontal displacement component may be given in a node. The condition on the pore fluid is that either there is no water supplied (in internal nodes or on an impermeable boundary), or the pore water stress is prescribed.

All input data are to be supplied from cards. A description of the input parameters is given in a separate list preceding the program.

It is to be noted that the values of the time parameter should be taken such that in each time step there is a reasonable progression of the consolidation phenomenon. For instance, in the case of Example 1 (see Figure 9.1) the first time-step can best be taken such that in that time step consolidation has progressed over approximately one element. This will be the case if the order of magnitude of the first time step is taken as follows

$$O(\Delta t) = \frac{(\Delta x)^2}{(\kappa/\mu)(K + \frac{4}{3}G)}$$

No precise prescription can be given. In general instabilities can be avoided by taking smaller time-steps, but it is to be noted that spatial instabilities can arise when the time-steps are taken too small.

In the computer program the pore stress is represented by a parameter TAU. In order to obtain a quantity of the same dimension as the displacement components a parameter W is introduced as W = TAU/ALPHA, with ALPHA = (COMPA + SHEARA)/0·75/CHARL. Here COMPA and

SHEARA are reference values for the compression modulus and the shear modulus (the most relevant values of the moduli in the field). CHARL is a reference length in the field, for instance an estimation of the average drainage length.

On the following pages a listing of the complete program is given, preceded by a list of input parameters.

List of input parameters

NAME	DESCRIPTION
NOD	NUMBER OF NODES.
NEL	NUMBER OF ELEMENTS.
NTIMES	NUMBER OF VALUES OF TIME PARAMETER, THE NUMBER OF TIME STEPS IS NTIMES–1.
CO(I, 1)	I = 1, . . . , NOD, X–COORDINATE OF NODE I.
CO(I, 2)	I = 1, . . . , NOD, Y–COORDINATE OF NODE I.
IT(I)	I = 1, . . . , NOD, INDICATOR FOR THE TYPE OF NODE I, IF (IABS(IT(I). EQ. 4) HORIZONTAL AND VERTICAL DISPLACEMENT PRESCRIBED, IF (IABS(IT(I). EQ. 3) HORIZONTAL FORCE AND VERTICAL DISPLACEMENT PRESCRIBED, IF (IABS(IT(I). EQ. 2) VERTICAL FORCE AND HORIZONTAL DISPLACEMENT PRESCRIBED, IF (IABS(IT(I). EQ. 1) HORIZONTAL AND VERTICAL FORCE PRESCRIBED, IF (IT(I). GT. 0) PORE WATER STRESS PRESCRIBED, IF (IT(I). LT. 0) NO WATER SUPPLY POSSIBLE.
DE(I, 1)	I = 1, . . . , NOD, HORIZONTAL COMPONENT OF PRESCRIBED DISPLACEMENT OF FORCE IN NODE I.
DF(I, 2)	I = 1, . . . , NOD, VERTICAL COMPONENT OF PRESCRIBED DISPLACEMENT OR FORCE IN NODE I.
NL(J, 1)	J = 1, . . . , NEL, FIRST NODE OF ELEMENT J.
NL(J, 2)	J = 1, . . . , NEL, SECOND NODE OF ELEMENT J.
NL(J, 3)	J = 1, . . . , NEL, THIRD NODE OF ELEMENT J.
PAR(J, 1)	J = 1, . . . , NEL, COMPRESSION MODULUS IN ELEMENT J.
PAR(J, 2)	J = 1, . . . , NEL, SHEAR MODULUS IN ELEMENT J.
PAR(J, 3)	J = 1, . . . , NEL, PERMEABILITY/VISCOSITY IN ELEMENT J. (OR HYDR. CONDUCTIVITY/VOL. WEIGHT)
PAR(J, 4)	J = 1, . . . , NEL, POROSITY*FLUID COMPRESSIBILITY IN ELEMENT J.
TIMES(K)	K = 1, . . . , NTIMES, VALUES OF TIME PARAMETER,
FAC(K)	K = 1, . . . , NTIMES, MULTIPLICATION FACTOR FOR PRESCRIBED DISPLACEMENTS OR FORCES AS A FUNCTION OF TIME. AT TIME = TIMES(K) THE PRESCRIBED DISPLACEMENTS OR FORCES ARE DF(I,1)*FAC(K) AND DF(I, 2)*FAC(K).

NOUT(K)   K = 1, . . . , NTIMES, OUTPUT PARAMETER,
                    IF (NOUT(K). GE. 0) THE DISPLACEMENTS AND
                    STRESSES AT TIME = TIMES(KKK) ARE PRINTED.
COMPA   REFERENCE VALUE FOR COMPRESSION MODULUS.
SHEARA   REFERENCE VALUE FOR SHEAR MODULUS.
CHARL   REFERENCE LENGTH IN THE PLANE.
EPS   AVERAGING FACTOR.


```
C       **********************************
C       *****                      *****
C       *****  PROGRAM PSC-1  *****
C       *****                      *****
C       **********************************
C
C
C       PLANE STRAIN CONSOLIDATION
C       ARNOLD VERRUIJT
C       DEPARTMENT OF CIVIL ENGINEERING
C       UNIVERSITY OF TECHNOLOGY
C       DELFT, THE NETHERLANDS
C       NOVEMBER 1975
C
C       NO RESPONSIBILITY FOR EVENTUAL ERRORS ACCEPTED
C
C
C
C       *****  DECLARATION BLOCK  ********************
C
        COMMON/LIST1/CO(200,2),PAR(350,4)
        COMMON/LIST2/AA(200,15,3,3)
        COMMON/LIST3/UA(200),VA(200),WA(200)
        COMMON/LIST4/U(200),V(200),TXX(350),TYY(350),TXY(350)
        COMMON/LIST5/IT(200)
        COMMON/LIST6/DF(200,2)
        COMMON/LIST7/NL(350,3)
        COMMON/LIST8/KT(200,15)
        COMMON/LIST9/NLM(200,9)
        COMMON/LIST10/IOR(200)
        DIMENSION W(200),TAU(200),TAUA(200)
        DIMENSION TIMES(50),FAC(50),NOUT(50)
        DIMENSION KTP(200,15),NLMP(200,9)
        NODMAX=200
        NELMAX=350
        KTMAX=15
        NLMMAX=9
        NTIMAX=50
C
C       *****  END DECLARATION BLOCK  ***************
C
C       *****  INPUT  ******************************
C
        READ(5,1) NOD,NEL,NTIMES
      1 FORMAT(3I6)
C
C               STORAGE CHECK
C
        I=0
```

```
      IF(NOD.LE.NODMAX) GOTO 2
      I=2
      WRITE(6,3) NODMAX,NOD
    3 FORMAT(1H0,' CHANGE VALUE',I6,' IN DECLARATION BLOCK INTO',I6)
    2 IF(NEL.LE.NELMAX) GOTO 4
      I=2
      WRITE(6,3) NELMAX,NEL
    4 IF(NTIMES.LE.NTIMAX) GOTO 5
      I=2
      WRITE(6,3) NTIMAX,NTIMES
    5 IF(I.GT.1) GOTO 999
C
C           END STORAGE CHECK
C
      DO 6 I=1,NOD
      READ(5,7) CO(I,1),CO(I,2),IT(I),DF(I,1),DF(I,2)
    7 FORMAT(2F12.6,I3,2F12.6)
      U(I)=0.0
      V(I)=0.0
      TAU(I)=0.0
      UA(I)=0.0
      VA(I)=0.0
      TAUA(I)=0.0
      DO 8 J=1,KTMAX
    8 KT(I,J)=0
      DO 9 J=1,NLMMAX
    9 NLM(I,J)=0
    6 CONTINUE
      DO 10 J=1,NEL
      READ(5,11) (NL(J,K),K=1,3),(PAR(J,K),K=1,4)
   11 FORMAT(3I6,4F12.6)
   10 CONTINUE
      DO 12 K=1,NTIMES
      READ(5,13) TIMES(K),FAC(K),NOUT(K)
   13 FORMAT(2F12.6,I3)
   12 CONTINUE
      READ(5,14) COMPA,SHEARA,CHARL,EPS
   14 FORMAT(4F12.6)
      T=0.001/(COMPA+SHEARA/0.75)
      DO 15 J=1,NEL
   15 IF(PAR(J,4).LT.T) PAR(J,4)=T
      ALPHA=(COMPA+SHEARA/0.75)/CHARL
      ALPHAA=1.0/ALPHA
      EPSA=1.0-EPS
      EPSB=1.0/EPSA
C
C     ***** END INPUT ****************************
C
C     ***** OUTPUT OF INPUT DATA *****************
C
      WRITE(6,16)
   16 FORMAT(1H1,' PLANE STRAIN CONSOLIDATION'/
     1' PROGRAM PSC-1')
      I=1
   17 K=1
      WRITE(6,18)
   18 FORMAT(1H1,' COORDINATES OF NODES')
      WRITE(6,19)
```

```
19 FORMAT(1H0,'    NODE       X           Y          IT',
  1'     HOR           VER'/)
20 WRITE(6,21) I,CO(I,1),CO(I,2),IT(I),DF(I,1),DF(I,2)
21 FORMAT(1H ,I6,2F12.6,I6,2F12.6)
   I=I+1
   K=K+1
   IF(I.GT.NOD) GOTO 22
   IF(K.GT.50) GOTO 17
   GOTO 20
22 J=1
23 K=1
   WRITE(6,24)
24 FORMAT(1H1,' PROPERTIES OF ELEMENTS')
   WRITE(6,25)
25 FORMAT(1H0,' ELEMENT          NODES        COMP',
  1'        SHEAR        PERM         BETAN'/)
26 WRITE(6,27) J,(NL(J,K),K=1,3),(PAR(J,K),K=1,4)
27 FORMAT(1H ,I6,I8,2I6,4F12.6)
   J=J+1
   K=K+1
   IF(J.GT.NEL) GOTO 28
   IF(K.GT.50) GOTO 23
   GOTO 26
28 CONTINUE
C
C    ***** END OUTPUT OF INPUT DATA *************
C
C    ***** CALCULATION OF KT AND NLM ***********
C
   CALL KONTAK(NOD,NEL,II)
   IF(II) 29,29,30
30 WRITE(6,31)
31 FORMAT(1H1,' OVERFLOW. INCREASE THE VALUE OF KTMAX'/
  1' IN DECLARATION BLOCK, THE VALUE OF M IN STATEMENT'/
  2' 100 IN SUBROUTINE KONTAK, AND THE SECOND DIMENSION'/
  3' IN LIST8.')
   GOTO 999
29 CALL STRUCT(NOD,NEL,II)

   IF(II) 32,32,33
33 WRITE(6,34)
34 FORMAT(1H1,' OVERFLOW. INCREASE THE VALUE OF NLMMAX'/
  1' IN DECLARATION BLOCK, THE VALUE OF MM IN STATEMENT'/
  2' 100 IN SUBROUTINE STRUCT, AND THE SECOND DIMENSION'/
  3' IN LIST9.')
   GOTO 999
32 DO 35 I=1,NOD
   DO 36 J=1,KTMAX
36 KTP(I,J)=KT(I,J)
   DO 37 J=1,NLMMAX
37 NLMP(I,J)=NLM(I,J)
35 CONTINUE
C
C    ***** START OF MAIN PROGRAM ***************
C
   NSTEPS=NTIMES-1
   DO 38 KKK=1,NSTEPS
   KKK1=KKK+1
   STEP=TIMES(KKK1)-TIMES(KKK)
   DO 39 I=1,NOD
39 WA(I)=TAUA(I)*ALPHAA
```

```
C
C               GENERATION OF MATRIX
C
        DO 40 I=1,NOD
        DO 41 J=1,KTMAX
        KT(I,J)=KTP(I,J)
        DO 41 K=1,3
        DO 41 L=1,3
     41 AA(I,J,K,L)=0.0
        DO 42 J=1,NLMMAX
     42 NLM(I,J)=NLMP(I,J)
     40 CONTINUE
        CALL MATRIX(NOD,NEL,KTMAX,STEP,ALPHA,EPS)
C
C               INCORPORATION OF BOUNDARY CONDITIONS
C
        FACT=EPS*FAC(KKK)+EPSA*FAC(KKK1)
        CALL BOUND(NOD,KTMAX,FACT)
C
C               SOLUTION BY FRONTAL ELIMINATION
C
        CALL FRONT3(NOD,3,II,KKK)
        IF(II.LT.0) GOTO 43
        WRITE(6,31)
        GOTO 999
     43 CONTINUE
C
C               DISPLACEMENTS AND PORE STRESS
C
        DO 44 I=1,NOD
        U(I)=AA(I,KTMAX,1,1)
        V(I)=AA(I,KTMAX,2,2)
        TAU(I)=ALPHA*AA(I,KTMAX,3,3)
        UA(I)=UA(I)+EPSB*(U(I)-UA(I))
        VA(I)=VA(I)+EPSB*(V(I)-VA(I))
        TAUA(I)=TAUA(I)+EPSB*(TAU(I)-TAUA(I))
        U(I)=UA(I)
        V(I)=VA(I)
     44 TAU(I)=TAUA(I)
C
C               EFFECTIVE STRESSES
C
        CALL STRESS(NOD,NEL)
C
C               OUTPUT
C
        IF(NOUT(KKK1).LT.1) GOTO 38
        I=1
     45 K=1
        WRITE(6,46) TIMES(KKK1)
     46 FORMAT(1H1,' TIME =',F12.6)
        WRITE(6,47)
     47 FORMAT(1H0,' DISPLACEMENTS AND PORE STRESS'//
       1'            X            Y            U',
       2'            V            TAU'/)
     48 WRITE(6,49) I,CO(I,1),CO(I,2),U(I),V(I),TAU(I)
     49 FORMAT(1H ,I6,5F12.5)
        I=I+1
        K=K+1
```

```
      IF(I.GT.NOD) GOTO 50
      IF(K.GT.50) GOTO 45
      GOTO 48
   50 J=1
   51 K=1
      WRITE(6,46) TIMES(KKK1)
      WRITE(6,52)
   52 FORMAT(1H0,' EFFECTIVE STRESSES'//
     1'          ELEMENT        TXX           TYY',
     2'          TXY'/)
   53 WRITE(6,54) (NL(J,K),K=1,3),TXX(J),TYY(J),TXY(J)
   54 FORMAT(1H ,3I6,3F12.5)
      J=J+1
      K=K+1
      IF(J.GT.NEL) GOTO 55
      IF(K.GT.50) GOTO 51
      GOTO 53
   55 CONTINUE
   38 CONTINUE
  999 CONTINUE
      STOP
      END
```

```
      SUBROUTINE KONTAK(NOD,NEL,II)
C         THIS SUBROUTINE CALCULATES THE COEFFICIENTS OF
C         THE MATRIX OF NODAL CONTACTS, KT, FROM THE
C         STRUCTURE OF ELEMENTS IN A MESH OF TRIANGLES,
C         AS DEFINED BY THE MATRIX NL.
C         NL(I,1), NL(I,2) AND NL(I,3) ARE THE THREE
C         NODES THAT TOGETHER CONSTITUTE ELEMENT I.
C         KT(J,1)=J,
C         KT(J,M) IS THE NUMBER OF NODES THAT ARE IN ONE
C         ELEMENT WITH NODE J, PLUS ONE,
C         KT(J,K), K=2,3,...,KT(J,M), ARE THE NODE NUMBERS
C         OF THE NODES THAT ARE IN ONE ELEMENT WITH NODE J.
      COMMON/LIST7/NL(350,3)
      COMMON/LIST8/KT(200,15)
C         NOD AND NEL MUST NOT BE GREATER THAN THE FIRST
C         DIMENSIONS IN LIST8 AND LIST7, RESPECTIVELY.
      II=-1
  100 M=15
      DO 1 I=1,NOD
      KT(I,1)=I
      KT(I,M)=1
      K=1
      DO 2 J=1,NEL
      DO 3 N=1,3
      IF(NL(J,N).EQ.I) GOTO 4
    3 CONTINUE
      GOTO 2
    4 DO 5 N=1,3
      JJ=NL(J,N)
      DO 6 L=1,K
      IF(KT(I,L).EQ.JJ) GOTO 5
    6 CONTINUE
      K=K+1
      IF(K.EQ.M) GOTO 7
      KT(I,K)=JJ
      KT(I,M)=K
    5 CONTINUE
    2 CONTINUE
    1 CONTINUE
      GOTO 8
    7 II=1
C         II=1 INDICATES THAT THE SECOND DIMENSION
C         IN LIST8 IS TOO SMALL, OTHERWISE II=-1.
C         IF(II.EQ.1) THE SECOND DIMENSION IN LIST8
C         AND THE VALUE OF M IN STATEMENT 100 MUST
C         BE INCREASED.
    8 RETURN
      END
```

```
      SUBROUTINE STRUCT(NOD,NEL,II)
C         THIS SUBROUTINE CALCULATES THE COEFFICIENTS OF
C         THE MATRIX INDICATING THE ELEMENTS IN WHICH
C         EACH NODE IS CONTAINED, NLM, FROM THE STRUCTURE
C         OF ELEMENTS IN A TRIANGULAR MESH, AS DEFINED
C         BY THE MATRIX NL.
C         NL(I,1), NL(I,2) AND NL(I,3) ARE THE THREE
C         NODES THAT TOGETHER CONSTITUTE ELEMENT I.
C         NLM(J,MM) IS THE NUMBER OF ELEMENTS THAT
C         CONTAIN NODE J,
C         NLM(J,K), K=1,2,...,NLM(J,MM), ARE THE ELEMENT
C         NUMBERS OF THE ELEMENTS THAT CONTAIN NODE J.
      COMMON/LIST7/NL(350,3)
      COMMON/LIST9/NLM(200,9)
C         NOD AND NEL MUST NOT BE GREATER THAN THE FIRST
C         DIMENSIONS IN LIST9 AND LIST7, RESPECTIVELY.
  100 MM=9
      II=-1
      DO 1 I=1,NOD
      NLM(I,MM)=0
      DO 2 J=1,NEL
      DO 3 K=1,3
      IF(NL(J,K).EQ.I) GOTO 4
    3 CONTINUE
      GOTO 2
    4 K=NLM(I,MM)+1
      IF(K.EQ.MM) GOTO 5
      NLM(I,MM)=K
      NLM(I,K)=J
    2 CONTINUE
    1 CONTINUE
      GOTO 6
    5 II=1
C         II=1 INDICATES THAT THE SECOND DIMENSION
C         IN LIST9 IS TOO SMALL, OTHERWISE II=-1.
C         IF(II.EQ.1) THE SECOND DIMENSION IN LIST9
C         AND THE VALUE OF MM IN STATEMENT 100 MUST
C         BE INCREASED.
    6 RETURN
      END
```

```
      SUBROUTINE MATRIX(NOD,NEL,KTMAX,STEP,ALPHA,EPS)
C         THIS SUBROUTINE GENERATES THE MATRIX AND THE
C         RIGHT HAND SIDE OF THE SYSTEM OF EQUATIONS.
      COMMON/LIST1/CO(200,2),PAR(350,4)
      COMMON/LIST2/AA(200,15,3,3)
      COMMON/LIST3/UA(200),VA(200),WA(200)
      COMMON/LIST7/NL(350,3)
      COMMON/LIST8/KT(200,15)
      DIMENSION B(3),C(3),D(3),X(3),Y(3)
      DIMENSION A(3,3,3,3),F(3,3)
      ALPHAS=ALPHA*ALPHA
      EPS1=1.0-EPS
      DO 1 I=1,NEL
      DO 2 K=1,3
      J=NL(I,K)
      X(K)=CO(J,1)
    2 Y(K)=CO(J,2)
      B(1)=Y(2)-Y(3)
      B(2)=Y(3)-Y(1)
      B(3)=Y(1)-Y(2)
      C(1)=X(3)-X(2)
      C(2)=X(1)-X(3)
      C(3)=X(2)-X(1)
      D(1)=X(2)*Y(3)-X(3)*Y(2)
      D(2)=X(3)*Y(1)-X(1)*Y(3)
      D(3)=X(1)*Y(2)-X(2)*Y(1)
      A2=0.5*(X(1)*B(1)+X(2)*B(2)+X(3)*B(3))
      AREA=ABS(A2)
      AP=0.25/AREA
      AS=AP*ALPHA
      AE=EPS1*AP*ALPHAS*STEP*PAR(I,3)
      AF=AP*ALPHAS*PAR(I,4)
      ZX=X(1)+X(2)+X(3)
      ZY=Y(1)+Y(2)+Y(3)
      ZXX=(X(1)*X(1)+X(2)*X(2)+X(3)*X(3)+ZX*ZX)/12.0
      ZYY=(Y(1)*Y(1)+Y(2)*Y(2)+Y(3)*Y(3)+ZY*ZY)/12.0
      ZXY=(X(1)*Y(1)+X(2)*Y(2)+X(3)*Y(3)+ZX*ZY)/12.0
      ZX=ZX/3.0
      ZY=ZY/3.0
      DO 3 K=1,3
      KK=NL(I,K)
      DO 3 L=1,3
      LL=NL(I,L)
      BB=B(K)*B(L)
      BC=B(K)*C(L)
      BD=B(K)*D(L)
      CB=C(K)*B(L)
      CC=C(K)*C(L)

      CD=C(K)*D(L)
      DB=D(K)*B(L)
      DC=D(K)*C(L)
      DD=D(K)*D(L)
      GK=PAR(I,1)-PAR(I,2)/1.5
      GG=PAR(I,2)
      A(K,L,1,1)=AP*((GK+2.0*GG)*BB+GG*CC)
      A(K,L,1,2)=AP*(GK*BC+GG*CB)
      A(K,L,1,3)=AS*(BB*ZX+BC*ZY+BD)
      A(L,K,2,1)=A(K,L,1,2)
      A(K,L,2,2)=AP*((GK+2.0*GG)*CC+GG*BB)
```

```
      A(K,L,2,3)=AS*(CB*ZX+CC*ZY+CD)
      A(L,K,3,1)=A(K,L,1,3)
      A(L,K,3,2)=A(K,L,2,3)
      F(K,L)=AF*(BB*ZXX+(BC+CB)*ZXY+CC*ZYY+(BD+DB)*ZX+(CD+DC)*ZY+DD)
      A(K,L,3,3)=-AE*(BB+CC)-F(K,L)
    3 CONTINUE
      DO 4 J=1,3
      JJ=NL(I,J)
      II=KT(JJ,KTMAX)
      DO 5 K=1,II
      DO 6 L=1,3
      IF(NL(I,L).EQ.KT(JJ,K)) GOTO 7
      GOTO 6
    7 DO 8 KK=1,3
      DO 8 LL=1,3
    8 AA(JJ,K,KK,LL)=AA(JJ,K,KK,LL)+A(J,L,KK,LL)
      GOTO 5
    6 CONTINUE
    5 CONTINUE
    4 CONTINUE
      DO 9 K=1,3
      KK=NL(I,K)
      DO 9 L=1,3
      LL=NL(I,L)
      A1=A(K,L,3,1)*UA(LL)+A(K,L,3,2)*VA(LL)-F(K,L)*WA(LL)
    9 AA(KK,KTMAX,3,3)=AA(KK,KTMAX,3,3)+A1
    1 CONTINUE
      RETURN
      END
```

```
      SUBROUTINE BOUND(NOD,KTMAX,FACT)
C        THIS SUBROUTINE INCORPORATES THE BOUNDARY
C        CONDITIONS INTO THE SYSTEM OF EQUATIONS.
      COMMON/LIST2/AA(200,15,3,3)
      COMMON/LIST3/UA(200),VA(200),WA(200)
      COMMON/LIST5/IT(200)
      COMMON/LIST6/DF(200,2)
      M=KTMAX
      DO 1 I=1,NOD
      IF(IABS(IT(I)).EQ.4) GOTO 1
      IF(IABS(IT(I)).EQ.3)   GOTO 2
      AA(I,M,2,2)=AA(I,M,2,2)+DF(I,2)*FACT
    2 AA(I,M,1,1)=AA(I,M,1,1)+DF(I,1)*FACT
    1 CONTINUE
      DO 3 I=1,NOD
      IF(IABS(IT(I)).LT.3) GOTO 4
      K=2
      A1=DF(I,2)*FACT
      IBACK=IABS(IT(I))
      GOTO 5
    4 IF(IABS(IT(I)).LT.2) GOTO 6
      K=1
      A1=DF(I,1)*FACT
      IBACK=3
      GOTO 5
    6 IF(IT(I).LT.0) GOTO 3
      K=3
      A1=WA(I)
      IBACK=2
    5. DO 7 J=1,M
      DO 7 L=1,3
    7 AA(I,J,K,L)=0.0
      AA(I,1,K,K)=1.0
      AA(I,M,K,K)=A1
      IF(IBACK-3) 3,6,4
    3 CONTINUE
      RETURN
      END
```

```
      SUBROUTINE FRONT3(NOD,NV,III,JJJ)
C         THIS SUBROUTINE SOLVES THE SYSTEM OF
C         EQUATIONS, BY FRONTAL ELIMINATION.
      COMMON/LIST2/A(200,15,3,3)
      COMMON/LIST8/KT(200,15)
      COMMON/LIST9/NLM(200,9)
      COMMON/LIST10/IOR(200)
      DIMENSION IROLL(105),NLM1(105)
      DIMENSION CC(3,3)
C         NOD MUST NOT BE GREATER THAN THE FIRST DIMENSION
C         IN THE COMMON STATEMENTS AND THE DIMENSION IN
C         THE FIRST DIMENSION STATEMENT.
C         NV MUST NOT BE GREATER THAN THE LAST TWO
C         DIMENSIONS IN THE COMMON STATEMENT LIST2, AND THE
C         LAST DIMENSION STATEMENT.
      III=-1
  100 M=15
      MM=9
      DO 1 I=1,NOD
      NLM1(I)=NLM(I,MM)
    1 IROLL(I)=-1
C         A NEGATIVE VALUE OF IROLL(I) INDICATES THAT THE
C         VARIABLES IN NODE I HAVE NOT YET BEEN ELIMINATED.
      DO 2 I=1,NOD
      IF(JJJ.GT.1) GOTO 3
C         IF(JJJ.GT.1) THE ORDER OF ELIMINATION IS GIVEN
C         BEFOREHAND IN THE VECTOR IOR.
      K=M
      L=MM+1
      DO 4 J=1,NOD
      IF(IROLL(J)) 5,4,4
    5 IF(KT(J,M)-M) 6,7,7
    6 IF(NLM(J,MM)-L) 8,9,4
    8 L=NLM(J,MM)
      KK=J
      K=KT(J,M)
      GOTO 4
    9 IF(KT(J,M)-K) 10,4,4
   10 KK=J
      K=KT(J,M)
    4 CONTINUE
      IROLL(KK)=1
      IOR(I)=KK
      KC=KT(KK,M)
C         KK IS THE NODE NUMBER OF THE NODE HAVING THE
C         SMALLEST VALUE OF NLM(J,MM), AND FROM THE
C         NODES HAVING THAT VALUE OF NLM(J,MM) THE
C         ONE HAVING THE SMALLEST VALUE OF KT(J,M).
C         IN CASE THERE ARE SEVERAL NODES SHARING
C         THESE PROPERTIES KK IS THE SMALLEST OF THESE.
C         KK IS THE NODE NUMBER OF THE VARIABLES TO
C         BE ELIMINATED. THIS NODE HAS KC CONTACTS.
      LL=NLM1(KK)
      DO 11 J=1,LL
      KI=NLM(KK,J)
      IF(KI.EQ.0) GOTO 11
      DO 12 KJ=2,KC
      KL=KT(KK,KJ)
      KM=NLM1(KL)
```

```
      DO 13 KN=1,KM
      LN=NLM(KL,KN)
      IF(LN.EQ.KI) GOTO 14
      GOTO 13
   14 NLM(KL,MM)=NLM(KL,MM)-1
      NLM(KL,KN)=0
      GOTO 12
   13 CONTINUE
   12 CONTINUE
   11 CONTINUE
    3 KK=IOR(I)
      KC=KT(KK,M)
      DO 15 KV=1,NV
      C=1.0/A(KK,1,KV,KV)
      DO 16 II=1,KC
      DO 16 LV=1,NV
   16 A(KK,II,KV,LV)=C*A(KK,II,KV,LV)
      A(KK,M,KV,KV)=C*A(KK,M,KV,KV)
      DO 17 LV=1,NV
      IF(LV.EQ.KV) GOTO 17
      C=A(KK,1,LV,KV)
      DO 18 II=1,KC
      DO 18 IJ=1,NV
   18 A(KK,II,LV,IJ)=A(KK,II,LV,IJ)-C*A(KK,II,KV,IJ)
      A(KK,M,LV,LV)=A(KK,M,LV,LV)-C*A(KK,M,KV,KV)
   17 CONTINUE
   15 CONTINUE
      IF(KC.EQ.1) GOTO 2
C         IF(KC.EQ.1) NO FURTHER ELIMINATION NECESSARY
      DO 19 J=2,KC
      JJ=KT(KK,J)
      L=KT(JJ,M)
      DO 20 JK=2,L
      IF(KT(JJ,JK).EQ.KK) GOTO 21
   20 CONTINUE
   21 DO 22 KV=1,NV
      DO 22 LV=1,NV
   22 CC(KV,LV)=A(JJ,JK,KV,LV)
C         THESE ARE THE MULTIPLICATION FACTORS.
      KT(JJ,JK)=KT(JJ,L)
      KT(JJ,L)=0
      DO 23 KV=1,NV
      DO 23 LV=1,NV
      A(JJ,JK,KV,LV)=A(JJ,L,KV,LV)
      A(JJ,L,KV,LV)=0.0
C         VARIABLES SHIFTED.
   23 A(JJ,M,LV,LV)=A(JJ,M,LV,LV)-CC(LV,KV)*A(KK,M,KV,KV)
C         RIGHT HAND SIDE ADJUSTED.
      L=L-1
      KT(JJ,M)=L
C         POINTER MATRIX ADJUSTED.
      DO 24 II=2,KC
      DO 25 IJ=1,L
      IF(KT(JJ,IJ).EQ.KT(KK,II)) GOTO 26
   25 CONTINUE
C         CONTINUED HERE IF VARIABLE KT(KK,II) IS NOT
C         IN ROW JJ.
      L=L+1
      IJ=L
```

```
       KT(JJ,M)=L
       KT(JJ,IJ)=KT(KK,II)
C         NOW VARIABLE KT(KK,II) IS IN ROW JJ, IN
C         POSITION IJ.
   26 DO 27 KV=1,NV
       DO 27 LV=1,NV
       DO 27 JV=1,NV
   27 A(JJ,IJ,KV,LV)=A(JJ,IJ,KV,LV)-CC(KV,JV)*A(KK,II,JV,LV)
   24 CONTINUE
   19 CONTINUE
    2 CONTINUE
C         BACK SUBSTITUTION
       DO 28 I=1,NOD
       J=IOR(NOD+1-I)
       L=KT(J,M)
       IF(L.EQ.1) GOTO 28
       DO 29 K=2,L
       JJ=KT(J,K)
       DO 29 KV=1,NV
       DO 29 LV=1,NV
   29 A(J,M,KV,KV)=A(J,M,KV,KV)-A(J,K,KV,LV)*A(JJ,M,LV,LV)
   28 CONTINUE
       GOTO 30
    7 III=1
   30 RETURN
       END
```

```
      SUBROUTINE STRESS(NOD,NEL)
C         THIS SUBROUTINE CALCULATES THE COMPONENTS OF THE
C         EFFECTIVE STRESS TENSOR IN EACH ELEMENT.
      COMMON/LIST1/CO(200,2),PAR(350,4)
      COMMON/LIST4/U(200),V(200),TXX(350),TYY(350),TXY(350)
      COMMON/LIST7/NL(350,3)
      DIMENSION B(3),C(3),X(3),Y(3)
      DO 1 I=1,NEL
      DO 2 K=1,3
      J=NL(I,K)
      X(K)=CO(J,1)
    2 Y(K)=CO(J,2)
      B(1)=Y(2)-Y(3)
      B(2)=Y(3)-Y(1)
      B(3)=Y(1)-Y(2)
      C(1)=X(3)-X(2)
      C(2)=X(1)-X(3)
      C(3)=X(2)-X(1)
      A1=X(1)*B(1)+X(2)*B(2)+X(3)*B(3)
      A2=(3.0*PAR(I,1)-2.0*PAR(I,2))/(6.0*PAR(I,2))
      T1=0.0
      T2=0.0
      T3=0.0
      DO 3 J=1,3
      K=NL(I,J)
      T1=T1+B(J)*U(K)
      T2=T2+C(J)*V(K)
    3 T3=T3+B(J)*V(K)+C(J)*U(K)
      TXX(I)=2.0*PAR(I,2)*(T1+A2*(T1+T2))/A1
      TYY(I)=2.0*PAR(I,2)*(T2+A2*(T1+T2))/A1
      TXY(I)=PAR(I,2)*T3/A1
    1 CONTINUE
      RETURN
      END
```

REFERENCES

Biot, M. A. (1941). 'General theory of three-dimensional consolidation', *J. Appl. Phys.*, **12**, 155–164.

Booker, J. R. and Small, J. C. (1974). 'An investigation of the stability of numerical solutions of Biot's equations of consolidation', *Res. Report No. R*.235, Civil Engineering Laboratories, The University of Sydney, Sydney.

Christian, J. J. and Boehmer, J. W. (1970). 'Plane strain consolidation by finite elements', *J. Soil Mech, and Found. Div., Proc. ASCE*, **96**, 1435–1457.

Courant, R. and Hilbert, D. (1937). *Methoden der Mathematischen Physik*, **II**. Springer, Berlin.

de Josselin de Jong, G. (1963). 'Three-dimensional consolidation' (in Dutch), *L.G.M. Mededelingen*, **7**, 57–63.

de Leeuw, E. H. (1964). 'Three-dimensional consolidation' (in Dutch), *L.G.M. Mededelingen*, **9**, 17–48.

Kenter, C. J. (1974). 'Dilatancy of soils' (in Dutch), *Civ. Eng. Thesis*, University of Technology, Delft.

Rowe, P. W. (1962). 'The stress dilatancy relation for static equilibrium of an assembly of particles in contact', *Proc. Royal Soc. A*, **269**, 500–527.

Sandhu, R. S. and Wilson, E. C. (1969). 'Finite element analysis of seepage in elastic media', *J. Eng. Mech. Div., Proc. ASCE*, **95**, 641–652.

Verruijt, A. (1969). 'Elastic storage of aquifers', in *Flow Through Porous Media*, de Wiest, R. J. M. (ed.), 331–376. Academic Press, New York.

Verruijt, A. (1971). *A Non-linear Isotropic Material Exhibiting Dilatancy* (in Dutch). University of Technology, Delft.

Verruijt, A. (1972). 'Solution of transient groundwater flow problems by the finite element method', *Water Resources Res.*, **8**, 725–727.

Verruijt, A. (1975). *The Generation of a Wave Front for a Mesh of Triangular Elements*. University of Technology, Delft.

Zienkiewicz, O. C. (1971). *The Finite Element Method in Engineering Science*. McGraw-Hill, London.

Chapter 10

Finite Elements for Foundations, Joints and Fluids

E. L. Wilson

10.1 INTRODUCTION

Several different elements for the analysis of foundations, joints and fluid–solid systems are presented. Problems with numerical sensitivity of stiffness coefficients of material interfaces are discussed, and new elements are introduced for two-and three-dimensional systems which are numerically stable. A fluid element is developed based on a pure displacement approach which can be used for the modelling of fluid–solid systems. For earthquake analysis of soil–structural systems a new free-field element is presented which reduces significantly the number of elements required in the finite element idealization of two- and three-dimensional foundations. In addition, variable numbers of node two- and three-dimensional isoparametric elements which are very useful in the idealizations of underground structures are summarized.

One of the first practical applications of the finite element method in civil engineering was to the analysis of a cracked dam on an orthotropic foundation (Clough and Wilson, 1963). During the past ten years the use of the method for the approximate solution of problems in geomechanics has been very successful. Except for the development of methods to represent the behaviour of joints (Goodman, Taylor, *et al.*, 1968; Zienkiewicz, Valliappan, *et al.*, 1970; Ghaboussi, Isenberg, *et al.*, 1973), special elements and efficient numerical methods for the solutions of problems in soil and rock mechanics have not been emphasized. Many computer programs which are currently used for these problems are based on combinations of two-dimensional triangular elements. Therefore, the purpose of this paper is to summarize some of the new elements which have been recently developed and can be effectively applied to the solution to a wide range of problems in geomechanics.

In general, the behaviour of soil and rock materials is non-linear and the exact determination of the material properties can only be approximate. In many cases this argument has been used to justify additional approximation

319

in the selection of the finite element idealization and in the numerical solution of the system. This rationalization of the use of obsolete elements and numerical methods can only be justified if a substantial saving of computer effort is obtained. However it has been demonstrated that the new isoparametric elements and other elements derived specifically for a particular problem result in a substantial saving of computational effort (Zienkiewicz, 1971).

In this paper only different types of finite elements will be discussed. Solution techniques for non-linear analysis of static and dynamic problems in geomechanics are presented in the reference list at the end of this chapter.

10.2 NUMERICAL SENSITIVITY OF FINITE ELEMENT SYSTEMS

At the interface of a structure and foundation or at joints there can be a significant change in stiffness of the different elements. In the case of crack closing in a non-linear problem the normal stiffness across the crack surfaces becomes infinite. In order to illustrate the numerical problem which may develop, a simple one-dimensional example will be studied. Two typical elements are connected by a small joint element as shown in Figure 10.1. The equilibrium equations are formulated in terms of the two absolute displacements at the sides of the joint. In order to present a numerical example the three elements are assigned the following stiffness coefficients:

$$\left\{\begin{matrix} P_1 \\ - \end{matrix}\right\} = \begin{bmatrix} 1 \cdot 5 & 0 \\ 0 & 0 \end{bmatrix} \left\{\begin{matrix} u_1 \\ u_2 \end{matrix}\right\} \quad \text{or} \quad \mathbf{P}_1 = \mathbf{K}_1 \mathbf{u} \qquad (10.1)$$

$$\left\{\begin{matrix} - \\ P_2 \end{matrix}\right\} = \begin{bmatrix} 0 & 0 \\ 0 & 1 \cdot 5 \end{bmatrix} \left\{\begin{matrix} u_1 \\ u_2 \end{matrix}\right\} \quad \text{or} \quad \mathbf{P}_2 = \mathbf{K}_2 \mathbf{u} \qquad (10.2)$$

$$\left\{\begin{matrix} P_1 \\ P_2 \end{matrix}\right\}_3 = \begin{bmatrix} 1000 \cdot 0 & -1000 \cdot 0 \\ -1000 \cdot 0 & 1000 \cdot 0 \end{bmatrix} \left\{\begin{matrix} u_1 \\ u_2 \end{matrix}\right\} \quad \text{or} \quad \mathbf{P}_3 = \mathbf{K}_3 \mathbf{u} \qquad (10.3)$$

The large stiffness assigned to the joint element illustrates the small size of the joint element compared to the other elements. The global node equilibrium equations are formed from

$$R = \left\{\begin{matrix} R_1 \\ R_2 \end{matrix}\right\} = \mathbf{P}_1 + \mathbf{P}_2 + \mathbf{P}_3 = \Sigma \mathbf{K}_i \mathbf{u} \qquad (10.4)$$

or if the external loads are given as $R_1 = 0$ and $R_2 = 1 \cdot 0$

$$\begin{bmatrix} 1001 \cdot 5 & -1000 \cdot 0 \\ -1000 \cdot 0 & 1001 \cdot 5 \end{bmatrix} \left\{\begin{matrix} u_1 \\ u_2 \end{matrix}\right\} = \left\{\begin{matrix} 0 \\ 1 \cdot 0 \end{matrix}\right\} \qquad (10.5)$$

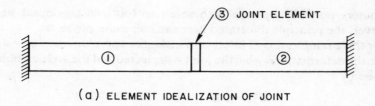

(a) ELEMENT IDEALIZATION OF JOINT

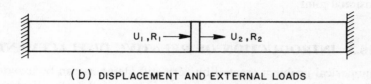

(b) DISPLACEMENT AND EXTERNAL LOADS

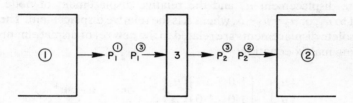

(c) DEFINITION OF POSITIVE INTERNAL FORCES

Figure 10.1 One-dimensional interface example

If five significant figures are retained in the stiffness matrix the solution of Equation (10.4) is

$$\begin{Bmatrix} u_1 \\ u_2 \end{Bmatrix} = \begin{Bmatrix} 0 \cdot 33283 \\ 0 \cdot 33333 \end{Bmatrix} \tag{10.6}$$

If only four significant figures are retained in the stiffness matrix the solution to the approximate equations will be

$$\begin{bmatrix} 1001 & -1000 \\ -1000 & 1001 \end{bmatrix} \begin{Bmatrix} u_1 \\ u_2 \end{Bmatrix} \begin{Bmatrix} 0 \\ 1 \cdot 0 \end{Bmatrix} \quad \text{or} \quad \begin{Bmatrix} u_1 \\ u_2 \end{Bmatrix} = \begin{Bmatrix} 0 \cdot 4995 \\ 0 \cdot 5000 \end{Bmatrix} \tag{10.7}$$

If only three significant figures are retained in the stiffness matrix the set of equations is singular and $u_1 = u_2 = \infty$. This example clearly illustrates that small stiff elements can cause numerical problems. Most modern digital computers normally operate with seven to fourteen significant figures; however, the principle illustrated here can still cause problems.

For this example, it is of interest to make the approximation $u_1 = u_2 = u$. Then, the deformation within the joint is neglected and the node equilibrium is given by

$$[3 \cdot 0]u = 1 \cdot 0 \qquad \text{or} \qquad u = 0 \cdot 333$$

This type of displacement approximation eliminates the problem in this case; however, it is not possible to use this for the general two and three dimensional joint.

10.3 INTRODUCTION OF RELATIVE DISPLACEMENT

The numerical problem created by very stiff elements can be avoided by transforming the equilibrium equations in terms of both absolute and relative displacements rather than in terms of absolute displacements only. The previous one-dimensional example can be written in terms of the absolute displacement u_1 and the relative displacement of node 2 with respect to u_1; or $u_2 = u_1 + \Delta$, where Δ is the relative displacement. Therefore, the obsolete displacements are related to the new set of displacements by the following matrix equation:

$$\begin{Bmatrix} u_1 \\ u_2 \end{Bmatrix} = \begin{bmatrix} 1 \cdot 0 & 0 \\ 1 \cdot 0 & 1 \cdot 0 \end{bmatrix} \begin{Bmatrix} u_1 \\ \Delta \end{Bmatrix} \qquad \text{or} \qquad \mathbf{u} = \mathbf{a}\mathbf{u}^* \tag{10.8}$$

The basic formulation of the equilibrium is still in terms of absolute displacements as given by Equation (10.4), or written in expanded form:

$$\mathbf{R} = [\mathbf{K}_1 + \mathbf{K}_2 + \mathbf{K}_3]\mathbf{u} \tag{10.9}$$

If Equation (10.8) is substituted into Equation (10.9) and the results premultiplied by $\mathbf{a}^T$ the modified equilibrium equations for the system are given by

$$\mathbf{K}^*\mathbf{u}^* = \mathbf{R}^* \tag{10.10}$$

in which

$$\mathbf{R}^* = \mathbf{a}^T\mathbf{R} = \begin{bmatrix} 1 & 1 \\ 0 & 1 \end{bmatrix} \begin{Bmatrix} 0 \\ 1 \end{Bmatrix} = \begin{Bmatrix} 1 \\ 1 \end{Bmatrix}$$

and

$$\mathbf{K}^* = \mathbf{K}_1^* + \mathbf{K}_2^* + \mathbf{K}_3^*$$

where

$$\mathbf{K}_1^* = \mathbf{a}^T \mathbf{K}_1 \mathbf{a} = \begin{bmatrix} 1 & 1 \\ 0 & 1 \end{bmatrix}\begin{bmatrix} 1{\cdot}5 & 0 \\ 0 & 0 \end{bmatrix}\begin{bmatrix} 1 & 0 \\ 1 & 1 \end{bmatrix} = \begin{bmatrix} 1{\cdot}5 & 0 \\ 0 & 0 \end{bmatrix}$$

$$\mathbf{K}_2^* = \mathbf{a}^T \mathbf{K}_2 \mathbf{a} = \begin{bmatrix} 1 & 1 \\ 0 & 1 \end{bmatrix}\begin{bmatrix} 0 & 0 \\ 0 & 1{\cdot}5 \end{bmatrix}\begin{bmatrix} 1 & 0 \\ 1 & 1 \end{bmatrix} = \begin{bmatrix} 1{\cdot}5 & 1{\cdot}5 \\ 1{\cdot}5 & 1{\cdot}5 \end{bmatrix}$$

$$\mathbf{K}_3^* = \mathbf{a}^T \mathbf{K}_3 \mathbf{a} = \begin{bmatrix} 1 & 1 \\ 0 & 1 \end{bmatrix}\begin{bmatrix} 1000 & -1000 \\ -1000 & 1000 \end{bmatrix}\begin{bmatrix} 1 & 0 \\ 1 & 1 \end{bmatrix} = \begin{bmatrix} 0 & 0 \\ 0 & 1000 \end{bmatrix}$$

Therefore, the numerical form of Equation (10.10) is

$$\begin{bmatrix} 3{\cdot}0 & 1{\cdot}5 \\ 1{\cdot}5 & 1001{\cdot}5 \end{bmatrix}\begin{Bmatrix} u_1 \\ \Delta \end{Bmatrix} = \begin{Bmatrix} 1{\cdot}0 \\ 1{\cdot}0 \end{Bmatrix} \tag{10.11}$$

The solution to this equation, to five significant figures is

$$\begin{Bmatrix} u_1 \\ \Delta \end{Bmatrix} = \begin{Bmatrix} 0{\cdot}33308 \\ 0{\cdot}00050 \end{Bmatrix} \tag{10.12}$$

and

$$u_2 = 0{\cdot}33358$$

In order to obtain this accuracy, Equation (10.5) would need to be solved using eight significant figures in the solution procedure.

It is important to note that if the stiffness coefficient $1001{\cdot}5$ is changed to 1000 and calculations are performed to an accuracy of two significant figures the solution is

$$\begin{Bmatrix} u_1 \\ \Delta \end{Bmatrix} = \begin{Bmatrix} 0{\cdot}33 \\ 0{\cdot}00050 \end{Bmatrix} \tag{10.13}$$

If the stiffness of the joint material approaches infinity, $u_1 = \frac{1}{3}$ and $\Delta = 0$, and no numerical difficulties occur.

10.4 TWO-DIMENSIONAL INTERFACE ELEMENT

The formulation of the two-dimensional interface element involves the introduction of two relative displacements at the interface nodes as shown in Figure 10.2. In order to avoid all numerical difficulties it is necessary for both the absolute and relative displacements of the interface nodes to be in the $n-s$ reference system. Therefore, all standard two-dimensional finite elements adjacent to the interface must have their element stiffnesses and loads for the i and j nodes transformed to the n and s directions. In order to simplify computer implementation it is important that all matrix transformations are performed at the element level prior to the addition of element stiffnesses and loads to global stiffnesses and loads.

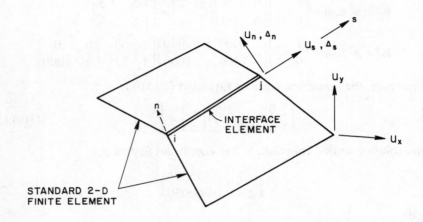

Figure 10.2 Two-dimensional interface element

The absolute displacement associated with the upper side of the interface is defined by:

$$u_{ni}^T = u_{ni} + \Delta_{ni}$$
$$u_{si}^T = u_{si} + \Delta_{si}$$
$$u_{nj}^T = u_{nj} + \Delta_{nj}$$
$$u_{sj}^T = u_{sj} + \Delta_{sj}$$

(10.14)

Therefore element stiffness on one side of the interface will be increased in size because of the addition of the relative displacements. Considering the quadrilateral elements shown in Figure 10.2 the upper element stiffness will be increased to a 12×12 matrix and the lower element stiffness will remain an 8×8 matrix.

The displacements associated with the interface element are shown in Figure 3. The interface thickness h is very small compared to the size of the two-dimensional finite element. Therefore, an assumption that the strains do not vary in the thickness direction is valid. Then the three components of

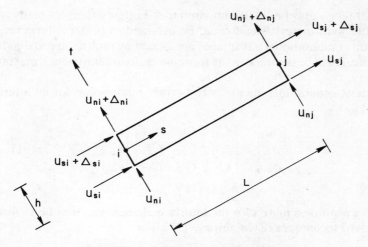

Figure 10.3 Interface element deformations

strain at position s within the interface element are given by:

$$\varepsilon_{ss} = \frac{u_{sj} - u_{si}}{L}$$

$$\varepsilon_{nn} = \frac{1}{h}\left[\Delta_{ni} + \frac{s}{L}(\Delta_{nj} - \Delta_{ni})\right]$$

$$\varepsilon_{ns} = \frac{1}{h}\left[\Delta_{si} + \frac{s}{L}(\Delta_{sj} - \Delta_{si})\right] + \frac{1}{L}(u_{nj} - u_{ni})$$

or written in matrix form

$$\left\{\begin{matrix} \varepsilon_{ss} \\ \varepsilon_{nn} \\ \varepsilon_{ns} \end{matrix}\right\} = (1/h)\begin{bmatrix} (h/L) & (h/L) & 0 & 0 & 0 & 0 & 0 & 0 \\ 0 & 0 & 0 & 0 & 1-(s/L) & (s/L) & 0 & 0 \\ 0 & 0 & -(h/L) & (h/L) & 0 & 0 & 1-(s/L) & (s/L) \end{bmatrix}\left\{\begin{matrix} u_{si} \\ u_{sj} \\ u_{ni} \\ u_{nj} \\ \Delta_{ni} \\ \Delta_{nj} \\ \Delta_{si} \\ \Delta_{sj} \end{matrix}\right\}$$

$$\boldsymbol{\varepsilon} = \mathbf{B}\mathbf{u}^* \tag{10.15}$$

The strain ε_{ss} may be small compared to the other strains for many types of flexible-joint materials and could be assumed to be zero; however, no significant computational advantages are gained by such an approximation. Therefore, it will be included in the formulation in order to obtain maximum generality.

The most general incremental stress-strain relationship for an interface material is

$$\begin{Bmatrix} \sigma_{nn} \\ \sigma_{ss} \\ \sigma_{sn} \end{Bmatrix} = \begin{bmatrix} C_{11} & C_{12} & C_{13} \\ C_{21} & C_{22} & C_{23} \\ C_{31} & C_{32} & C_{33} \end{bmatrix} \begin{Bmatrix} \varepsilon_{nn} \\ \varepsilon_{ss} \\ \varepsilon_{sn} \end{Bmatrix} \tag{10.16}$$

$$\boldsymbol{\sigma} = \mathbf{C}\boldsymbol{\varepsilon}$$

The 6×6 stiffness matrix for the interface element can now be evaluated by standard techniques (Zienkiewicz, 1971), or

$$\mathbf{K} = \int_{\mathrm{vol}} \mathbf{B}^T \mathbf{C} \mathbf{B} \, dv \tag{10.17}$$

As the strains vary in the s direction only

$$\mathbf{K} = A \int_0^L \mathbf{B}^T \mathbf{C} \mathbf{B} \, ds \tag{10.18}$$

where A is the area of the interface element normal to s. Equation (10.18) is best directly evaluated within a computer program by numerical integration. A one-point integration formula is the same as making the assumption of constraint within the element. Such an approximation may be acceptable for some problems; however, for many problems erroneous oscillations of displacements and stresses may result. Therefore, an exact or a two-point integration formula should be used for the two-dimensional interface element.

10.5 THREE-DIMENSIONAL INTERFACE ELEMENT

One of the most important advantages of the formulation of interface elements in terms of relative deformations is that the method can be used for both two- and three-dimensional problems. A schematic diagram of two eight-node solid elements and a four-node interface element is shown in Figure 10.4. The normal unknowns will be the three components of displacements u_x, u_y and u_z at each node and u_r, u_s, u_t, Δ_r, Δ_s and Δ_t at the interface nodes. It is essential to point out that the local r–s–t coordinate system can vary in definition at each interface node. The stiffness of both the standard and the interface elements can be formulated in reference to

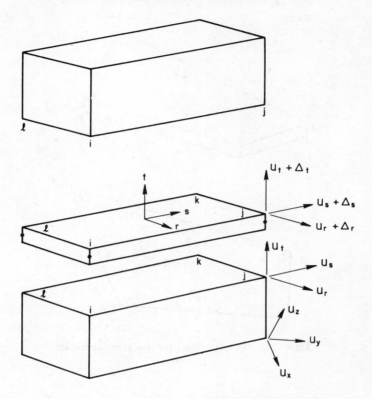

Figure 10.4   Three-dimensional interface element

different co-ordinate systems; however, all stiffnesses must be transformed to a unique r–s–t system at the interface nodes. It is apparent that only one interface nodal co-ordinate system will be required if the interface surface is flat. Also, if the interface surface corresponds to one of the global x, y or z planes no transformation will be required.

For the purpose of evaluating the stiffness matrix for the interface element it is necessary to define the three-dimensional displacements within the element in terms of the eight nodes as shown in Figure 10.5. All three components of displacements (u_r, u_s and u_t) are related to the eight-node displacement by the standard shape functions for an eight-node solid element. Or,

$$u = \sum_{i=1}^{8} H_i u_i \qquad (10.19)$$

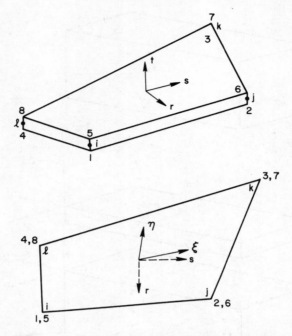

Figure 10.5 Local reference systems: general interface
element

Since the displacements of nodes 5 to 8 can be written as

$$u_i = u_{i-4} + \Delta_{i-4} \qquad i = 5 \ldots 8 \tag{10.20}$$

Also

$$H_i(\xi, \eta, \tau) = \frac{1-\tau}{2} N_i(\xi, \eta) \qquad i = 1 \ldots 4$$

$$H_i(\xi, \eta, \tau) = \frac{1+\tau}{2} N_i(\xi, \eta) \qquad i = 5 \ldots 8$$

in which

$$N_i(\xi, \eta) = N_{i-4}(\xi, \eta) \qquad \text{for} \qquad i = 5 \ldots 8$$

Therefore, Equation (10.19) can be written as

$$u = \sum_{i=1}^{4} \left[\frac{1-\tau}{2} N_i u_i + \frac{1+\tau}{2} N_i u_i + \frac{1+\tau}{2} N_i \Delta_i \right] \tag{10.21}$$

Since $(1+\tau)/2 = t/h$ in the global coordinate system Equation (10.21) can be further simplified and applied to all three global displacements

$$
\left.
\begin{aligned}
u_r &= \sum_{i=1}^{4} \left[N_i u_{ri} + \frac{t}{h} N_i \Delta_{ri} \right] \\
u_s &= \sum_{i=1}^{4} \left[N_i u_{si} + \frac{t}{h} N_i \Delta_{si} \right] \\
u_t &= \sum_{i=1}^{4} \left[N_i u_{ti} + \frac{t}{h} N_i \Delta_{ti} \right]
\end{aligned}
\right\}
\qquad (10.21)
$$

From the three-dimensional strain–displacement equations and by making the approximation that all strains are constant in the thickness direction t, the strains within the interface element are defined in terms of the absolute and relative displacements as

$$
\left.
\begin{aligned}
\varepsilon_{rr} &= \frac{\partial u_r}{\partial r} = \sum N_{i,r} u_{ri} \\[6pt]
\varepsilon_{ss} &= \frac{\partial u_s}{\partial s} = \sum N_{i,s} u_{si} \\[6pt]
\varepsilon_{tt} &= \frac{\partial u_t}{\partial t} = \sum \frac{1}{h} N_i \Delta_t \\[6pt]
\varepsilon_{rs} &= \frac{\partial u_r}{\partial s} + \frac{\partial u_s}{\partial r} = \sum N_{i,s} u_{ri} + N_{i,r} u_{si} \\[6pt]
\varepsilon_{rt} &= \frac{\partial u_r}{\partial t} + \frac{\partial u_t}{\partial r} = \sum \frac{1}{h} N_i \Delta_{ri} + N_{i,r} u_{ti} \\[6pt]
\varepsilon_{st} &= \frac{\partial u_s}{\partial t} + \frac{\partial u_t}{\partial s} = \sum \frac{1}{h} H_i \Delta_{si} + N_{i,s} u_{ti}
\end{aligned}
\right\}
\qquad (10.23)
$$

For many different types of interfaces some of these strains may be neglected and a simplified formulation obtained. Depending on what strains are retained a consistent set of material properties must be selected. The computer implementation of the element then proceeds in a similar fashion to the 8-node solid element. It is recommended that a two-by-two numerical integration formula be used to evaluate the 24×24 stiffness matrix for the three-dimensional interface element. Also, it may be necessary to transform these stiffness to different coordinate systems at the various interface nodes. In addition, the top element must be expanded to a 36×36 stiffness matrix before it is added to the global stiffness matrix. Of course, any local loads acting on the elements must be transformed in a consistent manner.

10.6 FLUID ELEMENTS

Many problems in geomechanics involve the interaction of fluids and solids during dynamic loading. The basic behavior of a fluid is not the same as that of a solid because a fluid cannot carry shear stresses. In addition, the only type of deformation which produces strain energy is a pure volume change. A typical quadrilateral with eight unknown node displacements is shown in Figure 10.6. It is clear that there exist seven independent modes of deformation which do not produce volume changes. Therefore, the rank of the resulting 8×8 stiffness matrix for a fluid element will be one, or the matrix will have seven zero eigenvalues.

For an axi-symmetric quadrilateral element the formulation of the fluid element stiffness is straightforward. From simple equations of geometry the

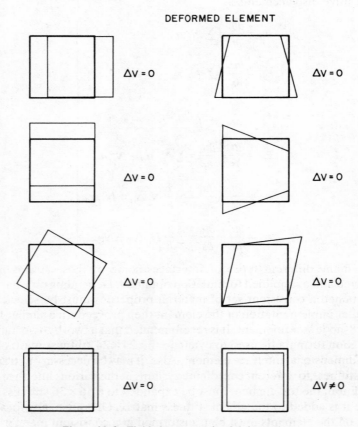

DEFORMED ELEMENT

$\Delta V = 0$

$\Delta V = 0$

$\Delta V = 0$

$\Delta V = 0$

$\Delta V = 0$

$\Delta V = 0$

$\Delta V = 0$

$\Delta V \neq 0$

Figure 10.6 Fluid element mode of deformation

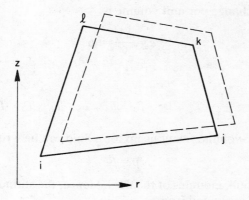

Figure 10.7 Deformed fluid element

change in volume of a one radian quadrilateral element as shown in Figure 10.7 can be expressed in terms of the eight node displacements

$$\Delta V = [T_1 \quad T_2 \quad T_3 \quad T_4 \quad T_5 \quad T_6 \quad T_7 \quad T_8] \begin{Bmatrix} u_{rz} \\ u_{rj} \\ u_{rh} \\ u_{rl} \\ u_{ri} \\ u_{rj} \\ u_{rh} \\ u_{rl} \end{Bmatrix} \quad (10.24)$$

in which

$$T_1 = 2r_1Z_2 + r_2Z_2 + r_4Z_1 - r_2Z_1 - r_4Z_4 - 2r_1Z_4$$

$$T_2 = 2r_2Z_3 + r_3Z_3 + r_1Z_2 - r_1Z_2 - r_3Z_2 - r_1Z_1 - 2r_2Z_1$$

$$T_3 = r_2Z_3 - r_3Z_3 - 2r_3Z_2 - r_2Z_2 + r_4Z_4 + 2r_3Z_4$$

$$T_4 = -r_3Z_3 - 2r_4Z_3 + 2r_4Z_1 + r_1Z_1 + r_3Z_4 - r_1Z_4$$

$$T_5 = r_4^2 + r_4r_1 - r_1r_2 - r_2^2$$

$$T_6 = r_1^2 + r_1r_2 - r_2r_3 - r_3^2$$

$$T_7 = r_2^2 + r_2r_3 - r_3r_4 - r_4^2$$

$$T_8 = r_3^2 + r_3r_4 - r_4r_1 - r_1^2$$

or the volume change per unit volume is

$$e = \frac{\Delta V}{V} = \mathbf{au} \qquad (10.25)$$

where

$$\mathbf{a} = \frac{1}{GV}[T_1 \quad T_2 \quad T_3 \quad T_4 \quad T_5 \quad T_6 \quad T_7 \quad T_8]$$

The pressure–volume relationship for a fluid can be written as

$$p = \beta e \qquad (10.26)$$

where β is the bulk modulus of the fluid. Hence, the stiffness matrix for the element can be evaluated from

$$\mathbf{k} = \int \mathbf{B}^T \beta \mathbf{B} \, dV \qquad (10.27)$$

Or, since all terms are not a function of space

$$\mathbf{k} = V \mathbf{B}^T \beta \mathbf{B} \qquad (10.28)$$

It is apparent that this formulation is extremely easy to implement within a computer program. In the case of two-dimensional plane analysis the equation can be simplified.

For three-dimensional elements the same physical approach to the formulation of the stiffness can be used. However, an equally valid approach is to use isoparametric shape functions and evaluate the unit volume change from

$$e = \varepsilon_{xx} + \varepsilon_{yy} + \varepsilon_{zz} \qquad (10.29)$$

A one-point integration method will then yield the correct stiffness.

An important physical behaviour of this fluid element should be noted. The fluid can move within the boundary of the element without causing a net change in volume. Therefore, compatibility within the element is not maintained on a microscopic level. As a result of this observation it is apparent that a diagonal lumped mass should be used in connection with this element rather than a consistent mass matrix which has been used for the analysis of solids.

10.7 EARTHQUAKE ANALYSIS OF SOIL STRUCTURE SYSTEMS

Most structures are constructed on foundations which are relatively stiff and massive compared with the above general structures. For this type of system it is clear that the dynamic behaviour of the structure during an earthquake is affected by the foundation, but the behaviour of the foundation is not affected by the properties of the structure. However, in the seismic analysis of this type of system it may still be necessary to model local footing and foundation stiffnesses in order to satisfy the correct boundary conditions for the structure and its components.

For massive structures, such as dams and large industrial plants, the dynamic behaviour of the structure can influence the motion of the foundation near the structure; therefore, the behaviour of both the structure and foundation are coupled. For simplified structures and linear material properties in the structure and foundation, each system may be analyzed separately and the results then superimposed by enforcing equilibrium and displacement compatibility at the interface (Parmalee, Perelman, *et al.*, 1969; Chopra and Gutierrez, 1974). For more complex structures and foundations with several different materials it is possible to perform a three-dimensional finite element seismic analysis for linear structure-foundation systems (Bathe, Wilson, *et al.*, 1974). However, a large amount of computer time will be required for only an approximate linear solution.

The type of waves which produced the surface accelerations cannot be identified directly from an examination of an earthquake record at a single point. Horizontal displacements and accelerations at a point may be produced by both surface compression waves and shear waves propagating vertically upward from a subsurface input. Also, vertical surface displacements may be produced by both vertical compression waves and surface waves. For foundations on a deep soft layer of soil above bedrock the assumption that the surface motions result from waves propagating up from the bedrock may be justifiable. However, for many foundations this assumption may be a gross over-simplification. At the present time experts in the field of soil-structure interaction do not agree on the fundamental question: '*Where is the appropriate location in the soil-structure model to specify the input?*' Perhaps the best approach at the present time is to select a model of the system which will allow for the earthquake input to be at the surface or at the base of the system. For the foundation element presented in this paper either type of input is possible.

A recently developed computer program, LUSH (Lysmer, Udaka, *et al.*, 1975), for the approximate non-linear seismic analysis of two-dimensional plane-strain soil-structure systems represents the most advanced approach for massive structures on deep non-linear soil foundations. Since this program extends most computer systems to their practical limits, with respect to both speed and storage requirements, it does not seem feasible directly to extend this two-dimensional approach to the analysis of three-dimensional soil-structure systems. In addition the acceleration input to this program must be assumed to be shear waves propagating up from a lower level.

A finite element idealization of a three-dimensional soil-structure system is shown in Figure 10.8. Such an idealization is possible; however, it cannot be assumed to be practical in all cases for the following reasons:

(1) The computer-time requirements would be extremely expensive because of the fine-mesh idealization of the foundation area.

(2) The boundary conditions on the sides of the foundation model are difficult to establish in a rational manner.

(3) The acceleration input is restricted to the base of the model. For some deep soil foundations this may be an excellent approximation.

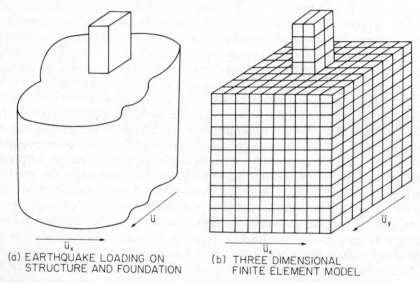

(a) EARTHQUAKE LOADING ON
STRUCTURE AND FOUNDATION

(b) THREE DIMENSIONAL
FINITE ELEMENT MODEL

Figure 10.8　Three-dimensional finite element idealization of structure and foundation

In the selection of a realistic finite element model for the foundation it may be necessary to consider both the local foundation stiffness effects near the base of the structure and accurately to represent the deep soil foundations. A logical approach to the idealization of the foundation is to use two different types of elements; one to represent the local deformation effects and one designed to transmit the earthquake motions from free-field to the vicinity of the structure. In two- and three-dimensions, standard solid finite elements can be used to model local foundation deformations. These elements should be used only in the immediate area of the structure (e.g. a distance beyond the base of the structure equal to the dimension of the structure). For a given class of structures a parameter study can be used to evaluate the required number of elements near the structure.

The free-field element shown in Figure 10.9 is designed to represent the foundation earthquake motions as if the structure were not present. This

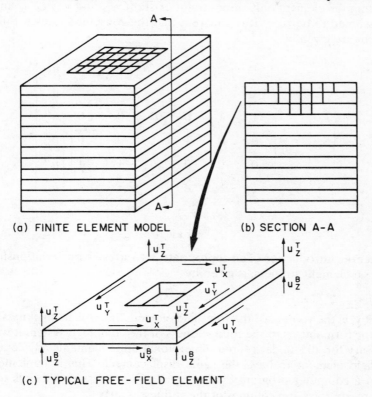

(a) FINITE ELEMENT MODEL   (b) SECTION A-A

(c) TYPICAL FREE-FIELD ELEMENT

Figure 10.9   Use of three-dimensional free-field elements for foundation idealization

element is designed to propagate shear and vertical compression waves to the structure from a point directly under the structure. The total mass of the finite elements near the structure will be several times the mass of the structure, and the mass of a typical free-field element should be selected to be an order of magnitude greater than the mass of the structure. Therefore, the dynamic behaviour of the structure will not affect the behaviour of the free-field elements. The foundation–structure interaction effects are confined to the area modelled by the standard finite elements.

The major advantage of the use of the free-field element is that a significant saving of computational effort is obtained, because only three unknown displacements are required at each level as shown in Figure 10.9c. In addition the boundary conditions at the sides of the foundation automatically satisfy the free-field boundary conditions.

Within the element only three strains exist: ε_z, γ_{xz} and γ_{yz}. ε_x, ε_y and γ_{xy} are assumed to be zero. It is apparent that the constant strains within the element are given by

$$\begin{Bmatrix} \varepsilon_z \\ \gamma_{xz} \\ \gamma_{yz} \end{Bmatrix} = \frac{1}{h} \begin{bmatrix} -1 & 1 & 0 & 0 & 0 & 0 \\ 0 & 0 & -1 & 1 & 0 & 0 \\ 0 & 0 & 0 & 0 & -1 & 1 \end{bmatrix} \begin{Bmatrix} u_z^B \\ u_z^T \\ u_x^B \\ u_x^T \\ u_y^B \\ u_y^T \end{Bmatrix}$$

or

$$\boldsymbol{\varepsilon} = \mathbf{au}$$

After the introduction of an appropriate 3×3 stress-strain relationship, $\mathbf{c}$, the 6×6 element stiffness, is given by

$$K = V\mathbf{a}^T\mathbf{ca}$$

where V is the volume of the free-field element and h is its thickness.

In the formulation of the total stiffness of the combined system it will be necessary for all standard three-dimensional finite elements adjacent to a free-field element to have the same displacement. This is implemented within a computer program by adding all the stiffness coefficients to the appropriate rows and columns of the stiffness matrix.

This free-field foundation element has not been extensively used on three-dimensional problems; however, experience with two-dimensional problems indicates that structure-foundation interaction is important only within a local area (Rukos, 1971).

10.8 VARIABLE-NUMBER-NODES TWO-DIMENSIONAL AND THREE-DIMENSIONAL ELEMENT

Most of the finite elements used in special purpose programs for geotechnical problems are based on lower order elements and use a triangular element for the purpose of altering the mesh size within an area. Variable-number-node iso-parametric elements, as shown in Figure 10.10, allow greater flexibility in mesh layout and, in most cases, a significant improvement of results for the same computational effort.

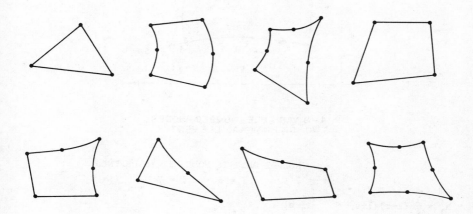

Figure 10.10 Typical nodal point configurations for 2/D continuum elements derived from the general 8-node element

While it is possible to write a separate set of interpolation fractions for each of the elements this approach requires separate computer coding for each element. The advantage of the elements shown in Figures 10.11 and 10.12 is that any number of nodes between the minimum and maximum is possible within the same computer code. The basic technique is one of starting with the four-node element in two dimensions or the eight-node element in three dimensions and adding an interpolation function for that node and correcting the interpolation function for the adjacent nodes. It should be mentioned that a constant strain triangle can be formed from the four-node element by superimposing appropriate corner nodes of the element. Similarly for three-dimensional elements, wedge elements or a constant-strain four-node solid can be formed from the basic eight-node brick element.

This technique for constructing variable node element is presented in reference (Bathe and Wilson, 1976); however, it is summarized here because of its special advantages in the modelling of underground structures as illustrated in Figure 10.20.

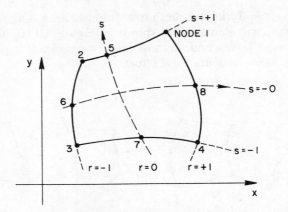

4 – 8 VARIABLE – NUMBER – NODES
TWO – DIMENSIONAL ELEMENT

INCLUDE ONLY IF NODE i IS DEFINED

	i = 5	i = 6	i = 7	i = 8

$$h_1 = \frac{1}{4}(1+r)(1+s) \qquad -\frac{1}{2}h_5$$

$$h_2 = \frac{1}{4}(1-r)(1+s) \qquad -\frac{1}{2}h_5 \qquad -\frac{1}{2}h_6$$

$$h_3 = \frac{1}{4}(1-r)(1-s) \qquad\qquad\qquad -\frac{1}{2}h_6 \qquad -\frac{1}{2}h_7$$

$$h_4 = \frac{1}{4}(1+r)(1-s) \qquad\qquad\qquad\qquad\qquad -\frac{1}{2}h_7 \qquad -\frac{1}{2}h_8$$

$$h_5 = \frac{1}{2}(1-r^2)(1+s)$$

$$h_6 = \frac{1}{2}(1-s^2)(1-r)$$

$$h_7 = \frac{1}{2}(1-r^2)(1-s)$$

$$h_8 = \frac{1}{2}(1-s^2)(1+r)$$

Figure 10.11 Interpolation functions of 4 to 8 variable-number-nodes two-dimensional element

10.9 LINEAR-ELASTIC ANALYSIS OF FOUNDATIONS

All elements presented in this paper can be used for linear or non-linear analysis. For a foundation which can be approximated by linear-elastic materials many different simplifications can be made in the solution techniques which greatly reduce the computational effort. For example, for the

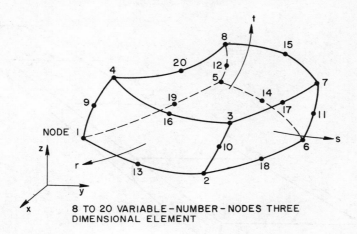

8 TO 20 VARIABLE-NUMBER-NODES THREE
DIMENSIONAL ELEMENT

$$h_1 = g_1 - (g_9 + g_{13} + g_{19})/2 \qquad h_6 = g_6 - (g_{11} + g_{14} + g_{18})/2$$

$$h_2 = g_2 - (g_{10} + g_{13} + g_{18})/2 \qquad h_7 = g_7 - (g_{11} + g_{15} + g_{17})/2$$

$$h_3 = g_3 - (g_{10} + g_{16} + g_{17})/2 \qquad h_8 = g_8 - (g_{12} + g_{15} + g_{20})/2$$

$$h_4 = g_4 - (g_9 + g_{16} + g_{20})/2 \qquad h_i = g_j \quad \text{for } j = 9, \ldots, 20$$

$$h_5 = g_5 - (g_{12} + g_{14} + g_{19})/2$$

$g_i = 0$ if node i is not included, otherwise

$$g_i = G(r, r_i) \ G(s, s_i) \ G(t, t_i)$$

$$G(\beta, \beta_i) = \frac{1}{2} (1 + \beta_i \beta) \quad \text{for } \beta_i \pm 1.$$

$$\qquad \qquad \qquad \qquad \qquad > \quad \beta = r, s, t$$

$$G(\beta, \beta_i) = (1 - \beta^2) \quad \text{for } \beta_i = 0$$

Figure 10.12 Interpolation functions of 8 to 20 variable-number-nodes three-dimensional element

case of certain structures on homogeneous foundations half-space theories may be appropriate. In the case of axi-symmetric structures on non-homogeneous axi-symmetric foundations, the expansion of the displacements in a series of trigonometric functions reduces the three-dimensional problem into a series of two-dimensional problems. In the case of earthquake loading the solution of only one two-dimensional problem is required

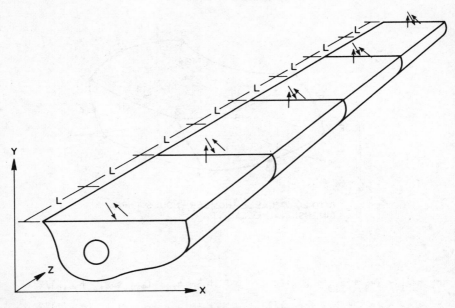

Figure 10.13 The prismatic space

(Bathe and Wilson, 1976). Also, for three-dimensional solids with constant properties and geometry in the third direction as shown in Figure 10.13, the problem is reduced to the solution of a set of two-dimensional problems (Rukos, 1971). The variable-number-node elements shown in Figure 10.10 can be used in analysis of prismatic or axisymmetric solids.

10.10 APPLICATIONS

Several examples of the application of the different elements will be summarized. However, it should be recognized that in the idealization of a complex structure it may be necessary to use interface elements, variable-number-node elements, liquid elements and free-field elements in order to accurately model the behaviour of the structure and to minimize computational costs.

10.10.1 Two-dimensional interface element

In Figure 10.14 a finite element representation of a foundation with a wedge-shaped block is modelled with standard two-dimensional finite elements and interface elements shown as heavy lines. The ambiguity created by intersecting joints is avoided by omitting interface elements from the immediate area. The mesh size selected in this area will define the size of the

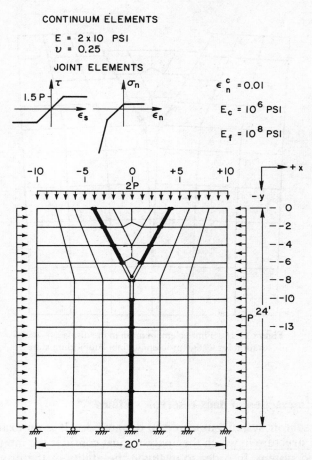

Figure 10.14 Geometry of example problem using plane slip element

gap. Such an approximation is consistent with the reliability of field information near intersecting cracks where additional small cracks are normally present. The joints (interface material) are assumed to be filled by non-dilatant material as shown in Figure 10.14 (Ghaboussi, Isenberg, *et al.*, 1973).

A magnified plot of the displacements is shown in Figure 10.15. The apparent overlap of the material near the joints arises from the large scale selected for the plot and does not exist if the scale was reduced.

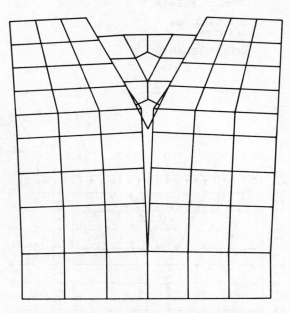

Figure 10.15 Finite element mesh in the displaced configuration for wedge problem in final equilibrium state

10.10.2 Interaction of dam–reservoir systems

A dam–reservoir system subjected to dynamic loads is an example of an important structure in which the analysis must consider the interaction of a liquid–solid system. In order to evaluate the ability of the proposed two-dimensional element the problem shown in Figure 10.16 was solved and compared to an exact solution (Chopra and Gutierrez, 1974). Figure 10.17 indicates that the basic behaviour of the liquid finite element model agreed with the exact solution.

In Figure 10.18 a simple gravity dam and finite reservoir was idealized and subjected to the gound accelerations of the 1940 El Centro earthquake. For this simplified model Figure 10.19 illustrates a singificant amplification effect due to the interaction of the dam and reservoir.

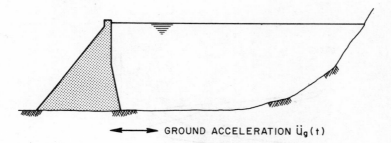

Figure 10.16a   Reservoir–dam system

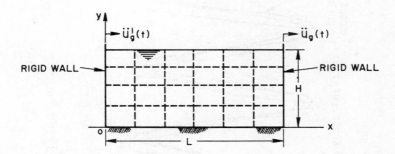

Figure 10.16b   Simple reservoir–dam system

It should be emphasized at this time that the significant advantage of the formulation of liquid elements in terms of displacement will be obtained in its extension to three dimensions or to problems with non-linearity and irregular geometry. For problems in which large deformation of the liquid is important the use of an interface element between the solid and liquid may prove to be necessary.

10.10.3   Application of variable-number-node elements

The finite element idealization of the underground opening shown in Figure 10.20 is an excellent illustration of the application of the variable node element. The use of the higher-order elements near the opening result in a good idealization of the curved geometry and in a higher-order approximation in the area of expected stress concentration. In this case the nonlinear material was assumed to have different properties in tension and compression and an incremental, step-by-step iterative solution method was

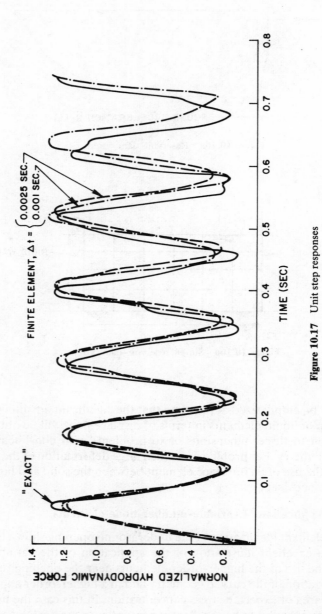

Figure 10.17 Unit step responses

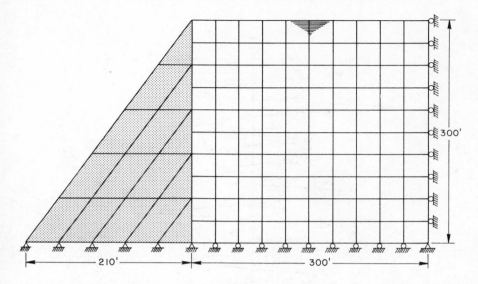

Figure 10.18 Finite element idealization of reservoir–dam system

employed (Bathe and Wilson, 1974). Results are shown in Figures 10.21 and 10.22.

10.10.4 Linear analysis of prismatic solids

Arbitrary loading on foundations which have two-dimensional properties and geometry which are constant with respect to a third direction is an important problem. Wheel loads near a joint or near the edge of a pavement surface produce a complex three-dimensional stress distribution (Wilson and Pretorins, 1970). The expansion of the displacements into a series avoids a time-consuming three-dimensional analysis. The results of such an analysis are shown in Figure 10.23. For problems of this nature non-linear material behaviour may be expected under static loads; however, under repeated dynamic loading the linear-elastic solution technique presented here may be a good approximation.

SUMMARY

Several different types of finite elements were discussed. The selection of the appropriate combination of elements for a given problem may result in a significant saving of computational costs, a reduction in the time required to

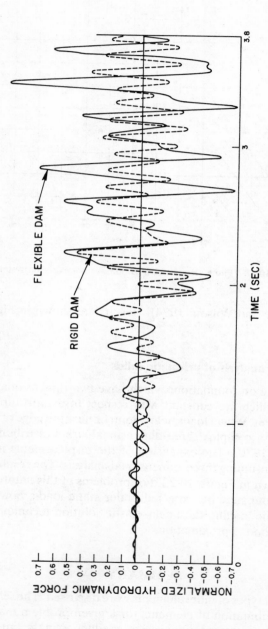

Figure 10.19 Response of reservoir–dam system to El Centro 1940 earthquake

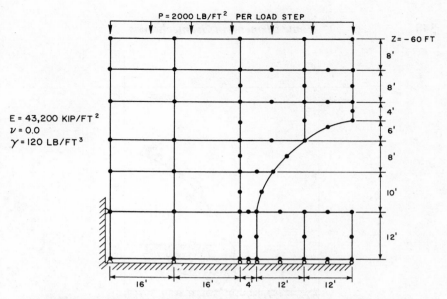

Figure 10.20 Finite element mesh for analysis of underground opening

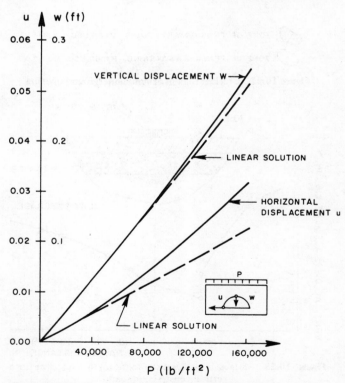

Figure 10.21 Load-deflection response of underground opening

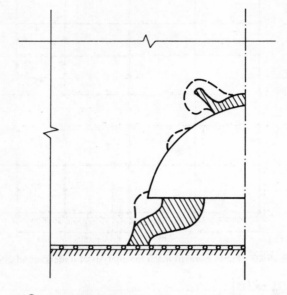

ZONE OF TENSION WEAKENING   P=64,000   lb/ft²

ZONE OF TENSION WEAKENING   P=160,000   lb/ft²

Figure 10.22   Cracked regions around underground opening

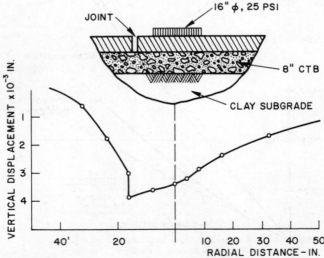

Figure 10.23   Surface displacement profile for a load close to a vertical construction joint

select a finite element mesh, and a minimization in numerical sensitivity problems.

At the present time all the elements presented are not incorporated into a single program. However, it is possible to develop a general purpose program for the static or dynamic analysis of problems in geomechanics including the effects of incremental construction and excavation. The elements presented in this paper can form the basis for such a program.

REFERENCES

Bathe, K. J., Ramm, E., and Wilson, E. L. (1975). 'Finite Element Formulation for Large Deformation Dynamic Analysis', *International J. for Num. Meth.*, **9**, 353–386.

Bathe, K. J. and Wilson E. L. (1974). 'NONSAP—A nonlinear structural analysis program', *Nuclear Engineering and Design*, **29**.

Bathe, K. J., Wilson, E. L., and Peterson, F. E. (1974). 'SAP IV, A structural analysis for static and dynamic response of linear systems', *EERC Report No. 73-11*, University of California, Berkeley, California.

Bathe, K. J. and Wilson, E. L. (1976). *Numerical Methods in Finite Element Analysis*, Prentice Hall.

Chopra, A. K. and Gutierrez, J. A. (1974). 'Earthquake Response Analysis of Multistory Buildings Including Foundation Interaction', *International Journal of Earthquake Engineering and Structural Dynamics*, **3**, 65–77.

Clough, R. W. and Wilson, E. L. (1963). 'Stress Analysis of a Gravity Dam by the Finite Element Method', *RILEM Bulletin No. 19*.

Ghaboussi, J., Isenberg, J., and Wilson, E. L. (1963). 'Finite Element for Rock Joints and Interfaces', *J. of Soil Mech.*, *ASCE*, SM10.

Goodman, R., Taylor, R. L., and Brekke, T. L. (1968). 'A Model for the Mechanics of Jointed Rock', *J. Soil Mech.*, *ASCE*, **94**, SM3.

Lysmer, J., Udaka, T., Seed, H. B., and Hwang, R. (1975). 'LUSH—A Computer Program for Complex Response Analysis of Soil-Structure Systems', *Report No. EERC 74-4*, Earthquake Engineering Research Center, University of California, Berkeley, California.

Parmalee, R. A., Perelman, D. S., and Lee, S-L. (1969). 'Seismic Response of Multistory Structures on Flexible Foundation', *Bulletin of the Seismological Society of America*, **59**, 1061–1070.

Rukos, E. A. (1971). 'Earthquake Analysis of Interacting Ground-Structure Systems', *Report No. UCSESM 71-9*, Department of Civil Engineering, University of California.

Wilson, E. L. and Pretorius, P. C. (1970). 'A Computer Program for the Analysis of Prismatic Solids', *Report No. UCSESM 70–21*, Department of Civil Engineering, University of California, Berkeley, California.

Wilson, E. L., Farhoumand, I., Bathe, K. J. (1973). 'Nonlinear Dynamic Analysis of Complex Structures', *Earthquake Engineering and Structural Dynamics*, **1**, 241–252.

Wilson, E. L. (1971). 'Earthquake Analysis of Reactor Structures', *Proceedings, ASME, First National Congress on Pressure Vessels and Piping, San Francisco, Ca.*, 53–73.

Zienkiewicz, O. C., Valliappan, S., Dullage, C., and Stagg, K. G. (1970). 'Analysis of Nonlinear Problems in Rock Mechanics with Particular Reference to Jointed Rock Systems', *Proc. of 2nd Conference of Int. Soc. for Rock Mech., Belgrade.*

Zienkiewicz, O. C. (1971). *The Finite Element Method in Engineering Science*, McGraw-Hill, London.

Chapter 11

Analysis in Jointed Rocks

R. E. Goodman

11.1 PROPERTIES OF JOINTED ROCKS

Rocks

Some rock masses are quite competent and virtually free of discontinuities, and have supported even giant sculptures with overhangs in canyon walls. These rocks are close to ideal materials, but analysis is rarely necessary in them. Those in which we find ourselves performing analyses for practical engineering and mining works are always non-ideal in one or more ways. Many are porous, penetrated by a network of roughly equidimensional spaces. Other rocks are continuously disrupted by planar cracks, denoted *fissures*. The closure of these cracks under compressive stresses shuts off their permeability and restores mechanical continuity, while tension directed normal to the fissures significantly increases permeability and quickly destroys cohesion. Fissures will be contained in rock specimens brought to the laboratory so laboratory measurements include their effect. Joints and other macrodiscontinuities are not usually contained in small sized test specimens and therefore special sampling and testing is required if their mechanical characteristics are to be measured.

A highly jointed rock mass is quite different from a continuous rock or a soil; all the cracks are perfectly mated with very little inter-block space, so that large shearing deformations are possible only if the rock itself is weak or if large amounts of dilatancy can occur. Joints change the behaviour mode from that in an unjointed rock mass and it is this change which we seek to estimate or calculate in engineering practice. The modification of rock mass behaviour brought about by jointing is not always to be considered bad; for example, vertical jointing in a layered rock forming the foundation of a dam may distribute the shear deformation in the foundation and consequently reduce shear stresses inside the lower levels of the dam itself.

Joints

Joints may be divided into extension type and shear type fractures. The former are typically clean fractures, without filling material, and may have

351

rough walls. Artificial joint surfaces produced by splitting rock blocks simulate this type of joint. The shear type joints are often composed of a myriad of intertwining surfaces, and can be approximated as smooth surfaces infilled with gouge. When the thickness of the filling material is more than about twice the height of the highest hills, the strength and deformability of the shear joint becomes that of the filling material (Goodman, 1970), except that, of course, the orientation of the joint controls the directions of allowable shearing in the filling material and the mass is consequently much stronger than a continuous mass of clay. Some early attempts at analysis assumed the rock to be composed of a filled joint in the worst possible orientation, but this is wrong, and far too costly. Most of the attention hereafter is addressed to the extension type fractures, that is rough, unfilled joints.

Parameters of behaviour

The mechanical behaviour of jointed rock masses is governed by the properties of each joint and the mutual arrangement of joint-bounded blocks. Hills rising above a mean plane through a joint surface create 'roughness' which in turn generates dilatancy and a dilatant contribution to shear strength. Idealized conceptual models of regular asperities have their counterparts in actual rock masses and yield useful conclusions. The compressive strength of the wall rock governs the loss of dilatancy with normal load and accordingly is an important parameter of jointed rocks in applications where the normal load is not very low, for example, in many applications underground. The flexural strength of the rock is important in the frequent cases where eccentric loads on joint-bounded blocks produce bending, as for example in rock slopes, foundations, and underground openings in stratified or schistose rock. The tension strength, as measured by a point load or Brazilian type indirect tension test, is especially relevant to blocky rock masses as the loosening occasioned by deformations on joints throws blocks into edge-to-face contacts, creating tension within blocks and, eventually, splitting the blocks. Tension cracks occur in sliding rock masses with non-persistent joints, the tension cracks crossing the rock bridges to complete the outline of the eventual rock slide (Goodman, 1972). When the spacing between joints of different sets is quite different, the resulting long blocks can overturn, leading to rotational shearing modes. Columns of several blocks can also overturn even when individual joint blocks are not slender. Frictional resistance in rotational shearing can be significantly lower than in plane sliding; in fact it can be lower than the 'residual' frictional resistance. Minor geological details are often quite important in particular cases and may overshadow other aspects of joint behaviour. For example, slight imbrication of blocks, i.e. a staggered arrangement, can significantly increase the resistance to toppling of slopes. The geologist needs to keep his eyes open for relevant details. (But this is only practicable if he is a full partner in the analytical process.)

Laboratory tests

Blocks containing joints can be drilled with the joint surface at about 25° to the long axis of the core and tested in triaxial compression. The ends of the specimen have to be smooth and properly aligned in order to permit unrestrained lateral motion. Intact triaxial samples can be failed at moderate confining pressure to simulate shear joints, which can then be tested without change of set-up. Block samples, drill cores containing joints, and casts of joint surface replicas (Schneider, 1975) can be tested conveniently in direct shear. Large deformation is then possible and controlled normal displacement as well as controlled normal stress testing modes are possible. However, most tests done to date have maintained the normal stress constant since this gives a lower strength estimate, as discussed later.

Behaviour laws

Normal deformations in joints are highly non-linear, the stiffness going from zero to infinity as the normal stress proceeds from zero to 10 or 20 MPa. This is easily demonstrated. Test a cylinder of rock in compression, producing curve A in Figure 11.1, and cycle the load to remove most of the hysteresis. Then produce a split across the specimen, reseat it, and curve B results. The curve B–A is hyperbolic, with a continuously variable normal stiffness, as noted, and a maximum closure, V_{mc}. Rotate the top of the specimen to produce a mis-match and reload, producing curve C. Curve C–A is similar to curve B–A but has a larger value of V_{mc}. Figure 11.1 presents an equation closely fitting the actual data for the particular granite tested. All joint closing was essentially irreversible; the slope on unloading was identical for all three curves and belonged to the rock.

Shearing deformation at constant normal stress exhibits a peak–residual behaviour in extension joints. Dilatancy starts at a shear load half-way or more to the peak load and the maximum rate of dilatancy accompanies the peak. Dilatancy continues at a diminishing rate until the residual strength is reached. The peak shear strength is fairly well predicted by Ladanyi and Archambault's equation (Ladanyi and Archambault, 1970) because this model correctly accounts for the reduction of dilatancy and the increase in the area shearing through the asperities as the normal load is elevated. For example, with rough model joints cast in sulphur capping compound (Cyclap), the area shearing through asperities, a_s, varies with normal stress as

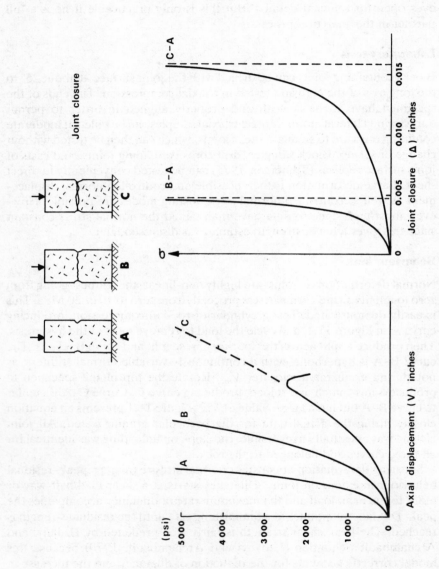

CLOSURE

$$\frac{\sigma - \sigma_o}{\sigma_o} = A \left(\frac{\Delta v}{v_{mc} - \Delta v} \right)^t$$

example: $\sigma_o = 67$ psi;

the mating joint gives:

$$\frac{\sigma - \sigma_o}{\sigma_o} = 3 \left(\frac{\Delta v}{0.0047 - \Delta v} \right)^{0.605}$$

the non mated joint gives:

$$\frac{\sigma - \sigma_o}{\sigma_o} = 5.95 \left(\frac{\Delta v}{0.0152 - \Delta v} \right)^{0.609}$$

Figure 11.1   Joint behaviour in compression

given in Figure 11.2, which agrees well with a formula included in Ladanyi's theory. The shear area in rock was estimated approximately by estimating the percentage of the total area exhibiting crushing after the test (research work performed by Rochard Thorpe, a graduate student in the Geological Engineering Group at Berkeley). The work was facilitated by colouring the crushed area black and comparing the appearance of the result to standards obtained by mixing varying percentages of black and white grains.

AREA SHEARING THROUGH ASPERITIES

Ladanyi: $\quad a_s = 1 - \left(1 - \dfrac{\sigma}{q_u}\right)^{1.5}$

our results: $\quad a_s = 1 - \left(1 - \dfrac{\sigma}{8000}\right)^{1.66}$

SHEAR AREA IN ROCK

$a_s = \%$ of surface sheared through asperities

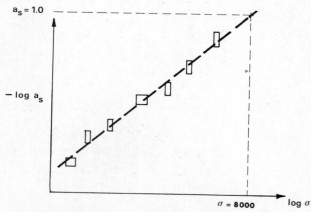

Figure 11.2 Dilatancy and shear under constant normal stress

Dilatancy at the peak shear stress can be measured at any normal stress directly from the direct shear test results. Figure 11.3 compares data for the Cylcap joints with Ladanyi's equation and again the comparison is favourable. The roughness angles on the joint surface can be measured as a function of wavelength according to the method of Rengers (1971). The measured rate of dilatancy extrapolated to zero normal stress agrees with a

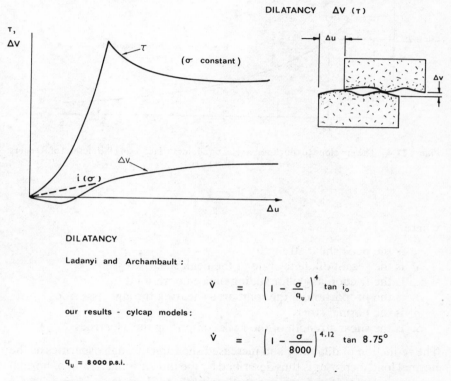

Figure 11.3 Proportion of shearing which occurs through asperities

roughness angle of $8 \cdot 75°$, which corresponds to a wavelength of $\frac{5}{8}$ inch (about $1 \cdot 5$ cm.) but this is about three times the peak shear displacement. The correct roughness angle corresponds to a base distance several times greater than the peak shear displacement because Renger's method uses the envelope to all roughness angles, whereas the joint finds some mean angle. Barton (1972) used a mean roughness measure.

$$\tau_p = \frac{\sigma(1 - a_s)(\dot{v} + \tan \phi_\mu) + a_s S_r}{1 - (1 - d_s)\dot{v} \tan \phi_\mu}$$

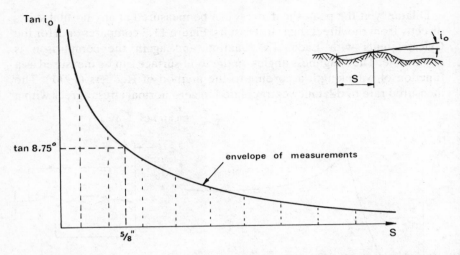

Figure 11.4 The envelope to roughness angles on a joint surface, using the method of Rengers (1971)

where

τ_p is the peak shear strength
$\dot{v}$ is the secant dilatancy rate at the peak shear stress
ϕ_μ is the friction angle for sliding on a smooth joint
a_s is the proportion of the joint area shearing through asperities
σ is the normal stress
S_r is the shear strength of the rock composing the asperities.

The reduction of dilatancy and increased shearing through asperities as the normal load increases is thus described by the dimensionless ratio of normal stress σ to unconfined compressive strength q_u (Ladanyi's formula has a transition pressure in place of q_u but the two are close in his examples). Comparison of shear specimens of hard quartz monzonite and a softer altered rhyolite porphyry are shown in Figure 11.5. Though both specimens were tested at the same normal pressure, the former has a low value of a_s and exhibited dilatancy whereas the latter has a high value of a_s and was non-dilatant.

Research

We are investigating shear tests at controlled normal displacement. A servo system, or a watchful operator, raises the pressure in the normal load ram to

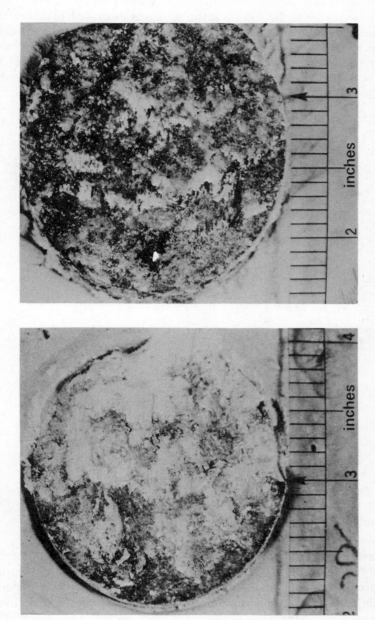

Figure 11.5 Photographs of two shear specimens after a shear test; left: quartz monzonite; right: altered rhyolite porphyry

maintain the normal displacement constant (Figure 11.6). The peak strength was increased by about 20 per cent in the two cases illustrated. In theory, the peakedness of the stress/strain curve can be lost entirely in this test mode, but it was not the case in these examples. This mode of shearing is applicable to natural cases where the direction of motion is prescribed, either by symmetry or by kinematics, as, for example, in the case of an acute wedge sliding down a line of intersection between two surfaces.

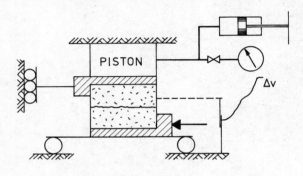

SHEAR WITH $\Delta V = 0$

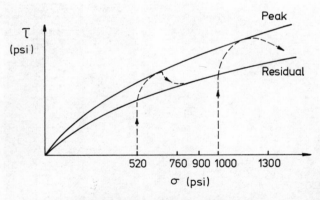

Figure 11.6 Shear with no dilatancy permitted

At elevated normal pressures, e.g. 20 MPa for smooth joints in granite, 'stick-slip' may occur, as shown in Figure 11.7. The instabilities during sliding are associated with sudden energy release and are a possible model for earthquake mechanisms on faults. We have observed associated and often precursory phenomena as this takes place (Wang *et al.*, 1975). The resistivity of saturated specimens undergoing stick-slip sliding first decreases

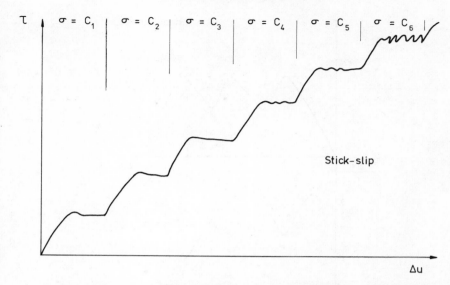

Figure 11.7 Stick-slip behaviour—a direct shear test series at successively higher normal pressures

and then increases as the stress is suddenly dropped on each event. (Figure 11.8). This is because the water is the electrical conducting element in the saturated granite; micro-cracks are presumed to occur as the shear stress builds up, with expulsion of water, as the instability progresses. (Figure 11.9 shows the contrasting resistivity changes in dry versus wet specimens, first reported by Brace *et al.*, 1965). Resistivity is a sensitive monitor of normal deformation in jointed rock. Changes in resistivity are mirrored by changes in pore pressure on each cycle, while dilatancy shows the opposite transient, i.e. an increase followed by a decrease when slip occurs (Figure 11.8).

Joint surveys

The prelude to all methods of analysis for jointed rock masses is a thorough joint survey, by means of which the system of discontinuities can be divided into sets, each scattered about a central tendency attitude (Müller, 1963). The latter is the direction of the vector representing the sum of all unit vectors normal to joints of a given set. Joints can be observed on walls of galleries, on outcrop surfaces, and in diamond drill cores and drill holes. In the latter case, the direction can be determined only by core orientation analysis. This may sometimes be based upon reference to known attitudes of

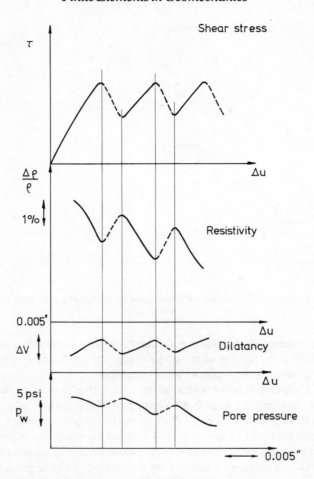

Figure 11.8 Variation of shear stress, resistivity, dilatancy and
water pressure with shearing displacement during stick-slip
events

recognizable reference planes, but will usually necessitate special down-the-
hole techniques, for example, marking the core stub with paint in inclined
holes; use of the Craelius core orienter in inclined holes; special drilling
techniques such as the Integral Sampling Method (Rocha, 1934) or the
Christensen orienting core barrel; or special geophysical surveys such as the
Dipmeter resistivity tool (Phillips, 1971) and the 'Seisviewer'. Some of these
tools and methods are discussed by Goodman (1975).

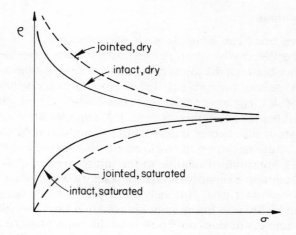

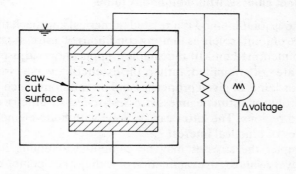

Resistivity Measurement

Figure 11.9 Resistivity changes during loading; above: variation with normal stress; below: experimental set-up

11.2 ANALYSIS OF STRESSES AND DEFORMATIONS

Stress analysis in jointed rocks is possible by a number of different numerical techniques including analogy to an equivalent continuum, ubiquitous joint analysis, finite element analysis, dynamic relaxation, and the boundary element method.

Equivalent continua

A jointed rock mass can sometimes be approximated as an equivalent continuum, the deformability properties of the joints together with the average distance between the joints being used to construct the constants of an 'equivalent' anisotropic material. Then closed form and series solutions of the theory of elasticity of an anisotropic elastic solid can be applied to rock mechanics problems. The method is potentially applicable to cases where one wishes to study the effect of small rock deformations on the stability of a man-made structure resting on the rock, especially where the stress changes within the rock are minimal relative to the initial stresses. An equivalent linear continuum approximation is not satisfactory when one's interest is centred in the rock mass itself, especially where joint deformations are large, because of the highly non-linear joint deformation laws previously introduced. For example, one does not know what dilatancy angle to input until the sign of the shear stress has been determined (Goodman and Dubois, 1972).

Finite element analysis with 'ubiquitous joints'

The ubiquitous joint method is a related numerical approach that examines the presence of joints solely as limiting conditions of a stress state computed for an unjointed medium. In the simplest application, adjustments to the stress state are not attempted; rather, the extent of 'overstressed' regions is examined for joints of given properties and orientations. Such an approach can provide only an estimate unless stresses are redistributed away from the overstressed regions. The latter can be done with finite element computations in cases of practical interest.

For example, the stresses may be computed assuming linear, elastic behaviour everywhere. An examination of sliding and opening conditions in any element is then possible if a direction is specified for the joint plane in that element. Such an examination of stresses in all elements provides a list of 'overstressed' elements. The applied loads are reduced until there is a limiting condition in only one, the most critically stressed, element in the list (de Rouvray and Goodman, 1972). This level of applied loading is a limiting load for elastic behaviour. However, it is far below the limiting load for stability and therefore the analysis must continue.

The critical element is considered to have 'failed' and is suitably modified, e.g. it is assigned low stiffnesses if opened and reduced stiffnesses if sheared. The 'failed' element must become anisotropic, with principal directions parallel to the joint plane. There is an additional increment of applied load that will then add one more element to the list of failed elements; this element will also be 'modified'. A number of such increments will produce an ultimate load for the structural system, dictated either by limiting deformations, geometric extent and location of the 'failed region', or instability. It is technically possible to treat two or more directions of jointing simultaneously, but only one can be permitted to 'fail'. Dilatancy, and joint closing can also be input. Large deformations can be accommodated more readily using joint elements explicitly in the mesh.

Finite element analysis with joint elements

Programs for two-dimensional finite element analysis with joint elements are in common usage. Linear stiffness matrices for joint elements are given in (Goodman and St. John, 1976). Iterations or loading in small increments is necessary, in practice, to satisfy the non-linear stress deformation laws previously discussed. Finite element analysis with joint elements is feasible where a few joints are important to a particular problem, as, for example, where several prominent discontinuities compromise the stability of a valuable structure like the roof or wall of an underground power house. In this case, the results of the analysis may be helpful in interpreting the meaning of instrument readings and in assessing the usefulness of alternative methods of remedial treatment. Finite element analysis may not be helpful when the locations and properties of individual joints are not well known and when the problem is not clearly presented.

In a typical problem of interest in applied rock mechanics, one wishes to compute the rock deformations resulting from an excavation which disturbs an initial state of equilibrium. The computation begins with the pre-excavation state of stress input in each element. To assure that the initial stresses are in equilibrium, it is simplest to input them identically throughout the mesh. If there is an initial free surface near the excavation, if the field of interest is large, or if the topography is irregular, initial stresses must vary from element to element. In such cases, an initial series of computer runs must precede excavation in order to compute an acceptable approximation for the pre-excavation stresses. Displacements will then be zeroed as the excavation begins.

To avoid numerical difficulties, one should not step out too far from this initial state of stress in any element on the first computation. By simulation of the excavation process the initial equilibrium can be changed gradually in all elements. Excavation sequence can be modelled in at least three different ways. The elastic moduli and Poisson's ratios of the elements to be excavated can be lowered progressively. Or, the mesh can be repeatedly reconstructed to omit elements as they are excavated; this would only be feasible if the computer does all the work of mesh regeneration. Another approach used by the writer is the insertion of joint elements along the excavation perimeter; the normal and shear stresses within these joints are zeroed gradually by adding normal and shear stress increments to the joint.

Since the normal stiffness of a joint varies greatly with changing normal stress, as previously shown, a continuous updating of normal stiffness in joint elements is required as excavation proceeds. Further, many joints will experience 'shear failure' as a result of reduced normal stress or excessive shear displacements. Consequently, either very small excavation steps, or iteration between excavation steps, must be used. Load transfer and variable stiffness algorithms for iterations with joints are discussed in Goodman (1975). For joint decompression, a load or stiffness correction is made by accepting the computed displacements and recomputing the normal stress. However, for joint compression, load or stiffness corrections should be made by accepting the computed normal stresses and recomputing the displacements. Computation past the peak shear stress is required as well, since the first joint element shear 'failures' invariably precede completion of the excavation. An elastic-plastic model is easiest to duplicate but a brittle elastic-plastic model is more realistic. Load transfer, or variable stiffness with negative stiffness coefficients can be used to move from the peak towards the residual strength as excavation proceeds. Difficulty will be experienced if increments of excavation are too large because of the close coupling between peak shear strength and normal stress, previously demonstrated.

To duplicate dilatant behaviour, St. John's procedure is recommended (Goodman and St. John, 1976). Presume that an increment of shear displacement (Δu) has just been computed in a joint element. Knowing the local normal stress, compute the current dilatancy rate ($\dot{v}$) (see Figure 11.3), and the current normal stiffness (k_n). The product (k_n)($\dot{v}$)(Δu) gives the normal stress increment that will develop if dilatant displacement is suppressed. Assume the latter to be true and add this increment of normal stress to the initial stress for the next computation run. If in fact normal displacement is permitted, it will occur on the next cycle, with consequent loss in the normal stress caused by dilatancy. On the other hand, if normal displacement is prevented, the element's normal stress will have been correctly enlarged.

Finite element analysis with joint elements to simulate fractures has been coupled with programs for flow in fractures to permit analysis of flow through fractured rock (Witherspoon and Gale, 1976). Such programs have wide potential application, including engineering for dams, groundwater in fractured rock, geothermal development; oil, gas or heat production from hydraulically fractured reservoirs; and analysis of reservoir-induced seismicity.

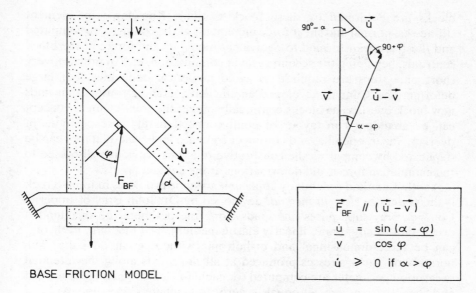

BASE FRICTION MODEL

$$\vec{F}_{BF} \; / / \; (\vec{u} - \vec{v})$$

$$\frac{\dot{u}}{v} \; = \; \frac{\sin (\alpha - \varphi)}{\cos \varphi}$$

$$\dot{u} \; \geqslant \; 0 \; \text{if} \; \alpha > \varphi$$

Figure 11.10 Base friction model test set-up

Other numerical methods

Finite difference methods, with time as an explicit variable, have been developed for dynamic problems. Some current codes used for computing effects of weapons have the capability of representing joints ('slip lines'). Such programs can offer solutions to problems posed by excavation in initially stressed jointed rock if computations are continued through the decay of all transients to a final state. It is not necessarily more expensive to compute the transient effects of a sudden unload in order to solve for its final effect, than to pursue the iterations or progressive excavation required to solve such problems with finite element methods. Cundall (1977) demonstrates this using dynamic relaxation to follow the movements of rock blocks after a sudden excavation. Dynamic relaxation is particularly attractive, however, for dynamic problems in jointed rocks and for problems with large deformations.

Cundall's method might be termed 'rigid element analysis'. Blocks are considered to move as rigid bodies with elastic contacts. Beginning with an initial configuration of blocks, the initial stresses and body forces are summed for each block to compute the forces and moments on each block's centroid. The equations of motion for each block are then integrated to give the translations and rotations of each block at the end of the first time step. (Critical damping is introduced to avoid 'bouncing'.) Joints between blocks are deformed by these block motions. Knowing joint element stiffnesses, normal and shear force increments at the contacts are computed and these are transformed to equivalent moments and forces at the block centroids, beginning the second cycle of computation, etc. In practice, very short time steps are required to avoid numerical difficulties. For large deformations, Cundall developed an efficient searching routine that finds new block overlaps as blocks continually move; the joint element concept can be abandoned in favour of point connections at these positions of overlap. Shear, opening, and closing of contacts, and even dilatancy can be duplicated by comparing the constitutive relations previously discussed to the cumulative forces and deformations at the contact points.

Another method potentially applicable to static problems in jointed rock is the *boundary element method*, developed by Dr. John Bray of Imperial College. Bray superposes line loads along the perimeter of an intended excavation in an infinite, linearly elastic medium. The medium, in theory, can be three-dimensional and orthotropic without great difficulty. The normal and shear stresses produced at all the points along the intended excavation perimeter are computed for each line load. When these normal and shear stresses are set equal to zero, to simulate excavation, a set of simultaneous equations is generated whose solution gives the line load magnitudes required to meet the boundary conditions. Summation of the effects of all these line loads (termed 'fictitious loads' by Bray) then gives the stresses at all points of the infinite medium. Non-zero boundary loads can be accommodated readily by entering them, instead of zero, in the right-hand side vector of the simultaneous equations. Presumably, joints could be included by considering them as part of the excavation perimeter, which does not have to be continuous. Thus the boundary element method, with its simple input that models only the edges, not the interior of the space, has the potential to compute stresses throughout three-dimensional, anisotropic, jointed rock masses, with excavation of arbitrary shape.

Physical models

It is important to see the numerical methods in comparison with other analytical methods at the command of engineers for problems in rock mechanics. Scaled physical models are expensive and require complete reconstruction after each test to failure. However, they are still very appropriate for problems in jointed rock masses, especially in three dimensions. The material can be chosen to simulate real, non-linear behaviour, including loading in the post-peak region and failure. This is difficult to achieve numerically. Large block systems can be incorporated.

A relatively new model technique is the Base Friction model method (Goodman, 1975), depicted in Figure 11.10. A two-dimensional model, with joints, is pushed over a board developing frictional forces. These forces act through the centroid of each piece which is in motion relative to the board. The base friction force is always in the direction of relative slip between a particle and the underlying surface, as a result, limit equilibrium of block systems under gravity loading is correctly modelled, presuming the friction angle to be properly chosen, even though the deformability of the material used is incorrectly scaled. Particles which would acquire momentum in reality are not correctly modelled, and progressive failure developments are therefore only approximately simulated (Figure 11.11).

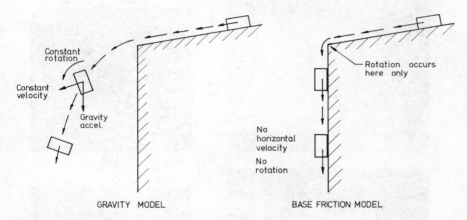

Figure 11.11 The approximation in the base friction experiment—momentum is not acquired by particles in motion

Using a mixture of plastic consistency containing flour, oil and sand, or alternatively using cork sheets, base friction models inexpensively include a large number of joints. Joint roughness, variable joint lengths, and other fine structural details can be input quickly. By employing an endless belt moving beneath the model, excavation sequence problems can be studied. Rock bolt systems can be studied by restricting movement of rocks along the lines of bolts and observing the changing failure modes with variations in bolt lengths, orientations and positions. Thus, the method is very useful for studying the effects of geological details on modes of failure in gravity loaded structures, such as the roofs of tunnels and mines and rock slopes (for examples, see Figure 11.12). As a result of base friction studies, the

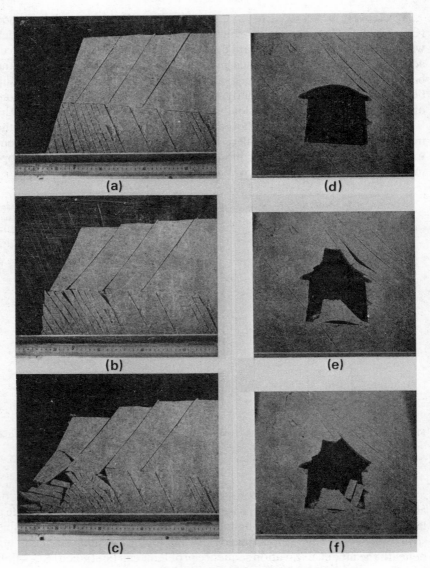

Figure 11.12 Examples of base friction model results

prototype for numerical or less distorted geomechanical models can be established more precisely, since neither the finite element model nor the scaled physical model can afford to include all structural features of the rock mass.

Limit equilibrium analyses

In cases involving rock failure, where the deformations up to the limit of equilibrium are not decisive, the direct calculation of limiting conditions can sometimes be accomplished satisfactorily. In fact, where the question of rock failure is foremost, the additional information that comes from a total study of the stresses and deformations may obscure the results and usefulness of the study. Limit equilibrium solutions have been developed for blocks and wedges sliding on joint planes (Wittke, 1966; John, 1968; and Londe *et al.*, 1970). A limit equilibrium solution can be developed for problems of toppling and sliding or multi-block systems in rock slopes. For example, Figure 11.13 shows a mode of failure of rock slopes involving

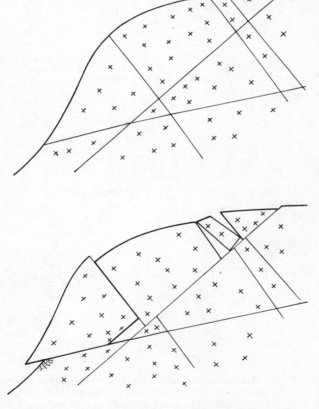

Figure 11.13   Two-block slide—an active block transfers load
to a passive block

sliding of a passive wedge by the transferred load from an active wedge. A limit equilibrium analysis of this mode is shown in Figure 11.14. Using stereographic projection procedures, complex three-dimensional wedges can be studied under varying water loads, gravity, and additional forces, so that dam abutment and foundation stability analyses can be made. The friction angle can be adjusted to account for uncertainty in joint orientations, a point that troubled Karl Terzaghi. Kinematic tests on the stereo-net

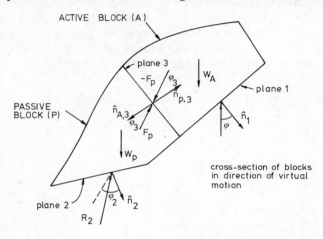

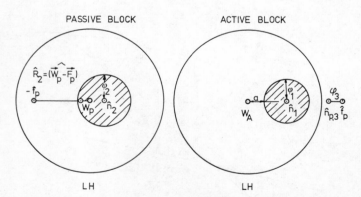

Figure 11.14 Two-block slide analysis on the stereographic projection. First, find the force $\vec{F}_p$ from the passive block to the active block required to stabilize the active block. Then, determine whether the opposite to this force $(-\vec{F}_p)$ can be supported by the passive block. W = weight. $\hat{\ }$ denotes a unit vector

allow critical block systems to be singled out for analysis. A theorem is helpful in this regard: of a large number of geometrically similar blocks, the largest is the most critical (Figure 11.15). This stems from the fact that friction decreases with normal stress. The larger the system of blocks, the higher the normal stresses along their bases, and therefore, the lower the friction will be.

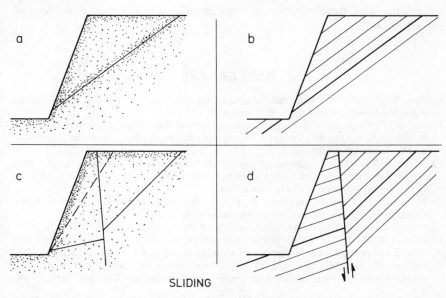

SLIDING

Figure 11.15 The most critical of a series of similar blocks is the largest one; in (a), the wedge for analysis is uniquely defined; in (b), the largest of five wedges is the one to analyse; in (c), a two block configuration is defined uniquely; in (d), the largest two block system is ruled more heavily. These are examples of conceptual models permitting limit equilibrium analyses

The importance of these analytical developments for limiting equilibrium calculations in jointed hard rocks is underscored by a number of case histories involving failure of large rock wedges, including the Malpasset Dam abutment, the Libby Reservoir slopes, and a number of mine pits. It is important to recognize when limit equilibrium analyses are acceptable and to save the more general tools for those situations where they can really be helpful and are necessary. These methods were elaborated by Goodman (1975), John (1968) and Londe *et al.* (1970).

11.3 CONCLUSION

Numerical methods are progressing rapidly as computers become more available. The powerful and general finite element methods are most useful where very specific problems are posed and where there is good knowledge about structure and properties. Other numerical schemes, including the boundary element methods and dynamic relaxation with rigid blocks, can be expected to find increasing application in rock mechanics, at the expense of finite element methods. The breadth of problems in rock mechanics and general uncertainty in the properties of jointed rock masses require continued use and development of limit equilibrium analyses and physical models as well.

REFERENCES

Barton, N. (1972). 'A model study of rock-joint deformation', *International Journal of Rock Mechanics and Mining Sciences*, **9**, 5.

Brace, W. F., Orange, A. S., And Madden, T. M. (1965). 'The effect of pressure on the electrical resistivity of water-saturated crystalline rocks', *Journal of Geophysical Research*, **70**, 5669.

Cundall, P. (1971). 'A computer model for simulating progressive large scale movements in blocky rock systems', *Proceedings of the International Symposium on Rock Fracture*, Nancy, ISRM, Paper 2–8.

de Rouvray, A. L. and Goodman, R. E. (1972). 'Finite element analysis of crack initiation in a block model', *Rock Mechanics*, **4**, 203.

Goodman, R. E. (1970). 'The deformability of joints', *ASTM, S.T.P. 477*, p. 174.

Goodman, R. E. (1972). 'Geological investigations to evaluate stability', *Proceedings of the 2nd International Conference on Stability for Open Pit Mines* (AIME), p. 125.

Goodman, R. E. and Dubois, J. (1972). 'Duplication of dilatancy in analysis of jointed rocks', *Journal of Soil Mechanics and Foundations Division, ASCE*, **98**, 399.

Goodman, R. E. (1975). *Methods of Geological Engineering in Discontinuous Rocks*, West Publishing Co., St. Paul.

Goodman, R. E. and St. John, C. (1976). 'Finite element analysis for discontinuous rocks', in *Numerical Methods in Geotechnical Engineering*, McGraw-Hill, New York.

John, K. W. (1968). 'Graphical stability analysis of slopes in jointed rock', *Proceedings of the 11th Symposium on Rock Mechanics*, AIME, p. 69.

Ladanyi, B. and Archambault, G. (1970). 'Simulation of shear behavior of a jointed rock mass', *Proceedings of the 11th Symposium on Rock Mechanics* (AIME), p. 105.

Londe, P., Vigier, G. and Vorneringer, R. (1970). 'Stability of rock slopes, graphical methods', *Journal of Soil Mechanics and Foundations Division*, ASCE, **96**, SM4.

Müller, L. (1963). *Der Felsbau*, Vol. 1, F. Enke, Stuttgart.

Phillips, F. C. (1971). 'The use of stereographic projection in structural geology', Edward Arnold, London.

Rengers, N. (1971), 'Unebenheit und Reibungswiderstand von Gesteinstrennflächen', Veröffentlichungen des Institut für Bodenmechanik und Felsmechanik, Karlsruhe, Heft 47.

Rocha, M. (1971). 'A new method of integral sampling of rock masses', *Rock Mechanics*, **3**, 1.

Schneider, H. J. (1975). 'Reibungs- und Verformungsverhalten von Trennflächen in Fels', Veröffentlichungen des Instituts für Bodenmechanik und Felsmechanik, Karlsruhe, Heft 67.

Wang, C. Y., Goodman, R. E., Sundaram, P. N., and Morrison, F. (1975). 'Electrical resistivity of granite in frictional sliding: applications to earthquake prediction', *Geophysical Research Letters*, **2**, 12, 525.

Witherspoon, P. A. and Gale, J. E. (1976). 'Mechanical and hydraulic properties of rocks related to induced seismicity', Proceedings of the Conference on Induced Seismicity, Banff, in *Engineering Geology* (in press).

Wittke, W. (1966). 'Berechnungsmöglichkeiten der Standsicherheit von Böschungen in Fels', Deutsche Gesellschaft für Erd- und Grundbau.

CHAPTER 12

The Elasto-Plastic Analysis in the Design Practice of Underground Openings

K. Kovári

12.1 INTRODUCTION

The increasing world-wide activity in the construction of underground openings and the frequency of larger projects even under difficult geotechnical conditions call for a continual improvement in design principles. As in every branch of engineering a rational approach in design procedures is sought for. This means that important constructional decisions should be made on the basis of a cautious qualitative and quantitative analysis of all relevant factors. Along with engineering judgement based upon the engineer's own fund of experience there are at his disposal today the modern technical aids of rock mechanics measurements and the use of computer programs.

An attempt is made in this paper to give a survey of the use of numerical procedures in the solution of certain problems connected with underground openings in which the resort to numerical analysis can be profitable. We shall discuss the scientific aspects of computer application only as far as they are relevant to engineering practice. The outlook of the researcher can differ considerably from that of the practising engineer. This could be one of the reasons for the fact that in tunnelling the use of numerical methods is, in many places, either rejected completely or excessively over-rated.

Commonsense computer application requires both a deep understanding and a 'feel' for the complex problems that arise in tunnelling. Therefore the use of computers cannot make up for inadequate experience of intuitive insight into the problems. The information obtained with the help of numerical analysis thus supplements the basic knowledge that is expected of a tunnelling engineer irrespective of the use of computer aids. One is less likely to go wrong, therefore, when one starts from the accumulated knowledge already available in tunnelling practice and then fits the information gained by the computer application into the framework of this basic knowledge.

The question: 'Under which circumstances and to what extent should stress analysis be carried out in a particular case?' can be answered from the purely economic point of view. The numerical results should justify the cost expenditure. The importance of the structure, the importance of a constructional decision (setting limits to certain risks) and experience in working with computer programs are some of the factors involved in the decision to use the computer. In any case there must be a healthy relationship between the totality of the assumptions and the real situation. In the following we shall not deal with cases in which stress and deformation analysis are required by some authorities, even if they are not at all appropriate.

12.1.1 The computational models

The mathematical models should, on the one hand, approximate as closely as possible the real situation and, on the other hand, be as simple as possible. Because of these opposing requirements the engineer is continually faced with the task of achieving some compromise.

In the process of simplification, that is idealizing the problems, it is advantageous to break the process down into three parts (Kovári, 1972). Thus the models for material behaviour, for the statical system, and for the load quantities will be discussed individually and in the interpretation of the results of the computation their influence will be handled separately. An overall view of all the simplifications must however be kept in mind to avoid unjustified refinement in one aspect of the modelling.

12.1.2 The material model

In the construction of underground openings all forms of occurrence of soil and hard rock can be encountered. For stress analysis it is the mechanical properties of the material on a large scale that is of consequence. When we consider that the material properties are dependent also upon the presence of water and the method of excavation, the limits that are set upon every computational method become apparent. In this paper we restrict ourselves to the discussion of elastic–ideal plastic material behaviour. This material model can be described by means of a small number of easily interpretable material parameters, even in the case of anisotropy. Despite the broad practical field of application of this concept of materials, its limitations and certain disadvantages are also apparent. Essentially, its limitations are conditioned by two factors: firstly, by the substantial simplification of the stress–strain relationships and secondly, by the fact that rheological behaviour is not taken into account.

12.1.3 The statical system

In engineering practice the dimensioning of underground structures is still dominated by the two-dimensional system under the condition of plane-strain. In many cases, however, the consideration of three-dimensional systems is not only desirable but also fully justified economically. The rock surrounding the opening is treated as a continuum which extends far enough away from the opening so that its effect on the stress distribution is negligible at the boundaries of the system. Particular shear zones or important joints can, however, be treated as discontinuities. In two-dimensional analysis constructional components, such as rock anchors and tunnel linings, are best simulated by rod and truss elements respectively (Kovári, 1969).

12.1.4 The load quantities

The primary state of stress (or the system of forces that derives from it) represents the most important and the most frequent type of loading. The primary state of stress is, however, the Achilles heel of stress analysis, since the possibilities of measuring stresses *in situ* are very limited (Grob, Kovári, *et al.*, 1975). Paradoxically the measuring techniques are not available just where the knowledge of the primary state of stress would be especially useful, namely in soil or soft rock. The one quantity that is known with some reliability is the vertical stress σ_V, which from statical considerations must be approximately equal to the overburden pressure. But even here exceptions are possible. These are due to the structure of the rock mass or its topography. The horizontal pressure σ_H is not known *a priori*. Calculations based upon elastic theory requiring a knowledge of the Poisson's ratio ν and predicted by the formula

$$\sigma_H = \frac{\nu}{1-\nu}\,\sigma_V$$

contradict the real nature of the primary stresses. Therefore, we are forced to assume a horizontal pressure coefficient λ (ratio of horizontal to vertical stress) which is independent of the material properties. Should there be some data on the strength of the rock mass, then it is at least possible to estimate the maximum and the minimum values of λ according to Rankine's theory. Even for plane-strain problems, in many cases the directions of the principal stresses should also be known, especially in the case of unsymmetrical cross sections. In the case of large cavities the knowledge of the complete stress tensor is desirable.

Further types of load that are introduced into the computations are the water pressure on the tunnel lining and loads simulating the rock pressure in some cases.

12.2 THE THEORETICAL BASIS OF THE ELASTO-PLASTIC ANALYSIS

12.2.1 General discussion

A material may be classified as elasto-plastic if after loading beyond a certain limit a permanent (plastic) deformation remains after unloading. A system is described as elasto-plastic if, in any part or zone of the system, plastic deformations occur. Such domains are called plastic zones.

The deformation and strength behaviour of an elastic-ideal plastic material is described by the basic concepts of Hooke's law, yield condition, and flow rule.

12.2.1.1 Hooke's law

Concerning Hooke's law, it needs only to be mentioned that an isotropic material is described by two material parameters, the transverse anisotropic material by five, and the general anisotropic material by twenty-one parameters.

12.2.1.2 The yield condition for geotechnical applications

In general, for geotechnical applications, the Coulomb yield condition is applied, either in its usual form or in the extended Drucker-Prager (1952) form. In both cases a further condition is introduced to account for the partial or complete reduction of tensile strength (tension cut-off). According to Coulomb's yield condition for an isotropic material no failure will occur if, at the point considered in the medium, the following condition is fulfilled for any arbitrary oriented element of area (Figure 12.1):

$$|\tau| < \sigma \tan \phi + c \qquad (12.1)$$

The material parameters ϕ and c are called the angles of internal friction and cohesion respectively. Shield (1955) has shown that the above condition (12.1) leads in terms of the principal stresses to six relationships of the form:

$$\sigma_i \leq m\sigma_j + b \qquad (\sigma_i > \sigma_j) \qquad (12.2)$$

where

$$m = \frac{1 + \sin \phi}{1 - \sin \phi} \quad \text{and} \quad b = \frac{2c \cos \phi}{1 - \sin \phi}$$

In principal stress space $(\sigma_1, \sigma_2, \sigma_3)$ the six relationships (12.2) are represented by a right, irregular hexagonal pyramid whose axis is equally inclined to the principal axes as shown in Figure 12.2.

In plane-strain problems only failure mechanisms are of interest in which the failure surface is normal to the plane. In these circumstances the analysis

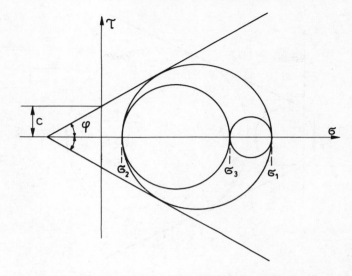

Figure 12.1 Mohr's representation of the Coulomb yield criterion

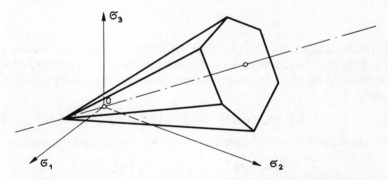

Figure 12.2 The Coulomb yield criterion in the principal stress space (Shield's representation)

may be restricted to a consideration of the two principal stresses σ_1 and σ_2 that lie in this plane. The yield condition is then defined in the plane of principal stresses (σ_1, σ_2) by the straight line

$$\sigma_1 = m\sigma_2 + b; \qquad (\sigma_1 > \sigma_2)$$

and its mirror image with respect to the 45°-line (Figure 12.3).

In order to obtain a uniform treatment of isotropic and anisotropic materials (at least for the two-dimensional case) it is necessary to express the

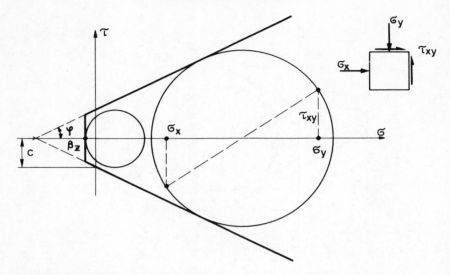

Figure 12.3   The Coulomb yield criterion for plane-strain conditions in terms of the stress components

basic relationship, Equation (1.12) in the general stress components σ_x, σ_y and τ_{xy} (Figure 12.3). If both sides of Equation (12.1) are squared and σ and τ are replaced by σ_x, σ_y, τ_{xy} the yield condition for the isotropic material is obtained, *viz.*

$$F_1 = 4\tau_{xy}^2 + (\sigma_x - \sigma_y)^2 - [(\sigma_x + \sigma_y) + 2\cot\phi]^2 \sin^2\phi = 0 \qquad (12.3)$$

For a material with tensile strength β_z the following condition also holds:

$$F_2 = 4\tau_{xy}^2 + (\sigma_x - \sigma_y)^2 - (\sigma_x + \sigma_y + 2\beta_z)^2 = 0. \qquad (12.4)$$

If the material is layered or contains a regular pattern of joints, then other yield conditions hold for these planes of weakness. If the shear resistance on these planes is described by the Coulomb parameters $\bar{\phi}$ and $\bar{c}$, there is, in addition to the conditions $F_1 = 0$ and $F_2 = 0$, a third condition $F_3 = 0$. Choosing the co-ordinate system so that the y-axis is normal to the direction of the layering, we obtain the simple relationship

$$F_3 = |\tau_{xy}| - \sigma_y \tan\bar{\phi} - \bar{c} = 0 \qquad (12.5)$$

writing Equation (12.3) in the form

$$(\sqrt{2}\tau_{xy})^2 + \left(\frac{\sigma_x - \sigma_y}{\sqrt{2}}\right)^2 = 2\left(\frac{\sigma_x + \sigma_y}{2} + \phi\right)^2 \sin^2\phi$$

and equation (4) in the form

$$(\sqrt{2}\tau_{xy})^2 + \left(\frac{\sigma_x - \sigma_y}{\sqrt{2}}\right)^2 = 2\left(\frac{\sigma_x + \sigma_y}{2} + \beta_z\right)^2$$

it may easily be seen that they each represent a right circular cone (Figure 12.4) in the stress space (σ_x, σ_y, $\sqrt{2}\tau_{xy}$). The axes of the cone coincide respectively with the bisector of the angle between the axes of the normal stresses. The vertex of the cone, for the condition of a complete tension

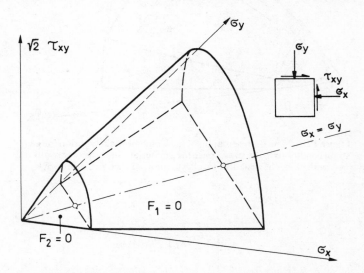

Figure 12.4 The representation of the Coulomb yield criterion with 'tension cut-off' for plane-strain conditions in the stress space

cut-off, lies at the origin of the co-ordinate system. The condition of anisotropy, Equation (12.5), is represented in the stress-space by two planes which intersect both cones. The yield conditions are shown in Figure 12.5 for the positive stress space $\tau_{xy} \geq 0$. In Figure 12.6 a section $((\sigma_x + \sigma_y)/2 = \text{constant})$ normal to the cone axis is shown.

The well-known Drucker–Prager yield condition

$$F = -\alpha I_\sigma + \sqrt{II_\sigma} - k = 0 \qquad (12.6)$$

is an extended form of the Coulomb condition. The quantities I_σ and II_σ represent the basic stress invariants of the stress tensor and the stress deviator respectively; α and κ are material constants. In the principal stress space, Equation (12.6) represents a cone with the same axis as the pyramid resulting from Shield's representation. The section in the deviatoric plane

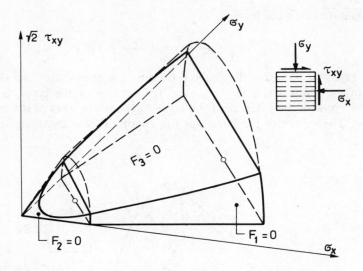

Figure 12.5   The representation of the Coulomb yield criterion for plane strain conditions in the stress space for a material with 'tension cut-off' and with planes of weakness parallel to the σ_x-direction (anisotropy)

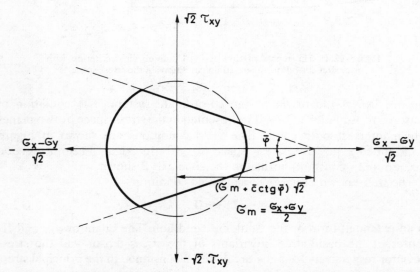

Figure 12.6   Section of the yield surface in the case of anisotropy in a plane $\sigma_x + \sigma_y =$ constant

(Figure 12.7) shows that it is possible in various ways to relate the two yield conditions or their associated material constants (Reyes, 1966). For the plane-strain conditions it is recommended that the cone inside and touching the pyramid is used. In this case the conversion formulas for the material parameters are:

$$\alpha = \frac{\tan \phi}{\sqrt{(g + 12 \tan^2 \phi)}} \quad \text{and} \quad k = \frac{3c}{\sqrt{(g + 12 \tan^2 \phi)}}$$

Because of its closed form and the continuity of the derivation (see Section 12.2.1.3–Flow Rule) the Drucker–Prager condition is frequently used in computer programs. In the case of anisotropy or under the condition of

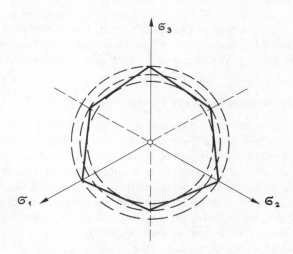

Figure 12.7 Section of the yield surface of Coulomb–Shield in a plane $\sigma_1 + \sigma_2 + \sigma_3 = $ constant indicating different possibilities for corresponding Drucker–Prager yield conditions

tension cut-off this advantage is partially lost. For two-dimensional application, the forms Equation (12.2) and Equation (12.6) are both of equal value for numerical analysis. But since the Coulomb condition is more deeply anchored in engineering practice and, in addition, it allows for a unique description of the anisotropic material, it is given preference over the Drucker–Prager condition. The Coulomb condition also permits a simple clear and rapid graphical check to be made on the state of stress with the aid of the Mohr stress circle.

12.2.1.3 *The flow rule*

The flow rule gives information about the plastic strain rate $\{\dot{\epsilon}\}^p$ in the state of flow. For the elastic-ideal plastic material (such as different metals) it appears that the so called normality condition

$$\{\dot{\epsilon}\}^p = \lambda \frac{\partial F}{\partial \{\sigma\}} \tag{12.7}$$

is appropriate both from the theoretical point of view (Hill, 1967) and from the results of experimental investigations (Nadai, 1950). In Equation (12.7) λ is a constant of proportionality not yet determined. The normality condition implies that the plastic strain rate $\{\dot{\epsilon}\}^p$ lies in the stress space in a direction normal to the yield surface. A direct consequence of this result is the fact that, theoretically, a volume change in the state of flow results for Coulomb materials. The validity of the normality condition is a matter of much dispute for materials of the earth's crust. For this reason it is considered quite valid if for the purpose of numerical analysis other relationships (Malina, 1969; Wittke, Wallner, *et al.*, 1972) and considerations are taken into account.

12.2.2 The verification of theory by experiment

Because the computational procedure for elasto-plastic analysis using the finite element method is well documented, it suffices here to draw attention to only a few of the important points. Because of the non-linear character of the problem, which is implicit in the flow rule [Equation (12.7)], the loads must, after the yield condition is reached (in any point of the system), be applied incrementally. For each increment an iterative method must be used. The well-known 'initial stress' approach of Zienkiewicz, Valliappan, *et al.* (1969) seems to be the most suitable method.

Several metals behave according to the elastic–ideal plastic material laws over a wide range of strains. Thus the possibility of an experimental verification of the theory, i.e. of the validity of the constitutive relationships and of the computational procedures, is offered. One such experimental study has been carried out on a steel plate with a central hole subjected to an uni-axial tensile force (Kovári, Amstad, *et al.*, 1971). The dimensions of the plate were $1500 \times 275 \times 5$ mm and the radius of the hole was 50 mm (Figure 12.8).

A total of 40 precision bolts were fixed to the plate surrounding the hole for the purpose of measuring changes of length in the direction of the longitudinal axis and at right angles to it. Four of these bolts are shown in Figure 12.8. The tensile force was increased in steps and at each stage the deformations were measured using a precision instrument. Numerical investigation of the system was carried out with the computer program STAUB

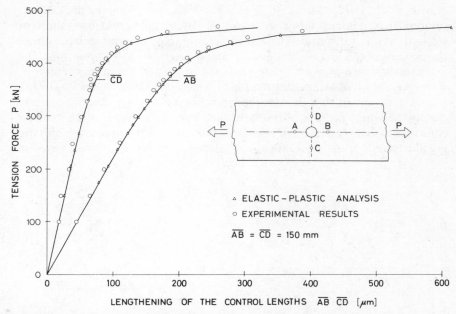

Figure 12.8 Axial tension of a perforated steel plate up to the state of collapse. Measured and computed load deformation relationship for the control lengths $\overline{AB}$ and $\overline{CD}$

employing experimentally determined material constants for the steel. The results obtained are exemplified by the load–deformation diagrams for the pairs of points AB and CD (Figure 12.8). The good agreement between computed and observed deformations shows that, at least for ideal material behaviour (metals), the theoretical basis of the method, i.e. the constitutive relationships and the algorithms are beyond criticism.

The theoretical (computational) check on the experimental results of other authors (Zienkiewicz, Best, *et al.*, 1970; Zienkiewicz, Nayak, *et al.*, 1972) has also shown similar agreement.

12.2.3 On the plastic behaviour of rocks

The actual behaviour of soft and hard rocks deviates—as was already mentioned—in many ways from the elastic–ideal plastic material model. We want to deal here with one point that has been given little attention, that is with the process of the loss of strength as the rock passes from the condition of the peak shear strength to that of the residual shear strength. The incorporation of the reduction of strength into finite element computations has already been attempted (Zienkiewicz, Best,. *et al.*, 1970; Zienkiewicz,

Nayak, *et al.*, 1972; Gates, 1972; Hoeg, 1972). As a basis for the calculations one has, it is true, information only about the upper and lower limits of strength at one's disposal. There is but scanty information available about the process of the loss of strength accompanying plastic deformations. The decisive influence of plastic deformations on the reduction of strength is, however, shown by strain-controlled tri-axial tests (Kovári and Tisa, 1975). In this new type of tri-axial test the lateral pressure is varied continuously during the whole process of fracture, such that the stress–strain curve ε, σ coincides with a prescribed straight line. In Figure 12.9 two tests of this type are illustrated for the ε_1, σ_1 and σ_2, σ_1 planes respectively. In this figure the

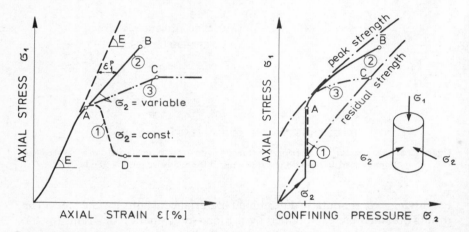

Figure 12.9 Strain dependence of the tri-axial compressive strength of rocks as shown by the 'strain-controlled tri-axial tests' II and III

classical triaxial test I under conditions of constant lateral pressure is also shown (by the dotted line). The strain-controlled tests are represented by the lines II and III. Until point A is reached (which indicates the start of non-linear behaviour) the lateral pressure is constant in all three tests and it remains constant in the conventional test I. In tests II and III, however, the lateral pressure is continuously changed (in this case increased), in order to obtain the straight lines, e.g. AB and AC in the ε_1, σ_1 (left hand) diagram. Since the slopes of these lines were chosen smaller than the elastic modulus E of the material, it is evident that plastic deformations ε_1^p are occurring in this loading region. It follows, therefore, that the material is continually in a state of failure or very close to failure. The corresponding loading history shown in the plane σ_2, σ_1 in the right hand side of Figure 12.9 represents the actual test result. Here it may be seen, that for test specimen II the plastic deformation is substantially less than for test specimen III. These tests show clearly that the peak and residual strength merely represent extreme values. The process of the loss of strength, which in real geotechnical situations is accompanied by stress changes, needs to be further investigated. It should be mentioned in passing, that it is possible with a single test specimen to determine the Mohr envelopes for the peak and residual strengths by appropriately running the strain controlled test (Figure 12.10).

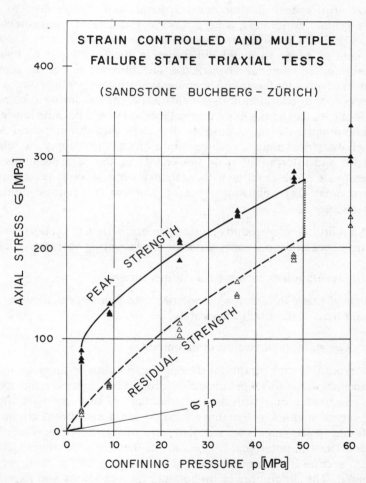

Figure 12.10 Peak and residual strength failure envelopes determined with a single test specimen in comparison with the results of 18 conventional tri-axial tests

12.3 TYPICAL COMPUTATIONAL PROBLEMS IN TUNNELLING

Static investigations may be required in the planning stage, during construction and sometimes after completion of the structure. At the planning stage the data forming the basis of the computations are often very uncertain. Despite this fact important and far-reaching constructional decisions (shape and size of profile, type and quantity of supports) must generally be made beforehand. This is especially true for highly mechanized constructional methods. But even if flexible constructional methods are used to meet variable ground conditions, a best-possible estimate of the geotechnical situation and the associated response of the construction is necessary beforehand in order to avoid difficulties in the settlement of financial accounts between owner and contractor. The dimensioning of the supports of a tunnel or other underground openings is not always possible on the basis of observations or considerations of field measurements during its construction. From rock mechanics this empirical method would be quite logical and should be practised as far as possible. But even with this empirical design approach numerical methods can be very useful as they supply the relevant theory for the interpretation of the results of the measurements. The overstatement 'no observation without theory' certainly contains some truth in this context. The following types of problem can require numerical computations:

(1) Stability of underground openings, determination of support system.

(2) Influence of tunnel excavations on neighbouring structures and vice versa.

(3) Interpretation of rock mechanics measurements.

Although in many instances all three problem types occur together, it is expedient here to treat them separately.

12.3.1 The stability of underground openings

Under favourable rock conditions the opening requires neither a temporary nor a permanent support. For very difficult conditions, however, the opening can be constructed only with the immediate aid of very extensive support arrangements. In quickly changing geological conditions, both extremes are often found at the same site, and there are many situations which lie in between. The computational models must, therefore, be adapted to the structure section-by-section depending on the type of the rock pressure anticipated. The differences in the model representations find expression especially in the investigation of the interaction of the tunnel lining with the surrounding rock mass.

12.3.1.1   Computational models for rock masses with loosening pressure
Rock masses with loosening pressure are substantially self-supporting. There is no noticeable reduction in the cross-section of the opening (Prader, 1972). The overall deformations of the rock take place essentially before the introduction of the supports. The danger of loosening and rock-fall due to the presence of local defects in the rock, however, call for permanent and, in many instances, for temporary support as well. Unfavourable combinations of layers and joints, shattering effects of blasting and percolation of ground water can all contribute to the settling of a certain volume of material on to the lining, which exerts a pressure according to its deadweight. It belongs to the art of tunnelling to excavate the opening in a manner which protects the surrounding rock and to restrain the whole loosening process by immediate support measures and stop it altogether by means of permanent supports (Rabcewicz, 1963). Figure 12.11 shows examples of inadequate construction of the supports and a loosening phenomenon which took place years after the completion of the excavation. In many instances heavy lining is necessary only because of excessive blasting. Such a case is shown in Figure 12.12 together with a tunnel in the same rock but with smooth surfaces and with no lining at all.

Because the process of loosening occurs in parts of the tunnel which cannot be determined in advance and is influenced by uncontrollable factors, its prediction computationally appears to be out of the question (Terzaghi, 1946/1968). In this type of rock a reasonable appproach is to assume a loading in the roof-zone of the tunnel which corresponds to the estimated volume of the loosened material. The interaction of the lining with the rock mass is taken into account by the partial embedment of the tunnel lining in an elastic continuum. The modulus, E, of the continuum corresponds to the deformability of the rock (Figure 12.13). The lining itself is simulated by a truss structure of the same flexural rigidity EI and stiffness of compressibility (Kovári, 1969). In the computation the condition is applied that no tensile stress is transmitted between the rock and the lining. In some circumstances this condition necessitates an iterative procedure. A criticism of this computational model is that all computed results are dependent upon the estimated loading and are thus questionable. One must consider, however, that by means of such computations useful relationships between important factors, like the shape and size of the cross-section, the stiffness of the lining and the deformability of the rock, may be established. In this way a reasonable parametric study can be carried out. Optimistic and pessimistic estimates of the loading q_v can be made, by considering the constructional method (protective or destructive excavation), the rock structure (jointing, stratification) and the size of the opening. Similar considerations are valid for the modulus, E, of the rock.

Figure 12.11 Overbreak in horizontally stratified rock as a result of inadequately constructed supports; abandoned tunnels (Photographs: ISETH)

Figure 12.12 Two different blasting techniques applied in the same rock at the construction of adjacent highway tunnels (Photographs: COEPE, Rio de Janeiro)

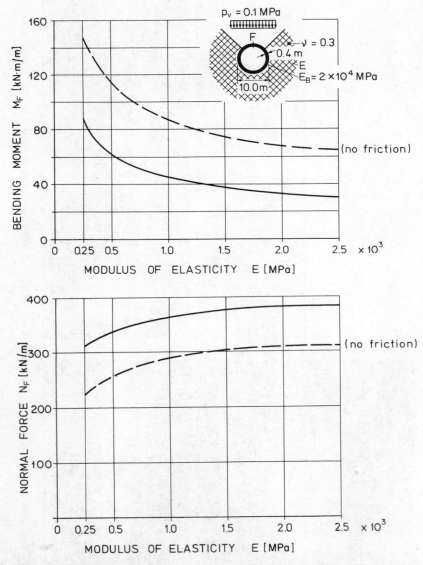

Figure 12.13 Moments and normal forces of an embedded tube in relation to the modulus of elasticity of the ground with or without wall friction

As an example of such an investigation we consider once again Figure 12.13. Here we see the influence of the deformability of the ground on the bending moment M_F and the normal force N_F of a concrete tunnel lining. With the diameter of $10 \cdot 00$ m and a thickness of lining of 40 cm, it is shown, for example, that the internal forces M_F and N_F are practically independent of the deformability of the surrounding rock for values of $E > 2500$ MPa. The influence of the friction on M_F and N_F is also easily seen in this figure.

A further example taken from tunnelling practice is shown in Figure 12.14. In connection with the construction of a hydroelectric power station in the Republic of Zaire, a parametric study had to be carried out for the design of several, parallel-running pressure tunnels of unusually large diameter each of them with a length of $3 \cdot 0$ km. The rock—a compact gneiss—was well-suited to the excavation of tunnels of up to $300 \, \text{m}^2$ cross-sectional area. The basis for the determination of the diameter of the opening as well as for the determination of the thickness of the concrete lining were provided by the parametric study. Several loading cases— different values of E for the deformability of the surrounding rock and different lining thickness—were considered. In Figure 12.14 the computational models for an assumed rock pressure q due to loosening and for the loading case of an external water pressure w (sudden emptying of the tunnel) is represented. The bending moments M and normal forces N of the lining were computed by an iterative procedure, in which the tensile stresses acting between the lining and the rock were eliminated.

12.3.1.2 *Computational models for rock masses with genuine rock pressure*

In contrast to the rock masses characterized by loosening pressure, in this kind of rock it is not the occurrence of accidental details such as the spacing and the orientation of the joints that is important, but the average properties of the material surrounding the tunnel. The deformations occur in all directions and make their presence felt in the form of a reduction in cross section (Prader, 1972). The ground exerts pressure onto the tunnel support from all sides. The movements are essentially time-dependent and reach a standstill as a consequence of the support measures. In order to follow, by means of computations, the occurrence of yield and the spread of the plastic zones, the redistribution of stresses and associated deformations, a continuum model is generally used. This model can also allow for major discontinuities with reduced shear-strength parameters. The dimensions of the model are chosen such that changes in stress due to the excavation of the opening are negligible at the boundaries of the model. The system is generally assumed to satisfy plane strain conditions. It is also assumed that the primary state of stress is known, and may, for example, be defined by the principal stresses (p_{10}, p_{20}) and the superimposed unit weight γ of the

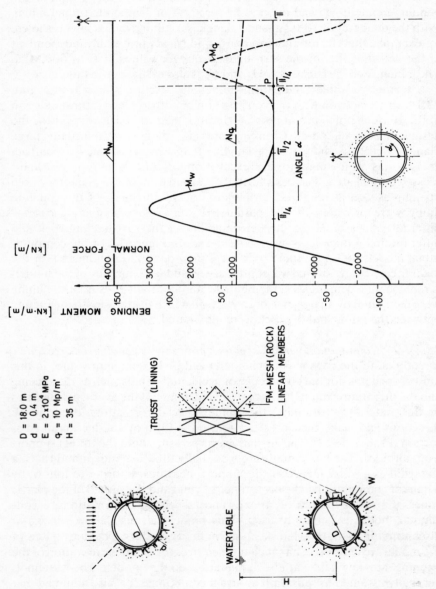

Figure 12.14   Large diameter pressure tunnels: moments and normal forces of the lining due to rock load *q* and water pressure *w*

material surrounding the opening (Figure 12.15). First of all an opening without lining is considered. The excavation of the hole causes its boundary to be stress-free. One proceeds, therefore, from the initial stress state, determines the corresponding nodal forces K_i at the boundary, and then applies these forces with reversed sign. In the elasto–plastic analysis the stress removal at the boundary of the opening is carried out in small steps using load increments. If, in the iterative calculation, no convergence is attained, this may indicate an instability of the underground opening.

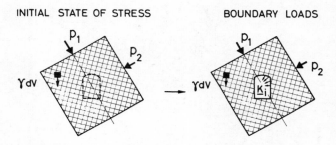

INITIAL STATE OF STRESS   BOUNDARY LOADS

Figure 12.15 Unlined opening: removal of boundary stresses by equivalent nodal forces

Next the possibilities for considering the lining in the statical system are looked at. The lining, for instance a tunnel lining, is introduced into the opening as a new and foreign structural element, by using a particular constructional method. The lining is stressed as a result of those rock movements that occur after the lining has been placed. These rock movements may be traced back to two basic causes:

(1) To a new step of excavation in the vicinity of the lining already introduced.

(2) To creep of the rock material (time-dependence of deformations and stress redistribution).

In Figure 12.16 these two causes may easily be distinguished where the results of convergence measurements in a slope tunnel are shown (Kovári, Amstad, *et al.*, 1974). Even if the tunnel is excavated in full-face operation and the lining is placed immediately at the face, the rock will still undergo stress changes and deformations before the lining begins to function. This behaviour of the rock in the neighbourhood of the tunnel face has been the subject to extensive theoretical (Lombardi, 1971; Daemen and Fairhurst, 1972; Descoeudres, 1974) and experimental investigations and *in-situ* measurement studies (Stroh and Chambosse, 1973; Lögters, 1974).

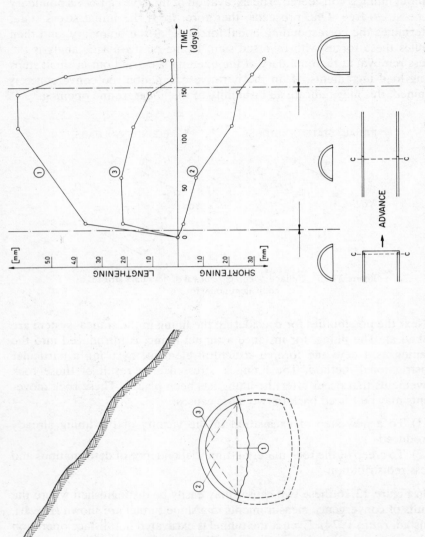

Figure 12.16 Variation of control lengths in a slope tunnel due to construction sequences and time effect. I advance of the face, II core removal

How is it possible for a two-dimensional computational model with time-independent material properties to describe this complicated process? It can do it, evidently, only by making extremely simplifying assumptions. These assumptions relate to deformation of the rock preceding placement of the lining and the rheological properties of the material.

The deformation of the rock before the functioning of the lining has to be estimated. The difficulties associated with the rheological behaviour of the rock are obviated by means of the use of a 'long-term modulus of elasticity' (Zienkiewicz, 1968). It should be realized that here also the computed results are dependent upon the estimates and the somewhat over-simplified assumptions made in the analysis. These assumptions make the results as uncertain as was the case in the behaviour of the loosened rock mass. In the static computations we shall concentrate less on the actual calculated values and much more on a parametric study. In keeping with such a 'sensitivity analysis' the initial rock deformations will be very often neglected and first brought to attention in the interpretation of the results. Therefore, the stressing of the lining turns out to be excessively large, so that for a certain value of the rock with a certain amount of overburden it gives irrational results which naturally do not agree with the experiences from tunnelling (Kovári, 1972).

The formal procedure in the computation is as follows. First of all—as in the case of an unlined tunnel—the nodal forces K_1 (Figure 12.17) are calculated from the primary state of stress at the boundary of the tunnel

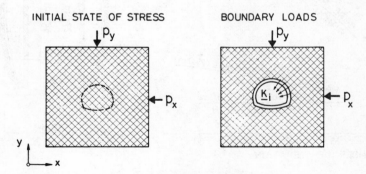

INITIAL STATE OF STRESS   BOUNDARY LOADS

Figure 12.17 Lined cavity, application of nodal forces K_i on the boundary of lining and rock

opening. These are then introduced with negative sign at the boundary (incrementally for plastic material behaviour) such that the rock and the lining are simultaneously acted upon by these forces. As a result, the re-adjustment of the stresses and deformations in the rock mass and the extent of possible plastic zones are obtained, as well as the bending moments and normal forces of the lining. Thus a functional relationship between the stresses, deformations, initial state of stress, deformation and strength properties of the rock, shape and size of the underground opening, as well as the stiffness of the lining is established.

An example of a stability analysis is illustrated in Figure 12.18. In the construction of a large underground opening for a power station in Poland it was necessary to investigate, amongst other things, the influence of the core removal on the displacement in the rock, which was, for the most part, already lined. The material was layered and both strain and strength anisotropy had to be considered. The unloading due to the removal of the core caused plastic zones to be formed. In Figure 12.18 the convergence of the heaving of the base δ_0 for the third and last unloading increment is shown as a function of the number of iterations. This figure shows clearly that only a quick placement of the invert vault guarantees the desired stability.

In this example the convergence of deformations has been interpreted as an indication of the mechanical stability of the system. Non-convergence was assumed to indicate a failure mechanism. Such interpretations are in this

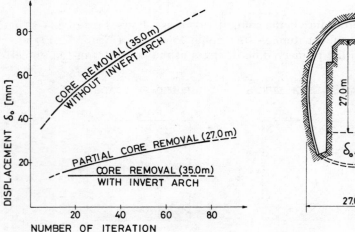

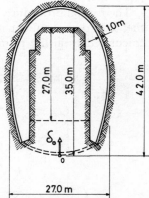

ROCK WITH HORIZONTAL STRATIFICATION :

E_1 = 12'000 MPa, E_2 = 3'000 MPa, G = 2'900 MPa
(ν_1 = 0.3 , ν_2 = 0.1)
φ = 40°, c = 0.01 MPa , $\bar{\varphi}$ = 17° , $\bar{c}$ = 0.18 MPa

Figure 12.18 Underground power-station in stratified rock. Convergence of the displacement δ_0 as a function of the number of iterations for different steps of the core removal procedure

specific case doubtless allowed because the global behaviour of the structure is well understood. On the other hand the stabilizing effect of an inverted arch is well-known in tunnelling. However in other cases we have always to ascertain that numerical instabilities should not be confounded with mechanical ones.

12.3.2 The interaction of structures

The interaction of structures is a type of problem in which the efficiency of numerical methods of analysis is especially evident. In the following a few typical cases which frequently occur in practice are summarized. Parallel traffic tunnels and an underground opening with parallel drainage gallery are shown in Figure 12.19a, while in Figure 12.19b situations for the interaction of a tunnel with another surface structure, as frequently encountered in subway construction, are illustrated. In the latter case, it could be an existing building and a projected tunnel or *vice versa*. A further example is shown in Figure 12.19c, that of a new highway cutting in the vicinity of an existing railway tunnel.

The special features in the numerical treatment of these problems are:

(1) Calculations must be carried out successively for different statical systems with different states of 'initial' stresses.

(2) The stresses and deformations produced in existing tunnel linings due to the influence of other structures can be adequately estimated.

The procedures used in the numerical treatment of such problems have been dealt with elsewhere (Kovári, 1972; Kovári and Hagedorn, 1975).

An example of the two-opening problem, taken from tunnelling practice, is shown in Figures 12.20a and 12.20b. In constructing highway connections in the region of Barcelona tunnels for a three-laned and a two-laned highway had to be built very close to one another over a certain stretch. The material was layered, with the strike of the bedding running almost parallel to the axis of the tunnel and its dip tangential to both profiles. In the first stage of the works it was planned to construct the larger of the tunnels (I), and to begin the second tunnel (II) only after the completion of the first. From the results of an extensive parameter analysis the moments M and normal forces N acting in the lining of the first tunnel, for a particular set of data, have been presented in Figures 12.20a and 12.20b. It is clear that despite the nearness of the two tunnels, the influence of the second tunnel on M and N is not important.

12.3.3 Computations for interpreting rock mechanics measurements

Measurements as a means of observation should promote our understanding both of the behaviour of the underground construction at hand and of the

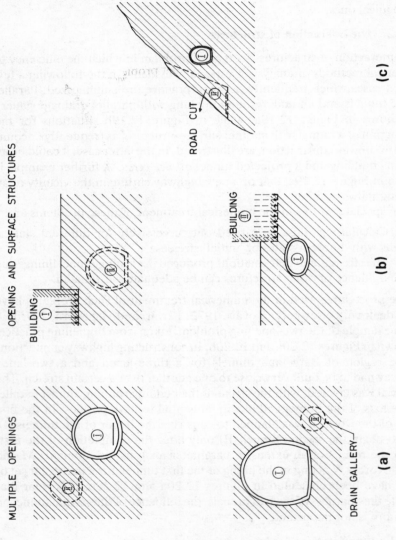

Figure 12.19 Typical cases of interaction of an underground opening with other structures

general problem. Thus understanding is deepened through the study of the results of measurements aided by numerical computations. Fortunately, more and more reports are available in which measurements are compared with the results of numerical analysis (Abraham and Pahl, 1974; Dolcetta, Capozza, *et al.*, 1972; Chang and Nair, 1974; Wittke, Carl, *et al.*, 1974) and this fact is important for the progress of the science of tunnelling. In this context we wish only to take a closer look at some of the possibilities for interpreting deformation measurements with the help of computational models. If displacements (relative or absolute) in the ground due to some step of the excavation process are measured, this can be considered to be a large-scale test to estimate the overall deformation properties of the rock mass or in some cases to estimate the initial state of stress. Since, in

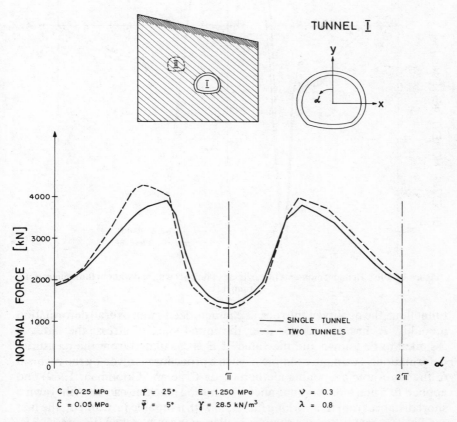

Figure 12.20a Interaction of two- and three-lane highway tunnels in stratified rock. Normal forces in the lining of tunnel I with and without influence of tunnel II

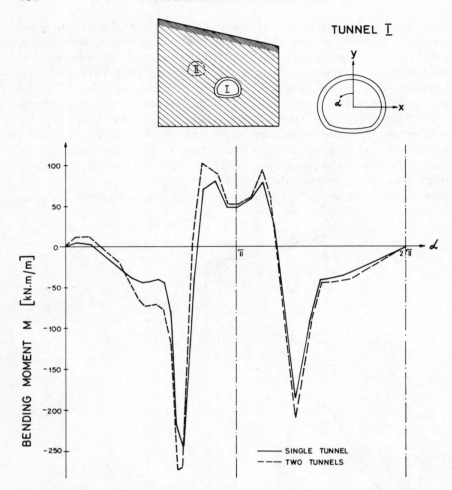

Figure 12.20b   Bending moments in the lining of tunnel I with and without the influence of tunnel II

tunnelling, the quality of the rock as characterized by an overall deformation modulus, E, has precedence over the initial state of stress: the latter is assumed to be known and the value of E is calculated from the measured deformations. A simple example of such a procedure is given by the reversal of the bore-hole deepening method (de la Crue and Goodman, 1969) and applied to a machine-bored tunnel. The boring machine can be withdrawn a short distance from the working face, and with a suitable instrument, the first readings for measuring the changes in diameter can be taken (Figure 12.21). The second set of readings are taken as soon as the machine has passed the

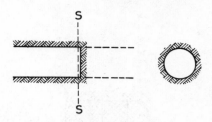

Figure 12.21 Measurement of the diameter contraction in a machine-bored tunnel due to the advance of the excavation front

measuring section. In this way the deformations due to the removal of the supporting tunnel face are obtained. In a sufficiently homogeneous and isotropic material values for the deformation modulus of the rock may be evaluated by means of the relationships established by de la Cruz and Goodman (1969). Such measurements have been carried out in some machine-bored tunnels in Switzerland.

Measurements with bore-hole extensometers offer even greater possibilities because they also give information about the deformations in the rock mass. A typical example for this is shown in Figure 12.22 in which three excavation stages are instrumented and thus an estimate of the overall value of E for the rock mass can be made. It should be emphasized that here also only an estimate of the order of magnitude of the quantities involved is possible, as the number of important parameters is too great. But even a rough quantitative characterization of the rock type is of great value in the process of decision-making for the design. In this way one also obtains a useful basis of comparison between different constructions in similar geotechnical situations.

12.4 GENERALIZATION OF THE RESULTS OF COMPUTER CALCULATIONS WITH THE AID OF THE LAWS OF SIMILITUDE

There is an obvious need for charts, which, at least for simple but frequently met problems, could replace time-consuming computer calculations. Because of the great number of factors which influence the behaviour of a construction and have to be taken into account in the computational model, a large number of charts would have to be produced for practical uses. However, if one considers the laws of similarity of the theory of model simulation the range of application of a chart can be considerably extended.

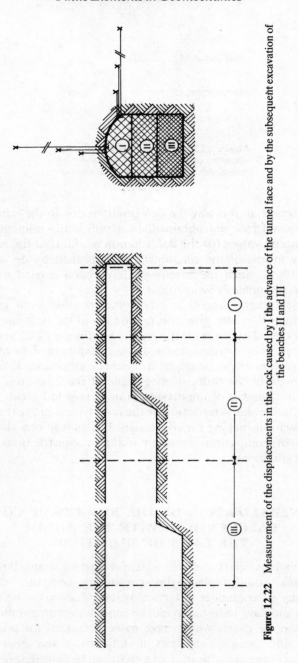

Figure 12.22 Measurement of the displacements in the rock caused by I the advance of the tunnel face and by the subsequent excavation of the benches II and III

We shall discuss this point in the case of a lined tunnel of circular cross-section in an elastic, homogeneous, isotropic material. The interaction between the lining and the rock mass is taken into account using the concept of the 'long-term' modulus (Zienkiewicz, 1968). The Poisson ratio ν for the rock, the coefficient of lateral pressure λ and the elastic modulus E_c for the concrete lining were chosen as follows:

$$\nu = 0.3 \qquad \lambda = 0 \cdot 7 \qquad E_c = 20\,000 \text{ MPa}$$

The objective is to find the fibre stresses σ_{min} and σ_{max} at a particular point of the lining and the changes in the diameter δ as a function of the tunnel diameter D, the thickness of the lining d, the deformation modulus of the rock E, the depth of overburden H and the unit weight of the rock material γ. It follows from the purely elastic analysis that the desired values σ_{min}, σ_{max} and δ are linearly dependent upon γ. Further, it may easily be shown that the influence of H on these values is practically linear as well. It is sufficient therefore, if only the two extreme cases, $H = D/2$ and, for example, $H = 4D$, are considered and linear interpolation is used for values lying in between this extreme. The charts in Figure 12.23 show the variation of the stresses in the concrete lining for the point F of the tunnel roof and Figure 12.24 associated changes of diameter δ for a model with the fixed parameters

$$\bar{D} = 10 \cdot 0 \text{ m} \qquad \text{and} \qquad \bar{\gamma}^* = 10 \text{ kN/m}^3$$

For the same geometry but with arbitrary values of $\bar{\gamma}$ we obtain the results

$$\bar{\sigma} = \bar{\gamma}\sigma^* \qquad \text{and} \qquad \bar{\delta} = \bar{\gamma}\bar{\delta}^*$$

respectively.

Now, in order to be able to use the charts for $D \neq \bar{D}$ the laws of similarity must be introduced. As fundamental quantities the ratio

$$\mu = \bar{D}/D \qquad \text{and} \qquad \rho = \bar{E}/E = 1$$

will be chosen (Fumagalli, 1968). The choice of ρ as one of the fundamental values facilitates the consideration of inhomogenity. In addition, with $\rho = 1$ neither the E (rock, concrete) nor the resulting stresses undergo any distortion. The system with $\bar{D}$, $\bar{d}$, $\bar{E}$, $\bar{\gamma}$, $\bar{\sigma}$ and $\bar{\delta}$ is regarded as the model and the prototype is defined by the values D, d, E, γ, σ and δ. As derived quantities we obtain from a dimensional analysis

$$\xi = \bar{\gamma}/\gamma = \bar{E}\bar{D}/ED = 1/\mu$$

and thus

$$\delta = \bar{\delta}/\mu = \bar{\gamma}\bar{\delta}^*/\mu = \gamma\bar{\delta}^*/\mu^2$$

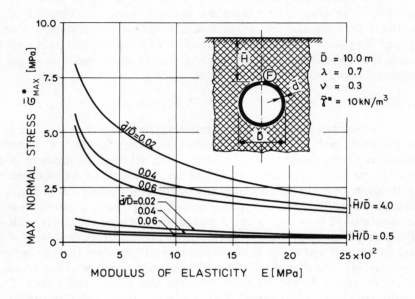

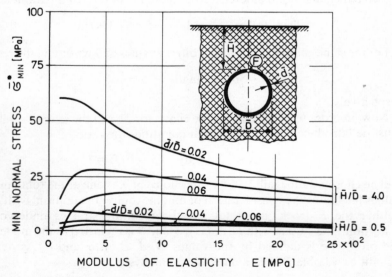

Figure 12.23 Charts for maximum and minimum axial stresses at the point F of the concrete lining of a 'tunnel-model' as a function of the E for the rock and the thickness of the lining

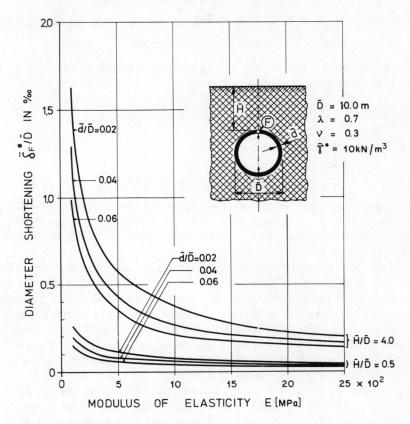

Figure 12.24 Charts for diameter shortening at the point F of the 'tunnel-model' as a function of the E of the rock and the thickness of the lining.

and

$$\sigma = \bar{\gamma}\bar{\sigma} = \gamma\bar{\sigma}^*/\mu$$

respectively. Thereby the following procedure results for the use of the charts in Figures 12.21 and 12.22.

(1) Determination of μ for a given D ($\neq 10 \cdot 0$ m).

(2) Determination of the model parameters according to

$$\bar{d} = \mu d, \qquad \bar{H} = \mu H, \qquad \bar{E} \equiv E$$

(3) Reading off the associated values of $\bar{\sigma}^*_{\min}$, $\bar{\sigma}^*_{\max}$ and $\bar{\delta}^*$ in the charts (with interpolation for intermediate values of $\bar{H}$ and $\bar{d}$).

(4) Conversion of these values for the prototype using the relationships

$$\sigma = \gamma\bar{\sigma}^*/\mu, \qquad \delta = \gamma\bar{\delta}^*/\mu^2$$

The moments and the normal forces per metre length of tunnel may be calculated using the simple formulae

$$N = \frac{\delta_{max} + \sigma_{min}}{2} d \qquad |M| = \frac{|\sigma_{max} - \sigma_{min}|}{12} d^2$$

with length measured in metres.

12.5 CLOSING REMARKS

The experience of the last ten years in using numerical methods in the design of underground constructions allows several conclusions to be made, which, without making any claims regarding their general validity, are summarized here.

A clear formulation of the particular problem facing the engineer is first required if a computer solution is to be sought. On the basis of this formulation of the problem suitable computational models can be established and the variations in the required input data can be defined by giving the values of the upper and lower bounds. The real purpose of the computations is mostly a parameter analysis. However, in order to keep the number of computed cases within practical limits, only those data combinations can be considered, which the engineer thinks to be the most important in the light of his experience. It is readily shown that even the problem of a single tunnel in a two-layered elasto-plastic material may easily lead to over 100 computations, if proper choice of combinations of input data is made (e.g. material properties, initial state of stress, support measures for the opening).

Computational results should be presented in the form of diagrams which give a good summary of the results and enable various computed cases to be easily compared. For conclusions affecting constructional decisions the computed deformations in the rock and stresses in the lining are of particular value.

Rock anchors introduced as a safety measure can also be included in the computational model. However, their doubtlessly useful effect cannot, in general, be verified numerically due to the many simplifications in the model.

A clear and thus a useful definition of the safety factor for underground openings does not exist even today despite the emergence of numerical computational methods. It is doubtful whether, in such a complex structure as a tunnel, a definition of safety can be reasonably expressed by a single figure.

Acknowledgements

The author wishes to express his sincere appreciation to Messrs P. Fritz and H. Hagedorn for their valuable comments on various parts of this report.

REFERENCES

Abraham, K. H. and Pahl, A. (1974). 'Planung und Berechnung grosser Felsbauten unter Berücksichtigung felsmechanischer Kontrollmöglichkeiten', *Proc. of the 3rd Congress of the Int. Soc. for Rock Mechanics, Denver*, **11A**.

Chang, C. Y. and Nair, K. (1974). 'Development and applications of a general computer program for evaluating stability of openings in rock', *Proc. of the 3rd Congress of the Int. Soc. for Rock Mechanics, Denver*, **IIB**.

Daemen, J. J. K., Fairhurst, C. (1972). 'Rock Failure and Tunnel Support Loading', *Proc. of the International Symposium on Underground Openings', Luzern*.

de la Cruz, R. and Goodman, R. E. (1969). 'The borehole deepening method of stress measurement', *Proc. of the International Symposium on the Determination of Stresses in Rock Masses, Lisbon*.

Descoeudres, F. (1974). 'Analyse tridimensionelle de la stabilité d'un tunnel au voisinage du front de taille dans une roche élasto-plastique', *Proc. of the 3rd Congress of the Int. Soc. for Rock Mechanics, Denver*, **IIB**.

Dolcetta, M., Capozza, M., and Martinetti, S. (1972). 'Rock load on the support structures of two large underground hydroelectric powerstations', *Proc. of the International Symposium on Underground Openings, Luzern*.

Drucker, D. C. and Prager, W. (1952). 'Soil mechanics and plastic analysis or limit design', *Quart. Appl. Math.* **10**, 2.

Fumagalli, E. (1968). 'Model simulation of rock mechanics problems', *Rock Mechanics in Engineering Practice*, Stagg, K. G. and Zienkiewicz, O. C. (Eds.), John Wiley.

Gates, R. H. (1972). 'Progressive failure model for clay shale', *Proc. of the Symp. on Application of the Finite Element Method in Geotechnical Engineering, Vicksburg, Mississippi*.

Grob, H., Kovári, K. and Amstad, Ch. (1975). 'Sources of error in the determination of *in situ* stresses', *Tectonophysics, Int. Journal of Geotechnics and the Geology and Physics of the Interior of the Earth*, **29**, 1–4.

Hill, R. (1967). *The Mathematical Theory of Plasticity*, Oxford University Press.

Höeg, K. (1972). 'Finite element analysis of strain-softening clay', *Journal of Soil Mechanics and Foundation Division, Am. Soc. Civ. Engrs*, **98**.

Kovári, K. (1969). 'Ein Beitrag zum Bemessungsproblem von Untertagbauten', *Schweiz. Bauzeitung*, **37**.

Kovári, K. (1972). 'Methoden der Dimensionierung von Untertagbauten', *Proc. of the Int. Symposium on Underground Openings, Luzern*.

Kovári, K., Amstad, Ch. and Vannotti, F. (1971). 'Numerisch Berechnete und gemessene Verschiebungen einer elastisch-plastischen Scheibe', *Schweiz. Bauzeitung*, **40**.

Kovári, K., Amstad, Ch., and Grob, H. (1974). 'Displacement measurements of high accuracy in underground openings', *Proc. of the 3rd Congress of the Int. Soc. for Rock Mechanics, Denver*, **IIA**.

Kovári, K. and Dudt, J. P. (in preparation). 'Parametrische Untersuchungen in der Tunnelstatik unter Anwendung der Aehnlichkeitsgesetze der Modelltheorie', *Mitteilungen des Institutes für Strassen- und Untertagbau ETHZ.*

Kovári, K. and Hagedorn, H. (1975). 'Berechnungsmodelle für die Ermittlung der Deformationen und Beanspruchungen in Tunnelbauwerken', *Proc. of the Int. Conference on Subway Construction, Budapest–Balatonfüred.*

Kovári, K. and Tisa, A. (1975). 'Multiple failure state and strain-controlled triaxial tests', *Rock Mechanics*, No. 7/1.

Lögters, G. (1974). 'Modellversuche zur Bestimmung des räumlichen Verformungsvorganges beim oberflächlichen Tunnelbau', *Rock Mechanics, Suppl. 3.*

Lombardi, G. (1971). 'Zur Bemessung der Tunnelauskleidung mit Berücksichtigung des Bauvorganges', *Schweiz. Bauzeitung*, **32**.

Malina, H. (1969). 'Berechnung von Spannungsumlagerungen in Fels und Boden mit Hilfe der Elementenmethode', *Veröffentlichungen des Instituts für Bodenmechanik und Felsmechanik der Universität Karlsruhe*, **40**.

Nadai, A. (1950). *Theory of Flow and Fracture of Solids*, McGraw-Hill.

Prader, D. (1972). 'Beispiele von Druckerscheinungen im Tunnelbau', *Proc. of the Int. Symposium on Underground Openings, Luzern.*

Rabcewicz, L. v. (1963). 'Bemessung von Hohlraumbauten, Die "Neue Oesterreichische Bauweise" und ihr Einfluss auf Gebrigsdruckwirkungen und Dimensionierung', *Rock Mechanics and Engineering Geology*, **I**, 3–4.

Reyes, S. F. (1966). 'Elastic Plastic Analysis of Underground Openings by the Finite Element Method', *Thesis*, University of Illinois.

Sauer, G. (1974). 'In-situ-Messungen und Berechnungen nach der Methode der Finite Element-Methode beim U-Bahnbau in Frankfurt/Main', *Interfels Messtechnik Information Bentheim BRD.*

Shield, R. T. (1955). 'On Coulomb's law of failure in soils', *Journal of the Mechanics and Physics of Solids*, **4**.

Stroh, D. and Chambosse, G. (1973). 'Messungen und Setzungsursachen beim Tunnelvortrieb im Frankfurter Ton', *Strasse, Brücke, Tunnel*, **2**.

Terzaghi, Karl (1946/1965). *Rock Tunneling with Steel Supports*, Youngstown Printing Co., Ohio.

Wittke, W., Carl, L., and Semprich, S. (1974). 'Felsmessungen als Grundlage für den Entwurf einer Tunnelauskleidung', *Interfels Messtechnik Information, Bentheim BRD.*

Wittke, W., Wallner, M., and Rodatz, W. (1972). 'Räumliche Berechnung der Standsicherheit von Hohlräumen, Böschungen and Gründungen in anisotropem, klüftigem Gebirge nach der Finite Element Methode', *Brücke, Strasse, Tunnel.*

Zienkiewicz, O. C. (1968). 'Continuum mechanics as an approach to rock mass problems', *Rock Mechanics in Engineering Practice*, Stagg, K. G. and Zienkiewicz, O. C. (eds.). John Wiley & Sons.

Zienkiewicz, O. C., Best, B., Dullage, C. and Stagg, K. G. (1970). 'Analysis of non-linear problems in rock mechanics with particular reference to jointed rock system', *Proc. of the 2nd Congress of the Int. Soc. of Rock Mechanics, Belgrade*, **3**.

Zienkiewicz, O. C., Nayak, G. C., and Owen, D. R. J. (1972). 'Composite and "overlay" models in numerical analysis of elasto-plastic continua'. *Proc. of the Symposium on Foundations of Plasticity, Warsaw.*

Zienkiewicz, O. C., Valliapan, S. and King, I. P. (1969). 'Elasto-plastic, solutions of engineering problems, initial stress, finite element approach', *Int. Journal for Numerical Methods in Engineering*, **1**.

Chapter 13

New Design Concept for Underground Openings in Rock

W. Wittke

13.1 INTRODUCTION

The following is concerned with the evaluation of the stability and the amount of required safety measures and lining for underground openings in jointed rock. A new design concept based on the Finite Element Method and recent developments in rock mechanics will be outlined and illustrated by means of three underground openings, which have been recently completed (Pfisterer, Wittke, *et al.*, 1974; Rodatz and Wallner 1974; Wittke, 1973; Wittke, in print; Wittke, Wallner, *et al.*, 1972; Wittke and Pfisterer, 1972; Wittke, Carl, *et al.*, 1974; Wittke, Pfisterer, *et al.*, 1974).

A very important aspect of the development of this concept is, that the rearrangement of the stresses due to the excavation of a deeply located underground opening almost completely takes place within the rock mass itself and that the safety measures only play a supporting role.

So for example in case of a tunnel with an overburden of $h = 100$ m and a unit weight of the rock of $\gamma = 2 \cdot 5 \times 10^{-2}$ MN/m^3, resulting over-burden pressures of $\sigma_v = 2 \cdot 5$ MN/m^2 during and after excavation are to be diverted around the tunnel. It is obvious that stresses of this magnitude cannot be transmitted with common standards of safety measures and lining.

Consequently for a stability analysis—an important part of the design concept—the stress–strain law of a rock mass and the development of a relevant model play a decisive role. Along with the development of a stress–strain law the following requirements have however to be observed:

The incorporation of the stress–strain law in the stability analysis should not lead to unreasonable computing costs.

It is necessary that the applied mechanical parameters can be determined by common rock testing techniques.

The stresses and displacements resulting from the stability analysis have to be close enough to reality for practical purposes.

413

13.2 STATEMENT OF PROBLEM FOR TUNNEL DESIGN

To begin with, the statement of problem of tunnel design—as far as it can be separated from the mechanical properties of the rock mass—shall be discussed.

An important influence on the stress–strain conditions around an opening is created by the *in situ* stresses. From measurements it is known that the orientation and magnitude of these stresses can vary considerably. So for example, the x- and z-co-ordinate axes as shown in Figure 13.1 need not coincide with the directions of the normal principal stresses ((1) Figure 13.1). Even if this however is the case and the vertical normal principal stress $\sigma_1\|z$ equals the weight of the overburden, the horizontal principal stress

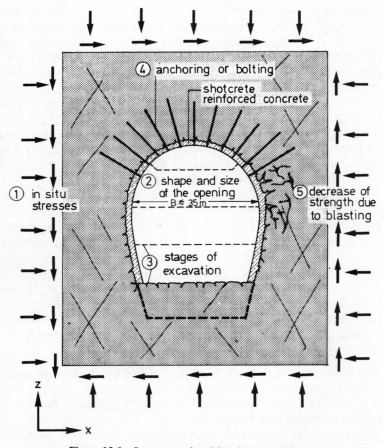

Figure 13.1 Statement of problem for tunnel design

$\sigma_3 \| x$ still can result to be a small portion or several times as much as σ_1 (Raleigh, 1974).

Depending on the purpose (traffic tunnel, underground power house, etc.) the shape as well as the dimensions of the cross-section of underground openings vary considerably and very often; for example, deviate from a circular cross-section, which in former calculative procedures was often postulated ((2), Figure 13.1). So for example underground power houses are mostly designed with horseshoe-shaped cross-section (Figure 13.1) and with widths of up to 35 m (Rescher, Abraham, *et al.*, 1973). Further, a calculation technique needs to account for various construction stages, because, for example openings with cross-sectional areas of $\geq 100 \, \text{m}^2$ are commonly excavated in stages ((3), Figure 13.1) and also the safety measures and linings consisting of reinforced shotcrete, anchoring and also reinforced concrete are installed stepwise ((4), Figure 13.1).

Another factor, decisive in many cases, is given by the three-dimensional state of stresses around the tunnel face (Figure 13.2). As a consequence of this, displacements already occur ahead of the excavated tunnels (Section B,

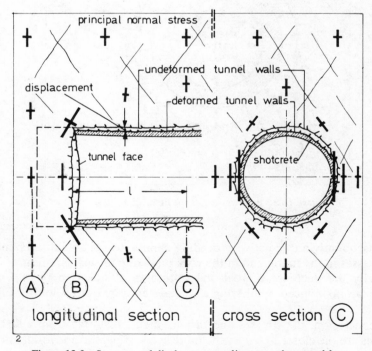

Figure 13.2 Stresses and displacements adjacent to the tunnel face

Figure 13.2), and the lining, which can only be installed after excavation of the tunnel, sustains only a part of the displacements of the cross-section due to excavation (Section C, Figure 13.2). A calculative technique, which does not account for these three-dimensional stress–strain conditions, consequently leads to an over-estimation of the stresses in the lining and on the other hand reveals too small displacements of the tunnel cross-section as well as, for shallow tunnels, of the settlements on the surface.

A design concept, frequently applied to concrete linings of pressure tunnels, consists of a radial pre-stressing of the lining by cement grouting (Figure 13.3).

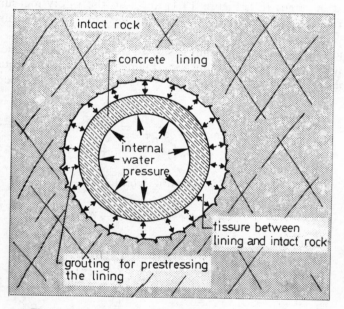

Figure 13.3 Pre-stressing of the lining of a pressure tunnel

Consequently a calculative procedure should also enable to account for the stresses in the lining and in the rock mass due to such a measure.

Finally the decrease of rock mass strength adjacent to the opening, which can be induced by blasting also plays an important role ((5), Figure 13.1).

In conclusion, the stresses and displacements resulting from a stability analysis are the closer to reality the more successfully the above-mentioned factors can be incorporated in the calculative technique.

13.3   A STRESS–STRAIN LAW FOR JOINTED ROCK MASSES

To elaborate a realistic stress–strain law we shall begin with a phenomenological description of a jointed rock mass. From the photograph of a rock slope in slate, represented in Figure 13.1, it can be realized that the siltstone is partly as well as completely separated by three series of approximately plane discontinuities with approximately equal orientations ($K_1 - K_3$, Figure 13.4).

Figure 13.4   Jointed rock mass

Such jointing, consisting of one or more series of discontinuities, is very common and encountered in most of the practical cases. Concerning the stability analyses of underground openings, as mentioned, usually it can be assumed that the discontinuities of one series or family are parallel (Figure 13.5).

Since along the discontinuities the shear strength in comparison to that of the intact rock is considerably diminished, the jointing reveals a considerable influence on the stress–strain behaviour of a rock mass. In addition to this homogeneous jointing faults and shear zones with considerable extent and thickness occur quite frequently. Discontinuities of this type are very often filled with cohesive soil and consequently reveal considerable compressibility and very low shear strength (Figure 13.5). Since the spacing and the

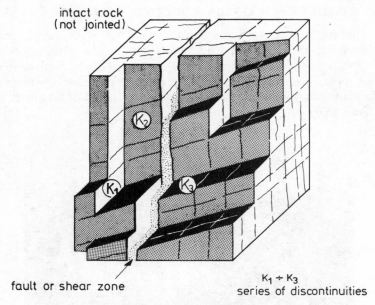

intact rock
(not jointed)

fault or shear zone

$K_1 \div K_3$
series of discontinuities

Figure 13.5   Model of a jointed rock mass

frequency of faults and shear zones is usually large in comparison to the dimensions of the underground openings, these discontinuities deserve special consideration regarding their stability.

Developing an idealized stress–strain law for a rock mass, we begin with the mechanical properties of intact rock, which in practical cases can be easily determined by laboratory tests. My personal experience reveals that when one considers the magnitude of stresses occurring in the every-day practice of tunneling, except in certain cases (e.g. salt rock or very high overburden) the stress–strain law of intact rock can be assumed to be linear-elastic. Isotropy however cannot be assumed in all cases. For example, in case of schistous rock the compressibility orthogonal to the schistosity very often is considerably higher than parallel to schistosity (Figure 13.6), (Pinto, 1970; Patton, 1966) and it could be proved that this stress–strain behaviour can be dealt with by five elastic constants (transversal anisotropy, Figure 13.7) as a good approximation. In case of a higher ratio of the two Young's moduli $a = E_1/E_2$, this intact rock property often even dominates the stress–strain behaviour of the jointed rock mass. Further it is obvious that in the case where the plane of schistosity diagonally intersects the tunnel axis, a two-dimensional stability analysis does not serve the purpose even if there are no other arguments against it. In this context it is of considerable

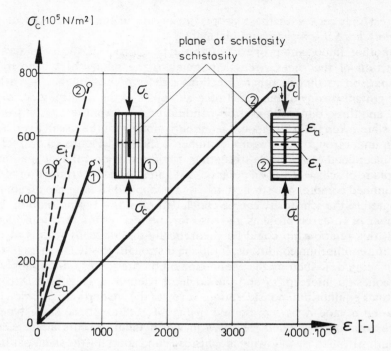

Figure 13.6   Stress-strain diagram of a clay slate

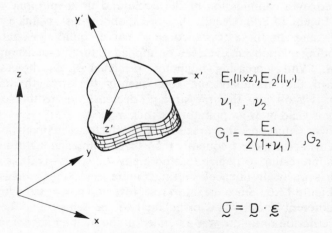

Figure 13.7   Transverse anisotropy

interest that rock with these properties occurs in the whole area of the *Rheinisches Schiefergebirge* in Germany.

Another important property of this type of rock is the considerable reduction of the shear strength parallel to the planes of schistosity in comparison to that in other directions and as a consequence a marked strength anisotropy of the intact rock as well as of the rock mass for one-, two- and three-dimensional stress conditions. A relevant test result from a clay slate taken from Vianden/Luxemburg along with the feasibility design of an underground air-pressure chamber is shown in Figure 13.8(a). Here the unconfined compressive strength σ_c is plotted against the inclination of the plane of schistosity α on polar co-ordinates. A distinct reduction of the unconfined compressive strength in case the applied stresses are diagonally oriented to the schistosity can be concluded from this representation. In a number of research projects and also for the test results shown in Figure 13.8, this relationship could be theoretically described by means of two limiting equilibrium conditions. If the shear strength parallel to the schistosity is being described by the Mohr–Coulomb criterion of failure, applying the cohesion intercept c_s and the angle of friction ϕ_s (Figure 3.18(b)), a limiting equilibrium consideration reveals the hyperbolic relationship between σ_c and α as represented in Figure 13.8(a). If the same type of representation is applied for cases in which failure occurs along planes deviating from those following the shistosity and adopting the shear parameters c and ϕ (Figure 13.8(b)) for those directions, the unconfined compressive strength as in case of an isotropic rock is independent of the angle α and can be represented in Figure 13.8(e) by a circle. If it is assumed that the smaller of the two calculated strengths is correct, then the strength can be represented by a combination of the circle and the hyperbolic curve as shown in Figure 13.8(a). Usually the corresponding test results except the transition zones fit these two theoretical curves quite reasonably. The corresponding relationship even can be applied to three-dimensional stress conditions. With increasing minimum principal stress, however, the influence of the schistosity and consequently the strength anisotropy decreases. It is obvious that the strength decrease due to the schistosity practically is valid in every point of the rock mass.

Local shear failures parallel to the plane of schistosity in practical tunneling problems occur more frequently than shear failures along other directions. It is interesting to realize that normally the stress–strain law of the intact rock is practically linear elastic until failure, e.g. along the schistosity is reached (Figure 13.6). Since the intact rock reveals a tensile strength, which again is different parallel and orthogonal to the schistosity, the Mohr-Coulomb criterion of failure was extended in the manner shown in Figure 13.8(b).

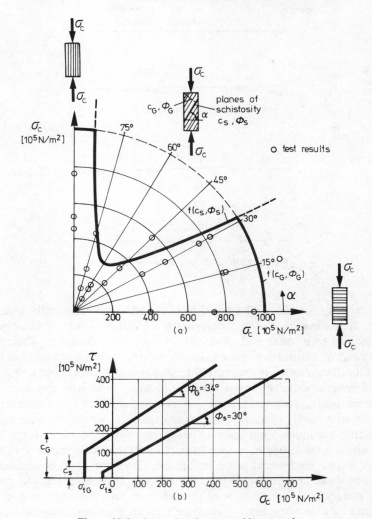

Figure 13.8 Strength anisotropy of intact rock

The sketch shown in Figure 13.9 in an idealized manner represents some different types of joints. It can be seen that, according to the shape of the walls one must distinguish between rough and smooth as well as even and uneven discontinuities. Further very often discontinuities only partly intersect the rock mass, so that areas of intact rock are left along the joints (material bridges, Figure 13.9). Also open discontinuities and fillings (as well

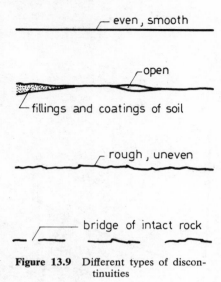

Figure 13.9 Different types of discontinuities

as the coatings of the walls) consisting of soil quite frequently occur in nature. It is obvious that the deformation characteristics of the discontinuities due to normal and shear stresses are very complex. Though in recent years much and extensive research dealing with this subject has been done (Goodman, 1970; Rengers, 1971; Müller and Pacher, 1965), relationships of general validity cannot yet be evaluated. However, the discontinuities lead to a reduction of the shear strength of the rock mass in directions parallel to the family of discontinuities in question. A reliable shear stress–shear strain law in practical cases however can only be found by large-scale *in situ* shear tests. Since in nature usually more than one series of discontinuities exists, and because of inhomogeneities for the discontinuities of each of these families more than one shear test is required, and such a testing programme normally is too expensive. Therefore in most of the practical cases stability analyses will have to be based on estimated shear parameters, which, for example, are evaluated from a detailed geometrical description of the discontinuities as well as from results of laboratory tests.

Therefore, in our present state of knowledge, it is justifiable to apply simplifying assumptions to describe the shear strength along the discontinuities by the Mohr–Coulomb criterion of failure and accordingly apply the shear parameters c_{Ki} and ϕ_{Ki} for joint set i. As the spacing of the discontinuities of one family is usually between one-tenth of a metre and a few metres, it is usually small in comparison to the dimension of the cross-section of an underground opening. Consequently, within an analysis it will not be possible to take separate account of each single discontinuity. According to the influence of the schistosity (Figure 13.8), it is therefore assumed that the oriented decrease of the strength of a rock mass due to one or more families of discontinuities is valid in every point and that it can be defined—as shown in Figure 13.10—by one limiting equilibrium condition for each joint family and in the case of an isotropic intact rock by one more condition (circle in Figure 13.10). Results of model tests have proved this assumption (John, 1969; Pfisterer, 1963). Of course the transition from the validity of one failure criterion to the other is smooth, as it was already explained for the schistous intact rock. As in Figure 13.8, in the case of incompletely separating discontinuities, reduced tensile strength is assumed perpendicular to the discontinuities.

The shear strength of faults and shear zones or master joints also will be described by the Mohr–Coulomb failure criterion. In most cases it will, however, be necessary to account for the increased deformability perpendicular to these discontinuities, which, for example, can be done by a corresponding reduction of Young's modulus.

In summary, with the given explanations as a first approximation, a linear elastic stress–strain law is assumed for the rock mass as long as the stresses do not exceed the above-defined strengths. In case of schistous rock this stress–strain law is assumed to be transversely anisotropic.

For intact rock, as previously outlined, this assumption applies, and it also applies to a jointed rock mass in between faults, shear zones, or master joints as experience has shown that this can normally be considered to be a reasonable approximation. Particularly when the discontinuities are closed over larger extents (Figure 13.9) it gives very good results. Further it is assumed that the strength of a rock mass is mainly determined by the shear strength along the discontinuities or an eventual schistosity and further in deviating directions by the intact rock strength. These strengths as outlined, are described by the Mohr–Coulomb failure criterion. No reasonable assumption however is at present available for a stress–strain law beyond failure or, in other words, for a flow rule.

The influence of faults, shear zones and master joints are accounted for separately in the above manner.

Normally at least one family of discontinuities diagonally intersects the tunnel axis and as a consequence, lest the strength is exceeded, the stress–strain analysis is a three-dimensional problem. In case of a schistous rock, even within the elastic range the stability analysis for a tunnel cannot be dealt with as a two-dimensional problem, as long as the schistosity intersects the tunnel axis diagonally. Further, at the face of the tunnel a three-dimensional stress–strain analysis is required.

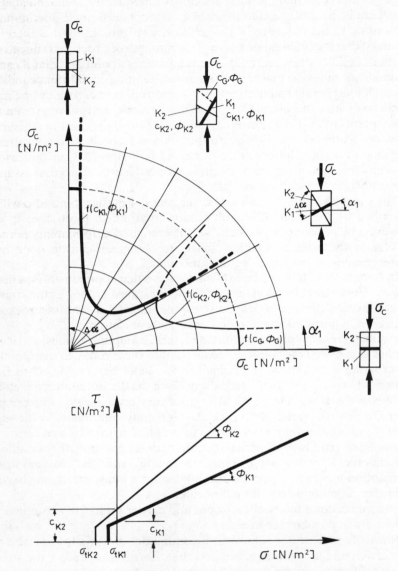

Figure 13.10 Unconfined compressive strength of a rock mass dependent on the orientation of the discontinuities

13.4 DEVELOPMENT OF A FEM-PROGRAM ACCOUNTING FOR THE ABOVE DESCRIBED ROCK MODEL

Because of the foregoing considerations, a three-dimensional finite element program was developed. The program is based on the assumption of constant strain within each element and consequently the continuum is sub-divided into eight-cornered, three-dimensional elements, which are · again being sub-divided into two tetrahedrons, which penetrate each other. This special sub-division was selected in order to reduce computing costs and to enable a better evaluation of the shear stresses to be made (Wittke, Wallner, *et al.*, 1972).

In situ stresses, as shown in Figure 13.1, can be allowed for by 'nodal force' and 'displacement' boundary conditions, whereas the cross-section of the opening is realized by a corresponding element mesh. Linings of shotcrete or reinforced concrete within this procedure are simulated by one or more rows of elements of the same type as used for the rock mass. It is remarkable how accurate the calculated results are, although these elements are extremely thin. Also a linear elastic stress–strain law and the Mohr–Coulomb criterion of failure are assumed for the lining. Pre-stressing loads of anchors are accounted for by concentrated loads at the anchor head and along the adhesive stretch. The stiffness of the anchor rod, however, needs not to be accounted for in a stability analysis, since it does not significantly influence the results.

An eventual loosening of the rock mass due to the selected procedure of excavation (Figure 13.1), can be approximately accounted for by a local reduction of the mechanical parameters as, for example, the shear strengths along the discontinuities. Various construction stages, as shown in Figure 13.1, can be simulated by a commonly applied procedure, that is, by a sequence of calculative steps in which the currently investigated construction stage is always the starting point for the calculation of the next stage. The fact that the shotcrete or another type of lining can only be installed after the respective part of the cross-section is excavated and consequently is loaded only after further excavation (Figure 13.11), is accounted for in the calculation sequence by corresponding initial stresses.

Also within the analysis of a pressure tunnel lining, which is prestressed by grouting (Figure 13.3), an initial stress principle is applied (Wittke, Wallner, *et al.*, 1972). The evaluation of the three-dimensional analysis of stresses and strains for the tunnel face follows the same line but will not be explained here in detail (Rodatz and Wallner, 1974).

In summary, the problem as outlined in Section 13.2 can be solved in a relatively simple manner and thus the Finite Element Method is an extremely useful tool for the stability analysis of underground openings.

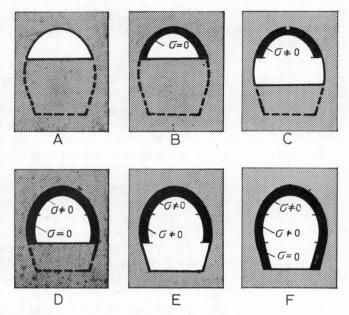

Figure 13.11   Simulation of the construction process

The incorporation of a transversely anisotropic, elastic stress–strain law, (see Section 13.3) in a finite element program does not create any major problems. Finally we shall show by means of an idealized example, how the analysis of cases, in which the strength locally is exceeded, is maintained by an iterative calculative procedure. The so-called 'initial stress approach' is also applied in this case.

An idealized, isotropic, weightless system consisting of nine quadratic elements is shown in Figure 13.12(a). This system is loaded by the maximum and minimum normal principal stresses $\sigma^0_{1(\text{max})}$ and $\sigma^0_{3(\text{min})}$, the corresponding state of stress being denoted as $\boldsymbol{\sigma}^0$. Further, plane strain conditions are assumed. For the middle element e a linear elastic behaviour is adopted until the criterion of failure, also represented in Figure 13.12(b), is violated, whereas the adjacent eight elements, the so called 'surrounding U', are assumed to behave linearly elastic at any stress level.

The graphic representation in Figure 13.12(b) shows that the state of stress $\boldsymbol{\sigma}^0$ violates the failure criterion for element e. The admissible state of stress, i.e. the residual strength, is given by $\boldsymbol{\sigma}_{Br,o}$, the corresponding stress circle touching the Mohr–Coulomb envelope (Figure 13.12(b)). The differential stress $\Delta\boldsymbol{\sigma}^1_e = \boldsymbol{\sigma}^0_e - \boldsymbol{\sigma}_{Br,e}$ or, in other words, the difference between the calculated stress and the residual strength has to be transmitted to the

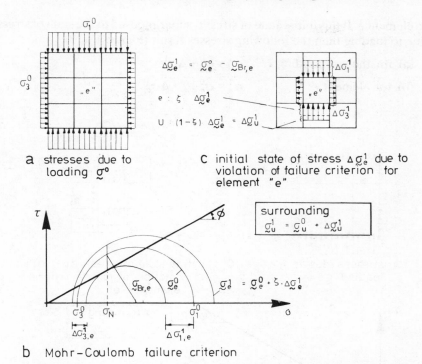

a stresses due to loading $\underset{\sim}{\sigma}^0$

$$\Delta\underset{\sim}{\sigma}_e^1 = \underset{\sim}{\sigma}_e^o - \underset{\sim}{\sigma}_{Br,e}$$

$$e : \zeta \; \Delta\underset{\sim}{\sigma}_e^1$$

$$U : (1-\zeta) \; \Delta\underset{\sim}{\sigma}_e^1 = \Delta\underset{\sim}{\sigma}_u^1$$

c initial state of stress $\Delta\underset{\sim}{\sigma}_e^1$ due to violation of failure criterion for element "e"

surrounding
$$\underset{\sim}{\sigma}_u^1 = \underset{\sim}{\sigma}_u^0 + \Delta\underset{\sim}{\sigma}_u^1$$

$$\underset{\sim}{\sigma}_e^1 = \underset{\sim}{\sigma}_e^0 + \zeta \cdot \Delta\underset{\sim}{\sigma}_e^1$$

b Mohr–Coulomb failure criterion

Figure 13.12 Illustration of the iterative calculation to account for stress rearrangement as a consequence of failure, calculative step 1

surrounding U. The residual strength $\sigma_{Br,e}$ within the described procedure is evaluated from the state of stress σ_e^0 in the manner described in Figure 13.12(b) where σ_N is the normal stress on the failure plane.

The redistribution of stresses from element e to the surrounding U is simulated by an iterative calculation applying the initial stress principle. Within a 1st iterative step the system is loaded by an initial stress state, given by the differential stress $\Delta\boldsymbol{\sigma}_e^1$. According to the stiffness of the system this stress is distributed as follows:

(1) to element e with the portion $\zeta \cdot \Delta\boldsymbol{\sigma}_e^1$; and
(2) to the surrounding U with the portion $(1-\zeta)\Delta\boldsymbol{\sigma}_e^1$, creating the state of stress $\Delta\boldsymbol{\sigma}_u^1$.

In these equations the factor ζ, which depends on the stiffness of the system and varies from $0 < \zeta < 1$ (note that for $\zeta \geq 1$ equilibrium within the system is not possible) describes the portion of the initial stresses distributed to element e. If this initial state of stress is superimposed to the state of stress due to loading then the following stresses result (Figure 13.13):

(a) for the surrounding U: $\boldsymbol{\sigma}_u^1 = \boldsymbol{\sigma}_u^0 + \Delta\boldsymbol{\sigma}_u^1$

(b) for element e: $\boldsymbol{\sigma}_e^1 = \boldsymbol{\sigma}_e^0 + \zeta \cdot \Delta\boldsymbol{\sigma}_e^1$

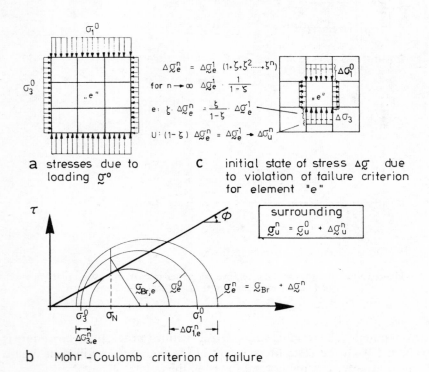

a stresses due to loading $\underset{\sim}{\sigma}^0$

c initial state of stress $\Delta\underset{\sim}{\sigma}$ due to violation of failure criterion for element "e"

b   Mohr – Coulomb criterion of failure

Figure 13.13   Illustration of the iterative calculation to account for stress rearrangement as a consequence of failure, calculative step n

This iterative calculation is continued towards step n (Figure 13.13). Then the initial state of stress results in:

$$\Delta\boldsymbol{\sigma}_e^n = \Delta\boldsymbol{\sigma}_e^1[1 + \zeta + \zeta^2 + \cdots + \zeta^n]$$

and for $n \to \infty$ the initial state of stress converges towards:

$$\Delta\boldsymbol{\sigma}_e^n = \Delta\boldsymbol{\sigma}_e^1 \cdot \frac{1}{1-\zeta}$$

This again is distributed according to the stiffness of the system as follows:

(1) To element e with the portion $\zeta \cdot \Delta\sigma_e^n = \dfrac{\zeta}{1-\zeta} \cdot \Delta\sigma_e^1$.

(2) To the surrounding U with the portion $(1-\zeta) \cdot \Delta\sigma_e^n = \Delta\sigma_e^1$ where it creates the state of stress $\Delta\sigma_u^n$.

If this final initial state of stress is superimposed to the state of stress due to loading then the following stresses result (Figure 13.13(b)):

(1) for the surrounding U:

$$\sigma_u^n = \sigma_u^0 + \Delta\sigma_u^n$$

where $\Delta\sigma_u^n$ just corresponds to the stress portion $\Delta\sigma_e^1$, which element e could not sustain.

(2) for element e:

$$\sigma_e^n = \sigma_e^0 + \zeta \cdot \Delta\sigma_e^n$$

$$= \sigma_e^0 + \frac{\zeta}{1-\zeta} \cdot \Delta\sigma_e^1$$

$$= \sigma_{Br} + \Delta\sigma_e^1 + \frac{\zeta}{1-\zeta} \cdot \Delta\sigma_e^1$$

$$= \sigma_{Br} + \frac{1}{1-\zeta} \cdot \Delta\sigma_e^1$$

$$\sigma_e^n = \sigma_{Br} + \Delta\sigma_e^n$$

(see Figure 13.13(b))

where the initial stress $\Delta\sigma_e^n$, by which the strength of element e at the end of the iterative calculation is exceeded, has just served to deform element e to such an extent that the non-admissible differential stress $\Delta\sigma_e^1$ of the 1st step would be redistributed to the surrounding U. By these means the required plastic deformation of element e has been simulated and for evaluation of the stresses resulting for element e it is assumed that this deformation does not create stresses. Therefore within the last iterative step the stress $\Delta\sigma_e^n$ is subtracted from the stress σ_e^n resulting in the residual strength $\sigma_{Br,e}$ for element e and consequently equilibrium for the total system is restored. For a general case the iterative calculation is performed correspondingly. The convergency ($n \rightarrow \infty$) then however cannot be proved as for the selected example.

In case the resulting zones, in which the strength is exceeded, are limited in extent and the calculated displacements converge towards a finite value, equilibrium of a system is possible. The incorporated flow rule valid for the plastic zones however is not clearly defined and results from the calculation itself. This of course is not satisfactory. In view of the present state of knowledge in rock mechanics this approach nevertheless seems to be justified.

13.5 ILLUSTRATION OF THE PROPOSED DESIGN CONCEPT

Subsequently the concept for the design of underground openings as applied by the author and his co-workers will be described and the important role the finite element method plays within this concept shall be illustrated.

For this purpose the applied rock mechanical parameters, which are based on the evaluated stress–strain law, are once more compiled in Figure 13.14.

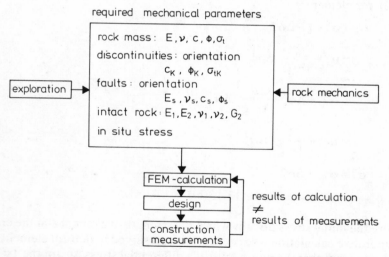

Figure 13.14 Representation of the design concept by a flow chart

An important condition for the determination of these parameters in any specific case, is a detailed and extensive engineering geological investigation. This investigation should be specially directed towards a detailed description of the geometry of the discontinuities and a petrographic description of the intact rock. The results of investigations of this type are a valuable aid for the evaluation of the mechanical parameters of the rock mass and in this course for the elaboration of a meaningful rock mechanical testing programme as well as for the extrapolation of the corresponding results to areas, which would not be tested (Figure 13.14).

Based on the rock mass parameters determined in this manner, a finite element analysis of the underground opening is performed. The results of this analysis serve as a basis for the design, i.e. to determine the required amount of safety measures and lining and the recommended construction procedure (Figure 13.14).

In spite of such a thorough investigation at the present state of knowledge it is still necessary to prove the results of the analysis and herewith the stability of the opening by in situ measurements during and after construction (Figure 13.14). It is even still possible that the results of such measurements can lead to changes of the amount of safety measures and lining during construction. In this context it is clear that the application of shotcrete and anchoring as a safety measure—because of its flexibility—is very suitable if this design concept is applied.

The details of this design concept vary from case to case and very much depend on the rock conditions encountered as well as on the type of underground structure in question. Also a certain amount of experience in dealing with rock mechanics problems and tunnel design in general and especially in the application of this concept will be very helpful. Therefore this concept subsequently will be outlined by examples of three underground openings, which have been designed and constructed in co-operation with the author.

13.6   UNDERGROUND POWER HOUSE WEHR

For a pumped storage scheme in the southern Black Forest in Germany (Pfisterer, 1963) the construction of an undergroud power house was required. It consists of a power house cavern 19 m wide, 33 m high and 219 m long, with valve cavern and the upstream and downstream manifolds (Figure 13.15). The overburden of the underground power house is about 350 m.

13.6.1   Geological investigations

Ten years before the construction was started, an exploration adit located 19 m above the designed cavern had been excavated. The exploration adit which also served as a starting point for some core drillings in the area of the power house, divides in the area of the cavern into two parallel and one connecting adit (Figure 13.15). For further exploration a so-called roof adit was excavated. This adit is parallel to the axis of the power house cavern and

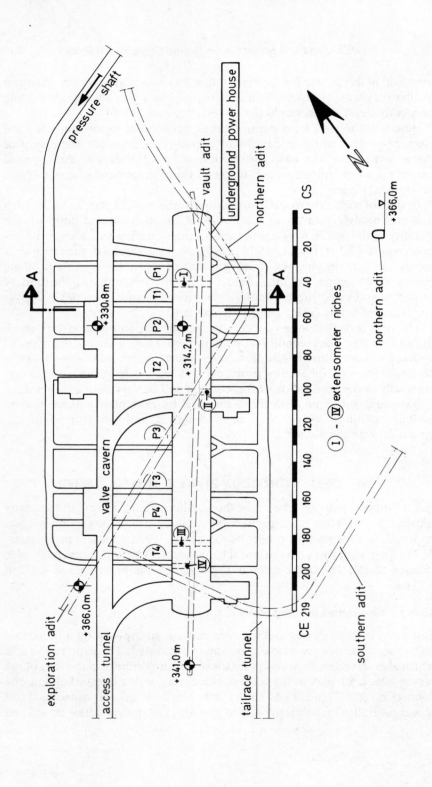

pressure shaft

vault adit

underground power house

northern adit

exploration adit

access tunnel

valve cavern

+ 366,0 m

+ 330,8 m

+ 314,2 m

A

A

P1

T1

P2

T2

P3

T3

P4

T4

I

II

III

IV

+ 341,0 m

tailrace tunnel

southern adit

CE 219

0 20 40 60 80 100 120 140 160 180 200 CS

N

① – Ⅳ extensometer niches

northern adit

+ 366,0 m

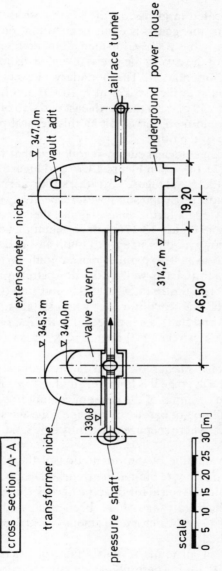

Figure 13.15 Location and cross-section of underground power house

is located within cross-section of the vault of the cavern. The cross section of this adit at four characteristic points was enlarged to that of the cavern vault (niches I–IV, Figure 13.15).

The cavern is located in gneiss. In the north east section of the power house the texture of this gneiss is equivalent to that of the nearby albtal granite. Consequently this rock was named albtal granitelike gneiss. In the south western area of the cavern the gneiss reveals a distinct parallel texture with interchanging orientation. The boundary between both rock types follows a vertical plane, which strikes at N 160° E and intersects the vault adit at a distance of 140 m from the north east end slab of the power house. No discontinuity could be observed along this vertical plane of transition from one rock type to the other.

As a result of the geological survey it followed that four throughgoing master joints ((1), (3), (4), (5) in Figure 13.16 and Figure 13.17(a)) and one fault ((2) in Figure 13.16 and Figure 13.17(a)) striking at N 150°–170° E and dipping steeply to north east and south west respectively exist in the area of the power house. Along a further master joint, the so-called parallel joint (PK, Figure 13.16 and Figure 13.17(a)) the orientation varies considerably. On the average it however dips steeply to south east and strikes at an acute angle to the cavern axis. The parallel master joint further intersects the southwestern end slab (CE) as well as the downstream and the upstream wall of the cavern. The upstream wall at this end slab (CE) is intersected at the elevation of the cavern roof, whereas at station CS + 150 m (CS = north eastern end slab) it is intersected at the floor level. The parallel master joint and the upstream wall form a rock mass wedge, which opens upwards.

The appearance of all master joints and the fault zone strongly varies from place to place, on the average it is however similar. Over large extents these discontinuities have openings of the order of centimetres to decimetres and have coatings and fillings of baryte, calcite and cohesive soils. Except along these discontinuities, where seepage frequently exists, the rock mass is more or less impermeable.

The statistical evaluation of the orientation of the 537 so-called small joints, which were much more limited in extent and mapped in the vault adit, reveals a scatter which is typical for this type of rock (Figure 13.17). Despite this scatter five idealized ranges have been evaluated as joint families K 1–K 5 (Figure 13.17), to which a total amount of 80 per cent of all mapped joints can be attached.

Only a minority of all joints reveals fillings of calcite, baryte, quartz, kaolin, and hematite iron. These fillings mostly are very thin and do not reach over a larger extent. Small quantities of seepage have been observed for only about 4 per cent of all joints.

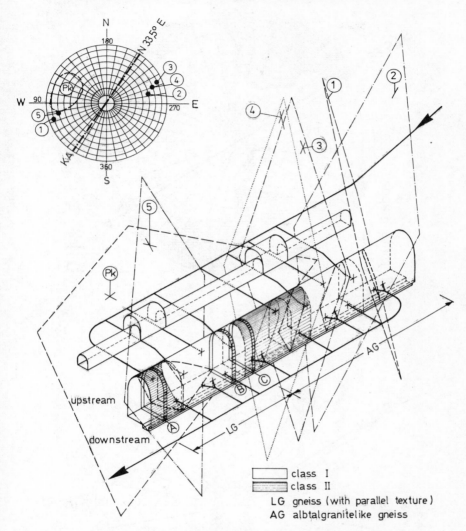

Figure 13.16 Faults, master joints and rock mass classification

The distribution of the joints of the five series along the length of the roof adit is irregular. From a statistical evaluation of the mapping with regards to the intensity of jointing assuming certain idealizations it could be concluded that there are two areas of homogeneous intensity of jointing, the one with a more intense degree and the other one with a less intense degree of jointing (rock mass classes I and II, Figure 13.16) (Wittke and Pfisterer, 1972).

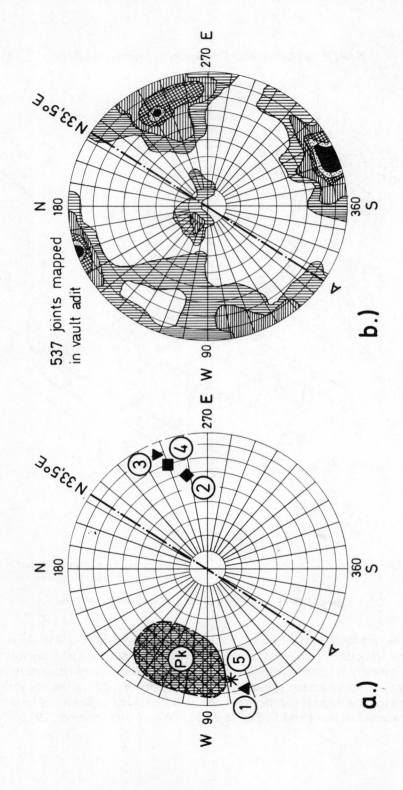

b.) 537 joints mapped in vault adit

a.)

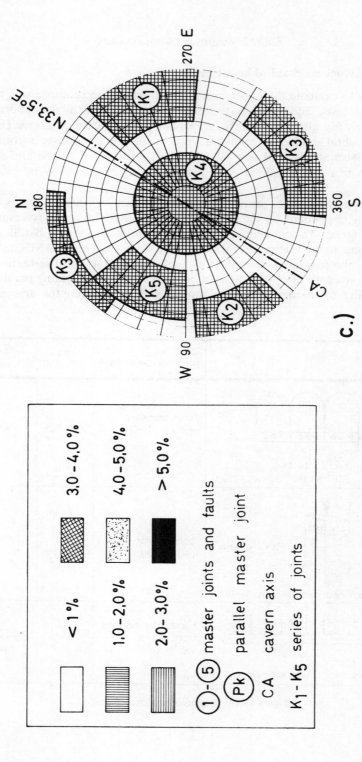

Figure 13.17 Orientation of master joints and faults, of joints and sub-division into series of joints

13.6.2   Rock mechanical investigations

In order to evaluate the intact rock strength unconfined compression tests, brazilian tests, and shear tests have been performed in the laboratory separately for 'albtal granitelike' gneiss and parallel textured gneiss. Hence for the 'albtal granitelike' gneiss the tests resulted in an average unconfined compressive strength of $\sigma_c = 82 \cdot 5 \, MN/m^2$, an uniaxial tensile and shear strength of $\sigma_t = 7 \cdot 2 \, MN/m^2$ and a cohesion of $c = 29 \cdot 4 \, MN/m^2$ respectively.

As expected the test results for samples of parallel textured gneiss were distinctly dependent on the orientation of the parallel texture versus the applied stress. The unconfined compression tests for loading parallel and orthogonal to the texture reveal an average strength of $\sigma_c = 63 \, MN/m^2$ and in cases the loading was applied at angles around 45° to the texture an average strength of $\sigma_c = 44 \, MN/m^2$ was measured. For loading parallel or diagonally to texture the mean tensile and shear strengths amount to

type of test	location / samples taken from	$V_{stat.}$ $[10^8 \, N/m^2]$	$V_{dyn.}$ $[10^8 \, N/m^2]$
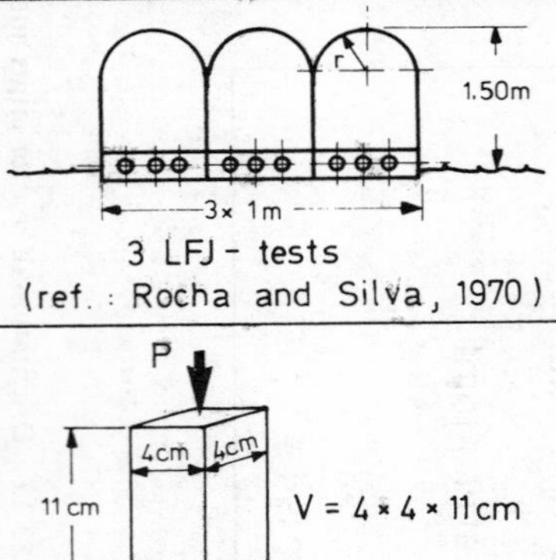 3 LFJ - tests (ref.: Rocha and Silva, 1970)	extensometer niches I − III	565÷865	—
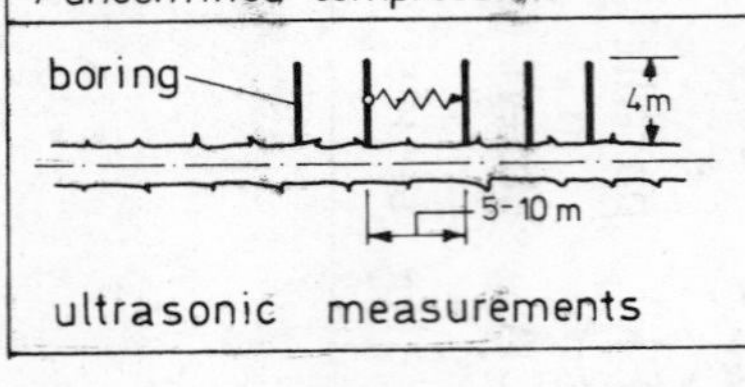 7 unconfined compression tests	boring for LFJ -tests	560÷800	—
ultrasonic measurements	horizontal borings from walls of vault adit	—	750÷850

Figure 13.18   Results of deformability tests

$\sigma_t = 8.6 \, \text{MN/m}^2$ and $c = 7.8 \, \text{MN/m}^2$. For loading orthogonally to the texture the corresponding figures are $\sigma_t = 4.2 \, \text{MN/m}^2$ and $c = 24 \, \text{MN/m}^2$.

By means of flat jack tests—system LFJ of LNEC (Rocha and da Silva, 1970)—and ultrasonic measurements the deformability of the rock mass was investigated. For comparison also prisms of intact rock taken from points next to the sites of the LFJ tests have been tested (Figure 13.18) (Wittke and Pfisterer, 1972).

The test results (Figure 13.18) reveal a relatively low deformability of the rock mass. A detailed evaluation of all tests, specially accounting for the correlation between static and dynamic moduli (Link, 1962) revealed for rock mass class I (Figure 13.16) a static modulus $V \approx 6$–$9 \cdot 10^4 \, \text{MN/m}^2$ and for rock mass class II a static modulus $V \approx 5$–$8 \cdot 10^4 \, \text{MN/m}^2$. Immediately adjacent to the fault zone and the master joints the deformability of the rock mass however will be higher.

From a longtime LFJ-test it was found that the time-dependency of the stress–strain characteristics of the rock mass is small. Only 20% of the total displacements occurred with a certain time delay.

13.6.3   Rock mass parameters for stability analyses

The representative mechanical parameters for the required stability analysis have been derived from the results of the geological and rock mechanical investigations and were applied to the calculations of the corresponding cross-sections ((A), (B), (C), see Section 13.6.4, Figure 13.16 and Table 13.1). For Young's modulus an average value was selected, which, because of the deviation of the moduli evaluated from the test results, can be applied to both the rock classes I and II. Shear strengths and angles of friction (Table 13.1) of the small joints of the five families were evaluated separately for the two rock mass classes I and II, according to the frequency and extension of the separated planes of the joints.

The determination of the mechanical properties of the master joints was of considerable importance. From the widths of the opening and the fillings of these discontinuities, as locally observed, it was concluded that the shear strength is very small and the tensile strength was zero. For the same reason the normal stiffness of the master joints was assumed to be very low.

With the exception of the parallel master joint the fault and master joints intersect the cavern approximately at right angles which is relatively favourable for stability. Therefore the stability analyses of the cavern were concentrated on the evaluation of the influence of the parallel master joint.

Table 13.1 Rock mass parameters adopted for the calculations of the underground power house Wehr

Cross-section (Figure 13.16)		A	B	C
Rock mass		LG	LG	AG
Amount of overburden above roof h(m)		350	350	350
Unit weight γ $(10^{-2}\,MN/m^3)$		2·5	2·5	2·5
Young's modulus E $(10^2\,MN/m^2)$*		700/400	700/400	700/400
Poisson's ratio		0·18	0·18	0·18
Intact rock				
Unconfined compressive strength σ_c (MN/m^2)		63	63	82·5
Unconfined tensile strength σ_t (MN/m^2)		4·2	4·2	7·2
Cohesion c (MN/m^2)		7·8	7·8	29·4
Jointing				
K_1—	tensile strength/ cohesion	σ_t/c $(10^{-1}\,MN/m^2)$ 8·6/14·7	0/0	0/0
K_2—		σ_t/c $(10^{-1}\,MN/m^2)$ 0/0	8·6/14·7	0/0
K_3—		σ_t/c $(10^{-1}\,MN/m^2)$ 0/0	0/0	0/0
K_4—		σ_t/c $(10^{-1}\,MN/m^2)$ —	0/0	0/0
K_5—		σ_t/c $(10^{-1}\,MN/m^2)$ 8·6/14·7	30/55·6	0/0

Angle of friction $\phi = 25°$; beyond failure $\phi' = 40°$ to $50°$

'Parallel' master joint $\sigma_t = 0$, $c = 0$

	A	B	C
Angle of friction ϕ (°)	10 to 25	25	—
Young's modulus E $(10^2\,MN/m^2)$	0·5	5/100 (alternatively)	
Thickness (Figure 13.19)	$d_{Pk}=0·1$ m	$d_{Pk}=1·0$ m	

*Most of the calculations are based on a Young's modulus of $700 \times 10^2\,MN/m^2$. Partly $E = 400 \times 10^2\,MN/m^2$ has been applied.

Arising from the results of the geological explorations the parallel master joint was assumed to be completely separated and consequently the tensile strength and the cohesion were assumed to be $\sigma_t = 0$ and $c = 0$. Also the adopted angle of friction was very low (Table 13.1). Because of the variation of the width, fillings and coatings along the parallel master joint, and since it was difficult to evaluate the success of the grouting measures (see Section 13.6) in advance, it was also very difficult to evaluate reliable figures which describe the normal stiffness as the Young's modulus and the effective opening of this discontinuities. Therefore the influence of a variation of the normal stiffness was investigated by calculating with a very small Young's modulus of $50\,MN/m^2$ and a thickness of $d_{PK} = 0·1$ m of $500\,MN/m^2$ and a thickness of $d_{PK} = 1·0$ m and also with a relatively high value of $10\,000\,MN/m^2$ and a thickness $d_{PK} = 1·0$ m (Table 13.1).

Extensive tests to determine the *in situ* stresses were not performed for this project. Only the displacements due to cutting the slot for the LFJ test applying vertically orientated flat jacks were available and revealed quite low horizontal stresses within the rock mass. By compensating for the displacements due to slot cutting for the horizontally orientated flat jack it was found that the vertical stress approximately equals the weight of the overburden. The *in situ* stresses within the undisturbed rock mass according to these measurements were then evaluated from the weight of the overburden (h, γ, Table 13.1) and a Poisson's ratio of $\nu = 0.18$. This Poisson's ratio also corresponds to the values obtained from the ultrasonic measurements.

13.6.4 FEM-analyses

Since the length of the cavern is very large in comparison to the dimensions of its cross-section, a comprehensive three-dimensional analysis including the total structure was neither necessary nor very useful. Therefore the stability analysis was performed for three cross-sections ((A), (B), (C), Figure 13.16) which were representative with regards to the location of the parallel master joint as well as to the degree of regular jointing (Wittke, Wallner, *et al.*, 1972). At these cross-sections, vertical slabs one metre thick were investigated.

Cross-section (A) is representative for zones in which the parallel master joint intersects the upstream wall of the cavern at the elevation of the roof, whereas cross-section (B) served for the investigation of the stability of the cavern in zones where the parallel master joint intersects the upstream wall at the elevation of the floor. Cross-section (C), finally, is a so-called 'standard cross-section' for zones not influenced by any fault or master joint. It is located in the NE-section of the cavern, because the most intensive regular jointing was found in that area. As boundary conditions, the displacements perpendicularly to the lower horizontal and the two vertically and parallel to the cavern axis oriented planes bounding the investigated slab were assumed to be zero. For the upper horizontal boundary nodal forces corresponding to the weight of the overburden were assumed, as can be seen for cross-section B in Figure 13.19. For the remaining vertical planes bounding the slab investigated it was assumed, that nodal points located on a line parallel to the cavern axis have equal displacements, if, in fact, they had any displacement. This boundary condition corresponds to the assumption of a cavern of infinite length having equal rock mass conditions. The analysis was also directed to the investigation of different construction stages. This was of special importance for cross-section (B), since—as subsequently described—the stability of the rock mass wedge bounded by the parallel master joint and the upstream wall of the cavern had to be permanently evaluated and observed during excavation, which started at the vault of the

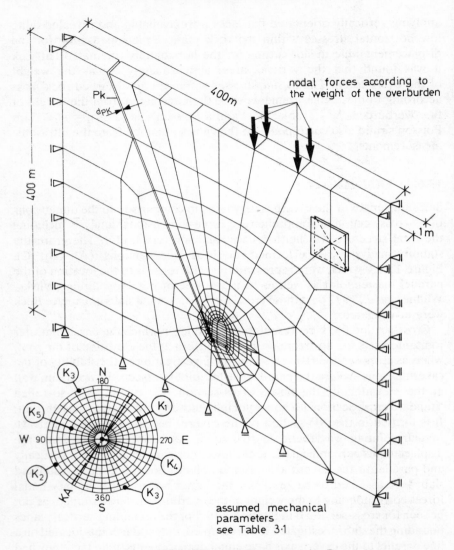

nodal forces according to
the weight of the overburden

Pk

dPK

400m

400 m

1m

K₃ N
180

K₅   K₁

W 90   270 E

K₂   K₄

KA   K₃
360
S

assumed mechanical
parameters
see Table 3·1

Figure 13.19   FEM-mesh for cross-section B

cavern and then was continued in benches. For this purpose two intermediate stages of construction (excavation of the cavern down to elevation +
326 m and + 320 m) have been analysed.

For cross-section (C) the analysis indicated stability of the power house
without any major lining or safety measures being required.

Also for cross-section (A), where the parallel master joint intersected at roof elevation stability of the power house was shown. It was, however, found that the stress transfer through the rock mass around the power house is strongly dependent on the normal stiffness and shear strength of the parallel master joint. In case of unfavourable conditions, i.e. small normal stiffness and shear strength, larger dislocations of the opposite walls of the parallel master joint occur. Consequently, with progressing excavation on both sides of the line of intersection with the parallel master joint relative displacements of the cavern wall occur. Furthermore, the state of stresses, which develops in the rock mass around the cavern is unsymmetrical.

The results of the analysis of cross-section (B) came out to be of special importance. Here along with the progress of excavation (Figures 13.20(a)–(f)) stress concentrations occur in the wedge between the parallel master joint and the upstream cavern wall and hence the shear strength in small joints is quite frequently exceeded, as marked by circles in the stress plots of Figures 13.20(a), (c), (e). As soon as the foot of this wedge is excavated the whole wedge slides on the parallel master joint towards the cavern and as a consequence is unloaded. Thus the upstream wall of the cavern moves towards the cavern and is stretched and the magnitude of the displacements increases from the roof towards the floor (Figure 13.20).

In connection with this process, the vertical stresses due to the weight of the overburden are transmitted from the sliding wedge towards the rock mass adjacent to the downstream cavern wall. Deviating from both the other cross sections the stability could not be shown by calculation unless additional measures were used. The above-mentioned iterative calculation gave increasing horizontal displacements of the tip of the wedge even after 40 iterative steps and no convergence could be reached. Consequently it could be concluded that the stability of the upstream wall of the cavern was endangered. By means of additional calculations it could however be found that by the installation of sufficiently dimensioned pre-stressed anchors (see Section 13.6.5) the horizontal displacements of the tip of the wedge could be limited to about one centimetre although the sliding of the wedge and the rearrangement of stresses towards the downstream side of the power house would still continue.

13.6.5   Rock-mass excavation—lining and safety measures of the cavern

For the cross sections not being influenced by master joints and faults, a light constructive lining accounting for the small joints was proposed despite the fact that the results of the calculations were so favourable. It consists of approximately 15 cm shotcrete reinforced by one layer of square wire mesh

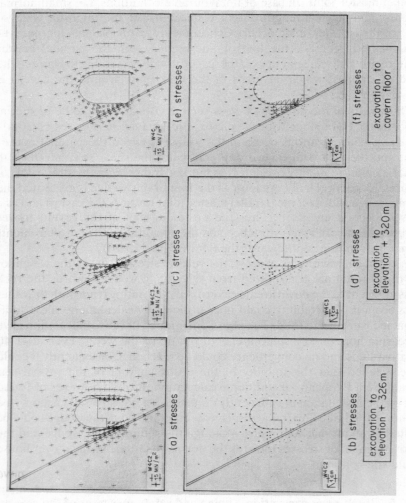

Figure 13.20 Results of the FEM-analysis

and of perfo bolts with a spacing of 1·5 to 2·5 m, diameter of 0·022 to 0·024 m and 4 m long. In order to increase the normal stiffness and to decrease permeability, the master joints and the fault-zone have been grouted, mainly from the vault adit, before the excavation was started. Further along the intersections of the master joints and the wall of the cavern, the amount of rock bolts, shotcrete and reinforcement was increased.

The same increase of safety measures was applied to those zones where the parallel master joint intersects the underground power house at roof elevation.

For improvement of the stability of the rock-mass wedge between the parallel master joint and the upstream cavern wall, a comprehensive grouting programme was carried out. As for the other master joints and the fault, the grouting started from the vault adit before excavation was started and it was extended stepwise from bench to bench over the total height of the cavern. Altogether 76 tons of cement have been grouted resulting in an average thickness of this discontinuity of three to four centimetres.

Furthermore, in accordance with the result of the analyses, 82 pre-stressed anchors with a capacity 1·7 MN each, with lengths from 13 to 30 m and an upward inclination of 30°, have been installed from the upstream cavern wall (Figure 13.21). They penetrate the parallel master joint and fix the rock-mass wedge into the rock-mass column between the valve cavern and the power-house cavern. In order to prevent rock loosening as far as possible the installation was conducted stepwise with the excavation of the benches. As, from the results of the calculations, it could be concluded that the wedge only slides off at the final stage of the excavation (Figure 13.20), an increase of the pre-stressing load of the anchors already installed was expected.

An evaluation of this increase of pre-stressing loads, assuming an unfavourable Young's modulus of the rock mass, revealed that depending on the length and location of the anchors an increase of tensional stresses ranging from 40 to 130 MN/m^2 had to be expected. Because of this reason the 1·7 MN anchors were only pre-stressed up to 1·4 MN. Moreover nine of the 82 anchors were installed as measuring anchors (Figure 13.21). Since the anchors were not grouted during the construction period it would have been possible to decrease the pre-stressing load according to any eventually unfavourable measurement.

In addition, in the zones where the pre-stressed anchors were applied, safety measures of reinforced shotcrete and rock bolts were applied to both cavern walls and at the roof. The amount of reinforcement was, however,

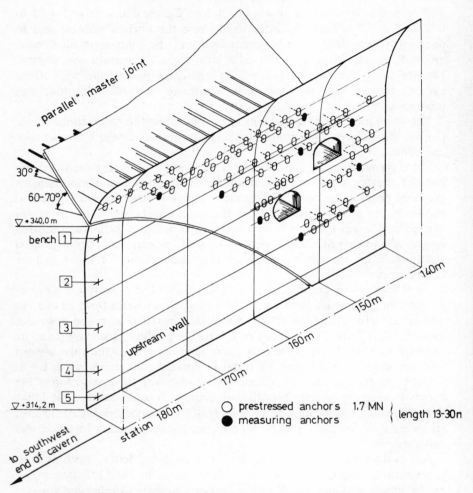

Figure 13.21 Prestressed anchors in the area of the parallel master joint

increased in comparison to that used in the zones of average jointing as described above.

Drainage and the reduction of pore pressures in the master joints and the fault was carried out by drainage holes located next to the floor of the cavern. The drainage of the parallel master joint required special attention. Here additional drainage holes were drilled at elevation + 330 m.

13.6.6 Monitoring during construction

For monitoring the rock-mass displacements in the area of the master joints, 13 multiple extensometers had been installed before the excavation started. Further additional one- and two-point extensometers served as a control measure for the pre-stressed anchors and for the eventual displacement of the cavern wall.

By comparing the results of the measurements with those of the FEM-analysis already made during construction it was possible to evaluate the stability of the cavern and, if necessary, it would have been possible to install additional safety measures.

Of special interest in this context were the results of extensometer S III (Figure 13.22), by which the displacements of the rock mass wedge between

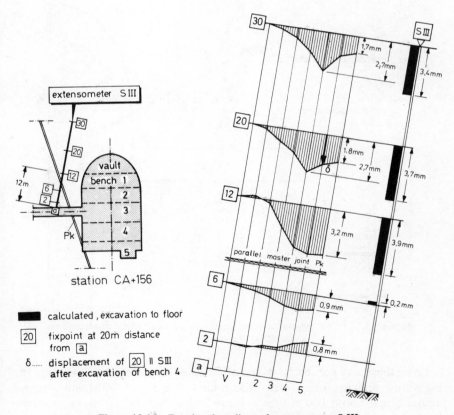

Figure 13.22 Results of readings of extensometer S III

the upstream cavern wall and parallel master joint could be monitored. From a comparison of the results of the calculated and measured displacements (Figures 13.22 and 13.23) it could be deduced that the rock-mass wedge during the excavation of the cavern actually moved according to the forecast. Calculated and measured displacements are in good agreement.

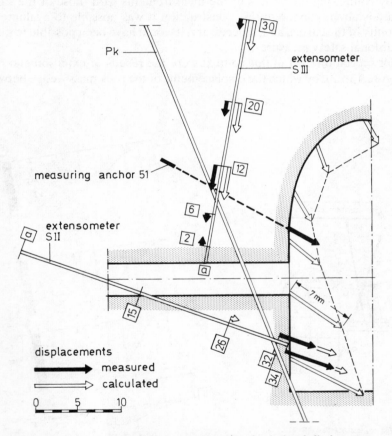

Figure 13.23 Comparison between measured and calculated displacements adjacent to cross-section B

From these and the results of the other extensometers as well as from the measured anchor forces—the maximum increase of tensional stresses amounting to about 100 MN/m^2—it can be concluded that the pre-stressing load of the anchors did not exceed the allowable limits. Also the trend, and in most of the cases the absolute magnitude, of the measurements of the multiple extensometers—not described here in detail—were in agreement with the results of the calculations.

It also is very interesting that by means of the extensometer readings even the instant of the re-arrangement of the stresses from the upstream to the downstream side of the power house due to excavation of the parallel master joint could be deduced (Figure 13.24). This stress rearrangement occurred in three steps, each being inititated by blastings close to the upstream wall and performed on February 14/15, February 28/March 1 and March 8 to 11, 1973. The extensometer readings plotted in Figure 13.24 obviously show an increase of displacements on those days.

In this context the readings of extensometer III 3 (Figure 13.24) located in the downstream wall of this area deserve special attention. As predicted, because of additional loading of the rock mass adjacent to the downstream cavern wall, displacements were also measured here after excavation of the parallel master joint on the opposite side.

It is also interesting to note that the geological mappings made during the whole time of construction show good agreement with the forecast based on the results of the vault adit. A picture of the cavern during construction is shown in Figure 13.25.

13.7 WATER TRANSMISSION TUNNEL—NÜRNBERG

In connection with a major project in the area of Nürnberg it was intended to cross the main water shed between Rhine and Danube by a tunnel approximately 2·2 km long. The diameter of this tunnel is 6·5 m; the rock overburden ranges from approximately 10 to 23 m. A 100 m long test tunnel was excavated in order to perform an extensive rock mechanical testing programme (Wittke, Carl, *et al.*, 1974; Wittke, Pfisterer, *et al.*, 1974). This structure later was part of the final tunnel, so that the costs of this test excavation in reality only amounted to those of the measuring programme. This example differs from the other two in so far, as the rock conditions are different and because the FEM analysis mainly served the purpose to simulate the deformations measured in the test tunnel and by this led to an improvement of the accuracy of the measurement of rock-mass properties, which in a first step were determined in laboratory tests. By this procedure the final design could be based on very reliable values for rock-mass properties. Since there was practically no deviation from the originally outlined design concept the same logical order as for the other two projects will be applied subsequently.

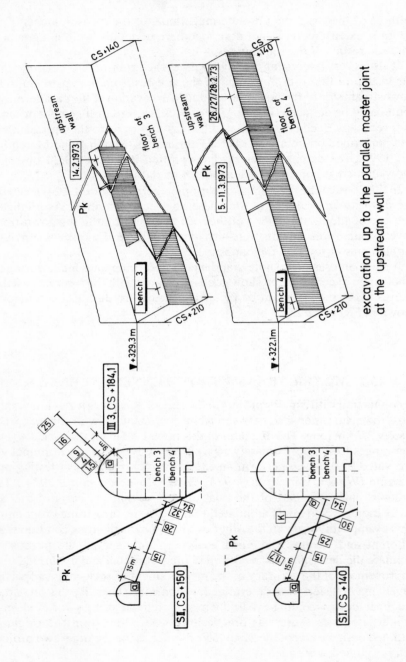

excavation up to the parallel master joint at the upstream wall

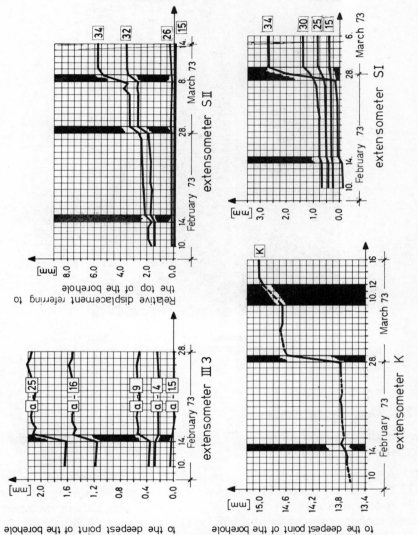

Figure 13.24 Time dependency of stress redistribution in the area of the parallel master joint

Figure 13.25 Underground power house, Wehr; stage of construction during Spring 1973

13.7.1 Geological explorations

The design of the test tunnel could be based on the following geological information:

(1) A geological map of Bavaria, sheet 6830, Gunzenhausen.

(2) Two expert opinions of the Bavarian Geological survey.

(3) A test pit located at the tunnel portal and being part of the open channel section of the water transmission system (Figure 13.26).

(4) The results of 31 core drillings located along and adjacent to axis of the tunnel.

In the area in question the sub-stratum consists of 'Burgsandstone', a formation belonging to the mean keuper. The Burgsandstone is separated

Figure 13.26   Test excavation and portal of the test tunnel

by two throughgoing silty clay layers into the lower, mean, and upper Burgsandstone. The planned tunnel is located within the mean Burgsandstone (Figure 13.27). For the area of the test tunnel borings and the test excavation yielded the idealized underground profile as shown in Figure 13.28. The layers of cohesive soil represented in this profile consist of dark red to dark brown clayey sandy silt and clayey silt and sand. The cohesive soil layers separating the upper, mean, and lower Burgsandstone have a very large extension whereas the soil layers within the mean Burgsandstone, as for example, the silty clay layers at the tunnel floor roof, do not extend too far.

In the boreholes two different groundwater tables were found, one in the upper and the other in the mean Burgsandstone. The reason for these two groundwater tables probably is the extremely low permeability of the thick and throughgoing cohesive soil layer separating the upper and mean Burgsandstone. The evaluation of the core borings and the slopes of the test excavation revealed 21 discontinuities. Plotting the measured angles of

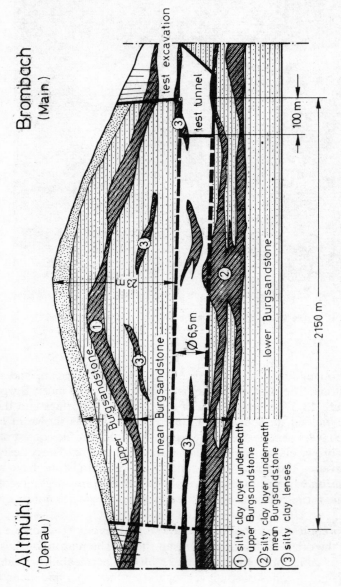

Figure 13.27 Water transmission tunnel, Nürnberg

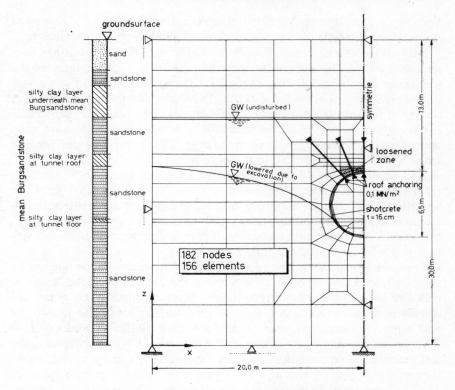

Figure 13.28 Finite element mesh and boundary conditions

strike and dip with the aid of a polar projection of the lower hemisphere resulted in a series of joints with a mean strike of N 80° E and 80° dip to south. The joints intersect the axis of the tunnel at an acute angle amounting to 15°. The mean extent of these discontinuities amounts to 35 m², i.e. approximately the area of the tunnel cross-section. The mean spacing of the discontinuities is 2·5 m. Further, at the slope of the test excavation horizontal sedimentation joints confining sandstone banks 0·8 to 1·0 m thick were exposed. Further, from the core borings it was found that the intact rock mass parallel to the bedding probably contains latent planes of reduced shear and tensile strength.

13.7.2 Mechanical investigations of the rock

Laboratory tests were carried out to evaluate the mechanical parameters of the intact rock and of the silty clay layers. By estimating the influence of the bedding and the above described discontinuities and from the results of these laboratory tests the decisive rock-mass parameters were evaluated.

Fifty-six sandstone samples were selected from the core borings in a manner such that the test results can be assumed to be representative of the sandstone. For 20 samples the unconfined compressive strength was determined resulting in a mean value of $\sigma_c \sim 15 \text{ MN/m}^2$ for air-dried samples. A scatter of the results from 6 and 22 MN/m^2 was observed. Further stress–strain curves measured in the unconfined compressive tests were only approximately linear. Depending on the stress level Young's moduli ranging from $1\cdot5 \times 10^3$ to $11 \times 10^3 \text{ MN/m}^2$ were evaluated.

According to the measured lateral strains, the Poisson's numbers ranged from $\nu = 0\cdot12$ for a stress level of $\sigma = 0-2 \, MN/m^2$ and $\nu = 0\cdot28$ for $\sigma = 10 \text{ MN/m}^2$. The tensile strength of the intact rock was investigated by means of 11 cylinder-splitting tests yielding values of $\sigma = 0\cdot5$ to 1 MN/m^2. Further 15 one-dimensional shear tests revealed minimum shear parameters of $\phi = 30°$ and $c = 2 \text{ MN/m}^2$.

From the slopes of the test excavation and from cores of the borings 86 samples were taken in order to determine the properties of the layers of cohesive soil. Within the corresponding test programme the grain size distribution, the natural water content, the Atterberg limits, the unit weight and degree of saturation were determined. Low plasticity indices of $I_P = 0\cdot19$ for the silty clay layers at floor level and $I_P = 0\cdot15$ at the roof level of the test tunnel resulted from the tests. Corresponding to a mean natural water content of $w_n = 0\cdot14$ and $w_n = 0\cdot11$ respectively, consistency indices of $I_c = 1\cdot26$ and $I_c = 1\cdot22$ respectively were obtained. The degree of saturation amounting to $S_r = 0\cdot95$ and $0\cdot88$ respectively for both layers is quite high. From these results it can be concluded that only small amounts of water can bring the water content of this soil close to the liquid limit, and further, that in case of additional loading of this soil layers excess pore pressures may occur. Confined compression tests were performed on three samples taken from the silty clay layers at the elevation of the roof of the test tunnel. The resulting Young's moduli for confined conditions and normal stress level of $\sigma = 0\cdot1$ to $0\cdot3 \text{ MN/m}^2$ amounts to $E \sim 10$ to 20 MN/m^2. The corresponding effective shear parameters derived from five triaxial shear tests on this cohesive soil amount to $\phi = 30°$ and $c = 0\cdot1$ to $0\cdot15 \text{ MN/m}^2$.

13.7.3   Mass properties of rock assumed for the stability analyses of the test tunnel

The parameters of the rock mass as introduced in the stability analyses of the test tunnel were evaluated from the results of the field and laboratory investigations accounting for experience gained from the design of comparable structures. The degree of separation along the horizontal, bedding parallel discontinuities was assumed to be $\varkappa = 90\%$. Applying the shear strength of the intact rock to the remaining 10% of intact rock along these discontinuities, the cohesion parallel to bedding was evaluated to $c_s = 0\cdot2\,\text{MN/m}^2$ and the tensile strength perpendicularly to the bedding $\sigma_{ts} = 0\cdot05\,\text{MN/m}^2$. For the vertical discontinuities even a higher degree of separation of $\varkappa = 95\%$ was assumed and consequently a cohesion $c_K = 0\cdot1\,\text{MN/m}^2$ and a tensile strength $\sigma_{tK} = 0\cdot025\,\text{MN/m}^2$ were taken into account. Since the spacing of the bedding parallel and the vertical discontinuities is small in comparison to the dimensions of the cross section of the tunnel, the reduced strength parallel to the discontinuities was assumed to hold in every point of the sandstone layers of the rock mass. As the applied degrees of separation are only estimated values, for comparative calculations (parametric studies) the cohesion along the horizontal and the vertical discontinuities was assumed to be zero and only an angle of friction of $\phi = 30°$ was applied (see values in brackets in Table 13.2).

Table 13.2 Mechanical parameters of the rock mass, soils and concrete for the feasibility calculations for the test tunnel, Nürnberg

	Young's modulus E [MN/m^2]	Poisson's ratio ν [−]	Cohesion c [10^{-1} MN/m^2]	Angle of friction [°]	Tensile strength σ_t [10^{-1} MN/m^2]	Unit weight wet/uplift γ_d γ' [10^{-2} MN/m^3]
Sandstone	3000	0·15	20	30	5	2·1/1·2
Sand	50	0·30	0	35	0	1·9/—
Silty clay layer at floor	5	0·30	0	30	0	2·2/1·2
Silty clay layer at roof	10	0·30	0	30	0	2·2/1·3
Concrete	20 000	0·18	70	20	15	2·4/—

Discontinuities	Orientation strike/dip	Degree of separation $\varkappa$ (%)	Cohesion c [10^{-1} MN/m^2]	ϕ [°]	Tensile strength σ_t [10^{-1} MN/m^2]
Bedding	0°/0°	90 (92·5/100)	2·0 (1·5)	30 (30)	0·5 (0)
Jointing	N80°E/80°S	95 (100)	1·0 (0)	30 (30)	0·25 (0)

According to the magnitude of stresses of $\sigma \sim 0\cdot1$ to $0\cdot15\,\text{MN/m}^2$ expected for the silty clay layers, a Young's modulus of $E = 5\,\text{MN/m}^2$ and a Poisson's ratio of $\nu = 0\cdot3$ were assumed, which correspond to the measured Young's modulus for confined strain conditions of the expected stress level.

For the silty clay layers at the roof of the tunnel a Young's modulus of $E = 10 \text{ MN/m}^2$ was assumed. The cohesion and the tensile strength of the silty clay layers of the floor and likewise of the roof were neglected. The effective angle of friction was derived from the test results as $\phi' = 30°$. The parameters for the concrete as well as for the sand next to the surface were assumed according to experience.

13.7.4　FEM-analyses

For the FEM-analyses of the test tunnel a circular cross-section with a diameter of $d = 6·5$ m was assumed. Further an overburden above the tunnel roof of $h = 13$ m and a 16 cm thick shotcrete lining were assumed.

Calculations were carried out for a vertical slab of 20 m wide, 30 m high and 1 m thick (Figure 13.28). As the problem was revealed to be symmetrical the calculations could be reduced to those for only one-half of the slab. As a boundary condition the displacements perpendicular to the lower horizontal and the two vertical confining planes, which are parallel to the tunnel axis, were assumed to be zero. The element mesh for the calculations consisted of 156 eight-cornered three-dimensional elements with 182 nodal points. The vertically oriented *in situ* stresses were assumed to equal the weight of the overburden ($\sigma_v = \gamma \cdot h$) and the corresponding horizontal stresses were evaluated by applying Poisson's ratio ν from the equations $\sigma_h = K_0 \cdot \sigma_v$, $K_0 = \nu/(1-\nu)$. Applying these assumptions the followings 5 cases were analysed:

B1: excavation of the total cross-section, no safety measures, lowering of the ground water table due to the drainage effect of the tunnel
B2: as B1, but zero strength of the sandstone layer between the tunnel roof and silty clay layer above the roof due to excavation
B3: as B2, but with a complete shotcrete lining and undisturbed ground water table
B4: as B1, but with roof anchoring of $0·1 \text{ MN/m}^2$
B5: as B2, but with roof anchoring of $0·1 \text{ MN/m}^2$

From the results of the above five loading cases, only those of case B5 are discussed further.

The magnitude and orientation of the evaluated normal principal stresses are plotted in Figure 13.29, the scale being given by means of a stress arrow. The plot shows that in the area not influenced by the excavation of the tunnel the maximum normal principal stress σ_1, which is vertical, increases approximately linearly with depth. Further it can be seen, that within the loosened silty clay layers above the roof the vertical normal stress is close to zero, i.e. the silty clay layer does not sustain any stresses. Thus the re-arrangement of

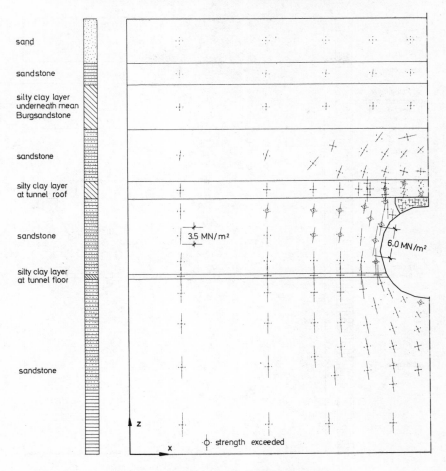

Figure 13.29   Loading case B 5, normal principal stresses

stresses due to excavation of the tunnel already takes place in the sandstone layer above the silty clay. In the sandstone adjacent to the tunnel wall this re-arrangement produces an increase of the vertical normal stress up to $\sigma_1 = 0 \cdot 6$ MN/m^2, which only amounts to $\sigma_1 = 0 \cdot 35$ MN/m^2 in a greater distance from the tunnel. Thus the rock-mass strength is locally exceeded, as marked in Figure 13.29. Underneath the tunnel the stress trajectories tend to be vertical again.

The resulting displacements as well as the horizontal and vertical components are also plotted for this loading case B5 in Figure 13.30. It can be seen that the surface sustains an approximately constant settlement of 5 mm. This

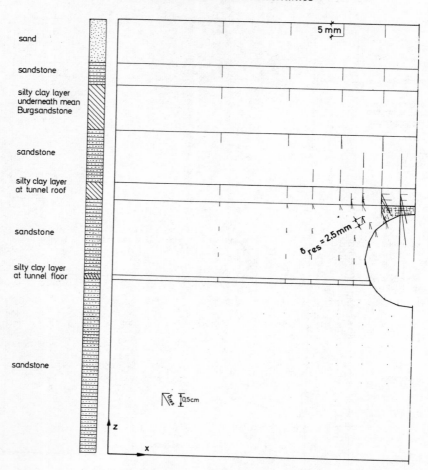

Figure 13.30 Loading case B 5, displacements

settlement results from a compression of the silty clay layers at the roof and at the floor level of the tunnel and is due to the re-arrangement of stresses, which takes place along with the excavation. The sandstone underneath the tunnel, except for a small heaving at the floor level due to unloading, hardly contributes to the overall displacements. The silty clay layer above the roof yields a remarkable vertical displacement towards the tunnel, whereas the sandstone at the walls only sustains negligibly small displacements towards the tunnel.

13.7.5   Recommendations for the design and the construction of the test tunnel

For the test tunnel a 16 cm thick lining of shotcrete with an unconfined compressive strength of $25 \, MN/m^2$ was recommended. This lining was reinforced by an inside and outside square wire mesh with $1 \cdot 58 \, cm^2/m$ cross section in both directions. Further rock anchoring with an average pre-stressing load of $0 \cdot 1 \, MN/m^2$ was recommended for the area of the tunnel roof. Further it was recommended that the shotcrete and the anchors be installed immediately after each or at least every second, blast.

13.7.6   Monitoring during construction

A measuring programme was recommended in order to monitor the stability of the testing tunnel and to evaluate representative design parameters for the main structure by comparison of the results of the above described calculations with the results of the measurements. The measuring programme consisted of extensometer and convergency measurements, precise levelling and stress measurements within the lining. The seepage was also measured and a rock mechanical mapping was carried out.

Since the extensometers could be installed from the surface it was possible to take zero readings before the construction started and by this the total displacements caused by the excavation were measured: this is often somewhat difficult in tunnelling. The settlement of the surface ranged between 3 and 7 mm. 20 to 30 per cent of the total displacements were measured immediately after the excavation passed the corresponding measurement cross section and levelling fixed point at the surface respectively. The total displacement was reached after the tunnel excavation arrived at a distance of 20 to 30 m ahead.

The results of one of the measured cross sections (II) are shown in Figure 13.31. It can be seen that a settlement of the tunnel roof of about 1 to 2 mm was recorded. Further, the convergence measurements reveal a relative displacement of the tunnel walls of $2\delta_h = 6$ to 9 mm and a vertical relative displacement of $2\delta_V = 1$ to 3 mm (Figure 13.31). Because the principle of the convergence measurement, the absolute displacements of the measuring points however cannot be evaluated from the readings. Further it has to be remembered that the convergence bolts could only be installed after the corresponding cross section was excavated and consequently only that portion of the displacements occurring later could be measured.

The pressure cells yielded tangential stresses in the lining of $\sigma = 1 \cdot 2$ to $1 \cdot 7 \, MN/m^2$ and radial normal stresses reaching from $\sigma = 0 \cdot 03$ to $0 \cdot 05 \, MN/m^2$. Another equally-equipped measurement cross-section revealed substantially the same results as those shown in Figure 13.31.

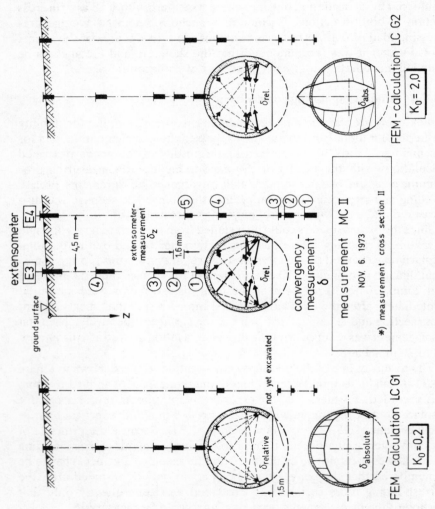

Figure 13.31 Comparison between measured and calculated displacements

13.7.7 Back analysis

To enable a meaningful comparison between analysis and measurements the stage of construction shown in Figure 13.31 (middle part) to which the measurement results refer was analysed by a FEM calculation, applying the original mechanical parameters as compiled in Table 13.2 (loading case G1).

A comparison of the resulting displacements (Figure 13.1, left side) with the corresponding extensometer readings reveals very good agreement, whereas for the horizontal convergence of the tunnel considerable discrepancy results. These differences were attributed to two reasons.

(1) The horizontal at right angles to the tunnel axis oriented *in situ* stresses within the rock mass were assumed too low.
(2) If this first reason is valid, then it follows that the Young's moduli for the rock mass were assumed too high.

Consequently the construction stage as shown in Figure 13.31 was calculated again (loading case G2), applying a Young's modulus of $1500\,\text{MN/m}^2$ for the sandstone and a modulus of $2\cdot5\,\text{MN/m}^2$ and $5\cdot0\,\text{MN/m}^2$ for the silty clay layers at the floor and at the roof of the tunnel respectively. Taking a Poisson's ratio of $\nu = 0\cdot4$, these Young's moduli are within the upper range of those determined in the laboratory tests for the silty clay. The vertical *in situ* stress was assumed to be the maximum normal principal stress and derived from the weight of the overburden. Orthogonally to the tunnel axis a horizontal *in situ* stress of $\sigma_h = 2 \cdot \sigma_v$ was assumed for the sandstone layers, whereas the normal *in situ* stress parallel to the tunnel axis was calculated according to Poisson's ratio for plane-strain conditions. All other parameters and the shape of the cross section correspond with loading case G1.

From Figure 13.31 it can be seen that the comparison of the calculated and the measured values again reveals very good agreement with the extensometer readings. In addition, however the horizontal convergence of the tunnel cross section is also reproduced by the analysis. It can therefore be stated that in this case the horizontal *in situ* stress, at right angles to the tunnel axis, amounts to twice the weight of the overburden, which is quite a surprising result for such a shallow tunnel. This conclusion is however additionally supported by the observation of a 11 m long shear crack in the partly-installed thin shotcrete at the tunnel roof, which occurred with considerable noise during excavation and can only be explained by means of high horizontal stresses within the rock mass (Figure 13.32). Further heavings measured at the tunnel portal, where locally an only 3 m thick rock-mass slab was left as overburden, and an additional horizontal convergence

Figure 13.32 Shear failure in the shotcrete of the tunnel roof

of the tunnel walls during excavation of the floor section, which took place at the end of the construction period, can only be explained by large horizontal *in situ* stresses.

13.8 CAVERN OF BREMM

Along with the feasibility design of a long-time pumped storage scheme of the Rheinisch-Westfälische Electricity Supply Commission at the river Mosel close to the village of Bremm, a 30 m long section of the vault of the underground power house has been excavated for testing purposes (Figure 13.33). The circular vault has a width of 24 m and a height of 9 m. The overburden amounts to 240 m. Since the rock conditions are different from those of the two previously discussed underground openings, this example is included in this paper (Wittke, in print; Wittke, Wallner, *et al.*, 1972).

13.8.1 Geological investigations

The geological investigations consist of deep core borings distributed over the project area and two exploration adits located in the area of the cavern. One of these two adits orthogonally crosses the cavern axis above the vault, the other one is located within the cross section of the vault and runs parallel to the cavern axis from north to south (Figure 13.33). Resulting from the geological mapping of the adits, the cavern is located in a clay slate with intercalations of quartzitic sandstone layers. The orientation of the schistosity K_3 which is approximately parallel to the bedding can be seen from Figure 13.34. From this figure the strike and dip of the two series of joints K_1 and K_2, which were also statistically evaluated from the mapping, can be derived. Since the dimensions of the test cavern are limited, the few shear zones occurring in the area do not significantly affect the stability of the cavern and consequently are neglected in the analysis.

13.8.2 Mechanical investigations of rock and adopted parameters

The rock mechanics testing programme was very limited and mainly consisted of unconfined compression tests on intact rock. In these tests the angle between the schistosity and the direction of the applied stress was systematically varied. The test results revealed a distinct stress–strain and strength anisotropy of the intact rock due to the schistosity. From the results of the laboratory tests and the mapping of the adits, the shear strength parallel to

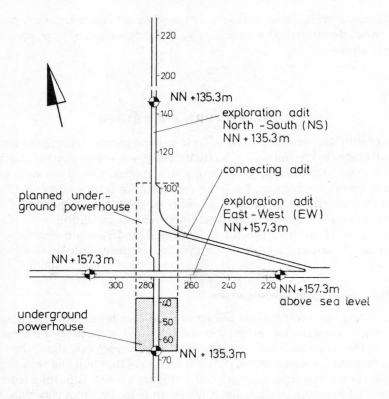

Figure 13.33   Lay-out of cavern and exploration adits

the series of joints was evaluated (Figure 13.35). Since the frequency and the degree of separation of the joints K_1 and K_2 are low and furthermore, since these joints are completely closed, it seemed to be justified in this case to apply the elastic constants determined for the intact rock to the rock mass. On the basis of these elastic constants, and assuming the weight of the obverburden as the only force acting on the rock mass, the *in situ* stresses have been evaluated from finite element calculations because corresponding measurements were not available.

13.8.3   FEM analyses and safety measures

Although the stabilizing influence of the end slabs was neglected in these calculations and therefore, theoretically, a cavern of infinite length was investigated, the problem could not be reduced to a two-dimensional one.

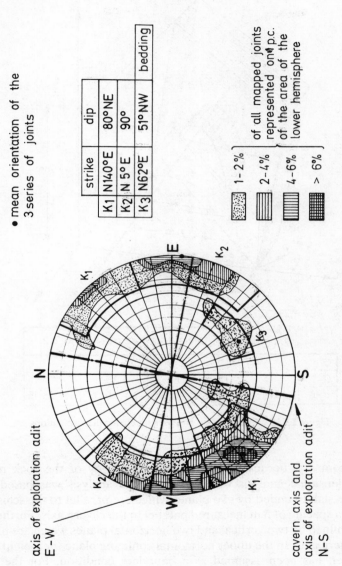

	strike	dip
K₁	N140°E	80°NE
K₂	N 5° E	90°
K₃	N62°E	51°NW
bedding		

● mean orientation of the 3 series of joints

1 - 2 %	of all mapped joints represented on p.c. of the area of the lower hemisphere
2 - 4 %	
4 - 6 %	
> 6%	

Figure 13.34 Orientation of joints mapped in the exploration adits

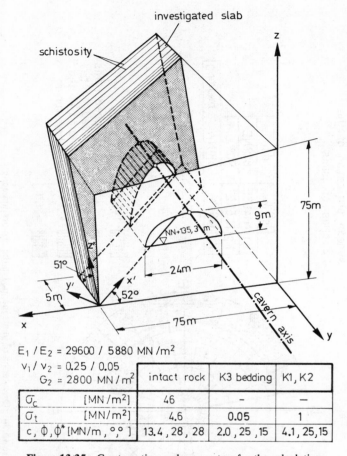

$E_1 / E_2 = 29600 / 5880$ MN/m²
$v_1 / v_2 = 0.25 / 0.05$
$G_2 = 2800$ MN/m²

	intact rock	K3 bedding	K1, K2
σ_c [MN/m²]	46	–	—
σ_t [MN/m²]	4.6	0.05	1
c, φ, φ* [MN/m, °,°]	13.4, 28, 28	2.0, 25 ,15	4.1, 25,15

Figure 13.35 Cross-section and parameters for the calculations

On the contrary, because of the elastic anisotropy of the rock mass a three-dimensional analysis was required. This analysis was based on a rock-mass slab bounded by two planes which are parallel to the schistosity and have a spacing of 5 m measured parallel to the cavern axis. Further, the slab is confined by two vertical and two horizontal planes which are parallel to the cavern axis. In the upper horizontal confining plane the weight of the overburden has been assumed as a boundary condition. For the lower horizontal plane the displacements have been assumed to be zero. For nodal points, located on straight lines parallel to the cavern axis and in the boundary planes which are parallel to the schistosity, equal displacements of any directions have been assumed as boundary conditions. By this assumption the analysis of a cavern of infinite length could be reduced to the analysis of the slab (Figure 13.35). In order to eliminate constraints due to the elastic anisotropy, the corresponding displacement boundary condition has been assumed for the two vertical confining planes.

A principle sketch of the resulting stresses is shown in Figure 13.36. It follows from the sketch and the calculations that, for the *in situ* stress state,

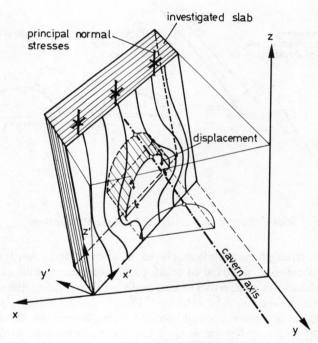

Figure 13.36 Three dimensional qualitative representation of stresses and displacements

the maximum principal normal stress is vertical and equals the weight of the overburden, that the intermediate principal normal stress is parallel and the minimum principal stress at right angles to the strike of the schistosity. Because of the excavation the maximum principal normal stresses are diverted around the vault and adjacent to the opening they tend to be parallel to the schistosity (Figure 13.36). As a consequence of this change in orientation of the maximum principal stresses, the rock mass at right angles to the schistosity is unloaded and the displacements resulting from the excavations are orientated approximately orthogonally to the schistosity. Further the distribution of the displacement around the vault is unsymmetrical (Figure 13.37). This phenomenon above and underneath the vault created larger zones where the shear strength parallel to the schistosity and

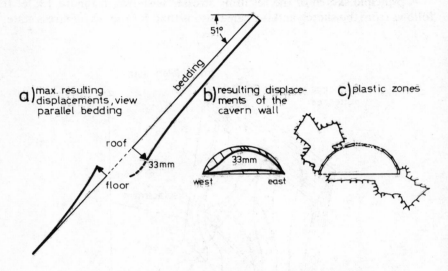

Figure 13.37   Characteristic results of the FEM-analysis

the tensile strength perpendicularly to it is exceeded. Applying safety measures consisting of 20 cm of reinforced shotcrete as well as 0·15 MN prestressed anchors, each 6 to 8 m long, with ~1·3 m spacing, the stability of the cavern however could be achieved (Figure 13.38). Within the analysis this resulted in a convergence of calculated displacements. In addition to these safety measures for the area of the above-mentioned shear zones a number of pre-stressed anchors was installed.

13.8.4   Monitoring of displacements during construction

Because of the relatively small amount of safety measures, the excavation was performed very cautiously and stepwise. The safety measures were installed immediately after each excavation step. To monitor the displacements six multiple extensometers (E1 to E6) have been placed. E1 and E2 are vertically orientated, E3 and E4 run parallel to and E5 and E6 at right angles to the schistosity. Altogether 30 fixed points were installed.

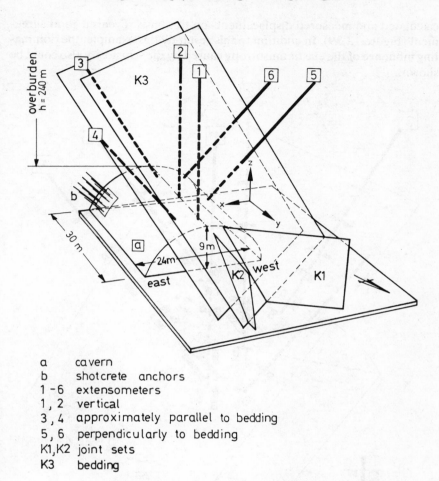

a   cavern
b   shotcrete anchors
1 - 6 extensometers
1, 2   vertical
3, 4   approximately parallel to bedding
5, 6   perpendicularly to bedding
K1,K2 joint sets
K3   bedding

Figure 13.38   Model of the cavern of Bremm

All extensometers, because of the deep location of the cavern could only be installed after excavation of the relevant part of the vault. Hence some displacements had already taken place when the measurements could be started. This part of the displacements was calculated in a separate analysis for the corresponding stage of excavation. By this procedure the results of the above described analysis (Figures 13.36 and 13.37) could be adjusted to the results of the measurements and a meaningful comparison was possible. Further for three of the 30 installed fixed points the influence of relative displacements along the shear zones was eliminated. A comparison of calculated and measured displacements on this basis reveals a good agreement (Figure 13.39). In addition to this result by this example, the dominating influence of the elastic anisotropy caused by the schistosity also could be shown.

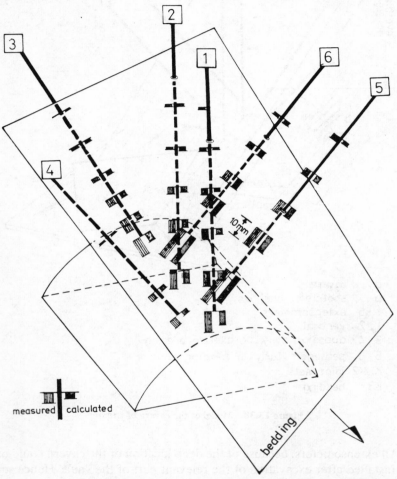

Figure 13.39 Comparison between measurements and calculations

13.9 CONCLUSIONS

On the basis of these encouraging experiences the above described method was applied to some other constructions. Some of the caverns shown in Table 13.3 are already completed, some of them are in the stage of design.

Table 13.3   Underground openings, constructed on the basis of the same design concept

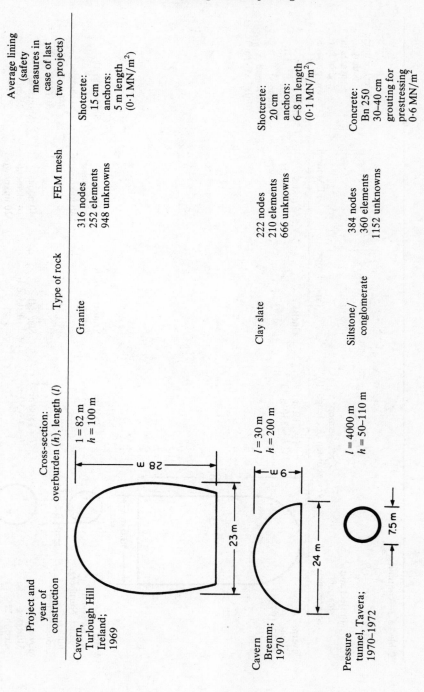

Project and year of construction	Cross-section: overburden (h), length (l)	Type of rock	FEM mesh	Average lining (safety measures in case of last two projects)
Cavern, Turlough Hill, Ireland; 1969	$l = 82$ m $h = 100$ m (28 m; 23 m)	Granite	316 nodes 252 elements 948 unknowns	Shotcrete: 15 cm anchors: 5 m length (0·1 MN/m^2)
Cavern Bremm; 1970	$l = 30$ m $h = 200$ m (9 m; 24 m)	Clay slate	222 nodes 210 elements 666 unknowns	Shotcrete: 20 cm anchors: 6–8 m length (0·1 MN/m^2)
Pressure tunnel, Tavera; 1970–1972	$l = 4000$ m $h = 50$–110 m (7.5 m)	Siltstone/ conglomerate	384 nodes 360 elements 1152 unknowns	Concrete: Bn 250 30–40 cm grouting for prestressing 0·6 MN/m^2

Table 13.3—continued

Project and year of construction	Cross-section: overburden (h), length (l)	Type of rock	FEM mesh	Average lining (safety measures in case of last two projects)
Cavern, Wehr; 1972–1973	$l = 219$ m $h = 350$ m	Gneiss	356 nodes 339 elements 1068 unknowns	Shotcrete: 15 cm anchors: 4 m length (0·025 MN/m^2)
Water transmission tunnel, Nürnberg; under construction	$l = 2650$ m $h = 10$–23 m	Sandstone/silty clay	182 nodes 156 elements 546 unknowns	Shotcrete: 16 cm anchors: 4–6 m length (0·1 MN/m^2)
Subway tunnel, Stuttgart section 12; under construction	$l = 1500$ m $h = 18$–50 m	Silt/soft siltstone	240 nodes 214 elements 720 unknowns	Shotcrete: 25 cm

Cavern, Straßberg; planned	17 m × 17 m	$l = 15$ m $h = 400$ m	Claystone	1032 nodes 777 elements 3096 unknowns	Shotcrete: 20 cm anchors: 5–6 m length (0·05 MN/m^2)
Vianden 11. machine (tunnel system); planned	5.5 m	$l = 2000$ m $h = 450$ m	Clay slate	275 nodes 262 elements 825 unknowns	Saftey measures only locally
Deutsche Bundesbahn Mannheim–Stuttgart (rapid railway line); planned	22 m × 13 m	$l = 2900$ m $h = 17$ m	Claystone/limestone	218 nodes 189 elements 654 unknowns	Shotcrete: 30 cm and bolting
	13 m × 14 m	$l = 9000$ m $h = 25$–55 m	Silt/sandstone	152 nodes 124 elements 456 unknowns	Shotcrete: 15–40 cm

Table 13.3—continued

Project and year of construction	Cross-section: overburden (h), length (l)	Type of rock	FEM mesh	Averaging lining (safety measures in case of last two projects)
Cavern, Taiwan; planned		Sandstone	400 nodes 397 elements 1200 unknowns	Shotcrete: 20 cm anchors: 6 m length ($0{\cdot}025$ MN/m^2)

With regards to all requirements of praetical problems in rock mechanics the method developed in many cases yields useful solutions.

Of course, further development of this procedure is envisaged. Thus, for instance, the material law adopted will be improved and checked by means of idealized model tests. Subsequently fundamental investigations referring to the stress–strain behaviour of discontinuities are very important. Further the FEM-program will be extended to other types of elements as used by other authors.

REFERENCES

Goodman, R. E. (1970) 'The deformability of joints', *ASTM, Spec. Techn. Publ.* 477, 174–196.

John, K. W. (1969). 'Festigkeit und Verformbarkeit von druckfesten, regelmäßig gefügten Diskontinuen', *Dissertation*, Universität (TH) Karlsruhe.

Link, H. (1962). 'Über die Unterschiede statisch, dynamisch und seismisch ermittelter Elastizitätsmoduln von Gestein und Gebirge', *Geologie und Bauwesen*, **3-4**, 131–145.

Müller, L. and Pacher, F. (1965). 'Modellversuche zur Klärung der Bruchgefahr geklüfteter Medien', *Felsmechanik und Ingenieurgeologie*, Suppl. II, 2–24.

Patton, F. D. (1966). 'Multiple modes for shear failure in rock and related materials', *Proc. 1. Congr. Int. Soc. Rock Mech.*, Lisbon, **1**, 509–513.

Pfisterer, E. (1963). 'Wasserkraftanlagen im Südschwarzwald und Hochrhein', *Die Wasserwirtschaft*, **53**, 5, 142–150.

Pfisterer, E., Wittke, W. and Rißler, P. (1974). 'Investigations, Calculations and Measurements for the Underground Powerhouse Wehr', *Proc. 3. Congress Int. Soc. Rock Mech.*, Denver, Colorado, USA, **II-B**, 1308–1317.

Pinto, J. L. (1970). 'Deformability of schistous rock', *Proc. 2. Congr. Int. Soc. Rock Mech.*, Belgrade, paper 2-30.

Raleigh, C. B. (1974). 'Crustal stress and global tectonics', *Proc. 3. Congress Int. Soc. Rock Mech.*, Denver, Colorado, USA, **I-A**, 593–597.

Rengers, N. (1971). 'Unebenheit und Reibungswiderstand von Gesteinstrennflächen', *Veröffentlichungen des Institutes für Bodenmechanik und Felsmechanik, Universität (TH) Karlruhe*, **47**.

Rescher, O.-J., Abraham, K. H., Bräutigam, F. and Pahl, A. (1973). 'Ein Kavernenbau mit Ankerung und Spritzbeton unter Berücksichtigung der geomechanischen Bedingungen', *Rock Mechanics*, Supplementum 2, 313–354.

Rocha, M. and Da Silva, J. N. (1970). A New Method for the Determination of Deformability in Rock Masses', *Proc. 2. Congress Int. Soc. Rock Mech.*, Beograd, Jugoslavija, **1**, 2–21.

Rodatz, W. and Wallner, M. (1974). 'Untersuchung des räumlichen Spannungs- und Verformungszustandes an der Ortsbrust eines Tunnels nach der Finite Element Methode', *Berichte der 1. Nationalen Tagung über Felshohlraumbau, Essen*, 107–118.

Wittke, W. (1973). 'Anwendung der Finite Element Methode auf den Entwurf von untertägigen Dämmen', *Erzmetall* **26**, 2, 66–74.

Wittke, W. (in print). 'Static Analysis for Underground Openings in Jointed Rock', *Chapter 18* in *Numerical Methods in Geotechnical Engineering*, C. S. Desai and J. Christian, (eds.).

Wittke, W., Carl, L. and Semprich, S. (1974). 'Felsmessungen als Grundlage für den Entwurf einer Tunnelauskleidung', *Straße Brücke Tunnel*, **27**.

Wittke, W. and Pfisterer, E. (1972). 'Geotechnical Investigations for the Underground Powerhouse Wehr of the Hotzenwald Pumped Storage Scheme West Germany', *Symposium on Hydro-Electric Pumped Storage Schemes*, Athens, Greece.

Wittke, W., Pfisterer, E. and Rißler, P. (1974). 'Felsmechanische Untersuchungen für die Maschinenkaverne Wehr', *Berichte der 1. Nationalen Tagung über Felshohlraumbau, Essen*, 123–148.

Wittke, W. and Semprich, S. (in print), 'Messungen als felsmechanische Grundlage beim Entwurf eines Stollens', *Diskussionsbeitrag am 3. Congress Int. Soc. Rock Mech., Denver, Colorado, USA*.

Wittke, W., Wallner, M. and Rodatz, W. (1972). 'Räumliche Berechnung der Standsicherheit von Hohlräumen, Böschungen und Gründungen in anisotropem, klüftigem Gebirge nach der Methode finiter Elemente', *Straße Brücke Tunnel* **24**, 8, 200–209.

Chapter 14

Interaction between Water Flow Phenomena and the Mechanical Behaviour of Soil or Rock Masses

C. Louis, J.-L. Dessenne and B. Feuga

14.1 INTRODUCTION

Water is often present in the materials which constitute the earth's crust. In addition to its physico–chemical effects, its influence on the mechanical behaviour of soil or rock masses is of utmost importance. The water flow induces hydrostatic pressures and seepage forces which have to be taken into consideration in order to solve geotechnical problems.

The presence of water in the pores as well as in the joints and cracks of soil or rock masses affects the inter-granular state of equilibrium. A close interaction exists between mechanical and hydraulic phenomena: the flow influences the state of stress, which in turn determines the hydraulic characteristics of the media. Generally speaking the state of stress governs the variations in the geometry of discontinuities in fractured media or the variations in the intergranular spaces in soil or porous media.

Experience, especially in the field of civil, mining and petroleum engineering shows the importance of the interaction between the ground water flow and the state of stress. Numerous practical examples exist on this subject (see Section 14.2).

Many geotechnical problems must therefore be solved by taking into account the presence of water in the soil or rock masses. This is not only true for dam studies, but also for the analysis of the behaviour of underground or open excavations, slopes, etc. which must be undertaken in aquifer media. For this subject it is important to know the laws controlling the mechanical effects of ground water flow and to define in which way these effects can be, for instance, introduced into mechanical models used in the simulation of mechanical behaviour of soil or rock masses (Finite Element Method). The numerical approach calls for coupling both the hydraulic and mechanical models. This method can be used for a fixed geometry medium (i.e. of constant permeability) or for a variable geometry medium (the permeability being a function of the state of stress). In this last case, the solution can be obtained by successive hydraulic and mechanical simulations.

Attention is drawn to the fact that errors are quite often found in the literature concerning the manner in which water influence is taken into consideration in the finite element method. With reference to practical examples (Arnon dam, Cher) it is noted that such errors can have a very important effect on the results and, therefore, on the final conclusions drawn from these studies.

14.2 PRACTICAL EXAMPLES

Many practical examples (sometimes historical) illustrate the importance of the role of water in the behaviour of soil or rock masses.

In fact, more and more often, projects require builders to work in aquifer media. The behaviour of abutments or of underground openings depends on the water-flow phenomena and on their effects at two separate stages in the history of the structure:

during the transient phase of construction,
during the life of the structure, after construction
  (transient or permanent phase, depending on the situation).

A dam (Figure 14.1), by its very nature, artificially creates a large hydraulic gradient. The potential energy of water is stored in a reservoir whose boundaries are predominantly made up of rock masses. Hydromechanical phenomena which affect these masses have to be analysed by the project engineer who is in charge of the optimisation of the structure. The phenomena are always very complex and can even endanger the dam stability (Figure 14.2). In the dramatic example of the Malpasset Dam, Bernaix (1967) has shown that under the load of the dam, permeabilities in the foundation were reduced in a ratio of approximately 10^2. As a result an 'underground hydraulic barrier' was created, where the concentrated action of seepage forces contributed to the failure by sliding of the dam foundation along a fault located under the structure.

The natural foundations of large structures and natural or man-made rock slopes are often subject to subsurface water flows which are related to natural hydrogeological conditions or rains. These conditions, like river floods, are essentially hazardous and their consequences can be dangerous because they are hard to forecast. Hydraulic gradients, in these cases, are certainly small in comparison to those induced by dams, but the important point is that these gradients generate forces of the same order of magnitude as those acting on the masses due to the gravity alone.

Figure 14.1 Monteynard dam on the river Drac (Isère, France). The behaviour of the dam is determined by water flow phenomena in the rock abutments (after Intrafor–Cofor photograph)

Figure 14.2 Upstream view of Malpasset dam site on the river Reyran (France). Hydromechanical phenomena in the foundation can lead to dam failure

Figure 14.3 shows in real terms the importance of this problem. Such a failure, though important, did not have the dramatic effect of other slides, like the one in Vaiont, Italy in 1963, where 300 million cubic metres of rock caused a sudden flood of the dam reservoir and a wave of water swept the town of Longarone killing more than 3000 people. One deplores the catastrophes (Roubault, 1971) resulting from man-made structures, but as in natural rock masses, their causes are unfortunately mainly related to the unpredictable behaviour of subsurface water flow.

Figure 14.3   Appearance of a motorway after a landslide in the Morava river valley south of Belgrade (Yugoslavia)

Mining people often have to deal with very difficult problems of rock hydraulics. Mineral ore exploitation in aquifer media is slowed down by seeping water.

Moreover the stability of surrounding rock masses (galleries, pillars, slopes of open-pits) is reduced by pore water pressures. Water in mining engineering has a double effect which increases in a non-negligible way the production cost of minerals. Figure 14.4 shows one example of possible water action, in which water infiltration in tension cracks (characteristic of open-pit mines) may cause an important slide.

The presence of water also affects the economies of exploitation because it influences the design of mine workings. Seepage forces induce a decrease in the span of unsupported underground openings or in the slope angles in open-pits or an increase in support structures. For instance, a decrease of one degree in the slope angle of the Tazadit open-pit in Mauritania

Figure 14.4 Atalaya open pit (Rio Tinto, Spain). The infiltration of rain water in tension cracks can lead to failure

(MIFERMA) necessitates the excavation of ten million cubic metres of additional waste. Water effects are often extremely marked due to the large hydraulic gradients surrounding mine workings. In South African deep-level mines (gold mines), dewatering reduces water pressure by more than 2000 metres in aquifers which are commonly separated by impervious layers. Such conditions produce hydraulic gradients which are definitely greater than those which are measured under the largest dams in the world. They represent hydromechanical problems of extreme importance. For instance, at West Driefontein mining carried out in 1968 caused a sudden local inrush of water at a rate of 5 m^3/s, flooding the mine to a depth of more than 1300 m of water.

In a very general way, the presence of water in rock masses is highly dangerous from the point of view of stability. It is not the absolute value of the pore-water pressure nor of the discharge ratio of the induced seepage forces to the total forces applied to the masses which are important. Studies of the existing flow conditions and their effects must be carried out for foundation design, slope or abutment stability analyses or optimization studies in mining engineering.

Underground water also plays an active role in seismo-tectonic phenomena, especially earthquakes. Evans (1966) pointed out that the observed seismic activity in Denver from 1962 to 1966 was directly related to industrial liquid waste-injections in deep layers through the Rocky Mountains deep wells, close to Denver. The pore pressure increase, induced by the injections reduced the normal stresses on discontinuity planes. The consequence was a decrease of shear strength along the rock discontinuities, and sudden displacements under the pre-existing tectonic stresses. Permeability tests generally show that higher permeability values are obtained when measured by injection (decrease in effective stress and joint opening) than by pumping (increase in effective stress and joint closure).

14.3 HYDRAULIC CHARACTERISTICS OF THE MEDIUM

In order to characterize a medium, in relation to a particular state or given property the six following terms are commonly used (coupled in opposites):

> continuous   — discontinuous
> homogeneous — heterogeneous
> isotropic   — anisotropic.

In rock masses, on the scale of man-made structures, one is operating with the most complex properties in regard to both hydraulic and mechanical behaviour. In fact, they constitute discontinuous, heterogeneous, and anisotropic materials. The rock mass complexity is not only due to the many natural crystalline constituents, which form rock masses, but above all to the discontinuities. Rock discontinuities are found at many different levels, from the microscopic defect in crystals to the major plurikilometric fault in geological formations.

The geotechnical engineer simplifies the problem by considering two major types of rock discontinuities: the micro-discontinuities at a smaller scale than the sample (decimetric) and the macro-discontinuities (greater than a decimetre) on the scale of the work. He models the rock mass as rock blocks separated by macro-discontinuities, cracks or fractures. The rock block is supposedly made up of porous intact rock, i.e. without apparent cracks. This material is called the 'rock matrix'. The assemblance of rock blocks on the scale of the engineering structure is called the 'rock mass'. Cracks and fractures are used in a general sense to include all defects and discontinuities, regardless of their geological source: bedding or schistose surfaces, joints, faults, etc.

The cracks and fractures, that intersect rock masses, obviously offer preferential paths to underground water. The rock mass discontinuities are therefore a determining factor in rock hydraulics. A quick computation shows that even with thin cracks a very high rock mass permeability coefficient is obtained compared to that of the rock matrix.

A physical and geometrical quantitative analysis of rock mass voids (pores and fractures) shows that rock masses have on the one hand high hydraulic conductivity and a low fracture porosity; on the other hand rock matrices are characterized by low permeability and high porosity. This is a very general statement. Exceptions to this rule may, however, be encountered especially when fractures are filled with an impervious clayey material which forms hydraulic barriers dividing the medium, or when the rock matrix permeability is abnormally high, which is the case for certain sandstones or conglomerates.

It appears that the hydraulic behaviour of rock masses is closely related to the nature, geometry and distribution of the fractures which divide the medium. Therefore the solution of any rock hydraulics problem necessitates at the beginning a structural analysis of the medium in order to obtain a spatial description of the fracturation and, then, a quantitative analysis of all the parameters governing seepage flow.

Five fundamental models are generally admitted to classify the hydraulic properties as shown in Figure 14.5 (Louis, 1976).

(a) Porous medium, generally homogeneous (Figure 14.5a):
The rock matrix on the macroscopic scale is made up of a porous medium, generally homogeneous (with thin pores of relatively equal dimensions in three directions). On the engineering scale, and especially at shallow depths, rock masses are generally always fractured. This type of model is retained for very deep strata, where cracks or fractures may exist, but are closed because of the high state of stress at these levels.

(b) Fractured porous medium, with different sets of parallel, plane discontinuities (Figure 14.5b).

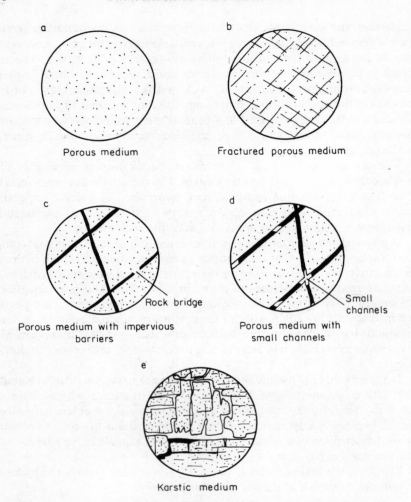

Figure 14.5 Representation of hydraulic properties of rock matrix and rock masses

This medium is similar to the one described above for a porous medium, to which is added the 'collector' network of discontinuities which totally alter the hydraulic characteristics of the medium. In most cases the influence of the matrix permeability is negligible. One can distinguish the case of fractured media with an impermeable matrix from the case of fractured media with a porous permeable matrix.

(c) Porous medium with impervious barriers (Figure 14.5c).

In rock mass discontinuities a fine particle filling can be found (for instance alteration clay). This filling, often overconsolidated or of swelling type (under the influence of water) is generally impermeable.

Subsurface water can therefore circulate only through the rock matrix, in a medium characterized by impermeable barriers. The medium can partially or totally be partitioned. In the rock mass, seepage can take place only through 'rock bridges' which provide hydraulic connection between the 'aquifer compartments'.

(d) Porous medium with small channels (Figure 14.5d).

In-situ observations have shown that water can circulate in small 'uni-directional' channels generally located in large fractures with impermeable fillings. It is the same case as the medium described in (c), only with open channels in the fractures. Water circulation therefore establishes itself in a more or less inter-connected meshed network, potential equilibrium being obtained by percolation between small channels inside the rock matrix. This case can be considered restricted, only a few authors making reference to it in the literature (Sabarly, Pautre, *et al.*, 1970; Bernaix, 1970; Wolters, Reinhardt *et al.*, 1972).

(e) Medium with dissolution channels (Figure 14.5e).

Under this heading falls the big variety of soluble rocks which comprise the karstic media. These media were initially fractured exactly as in (b) above. Following this periodic water circulation shaped the channels by a dissolving action. These channels, often of very large dimension have a geometry and a distribution which is totally hazardous according to the history of subsurface water flow.

The name 'karst' is a geomorphological and morphogenetic term, it is generally used as in the term 'karstic region', a region formed of carbonated, compact and soluble rocks in which appear characteristic morphological features (this idea has been extended to other soluble rocks: gypsum, salt, etc., Paloc, 1975).

The above sketch is obviously crude and generalized; it needs considerable developments for each medium in order to study the flow laws. The authors have essentially tackled the cases (a) and (b) of the porous and fractured media, which are certainly the most frequent, from the practical point of view.

14.4 WATER FLOW LAWS IN ROCK MASSES

The laws governing water flow in rock masses (and the numerical solution methods) have a different formulation depending on the chosen scheme: porous medium or discontinuous one (flow in fractures).

14.4.1 Porous medium

The laminar state of flow in porous media is governed by Darcy's law, which can be expressed in the following simplified form:

$$\mathbf{v} = \mathbf{kJ} \tag{14.1}$$

The combination of this equation and the equation of continuity leads to the general equation of flow in a porous medium, which can be expressed for the steady state by (Schneebeli, 1966):

$$\frac{\partial}{\partial x}\left(k_x \frac{\partial \varphi}{\partial x}\right) + \frac{\partial}{\partial y}\left(k_y \frac{\partial \varphi}{\partial y}\right) + \frac{\partial}{\partial z}\left(k_z \frac{\partial \varphi}{\partial z}\right) + q = 0 \tag{14.2}$$

Many numerical methods are able to solve this equation once the boundary conditions are known.

14.4.2 Fractured media

Flow phenomena in the fractures have been studied in a theoretical and experimental way by Louis (1967). If flow in smooth fractures follows the classical laws applied to pipes (Poiseuille, Blasius, Nikuradse), it appears that large discrepancies from these laws exist for rough fractures.

14.4.2.1 Hydraulic conductivity of a single fracture
Let us consider the open and unfilled fracture, possibly with bridges of rock. In rock, fractures constitute channels characterized by a high value of relative roughness, k/D_h (where k is the absolute roughness, and is represented by the height of its asperities, and D_h, the hydraulic diameter, represented by twice the opening of the fracture). The relative variations in the opening of the fracture are therefore most important, since they cause, during flow, a very high pressure drop coefficient (much higher than that which may be computed from Poiseuille's law, for instance).

The laws of flow in a single fracture can be expressed as follows:

laminar or steady flow: $v = k_f J_f$ $\hspace{2cm}$ (14.3)

turbulent flow: $\hspace{1.5cm} v = k_f' J_f^\alpha$ $\hspace{2cm}$ (14.4)

In these expressions, v stands for the mean velocity, k_f for the hydraulic conductivity of the fracture, k_f' its turbulent conductivity, J_f for the perpendicular projection of the hydraulic gradient ($\mathbf{J} = -\operatorname{grad} \varphi$) on the plane of the fracture and, finally, α for the degree of non-linearity ($\alpha = 0.5$ for completely rough turbulent flow).

For fracture flow, the transition from laminar to turbulent flow takes place at very low values of the Reynolds number (down to 100 or even 10), decreasing as the relative roughness of the fracture increases. (The Reynolds number, defined by the relationship $Re = vD_h/v$, in fact has a value that is extremely difficult to determine in the case of fissured rocks, since for a given type of flow it can vary enormously from one point to another along the same fracture $(D_h \simeq 2e)$.]

Within the fracture itself, the transition from laminar flow $(\alpha = 1)$ *to* completely rough turbulent flow $(\alpha = 0 \cdot 5)$ is quite progressive; the exponent slowly changes from 1 to $0 \cdot 5$ when the Reynolds number changes, for instance from 100 to 2000.

The hydraulic conductivities defined in relations of Equations (14.3) and (14.4) are given by the following expressions:

Laminar flow:
$$k_f = \frac{\kappa g e^2}{12 \nu C} \tag{14.5}$$

turbulent flow:
(completely rough)
$$k_f' = 4\kappa \sqrt{(ge)} \log \frac{d}{k/D_h} \tag{14.6}$$

In these expressions, g is the acceleration of gravity, κ is the degree of continuity of the fracture (ratio of the open surface and the total surface of the fracture), e is the mean width of the fracture, ν is the kinematic viscosity of the fluid, and, lastly, C and d are two coefficients which depend on the relative roughness k/D_h of the fissure [according to Louis (1967), $C = 1 + 8 \cdot 8 (k/D_h)^{1 \cdot 5}$, and $d = 1 \cdot 9$ for a relative roughness greater than $0 \cdot 033$; this, in general, is the case for fractures in rock].

In the case of fractures with filling, the hydraulic conductivity is equal to the permeability of the filling, provided, of course, that this permeability is definitely higher than that of the rock matrix.

14.4.2.2 *Hydraulic conductivity of a set of fractures*

As pointed out in Section 14.3, it is assumed that fracturing in a rock mass is made up of several sets of parallel plane fractures. To characterize the hydraulic properties of such a medium it will be sufficient to know the hydraulic conductivity K (laminar or turbulent) of each set of fractures. This hydraulic conductivity may be defined, as above, through the relation between the flow velocity V (flow rate in the direction of the fractures, divided by the total cross-section of the mass) and the active hydraulic gradient, as given by the relations:

laminar state:
$$V = KJ \tag{14.7}$$

turbulent flow;
$$V = K'J^\alpha \tag{14.8}$$

The scale of the phenomenon studied is of great importance. In a given volume, individual fractures may, within their own plane, be continuous or discontinuous; these two cases must be studied separately:

Set of continuous fractures

Directional hydraulic conductivity of a set of continuous fractures follows directly from the hydraulic conductivity of the individual fractures. It is given (in laminar or turbulent flow) by the expression

$$K = \frac{e}{b}k_f + k_m \qquad (14.9)$$

This relationship can be obtained by dividing the flow-rate by the total cross-section of the rock mass. In this equation, e stands for the mean width of the fractures, b the mean distance between them, k_f their hydraulic conductivity and k_m the permeability of the rock matrix.

In practice, k_m is very often negligible compared with the term $(e/b) \cdot k_f$. On the other hand, if there are no cracks or if they are bounded ($e = 0$ and $k_f = 0$) only the k_m-term remains in Equation (14.9), this case corresponding to that considered in Section 14.4.1.

Set of discontinuous fractures

A numerical study shows very clearly that a set of continuous fractures, even when they are extremely narrow, has a very large hydraulic conductivity (a single fissure per metre with a width of 0.1 mm corresponds to a conductivity of about 10^{-4} cm/s; with a 1 mm width and with the same frequency, the corresponding value if $0 \cdot 1$ cm/s). These theoretical values are therefore noticeably greater than the ones met with in practice, although most of the time, fissures with a width greater than 1 mm do exist. The low values of the hydraulic conductivities observed in nature can be explained simply by the fact that the fractures, even when of notable width, are of limited extent. Within their own plane, the fractures are therefore discontinuous. Within such a medium, flow is evidently anisotropic. While they do not communicate with each other, the fractures 'short-circuit' any flow along their direction. The fractures are at a constant potential and the circulation of water occurs through the rock matrix.

This problem, considered three-dimensionally, has been programmed on a computer to obtain the hydraulic conductivities of such media, whatever their geometric configuration. It must be noted that in rock masses with discontinuous fractures the degree of continuity and the frequency of the factures are the only important hydraulic parameters. The permeability of the matrix occurs merely as a proportionality coefficient in the hydraulic conductivities of the different sets of fractures; its influence only becomes noticeable in the computation of flow rates. The opening and the roughness of the fissures, as well as the geometry of the fracture wall have no bearing on the problem. In these media, the flows occur partly through the rock matrix and therefore generally remain laminar.

Many approaches exist for solving flow problems in fracture media. The first is a deterministic approach in which each fracture is individually considered (Wilson and Witherspoon, 1967).

The second is a statistical approach (Snow, 1967): knowing the hydraulic conductivity of an elementary fracture, it is easy to define the directional hydraulic conductivity of a set of fractures (Louis, 1976), by making a distinction between the continuous networks of fractures and the discontinuous ones, which have very different hydraulic roles.

A fractured medium can also be treated as an equivalent porous medium for which one can calculate the anisotropic permeability tensor from the hydraulic characteristics and the orientation in three dimensions of each set of fractures.

Finally, a third approach combines the two preceding ones by considering at the same time the hydraulic flow in the fractures and in the porous matrix (Warren and Root, 1963).

In fact the choice between these approaches depends upon the ratio of the average fracture spacing and the size of the engineering structure (Figure 14.6). In rock hydraulics the scale-effect plays a very important role.

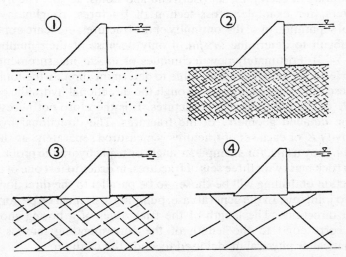

Figure 14.6 Continuous or discontinuous medium. Cases 1 and 2 = continuum, cases 3 and 4 = discontinuum

Before starting on a study of flow in a fractured medium, it is essential to determine whether the problem is to be considered as continuous or discontinuous. There is no general rule, and this notion only depends on the relative scale of the phenomenon studied and of the modulus of jointing characterized, for instance, by the mean distance between single fractures. This question of relative scale is outlined in (Figure 14.6) which shows the same hydraulic problem, but for four different media.

It will be correct to consider a fractured medium as being continuous if the dimension of individual blocks is negligible as compared to the phenomenon considered (Case 2, Figure 14.6) that is, if one can count, say, approximately 10 000 fissures in any plane section. On the other hand, if the number of fissures is between, for instance, 100 to 1000, the hypothesis of a discontinuous medium is necessary (Case 3) and finally, if in a given section the number of fissures is less than 10, each fissure will have to be individualized in the mathematical or physical model used (Case 4). The number of fissures given here is subjective; in fact, the hypothesis to be chosen will have to be very carefully analyzed for each given problem.

14.5 DETERMINATION OF THE HYDRAULIC CHARACTERISTICS

With the new methods of structural geology, it is now possible to determine the spatial distribution of discontinuities, viz. the orientation, frequency, and continuity of each joint set (Bertrand and Louis, 1976). The hydraulic parameters (for example: cross-section of fractures, roughness, filling, degree of separation or of discontinuity of the fractures, etc.), are apparently more difficult to determine *in situ*, if only because of their number (see Section 14.3). Fortunately new techniques of *in situ* measurements have been perfected, which make it possible to determine directly the total effect of all these different parameters through the directional hydraulic conductivities K of the different sets of factures. It is therefore not necessary to know the detailed geometry of the fractures. The directional hydraulic conductivity K of each set of fractures is measured separately, as shown in Figure 14.7, by using, for example, a single or triple hydraulic probe. In the case of a rock mass with three sets of fractures, in order to test one of the sets the direction of drilling will be chosen to be parallel to the direction of the other two joint sets. In the general case, pumping tests must be performed in different directions. The length of the trial zones of a boring should, in theory, correspond to the length of the corresponding meshes in the mathematical or physical model used to study the medium.

It is pointed out that no definite conclusions (for instance, for calculation of hydraulic conductivities) can be made regarding the opening of the

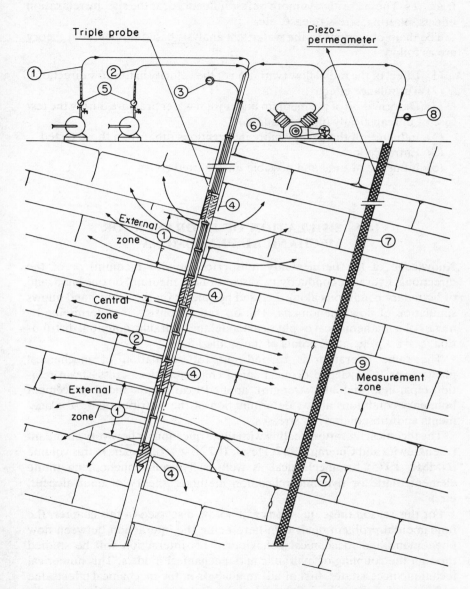

Figure 14.7   Water test by using the triple hydraulic probe and the piezopermeameter (after Louis, (1976)).

fractures. These are always more or less influenced, at the site, by relaxation effects, blasting, stress release, etc.

The main objections to the water test analysis based on potential theory are as follows:

(1) Effect of the radial flow (variation of the velocity in the flow direction).
(2) Turbulence effect.
(3) Deformation of the medium under joint water pressure during the test (use of unrealistically high pressures).
(4) Influence of the permeability in directions other than those tested.
(5) Entrance loss.
(6) Influence of time and possible unsaturated zones.

14.6 SIMULATION OF HYDRAULIC OR MECHANICAL PHENOMENA

Knowledge of the permeability tensor (continuous medium) or of the directional hydraulic conductivity (discontinuous medium) on one hand, and of boundary conditions along a closed perimeter on the other hand allows simulation of flow phenomena. The operation consists in determining by means of a mathematical or physical model the hydraulic potential distribution, $\varphi = z + p/\gamma_w$ at all points of the studied field.

The same operation is carried out for simulation of mechanical phenomena. Knowledge of mechanical characteristics (stress–strain relationships, deformability, strength). applied load, stress and displacement boundary conditions allows determination of the distribution of displacements and subsequently of stresses.

The technical literature dealing with these questions is now very abundant (Zienkiewicz and Cheung, 1967; Desai, 1972); several papers in this volume (NMSR, 1975) for mechanical as well as hydraulic phenomena (finite element, finite or dynamic relaxation methods, theory of equivalences, etc.)

For this reason these questions will not be discussed in this chapter, the fundamental problem dealt with here being the interaction between flow phenomena and mechanical behaviour. This interaction will be studied through the coupling of hydraulic and mechanical models. This numerical technique necessitates, first of all, an analysis of the mechanical effects due to flows and of the stress influence (mechanical or thermal) on the hydraulic characteristics which condition in their turn the flow network.

It must be. noted that the hydraulic and mechanical models used for coupling are classical ones (finite element models for instance).

14.7 MECHANICAL ACTION OF WATER FLOW ON THE ROCK MASS

The study of the mechanical action of water flow on a rock mass requires that a distinction be made between continuous and jointed discontinuous media.

14.7.1 Continuous medium

The water present in continuous media exerts on these media a body force, which is equal to:

$$\mathbf{F} = -\operatorname{grad} p \tag{14.7}$$

where $p = \gamma_w(\varphi - z)$.

That means $\mathbf{F} = -\gamma_w \operatorname{grad} \varphi + \gamma_w \operatorname{grad} z$

This force can be divided in: $\mathbf{F} = \mathbf{A} + \mathbf{S}$

$\mathbf{A}$ is the hydrostatic thrust: $\mathbf{A} = \gamma_w \operatorname{grad} z = -\rho_w \mathbf{g}$

$\mathbf{S}$ is the seepage force: $\mathbf{S} = -\gamma_w \operatorname{grad} \varphi = \gamma_w \mathbf{J}$

14.7.2 Jointed discontinuous media

The mechanical action due to water flow in discontinuous media has been studied in details in three-dimensions by Louis (1967). It has been shown that fissured rock masses, where seepage occurs, are submitted to three body forces due to the action of water in the fractures. These forces can be expressed by:

Tangential force, due to water viscosity (for a joint set K_i)

$$\mathbf{T}_i = n_i \gamma_w \mathbf{J}_i$$

hydrostatic thrust or Archimedes thrust

$$\mathbf{A} = -\rho_w(1-n)\mathbf{g} \tag{14.8}$$

Hydrodynamic force or seepage force

$$\mathbf{S} = \gamma_w(1-n)\mathbf{J}$$

$\mathbf{J}$ is the global hydraulic gradient in space ($\mathbf{J} = -\operatorname{grad} \varphi$), $\mathbf{J}_i$ is the active gradient in the fractures K_i and n_i the porosity of the fracture system K_i ($n_i = e_i/b_i$). The correction factor $1-n$ corresponds to the fracture porosity of the whole rock mass. This global fracture porosity in the case of rock masses having three sets of fractures, is expressed by the relationship:

$$n = 1 - \prod_{i=1}^{3}\left(1 - \frac{e_i}{b_i}\right) \tag{14.9}$$

In this expression e_i and b_i are respectively the opening and the average distance between fractures of family K_i.

The fractural porosity in rock masses is generally very low compared to unity. As a simplification one can assume with a good approximation that forces due to water flow reduce to the following:

$$\left. \begin{array}{l} \mathbf{T}_i \simeq \mathbf{o} \\ \mathbf{A} \simeq -\rho_w \mathbf{g} \\ \mathbf{S} \simeq \gamma_w \mathbf{J} \end{array} \right\} \qquad (14.10)$$

14.7.3 Introduction of forces due to water in computations

The analytical expressions for forces, due to the presence of water, are approximately the same for continuous media and discontinuous ones. It is noted that these forces can be taken into account in calculations in two distinct ways, as shown in Figure 14.8:

body forces **A** and **S**, conforming to paragraphs (a) and (b) above.
surface forces due to water pressure distributed on the perimeter of the studied element.

Body forces A and S   **External forces**

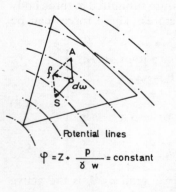

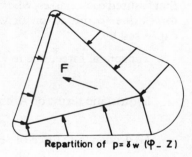

Figure 14.8   The two methods of taking into account the mechanical action of groundwater flow in porous or jointed media

More practical detailed information will be given in the section of the HYMEC program, which allows the introduction of effects due to water flow in the mechanical models.

Before ending this section on the mechanical action of water, it is important to note the frequent errors made on the subject. In the case of slope or dam stability analysis, some authors introduce simultaneously and incompletely the external forces (water pressure) on the volume susceptible to slide and the body forces (buoyant unit weight which is in part a result of these external forces). So the hydrostatic thrust is taken into account twice. Figure 14.9 illustrates this common mistake.

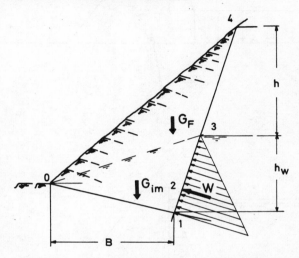

Figure 14.9 Example of wrong analysis of the mechanical effect of groundwater flow in a slope

Similarly, in a dam foundation analysis of stresses and strains, it is important to be very clear about assumptions concerning water forces:

(1) The instantaneous forces due to a quick reservoir filling; these forces are external, they act before the steady state flow is established (Figure 14.10a).

(2) The water forces in a steady state flow; these are body forces evenly distributed in the foundation (Figure 14.10b).

It is often found in the literature that forces (1) and (2) are taken into account simultaneously, either partially or totally, and this can be a source of error.

14.8 COUPLING CONCEPT OF HYDRAULIC AND MECHANICAL MODELS

The coupling of classical hydraulic and mechanical models, is realized in the HYMEC program (this name covers the first letters of the two names

(a) Instantaneous filling

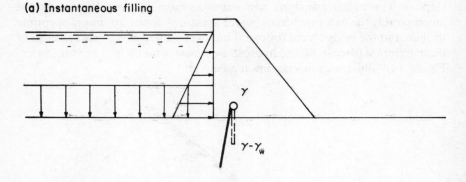

(b) Steady state

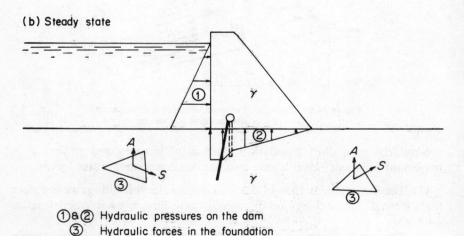

①&② Hydraulic pressures on the dam
③ Hydraulic forces in the foundation

Figure 14.10 Mechanical effects of water on dams and their foundation

'HYdraulic and MEChanical' and clearly suggests the coupling of models). This program has been prepared in detail by Feuga (1975). Only the principle of this program will be explained below.

The general scheme of the coupling of hydraulic with thermal (eventually) and mechanical models is given in Figure 14.11.

As concerns hydraulic–mechanical coupling, the basic data necessary to determine the seepage forces are the distribution of the hydraulic potential gradient $\mathbf{J} = -\operatorname{grad} \varphi$ in the medium. The calculation of this gradient

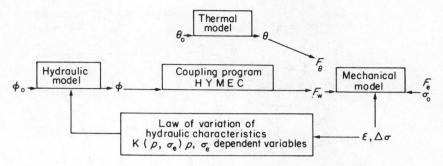

Figure 14.11 Schematic representation of coupling between hydraulic, thermal and mechanical simulations

constitutes one of the stages of hydraulic potential computation in a finite element program.

The gradient values obtained in this computation using, for instance, ELFES program (Sauty, 1972) or any other similar program are stored. By integration over the elements of the mechanical model (which can be different from the mesh of the hydraulic one), the coupling program determines the seepage nodal forces, which will act as 'external' forces in the finite element computation of displacements and stresses. Figure 14.12 illustrates this process. The hydrostatic thrust is introduced by taking into account the buoyant unit weight of the materials.

The mechanical simulation is then carried out using the classical finite element method, with the specified loading of the mesh elements. After a first run, an interaction between stress state and flow parameters can be introduced using an iterative computing technique. This analysis requires information on the permeability or hydraulic conductivity–effective stress function.

Similar analyses have been completed in different ways, independently of our own contribution, by other specialists (Rodatz, 1973 or Neorishad, Witherspoon, *et al.*, 1971). The studies are often incomplete because of the lack of numerical (laboratory or *in situ*) data and the partial ignorance concerning the relation between the state of stress and hydraulic parameters.

14.9 VARIATION OF SOILS OR ROCKS HYDRAULIC CHARACTERISTICS

The hydraulic conductivity of a medium, whether it be continuous or discontinuous, depends on the state of stress, which influences the intergranular spaces or the fracture openings, and the solid skeleton

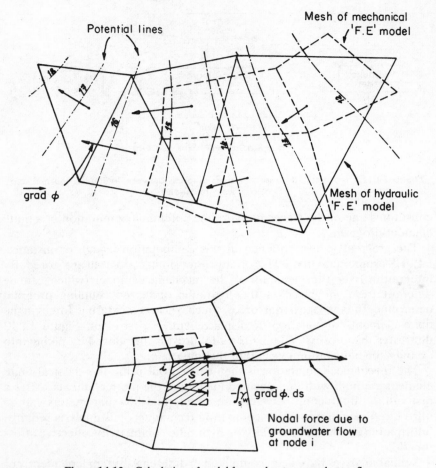

Figure 14.12 Calculation of nodal forces due to groundwater flow

compactness. The temperature also has an influence on the geometric characteristics of the medium (not to mention the variations of water viscosity). In this interaction, the fluid pressure, is related to the state of stress by an equation of the type:

$$\sigma = \sigma_e + \eta p \tag{14.11}$$

where σ is the total stress, σ_e is the effective stress, and η is a coefficient equal to 1 for soils and jointed rock or lower than 1 for the rock matrix (Serafim, 1972).

As for the state of stress, it depends on external forces, thermal effects and seepage forces; the latter forces depend on the hydraulic potential distribution, which is in itself a function of permeabilities.

14.9.1 Influence of the state of stress

The laws of variation of each parameter entering the expression for the hydraulic conductivity of a set of continuous fractures are unknown. They depend on the mechanical behaviour of each type of fracture. Only an experimental approach seems realistic.

14.9.1.1 In situ tests
Many *in situ* water tests in boreholes at various depths in homogeneous fissured formations have shown that the empirical law which most accurately describes the phenomenon of permeability variation is of the type:

$$K = K_0 \exp(-\alpha\sigma_e) \qquad \text{with } \sigma_e \simeq \gamma t - p \qquad (14.12)$$

where K_0 is the superficial permeability, or reference permeability, γt the weight of overlaying formations and p the water pressure.

14.9.1.2 Laboratory tests
Laboratory tests have been performed on parallelipipedic samples crossed by one fissure only, or on porous or fissured rock cores of smaller size, ($\phi = 4$ cm) (Figure 14.13). The samples can be studied under an axisymmetric stress field by use of a permeameter with longitudinal flow.

Exponential laws of variation of hydraulic conductivity, $K = K_0 \exp(-\alpha\sigma_e)$, were also commonly found (Louis, 1976).

14.9.2 Influence of temperature

Temperature influences permeability by its effect on water viscosity and on the opening or closing of voids or fractures due to thermal dilatation.

The hydraulic conductivity of a set of fractures for laminar flow is given by the relation (see Section 14.4):

$$K(\theta) = \frac{g}{12\nu C} \cdot \frac{e^3}{b} \qquad (14.13)$$

In this equation e, ν, C and b are functions of the temperature. The relationship 'kinematic viscosity–temperature' is well known and is given by the formula:

$$\frac{1}{\nu} = 2 \cdot 1482\{(\theta - 8 \cdot 435) + [8078 \cdot 4 + (\theta - 8 \cdot 435)^2]\} - 120 \cdot 00$$

$$(14.14)$$

where θ is in degrees Celsius (around 10°C), and ν is in stokes.

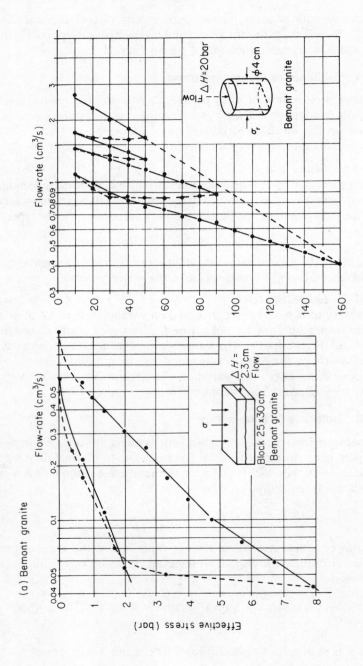

(a) Bemont granite

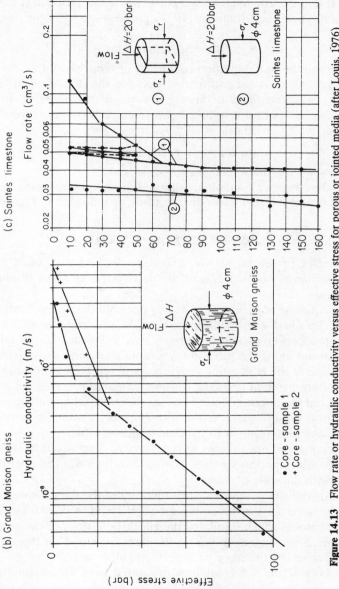

Figure 14.13 Flow rate or hydraulic conductivity versus effective stress for porous or jointed media (after Louis, 1976)

The width of the fracture varies as a function of the matrix dilatation between fractures. The analytical expression for this function is difficult to establish. Rayneau and Jouanna (1974) propose a too simple, unrealistic law:

$$e(\theta) = e_0 - \lambda(\theta - \theta_0)b \qquad (14.15)$$

where λ is the thermal dilatation coefficient of the rock matrix.

This relationship is very simplified because the dilatation of the rock matrix occurs in a confined medium with variable deformability. In a more general case, temperature influence on fracture width is expressed by a relationship which incorporates all the active factors:

$$e \text{ (or } K) = e_0 \text{ (or } K_0) \cdot \exp(-\alpha\sigma\theta) \qquad (14.16)$$

σ_θ represents the thermally generated stresses.

This analysis needs a preliminary thermal computation in order to get the temperature and thermal stress distributions, as indicated in Figure 14.11.

14.10 PRACTICAL EXAMPLE

The principles presented above have been applied to a small concrete gravity dam under construction in the department of Cher (France): the Arnon dam.

This dam has the particularity of having been built on a large fault, with an upstream dip filled with highly compressible and impermeable material. This fault occupies an oblique position relative to the dam axis and the study was carried out along the most unfavourable transverse cross-section, the upper section of the fault being excavated and replaced with concrete.

The medium was assumed to be continuous and a finite element computation delivered the potential lines in the foundation, taking into account the presence of a grout curtain and a drainage system and also permeability variations due to the weight of the dam (Figure 14.14).

The rock mass permeabilities were estimated from *in situ* water tests at different depths. Laboratory tests showed that there was little permeability variation with the state of stress.

Knowledge of the potential distribution under the dam allowed calculation of the seepage thrusts acting on each element of a finite element mechanical model which simulated the elastic behaviour of the ground and of the dam. Flow thrusts acting on the dam itself and on the fault were computed assuming that they were perfectly inpermeable.

The results of the stress analysis presented here are preliminary (see Durand, Louis, *et al.*, 1976; for the final computation).

These results are shown in Figure 14.15. They are strongly influenced by the introduction of the accurate distribution seepage force in the rock mass;

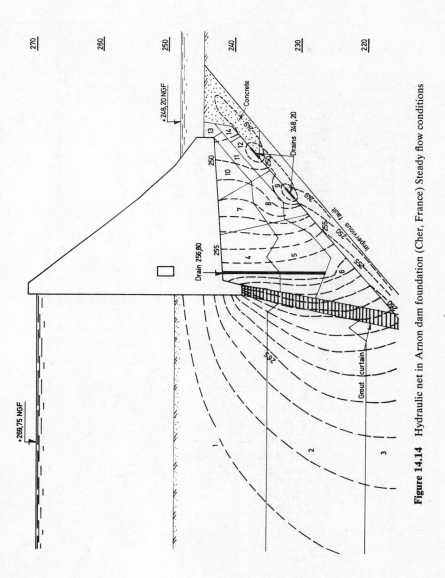

Figure 14.14 Hydraulic net in Arnon dam foundation (Cher, France) Steady flow conditions

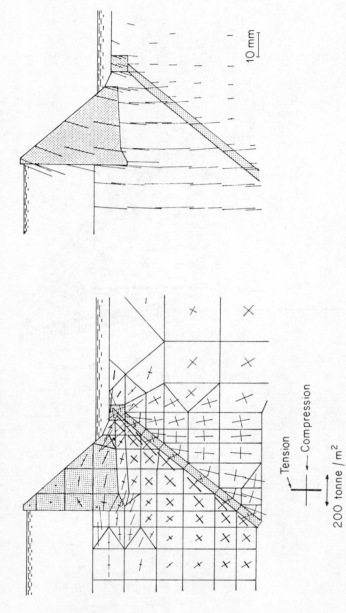

Figure 14.15 Arnon dam. Stresses and displacements due to the weight of the dam and the hydraulic forces in the foundation. Case of steady water flow

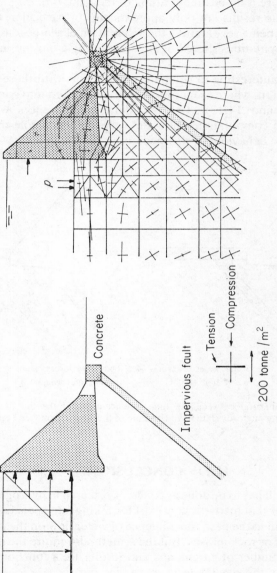

Figure 14.16 Arnon dam. Stress distribution in the foundation. External hydraulic forces only. Case of instantaneous filling (see Figures 14.15 and 14.17)

in particular under the downstream part of the dam a highly developed tension zone develops (also due in part to the concrete wedge). It must also be noted that there is an upstream tilting of the dam.

However, these results are only approximate. In particular, the tensile strength of rocks being very limited, the assumption of a large tension zone is unrealistic. Computations should be repeated using a 'no-tension' process (Zienkiewicz, 1968).

However it is interesting to compare these results with those of a more classic computation, where seepage forces are not taken into consideration (Figures 14.16 and 14.17). The considerable differences which exist between the two computations show the very important role the seepage forces play in the behaviour of the medium.

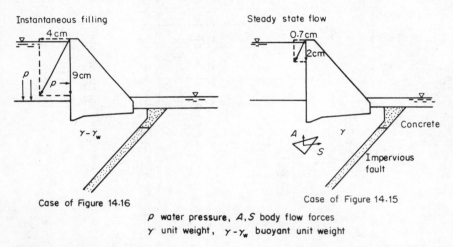

Figure 14.17 Comparison between the total displacements of the top of the dam for instantaneous filling or steady state flow. Example of the Arnon dam (see Figure 14.14)

14.11 CONCLUSIONS

Although a lot still has to be done as concerns research in hydrogeotechnics, one may consider that methods now exist for taking into account, in a more accurate way than in the past, the influence of water flow on the mechanical behaviour of soil or rock masses. But these methods require the determination of a large number of parameters and results are a function of testing techniques and of the way the tests are carried out.

One should keep in mind that a computation method, sophisticated as it may be, cannot represent nature in all its complexity; this fact should emphasize the need for *in situ* instrumentation in hydraulics (pressure and discharge flow measurement) as well as in mechanics (displacement and eventually stress measurements). Hydraulic and mechanical monitoring, which should start at the earliest stage of construction, constitutes an indispensable check for all computations. It allows us to verify that the assumptions conform to the reality or to modify the computations; If the difference between their analytical results and the *in situ* measurements are too great, this could eventually change the project. This approach is also the only way of better understanding of the hydromechanical behaviour of soil and rock masses.

REFERENCES

Bernaix, J. (1967). *Etude Géotechnique de la Roche de Malpasset*, Dunod, Paris.

Bernaix, J. (1970). 'Drainage des fissures à canalicules', *Proc. Zème congrès de la Soc. Intern, de Mécanique des roches, Belgrade*, **4**, 499–501.

Bertrand, L. and Louis, C. (1973). 'Analyse structurale appliquée à la géotechnique', *B.R.G.M. (France)*, Rapport à paraître.

Desai, C. and Abel, J. (1972). *Introduction to the Finite Element Method*, Van Nostrand Reinhold, New York.

Dupeyrat, J. M. (1975). 'Méthodes de calcul des massifs discontinus à comportement non linéaire', *Thèse de Docteur-Ingénieur*, Université de Paris VI.

Durand, E., Louis, C., and Masure, Ph. (1976). 'Foundation problems of the Arnon dam', *Water Power and Dam Construction*, 26–29.

Evans, D. M. (1966). 'The Denver area earthquakes and the Rocky Mountain Arsenal well', *The Mountain Geologists*, **3**, No. 1.

Feuga, B. (1975). 'Prise en compte des poussées d'écoulement dans un calcul par éléments finis des contraintes et déplacements dans un massif rocheux', *B.R.G.M.* (France), Rapport No. 75 SGN 393 AME.

Gale, J. E. (1975). 'A numerical field and laboratory study of flow in rocks with deformable fractures', *Ph. D. Dissertation*, University of California, Berkeley.

Goodman, R. E. and Dubois, J. (1971). 'Duplication of dilatant behaviour in the analysis of jointed rocks', *US Army Corps of Engineers*, Contract DACA 45-70-C0088 NEG. Final report.

Gray, D. H. *et al.* (1963). 'The effect of stress on permeability of sandstone cores', *SPE Journal*, **3**, No. 2.

Harper, T. R. (1973). 'Field evaluation of the hydraulic behaviour of rock masses for engineering purposes', *Ph. D. Thesis*, Imperial College, London.

Jouanna, P. (1972). 'Effet de sollicitations mécaniques sur les écoulements dans certains milieux fissurés', *Thèse Doc. es Sc.*, Université de Montpellier.

Kirschke, D. (1974). 'Druckstossvorgänge in wassergefüllten Felsklüften', *Dissertation*, Universität Karlsruhe, Publ. Inst. für Bodenmechanik und Felsmechanik, **61**.

Louis, C. (1964). 'Rock hydraulics', in *Rock Mechanics*, L. Müller (ed.). Intern. Centre for Mechanical Sciences, Courses and Lectures No. 165, Udine, Italy, 299–387.

Louis, C. (1967). 'A study of groundwater flow in jointed rock and its influence on the stability of rock masses', *Dissertation*, Universität Karlsruhe (W. Germany) (original in German). Published in English in Imperial College Rock Mechanics report No. 10.

Louis, C. (1976). 'Introduction à l'hydraulique des roches', *Thèse Doc. es Sc.*, Université Pierre et Marie Curie, Paris.

Maini, Y. N. (1971). 'In situ hydraulic parameters in jointed rock. Their measurement and interpretation', *Ph.D. Thesis*, Imperial College, London, University Microfilms, Pen. Bucks.

Noorishad, J., Witherspoon, P. A., and Brekke, T. L. (1971). 'A method for coupled stress and flow analysis of fractured rock masses', *Geotechnical Eng. Publ.*, No. 71–6, University of California, Berkeley.

Paloc, H. (1975). 'Glossaire d'hydrogéologie du karst', in *Hydrogeology of Karstic terrains*, Int. Ass. of Hydrogeologists, Paris, Int. Union Geol. Sc. Series B, N3, 151–186.

Rayneau, C. and Jouanna, P. (1971). 'Influence de la température sur l'écoulement en milieux fissurés', *Symposium of the Int. Soc. for Rock Mechanics, Nancy*, **2**, 5.

Roubault, M. (1971). *Peut-on Prévoir les Catastrophes Naturelles?* Presses Universitaires de France, Paris.

Rodatz, W. (1973). 'Berechnung räumlicher, hydraulisch-mechanischer Wechselwirkungen im klüftigen Fels', *Dissertation*, Universität Karlsruhe.

Sabarly, F. (1968). 'Les injections et les drainages des fondations de barrages', *Géotechnique*, 18.

Sabarly, F., Pautre, A., and Londe, P. (1970). 'Quelques réflexions sur la drainabilité des massifs rocheux', *Proc. 2ème Congrès de la Soc. Intern. de Mécanique des roches, Belgrade*, **3**, 213.

Sauty, J. P. (1970). 'Programme ELFES. Modèle mathématique de simulation des écoulements plans permanents en milieu poreux par la méthode des éléments finis', *B.R.G.M.* (France), Rapport No. 72 SGN 141 AME.

Schneebeli, G. (1966). *Hydraulique Souterraine*, Eyrolles, Paris.

Serafim, J. (1972). 'Influence of interstitial water on the behaviour of rock masses', in *Rock Mechanics in Engineering Practice*, K. G. Stagg and O. C. Zienkiewicz (eds.), John Wiley, London.

Sharp, J. C. (1970). 'Fluid flow through fissured media', *Ph.D. Thesis*, Imperial College, London.

Snow, D. T. (1965). 'A parallel plate model of fractured permeable media', *Ph.D. Thesis*, University of California, Berkeley.

Snow, D. T. (1967). 'Anisotropy of permeable fractured media', in *Hydrology and Flow Through Porous Media*, R. J. M. de Weist (ed.), Academic Press, New York.

Symposium of the International Society for rock mechanics and Association of Engineering geology (1972). *Percolation Through Fissured Rocks* (36 publications), Stuttgart (West Germany).

Warren, J. E. and Root, P. J. (1963). 'The behaviour of naturally fractured reservoirs', *Trans. AIME*, **228**.

Wilson, C. R. and Witherspoon, P. A. (1970). 'An investigation of laminar flow in fractured rocks', *Geotechnical report No.* 70-6, University of California, Berkeley.

Wolters, R., Reinhardt, M., and Jager, B. (1972). 'Observations sur l'ouverture des fissures', *Symposium de la Soc. Intern. de Mécanique des roches, Stuttgart (West Germany)*, **1**, 1–13.

Zienkiewicz, O. C. and Cheung, Y. K. (1967). *The Finite Element Method in Structural and Continuum Mechanics*, McGraw-Hill, London.
Zienkiewicz, O. C., Valliappan, B. E., and King, I. P. (1968). 'Stress analysis of rock as a no-tension material', *Geotechnique*, **18**.

Chapter 15

Accuracy in Data Input and in Stress Calculations

R. H. Gallagher

15.1 INTRODUCTION

The initial development of the Finite Element Method, in the early 1950s, was along two lines. These were the force and displacement methods. The force method in effect vanished from practical application in two- and three-dimensional analysis by the early 1960s, due mainly to practical difficulties in the definition of the unknowns to be solved. During the era in which the two methods were competititive, however, there was considerable controversy regarding their relative merit. The force method was claimed to be superior in the calculation of stresses since it is based on equilibrium stress fields. By implication, therefore, the displacement method possesses disadvantages in stress computation.

A principal objective of this paper is to examine the disadvantages and to describe approaches to the improvement of stress calculations in the finite element method. Melosh (1974a), in a recently published overview of finite element analysis, has identified this topic as a source of new computational techniques and research in finite element analysis.

A second objective of this paper is a discussion of the integrity of solutions in finite element analysis from the standpoints of predicting errors *a priori* or *a posteriori* and of the steps to be taken for their reduction or elimination. Questions of accuracy in data input are a part of this topic. The topic is one of the most important in finite element analysis since, if the method is capable of producing solutions to problems for which no adequate alternative solutions exist, procedures for establishing confidence in the computed results must be devised.

The next section gives a categorization of errors in finite element analysis and subsequent sections examine certain of these in greater detail. The treatment of the various sources of error is not even and is not taken in the sequence in which it appears in practical analysis. In particular, matters pertinent to errors in the computation and representation of stress are examined first, followed by a review of procedures in the area of numerical manipulation errors.

15.2 SOURCES OF ERROR IN FINITE ELEMENT ANALYSIS

A rational approach to confirmation of the integrity of solutions in finite element analysis requires a categorization of the sources of error. Melosh (1970) is among the first to have undertaken this categorization and in the following we employ his groupings. Their order of appearance corresponds to the sequence of operations in the usual application of the finite element method.

(1) *Input Data Errors*: These result from not only mistakes in the definition of problem data but also from random errors or uncertainty in the input data.

(2) *Discretization Errors*: Such errors are due to the replacement of the continuum by the finite element model with its attendant assumed displacement fields, or with whatever fields must be chosen in the theory being employed.

(3) *Numerical Manipulation Errors*: These derive fundamentally from round-off and truncation operations and represent the amplification in the computational process of approximations made at the source of the computations.

(4) *Output Interpretation Errors*: In consequence of the approximations made in the representation of certain solution quantities, notably the stresses in an assumed-displacement formulation, further decisions must be made in the interpretation of the solved-for values of these quantities. There is presently no unique or preferred basis for these operations.

We first examine, in the following, the interpretation of calculated stress in finite element analysis (Item 4). Then, numerical manipulation errors (Item 3) are discussed with inclusion of considerations that derive from input data errors (Item 1). The topic of discretization errors (Item 2) has grown enormously in recent years and any summary of it would be beyond the scope of this review. For such reviews the reader is advised to consult Strang and Fix (1973), Whiteman (1973), Oden (1972), and Aziz (1973).

15.3 CALCULATION OF STRESS

It bears emphasis that when the finite element displacement method is rigorously applied, i.e. such conditions as inter-element continuity of displacement are adhered to, the conditions of stress and boundary traction equilibrium are violated. The equilibrium equations are the *Euler–Lagrange equations* and the boundary traction conditions are the natural boundary conditions. Some elements, such as the constant strain triangle, meet the condition of stress equilibrium inside the element but equilibrium is violated along inter-element boundary lines. All higher-order triangles based on complete polynomials violate the equilibrium conditions within the elements.

The 'standard' approach to the calculation of stress is as follows. The stress–strain law, in the presence of initial strain $\{\boldsymbol{\varepsilon}^i\}$ can be written as

$$\{\boldsymbol{\sigma}\} = [\mathbf{E}]\{\boldsymbol{\varepsilon}\} - [\mathbf{E}]\{\boldsymbol{\varepsilon}^i\} \tag{15.1}$$

where $[\mathbf{E}]$ is the matrix of elastic constants and $\{\boldsymbol{\sigma}\}$ and $\{\boldsymbol{\varepsilon}\}$ list the relevant stress components, e.g. $\{\boldsymbol{\sigma}\} = \{\sigma_x \sigma_y \sigma_z \tau_{xy} \tau_{yz} \tau_{xz}\}^T$. The displacement method is based on shape function representation of displacement fields

$$\{\boldsymbol{\Delta}^*\} = [\mathbf{N}]\{\boldsymbol{\Delta}\} \tag{15.2}$$

where $\{\boldsymbol{\Delta}^*\}$ lists the displacement components $\{\boldsymbol{\Delta}^*\} = \{u, v, w\}^T$, $\{\boldsymbol{\Delta}\}$ lists the values of displacement at the element nodes and $[\mathbf{N}]$ is the matrix of shape functions. Application of the pertinent strain-displacement relationships to $\{\boldsymbol{\Delta}^*\}$ results in

$$\{\boldsymbol{\varepsilon}\} = [\mathbf{D}]\{\boldsymbol{\Delta}\} \tag{15.3}$$

where $[\mathbf{D}]$, in general, will contain functions of the coordinate variables since the matrix $[\mathbf{N}]$ contains such functions prior to differentiation. By substitution of Equations (15.3) into Equations (15.1):

$$\{\boldsymbol{\sigma}\} = [\mathbf{S}]\{\boldsymbol{\Delta}\} - \{\boldsymbol{\sigma}^i\} \tag{15.4}$$

where $[\mathbf{S}] = [\mathbf{E}][\mathbf{D}]$ is the *element stress matrix* and $\{\boldsymbol{\sigma}^i\} = [\mathbf{E}]\{\boldsymbol{\varepsilon}^i\}$ is the *initial stress*.

It is of interest to observe that Equation (15.4) can be regarded as a step on the way to the formulation of the stiffness equations

$$\{\mathbf{F}\} = [\mathbf{k}]\{\boldsymbol{\Delta}\} - \{\mathbf{F}^i\} \tag{15.5}$$

In this, $[\mathbf{k}]$ is the element stiffness matrix and $\{\mathbf{F}^i\}$ is the initial force vector,

$$[\mathbf{k}] = \int_{\text{vol}} [\mathbf{D}]^T [\mathbf{E}][\mathbf{D}] \, d(\text{vol}) \tag{15.6}$$

$$\{\mathbf{F}^i\} = \int_{\text{vol}} [\mathbf{D}]^T [\mathbf{E}]\{\boldsymbol{\varepsilon}^i\} \, d(\text{vol}) \tag{15.7}$$

with (vol) designating the element volume.

Now, in the case of distributed loads the stiffness equations are of the same form as Equations (15.5), with $\{\mathbf{F}^d\}$, the 'work-equivalent' or 'consistent' load vector replacing $\{\mathbf{F}^i\}$. The quantity $\{\mathbf{F}^d\}$, however, is not associated with an initial strain term and it would appear that the stress for this case is simply given by $\{\sigma\} = [S]\{\Delta\}$. A rather different view emerges if one considers the notion of a matrix $[A]$ which transforms force into stress:

$$\{\sigma^*\} = [A]^{-1}\{F\} \tag{15.8}$$

(Here, $\{\sigma^*\}$ gives stresses at specified points.) In the case of distributed load, Equations (15.5) and (15.8) give

$$\{\sigma^*\} = [A]^{-1}[k]\{\Delta\} - [A]^{-1}\{F^d\}$$
$$= [\hat{S}]\{\Delta\} - \{\hat{\sigma}\} \tag{15.9}$$

where $[\hat{S}]$ is the newly-defined stress matrix and $\{\hat{\sigma}\}$ is a stress correction for distributed load.

The considerations represented by Equation (15.9) have been taken up by Filho (1968), Stricklin (1966), and Tong (1969) for axial and flexural members and are detailed by Gallagher (1975). This work demonstrates a substantial improvement in the representation of stress when $\{\hat{\sigma}\}$ is present. (Indeed, this procedure is standard in the matrix analysis of frameworks.)

The term $\{\hat{\sigma}\}$ is generally ignored, however, in two- and three-dimensional finite element analysis. It cannot be established uniquely in such cases. Firstly, the conventional forces at a point are fewer in number than the stress components at that location. Planar elements will have two forces at a joint, but three stress components at that point within the element. In three-dimensional situations there are three forces and six stress components.

When an element is based on equilibrium stress fields a relationship betweeen corner forces can be constructed, but not however, uniquely. Consider the constant-strain triangle. There are three stress components and three independent joint force components because three of the forces are related to the other three by overall equilibrium. There are various combinations of the three chosen forces, however, and these lead to different calculations of stress. (See Figure 15.1.)

The above considerations are not of major concern in soil mechanics analysis since distributed loads usually occur over only a small portion of the total finite element idealization. What is more important is that discontinuity of the tractions will exist across the element interfaces for virtually all

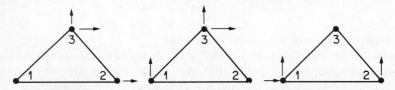

Figure 15.1 Some alternative choices of joint force for transformation to stress

formulations employed in practice and for many of these there is violation of equilibrium conditions within the element as well. Two general avenues that are open to the analyst in resolution of this problem are through the use of schemes which yield improved *interpretation* of the solution data, or through reconstruction of the theoretical basis of the computation so as to produce equilibrium and inter-element-continuous stress field. These alternatives are reviewed in the next two sections.

15.4 IMPROVED STRESS CALCULATION THROUGH INTERPRETATION PROCEDURES

There is no doubt, a wealth of practical experience in the interpretation of stresses in finite element analysis. A prevalent approach is to identify stress values at key points in the element, e.g. the element centroid, and to use such data in construction of contour plots of stress. This procedure masks the errors defined previously but depends for its success on idealizations with very large numbers of elements. Since the use of a large number of elements is often prevented by the economic limitations of the analysis project, situations in which the previously described errors are significant demand attention.

It is surprising that the finite element analysis quantities which govern design in most cases, the stresses, have been given so little attention in the literature. Turner, Martin, *et al.* (1964) discussed a scheme for calculating stress at a point of intersection of a number of elements. In its simplest form their approach is an averaging technique that uses the net joint force to one side of a section at that joint. Similar ideas are discussed by Hrennikoff (1969). These and other *averaging techniques* are examined in some detail by the present writer (Gallagher, 1975).

A more elegant approach to stress interpretation is the conjugate stress procedure, proposed by Oden and Brauchli (1971) and Oden and Reddy (1973) which involves a fitting of stress values, to some criteria, at the nodal points to form a continuous field. For example, if in the case of a displacement field the shape functions $[\mathbf{N}]$ give inter-element continuity, then a conforming stress field $\{\hat{\boldsymbol{\sigma}}^c\}$ can also be constructed on the basis of

$$\{\hat{\boldsymbol{\sigma}}^c\} = [\mathbf{N}]\{\boldsymbol{\sigma}\} \tag{15.10}$$

This is termed a *displacement-consistent* stress field.

Now, in accordance with the conjugate stress approach of Oden and Brauchli (1971), two types of element matrices are formed. One is a square matrix formed of the integral of the product of the conforming stress field and the virtual displacements $\{\delta\Delta^*\} = [N]\{\delta\Delta\}$

$$\{\hat{\boldsymbol{\sigma}}^c\}^T \int_{\text{vol}} [N]^T[N] \, d(\text{vol})\{\delta\Delta\} = \{\hat{\boldsymbol{\sigma}}^c\}^T[M]\{\delta\Delta\}$$

This term can be viewed as the virtual work or the conjugate stresses or, more precisely, as a least-square representation of the assumed stress field. Note that the central matrix $[M]$ is of the form of a 'consistent' mass matrix for an isotropic element. The second matrix to be formed is a row matrix that represents the virtual work of the element stress field $\{\boldsymbol{\sigma}\}$ calculated in the usual way (Equation 15.1)

$$\int_{\text{vol}} \{\boldsymbol{\sigma}\}^T \cdot [N] \, d(\text{vol})\{\delta\Delta\} = \{\boldsymbol{\Sigma}\}^T\{\delta\Delta\}$$

These respective element work terms are summed globally by use of the summation procedure of direct stiffness analysis. Retaining the same nomenclature for global representation, the condition of equality of work gives the vector of conjugate stresses as

$$\{\boldsymbol{\sigma}^c\} = [M]^{-1}\{\boldsymbol{\Sigma}\} \tag{15.11}$$

In a strict sense, this approach requires the formation and inversion of a matrix ($[M]$) which is more difficult to form and which is generally larger than the stiffness matrix. Simplifications to a local basis are possible, however (Oden and Reddy, 1973).

Several generalizations of the conjugate stress idea suggest themselves. Two are mentioned here:

(1) Conforming but non-displacement-consistent stress representations could be used. This would of course result in a loss of convenience of having $[N]$ on hand from previous displacement calculations. Indeed, one might refer to the procedure described above as the 'iso-conjugate stress representation'.

(2) A different stress than $\{\boldsymbol{\sigma}\}$ might be used in forming the row vector. If some stress can be defined that comes closer toward satisfying the local equilibrium conditions, its use could conceivably produce better conjugate stresses.

In their study of methods of stress interpretation, Stein and Ahmad (1974) have identified, as a key aspect of the problem, that the element edge-stresses are related to element nodal forces, rather than to node-point internal forces on sections through such points. This is the same consideration discussed earlier in connection with Equation (15.9), where the stresses are obtained through premultiplication of the element joint forces by a matrix [**A**]. In the work of Stein and Ahmad (1974), which is limited to rectangular structures, the decomposition from element joint forces to stresses is accomplished through virtual work concepts.

Figure 15.2 gives a simple illustration of some aspects of interpretation which we have discussed above. An axial member if subjected to a linearly-varying applied load and for analysis purposes is divided into two segments.

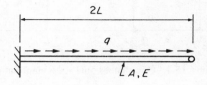

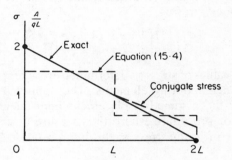

Figure 15.2 Alternative solutions and interpretations of stresses

Use of the standard stress matrix, Equation (15.1), gives the constant values of stress in each element. Application of the conjugate stress approach gives the exact stress distribution in the interval 1–2 but departs from the exact solution at the free end (point 3). The approach represented by Equation (15.9)—transformation of the element node point forces into stresses—gives the exact solution. In this case the matrix [**A**]$^{-1}$ is simply $1/A$, where A is the cross-sectional area of the element.

A simple approach to stress interpretation, which is grounded in theory, is the 'least squares smoothing' procedure described by Hinton and Campbell (1974) and by Hinton, Scott, *et al.* (1975). When done on a local (element) basis, with elements formulated with use of quadratic displacement fields, this scheme consists of passing a linear function through the stress values at the numerical integration (Gauss) points. This is shown in Figure 15.3, which portrays a one-dimensional segment with node points at $\xi = -1, 0, 1$. The Gauss points are at $\xi = \pm 1/\sqrt{3}$. The fit of a straight line through these points

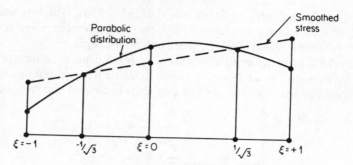

Figure 15.3 One-dimensional stress smoothing

gives the following expressions for the end node point stresses in terms of the sampled Gauss point stresses.

$$\begin{Bmatrix} \sigma_1 \\ \sigma_2 \end{Bmatrix} = \frac{1}{2}\begin{bmatrix} 1+\sqrt{3} & 1-\sqrt{3} \\ 1-\sqrt{3} & 1+\sqrt{3} \end{bmatrix}\begin{Bmatrix} \sigma_A \\ \sigma_B \end{Bmatrix} \tag{15.12}$$

The end-point values of stress so determined are averaged with the values of stress of the neighbouring elements. The approach is allied with an interpretation of the assumed-displacement finite element method as a least-squares error procedure where the measure of error is a weighted function of the error in the stresses; this interpretation has been made by Herrmann (1972).

15.5 THEORETICAL APPROACHES TO IMPROVED STRESS CALCULATIONS

A straightforward theoretical approach to the improved interpretation of stress would appear to be through the use of higher-order displacement functions which include displacement derivatives, interpretatable as strains or as degrees of freedom. Thus in construction of the stiffness matrix for a planar triangular element, using a cubic polynomial, the displacement and its first derivatives might be employed as degrees-of-freedom. (See Figure 15.4). This has been termed a Hermitian representation because of the type of interpolation formula used in its construction. The awkwardness of these degrees-of-freedom, in comparison with the representation based on values of the function itself at a greater number of points (the Lagrangian representation), makes it less attractive, although the efficiencies it furnishes in limited equation bandwidth should be noted. Also, from a practical view, as the analyst considers use of higher-order triangular elements he may regard it to be sufficient to progress from a linear-field formulation to a quadratic.

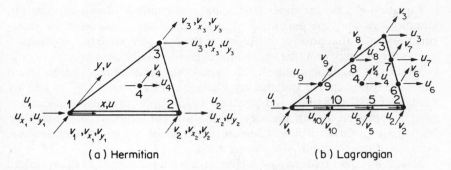

(a) Hermitian (b) Lagrangian

Figure 15.4 Alternative representation of triangles based on cubic polynomials ($u_{x_1} = \partial u/\partial x$ at 1, etc.)

The most promising alternatives are found in alternative variational principles and hybrid methods of element formulation. A review of all possibilities in this connection is beyond the scope of this paper, but can be found in Chapter 6 of Gallagher (1975).

The most obvious alternative variational principle is the one using the dual functional, complementary energy. The disadvantages of complementary energy when represented by the matrix force method have been alluded to earlier. It is not necessary, nor appropriate, to construct a dual in the form of the force method, however. Consider the stress–strain law given by Equation (15.1). Stress is the dual of strain, which is obtained by differentiation of the variables of the potential energy representation, the displacements. Quantities which, when differentiated, gives stresses are *stress functions*. When stress functions are employed as the solution parameters of the complementary energy formulation a process of direct addition can be used in construction of the global equations and stress fields which are continuous across element boundaries and meet all equilibrium conditions.

Under planar conditions, for example, the Airy stress function Φ can be introduced, given by

$$\sigma_x = \frac{\partial^2 \Phi}{\partial y^2} \qquad \sigma_y = \frac{\partial^2 \Phi}{\partial x^2} \qquad \tau_{xy} = \frac{-\partial^2 \Phi}{\partial x \partial y} \qquad (15.13)$$

The functional to be approximated in finite element analysis is then

$$\Pi_c = \frac{1}{2} \int_A \{\Phi''\}^T [E]^{-1} \{\Phi''\} \, dA - \int_{S_u} \{\bar{u}\}^T \cdot \{\Phi\} \, dS \qquad (15.14)$$

where

$$\{\Phi''\} = \left\{ \frac{\partial^2 \Phi}{\partial y^2}, \frac{\partial^2 \Phi}{\partial x^2}, \frac{-\partial^2 \Phi}{\partial x \partial y} \right\}^T,$$

and $[E]^{-1}$ denotes the material compliances.

Equation (15.14) identifies a principal disadvantage of this approach in situations of the type encountered in soil mechanics, the need for stress function-fields that possess continuity of the first derivative (C^1 continuity) across the element boundaries. Displacement formulations require only the continuity of the function itself. This and other disadvantages of the stress function approach are detailed by Gallagher and Dhalla (1971) and by Gallagher (1975). Sander and Beckers (1973) report practical applications of this approach, but in the view of the present writer it does not have immediate promise in finite element methods of soil mechanics analysis because of the C^1 continuity requirement.

Mixed variational principles, which have been postulated in many different forms, are functionals containing both stress and displacement variables. In finite element approximation we define these as functionals which are discretized in terms of both stress and displacement physical variables at the nodes. The most widely employed mixed functional, due to Reissner (1950), among others, does not demand inter-element equilibrium and therefore does not demonstrate special advantages over a displacement formulation. Moreover, there are a large number of parameters per node and a possibly awkward lack of positive-definiteness of the global analysis equations.

Hybrid formulations, pioneered by Pian (1973) can be defined as modified forms of conventional variational approaches (e.g. complementary or potential energy) in which one field is described in terms of generalized parameters and the others in terms of node point physical parameters. Imposition of the stationary condition of the functional enables the removal of the generalized parameters from the element equations and leads to element stiffness or flexibility equations, as appropriate.

One of the more pertinent hybrid approaches in the context of this discussion is the hybrid stress method, in which an equilibrium stress field is written for the element in terms of undetermined parameters and an inter-element-compatible displacement field is independently described for the element boundary in terms of joint displacements. The concept is illustrated in Figure 15.5. This approach results in a conventional element stiffness matrix, which fits in well with prevalent general prupose finite element analysis programs. It is especially useful in the representation of singular stress fields (Pian, 1973) and in the enforcement of stress boundary conditions. It bears emphasis, however, that element interface tractions remain discontinuous, a point which is emphasized in shell analysis solutions published by Edwards and Webster (1976).

Finally, attention should be called to 'generalized' variational principles, in which constraint conditions are written to enforce conditions which are not basically met in the conventional variational principle being employed.

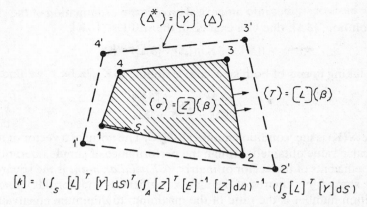

Figure 15.5   Representations of fields in the assumed-stress hybrid method

These would be the equilibrium conditions in a potential energy formulation (Gallaher, 1975).

15.6   NUMERICAL ERRORS

Considerable work has been done by applied mathematicians on the topic of numerical error. Summaries of the earlier work can be found in the work of Westlake (1968), Wilkinson (1963), and Rall (1963). The practical implementation of derived formulae, however, requires numerical experimentation. This means that the specific conditions encountered in structural design analysis must be accounted for in the studies performed. During the past ten years there have been a number of studies of this type, although the number of different organizations involved in them has not been widespread. Fortunately, they have been done with large-scale, general purpose programs in mind, such as ASKA and NASTRAN (Roy, 1971; Melosh, 1974b).

The following remarks are concerned with the numerical errors in the solution process. Rosanoff, Gloudemann, *et al.* (1968) emphasized the significance of two sources of error, round-off and initial truncation. Round-off errors result from the use of floating-point arithmetic in the computer. Initial truncation is due to the use of a constant word-length in the computer in the representation of the equation coefficients. The distinction can perhaps be clarified by the test that can be employed in assessing rounding errors, which consist of a comparison of single- and double-precision solutions to a problem wherein the stiffnesses of the latter are obtained by supplementing the stiffnesses of the former with zeros.

The basis of studies into numerical error is the examination of the change in a solution, $\{\delta\Delta\}$, due to a change in the stiffness, $[\delta\mathbf{K}]$,

$$([\mathbf{K}]+[\delta\mathbf{K}])(\{\Delta\}+\{\delta\Delta\})=\{\mathbf{P}\} \tag{15.15}$$

By taking norms of both sides and assuming $\|\delta\mathbf{K}\|/\|\mathbf{K}\|\ll 1$, we find

$$\frac{\|\delta\Delta\|}{\|\Delta\|}\leqslant N(\mathbf{K})\frac{\|\delta\mathbf{K}\|}{\|\mathbf{K}\|} \tag{15.16}$$

where $N(\mathbf{K})$ is the 'condition number' of $[\mathbf{K}]$. The norm of a vector or matrix is a scalar value obtained through the performance of simple operations on the coefficients of the vector or matrix. A *Euclidian norm* is the square root of the sum of the squares of the matrix coefficients and, for this choice, the condition number is the ratio of the maximum to minimum eigenvalues of $[\mathbf{K}]$:

$$N(\mathbf{K})=\lambda_{\max}/\lambda_{\min} \tag{15.17}$$

In order for $N(\mathbf{K})$ to be a practical tool for *a priori* assessment of numerical error it is necessary that efficient methods for eigenvalue approximation be available. Tong (1971) and Fried (1971) have suggested such approximate methods. Meyer (1975) notes that the Hölder norm, $\|\mathbf{K}\|=\max_{1\leqslant j\leqslant n}(\sum_{i=1}^{n}K_{ij})$, is an upper bound for $\lambda_{\max}$ and that $\lambda_{\min}$ can be obtained from inverse vector iteration after triangularization of $[\mathbf{K}]$.

Equation (15.16) indicates the loss of a significant figure in the solution for each power of 10 in the norm. A more rigorous criterion can be established, but results of numerical experiments (e.g. Rosanoff *et al.*, 1968) are often measured against the relationship

$$s\geqslant p-\log N(\mathbf{K}) \tag{15.18}$$

where p is the number of decimal places to which the matrix $[\mathbf{K}]$ is represented in the computer and s is the number of correct decimal places in the machine. Equation (15.18) accounts for initial truncation error, but not round-off. Also, it does not account for the effects on errors in the displacement vector due to different loads. This can be dealt with through an assessment based on the eigenvectors of $[\mathbf{K}]$, as described by Roy (1961).

The considerations cited above imply a substantial cost for *a priori* error assessments. At present, therefore, only *a posteriori* assessments may be practical in the general case. One important advantage of *a posteriori* assessments of solution adequacy is that they account for the loading conditions of the problem.

A simple way to check the accuracy of a solution would appear to be to substitute the solution into the original equations and assess the discrepancy $\{\Delta\mathbf{P}\}=\{\mathbf{P}\}-\{\mathbf{P}_c\}$, where $\{\mathbf{P}_c\}$ is the load vector calculated from the solution, but this is not a reliable test. Although an accurate solution will produce small residuals, a rather large difference between the true $\{\Delta_T\}$, and computed $\{\Delta_c\}$ displacements may exist for small $\{\Delta P\}$. This can be seen by examination of the application of $\{\Delta P\}$ to the inverse of $[K]$

$$\{\Delta_T\} - \{\Delta_c\} = [K]^{-1}\{\Delta P\} \tag{15.19}$$

It is clear that the difference between the terms on the left can be great even for small $\{\Delta P\}$ since terms in $[K]^{-1}$ might be large. Equation (15.19) represents a scheme for 'iterative improvement' of the solution, but which may prove ineffective for the above reason.

Visser (1968), who has also presented numerical evidence of the inadequacy of the above criterion, has suggested that an appropriate measure for the deviation of the unknowns from the exact solution is given by the difference between the unknowns as obtained by solutions for two different forms of the equations. Such different forms can be obtained simply be the interchange of two or more rows and columns of the matrix being solved. Test cases given by him point towards the validity of the procedure.

With respect to the steps which might be taken to improve the conditioning of finite element analysis equations, 'scaling' is the most obvious and simplest to implement. Bauer (1963) has described procedures which yield optimal scaling, but these may be computationally expensive in themselves.

Substructuring, which heretofore has been regarded as highly advantageous in soil-structure interaction problems, has a beneficial effect. Yamamoto (1972) has conducted studies of this technique and gives a number of rules for the formation of substructures which lead to reduced errors, such as elimination of displacements near to applied-load boundaries in the early stage of the elimination process. The 'partial analysis' approach, discussed by Meyer (1975) bears a relationship to sub-structuring. The idea is to perform an analysis for a coarse-mesh idealization of the problem at hand, isolate regions of design interest, and perform design analyses of these using boundary conditions calculated in the coarse-mesh analysis. This, however, requires capabilities in general-purpose analysis programmes which might be somewhat beyond the substructuring capabilities which are now so prevalent.

An understanding by the analyst of his own finite element representation is a very effective means of constructing well conditioned systems. He should seek, for example, to identify regions where there is a disparity of stiffness between the local and global representation, e.g. stiff elements in flexible structures and *vice-versa*. The imposition of constraints in suppressing such disparities is effective. The judicious choice of coordinate systems has also been recommended (Rosenoff, Gloudemann, *et al.*, 1968).

15.7 CONCLUDING REMARKS

Soil and rock mechanics, which most often involve non-linear behaviour, is sensitive to the definition of the relevant material and physical parameters. The relationship between solution accuracy and the accuracy of this input data is a relatively unexplored topic and should be the basis for much research in the future. Meanwhile, numerical methods in soil and rock mechanics depend heavily on earlier developments in structural mechanics and applied mathematics for solution accuracy guidelines. Rather few contributions have been made in consequence of soils numerical analyses.

This situation must change since, due to the incomplete understanding found in general theories of solution accuracy, useful tools derive mainly from studies of the specific type of physical problem at hand.

REFERENCES

Aziz, K. (ed.) (1973). *The Mathematical Foundations of the Finite Element Method*, Academic Press, N.Y.

Bauer, F. L. (1963). 'Optimally scaled matrices', *Num. Math.*, **5**, No. 1.

Edwards, G. and Webster, J. J. (1976). 'Hybrid Cylindrical Shell Elements', in *Finite Elements for Thin Shells and Curved Elements*, D. Ashwell and R. Gallagher (eds.), J. Wiley Book Co., London.

Filho, F. V. (1968). 'Comment on "Computation of stress resultants and element stiffness matrices" ', *AIAA J.*, **6**, 3, 571–572.

Fried, I. (1971). 'Accuracy of finite element eigenproblems', *J. Sound Vibr.*, **18**, 1971, 289–295.

Gallagher, R. H. (1975). *Finite Element Analysis: Fundamentals*, Prentice-Hall Book Co., Englewood Cliffs, N.J.

Gallagher, R. H. and Dhalla, A. K. (1971). 'Direct flexibility—finite element elastoplastic analysis', *Proc. of First SMIRT Conf.*, *Berlin*, **6**, Part M.

Herrmann, L. R. (1972). 'Interpretation of finite element procedure as stress minimization procedure', *Proc. ASCE, J. of the EM Div.*, **98**, EM5, 1330–1336.

Hinton, E. and Campbell, J. S. (1974). 'Local and global smoothing of discontinuous finite element functions using a least squares method', *Int. J. for Num. Methods in Engrg.*, **8**, 461–480.

Hinton, E., Scott, F., and Ricketts, R. (1975). 'Local least squares stress smoothing for parabolic isoparametric elements', *Int. J. for Num. Methods in Engng.*, **9**, 235–256.

Hrennikoff, A. (1969). 'Precision of finite element method in plane stress', *Publ. Int. Assoc. Bridge and Struct. Eng.*, **29–II**, 125–137.

Melosh, R. J. (1970). 'Manipulation errors in finite element analysis', in *Recent Advances in Matrix Methods of Structural Analysis and Design*, R. Gallagher, Y. Yamada, and J. T. Oden (eds.), University of Alabama Press.

Melosh, R. J. (1974a). 'A status report on computational techniques for finite elements analysis, *Nucl. Engng. Des.*, **27**, 274–285.

Melosh, R. J. (1974b). *Manipulation errors in Computer Solution of Critical Size Structural Equations*, NASA CR-1784.

Meyer, C. J. (1975). 'Special problems related to linear equation solvers', *Proc. ASCE J. of the Struct. Div.*, No. ST6, 869–890.

Oden, J. T. (1972). *Finite Elements of Nonlinear Continua*, McGraw-Hill Book Co., N.Y.

Oden, J. T. and Brauchli, H. (1971). 'On the calculation of consistent stress distributions in finite element approximations', *Int. J. Num. Methods in Engrg.*, **3**, 317–322.

Oden, J. T. and Reddy, J. N. (1973). 'Note of an approximate method for computing consistent conjugate stresses in elastic finite elements', *Int. J. Num. Meth. in Engng.*, **6**, 1, 55–62.

Pian, T. H. H. (1973). 'Hybrid models', in *Numerical and Computer Methods in Structural Mechanics*, S. J. Fenves, N. Perrone, A. R. Robinson, and W. C. Schnobtich (eds.), Academic Press, N.Y.

Pian, T. H. H., Tong, P., and Luk, C. H. (1973). 'Elastic Crack Analysis by a finite Element Hybrid Method', *Proc. of Third Conf. on Matrix Methods in Struct. Mech.*, AFFDL-TR-71-160, December, 661–682.

Rall, R. (ed.). (1963). *Error in Digital Computation*, **1**, J. Wiley Book Co., N.Y.

Reissner, E. (1950). 'On a variational theorem of elasticity', *J. Math. Phys.*, **29**, 90–98.

Rosanoff, R. A., Gloudemann, J. F., and Levy, S. (1968). 'Numerical conditioning of stiffness matrix formulations for frame structures', *Proc. of 2nd Air Force Conf. on Matrix Methods in Struct. Mech.*, AFFDL–TR–68-150, 1020–1060.

Roy, J. R. (1971). 'Numerical error in structural problems', *Proc. ASCE, J. of the Struct. Div.*, **97**, ST4, 1039–1054.

Sander, G. and Beckers, P. (1973). 'Improvements of finite element properties for structural and nonstructural applications', *Proc. Third Conf. on Matrix Methods in Structural Mechanics*, AFFDL-TR-71-160, 305–346.

Stein, E. and Ahmad, R. (1974). 'On the stress computation in finite element models based upon displacement approximations', *Comp. Methods in Applied Mech. and Engrg.*, **4**, 81–96.

Strang, G. and Fix, G. (1973). *An Analysis of the Finite Element Method*, Prentice-Hall Book Co., Englewood Cliffs, N.J.

Stricklin, J. A. (1966). 'Computation of stress resultants from element stiffness matrices', *AIAA J.*, **4**, 6, 1095–1096.

Tong, Pin, (1969). 'Exact solution of certain problems by finite-element method', *AIAA J.*, **7**, 1, 178–180.

Tong, Pin (1971). 'On the numerical problems of the finite element methods', in *Computer-Aided Engineering*, G. L. M. Gladwell (ed.), University of Waterloo Press, 539–558.

Turner, M. J., Martin, H. C., and Weikel, R. (1964). 'Futher development and applications of the stiffness method', *Matrix Methods of Structural Analysis*, B. Fraeijs de Veubeke (ed.), Pergamon Press, Oxford, 203–266.

Visser, W. (1968). *The Finite Element Method in Deformation and Heat Conduction Problems*, Ph.D. Diss., Delft, Netherlands.

Westlake, J. (1968). *A Handbook of Numerical Matrix Inversion and Solution of Linear Equations*, J. Wiley Book Co., N.Y.

Whiteman, H. R. (ed.) (1973). *The Mathematics of Finite Elements and Applications*, Academic Press, N.Y.

Wilkinson, J. H. (1963). *Rounding Errors in Algebraic Processes*, Prentice-Hall Book Co., Englewood Cliffs, N.J.

Yamamoto, Y. (1972). 'Round-off errors of the finite element method', in *Advances in Computational Methods in Struct. Mechanics and Design*, J. T. Oden, R. W. Clough, and Y. Yamamoto (eds.), University of Alabama Press.

Chapter 16

Boundary Element Methods in Geomechanics

P. K. Banerjee and R. Butterfield

16.1 INTRODUCTION

The great majority of realistic geotechnical problems related to steady-state and transient water flow and static and dynamic stress–deformation behaviour involve bodies of very complex geometry. In addition, such bodies will usually contain many zones of different materials each of which will be anisotropic and, in general, best described by non-linear constitutive equations. Even if these equations are assumed to be either incrementally linear or fully linear the problem of obtaining an analytical solution is still formidable.

In practice solutions can only be obtained *via* some form of numerical analysis for which the principal techniques available fall into two main categories—differential methods and integral methods. The former involve either a discrete approximation of the governing differential equations (as in finite difference methods) or a discrete approximation to the actual connectivity of the elements of the body (as in finite element analyses). Both methods can, in principle, cope with systems of any complexity and, largely because of the ease with which boundaries and boundary conditions can be incorporated, the latter method has now reached a high level of performance and hence popularity.

Nevertheless there are two clear areas in which considerable basic improvements might be achieved. One would be to reduce the number of elements required to represent homogeneous zones of a body and the other to ensure fully continuous variation of parameters such as stress, strain etc. throughout an element.

The techniques of the second major category—integral equation methods—do in fact operate by discretizing only the boundaries of the region being analysed and produce fully continuous solutions to the problem within that region. The method presented below is of this kind and, since it requires only boundary discretization of each homogeneous zone of the body, can be aptly described as the Boundary Element Method. Each

529

homogeneous zone becomes one large sophisticated finite element within which there is fully consistent and continuous variation of all the problem parameters. A number of major advantages of such a method are immediately evident:

(1) As only boundaries are discretized very much smaller systems of algebraic equations are developed than when internal sub-divisions are used. (The matrices generated are usually much smaller than those from finite element methods but relatively highly populated.)

(2) Values of the solution variables are obtained only where required at any specifically selected internal points.

(3) The solution variables of main interest (potentials and velocities, stresses and displacements) are obtained directly without the need for numerical differentiation.

(4) Because only boundaries are discretized the errors introduced thereby are mainly confined to the boundaries of the zone.

In principle an integral equation analysis produces an exact solution of the governing differential equations of a problem and numerical errors need only arise when a boundary has to be discretized in order to perform the integrations required.

The method utilizes superposition of particular solutions of the differential equations and therefore the constitutive laws for the materials involved have to be at least incrementally linear. The basic particular analytical solutions used are those for unit excitations applied within an infinite region. (For example, a point source in an infinite plate for steady-state potential flow in two dimensions and a concentrated point load in an infinite space for three-dimensional elasticity problems, etc. all of which are well known.) The underlying formulation of the solution is identical in any number of space dimensions and consequently boundary element methods become particularly attractive in three-dimensional regions. If however the constitutive laws for the material are only incrementally linear then progressively increasing internal subdivision of a region into discrete cells becomes necessary. Nevertheless such cells need only be introduced in locations where material properties change from their initial values and even then including them does not increase the order of the system matrices involved.

In problems governed by elliptic differential equations the solution is direct whereas in parabolic and hyperbolic problems, such as transient potential flow and elastodynamics respectively, the analogous unit solutions are incorporated but a marching process in time has to be introduced.

16.2 A BRIEF REVIEW OF PREVIOUS WORK

Although it is only relatively recently that integral equation methods have emerged as a powerful and practical numerical tool a considerable literature already exists illustrating their application to the solution of boundary value problems in elasticity, plasticity, visco-elasticity, field theory, elastodynamics etc. The given references are a representative selection from published papers on these topics which may be of interest to workers in geotechnical engineering, a field in which integral equation methods have been little used in spite of their great potential.

The methods described in the above literature may be classified into three groups: indirect, semi-direct and direct. We are advocating the former of these three as much the easiest to comprehend and, in our opinion, the most efficient computational algorithm for foundation engineering problems. The basic differences between the three techniques are briefly described below.

In indirect methods the discretized integral equations are formulated in terms of 'fictitious' distributions of the singular solutions mentioned previously over the problem boundaries. The fictitious density functions have no physical significance themselves but once they have been determined the stresses and displacements at all points in an elasticity problem, for example, can be obtained very easily.

Banerjee (1971, 1975a, b, c, 1976), Banerjee and Driscoll (1975), Banerjee and Commons (1976), Benjumea and Sikarskie (1972), Butterfield (1971), Butterfield and Banerjee (1970, 1971a, b, c), Butterfield and Tomlin (1972), Massonnet (1965), Oliviera (1968), Tomlin (1972), Tomlin and Butterfield(1974), Van Buren (1968) and Watson (1968, 1972a, b) have developed algorithms based on such an indirect approach and used them to solve a wide range of engineering problems.

In the semi-direct method the integral equations are formulated in terms of unknown functions which are related to stress functions and are therefore more familiar. The stresses can then be obtained from them by simple differentiations. Jaswan (1961), Jaswan and Ponter (1963), Rim and Henry (1967, 1969) and Symn (1963) have described algorithms based on this approach.

In the direct formulation the unknown functions in the integral equations are in fact the physical tractions and displacements on the boundaries. The solution of the integral equations yields all the stresses and displacements on the system boundary directly and those elsewhere are obtained by numerical integration. Algorithms based on this formulation have been described by Boissenot, Lachat *et al.* (1964), Cruse (1968a, b, 1969, 1972, 1973, 1974), Cruse and Rizzo (1968, 1975), Cruse and Van Bauren (1971), Lachat

(1975), Lachat and Watson (in Cruse and Rizzo, 1975) and Ricardella (1972, 1973).

Usually the indirect methods involve the least amount of computation and can be used in conjunction with a range of singular solutions of the differential equations one of which may be particularly suitable for the particular problem in hand as explained below. This may result in a very considerable reduction in the computer time (Butterfield and Banerjee, 1970, 1971a, b, c). One major disadvantage of the method is that for three-dimensional domains with large specific surface (i.e. large surface area-to-volume ratios) in relation to a sphere then the surface discretization causes quite substantial errors in the stresses on and near the surfaces of the domain (Van Baurens, 1968; Watson, 1968, 1972a, b). This particular difficulty arises also in semi-direct methods, and in numerical methods generally, but appears to be largely overcome in the direct formulation because of the use of physical boundary tractions and displacements. Fortunately most foundation engineering problems have low relative specific surface values.

In what follows the boundary element method algorithm is presented for steady-state potential flow, transient potential flow (diffusion), elastostatics and classical plasticity together with examples of solved problems and an Appendix in which more details of the solution process are provided. We have attempted to describe the method very much from an applied point of view and mathematical discussions have been minimized quite deliberately.

16.3 THE SOLUTION OF STEADY STATE POTENTIAL FLOW PROBLEMS

Figure 16.1(a) shows a homogeneous body I^* with boundary S^* over part of which the potential p^* is specified together with the normal velocity component u^* over the remainder of S^*. We are to obtain solutions to Laplace's equation $\nabla \cdot \nabla p = 0$ within I^* subject to the prescribed boundary conditions on S^*. In Figure 16.1(b) a 'fictitious' body I, surface S, geometrically identical to S^*, is shown embedded within an infinite region R of the material comprising I^*. The potentials p and normal velocity components u over S are to be maintained equal to those specified (p^*, u^*) around corresponding portions of S^*. This is to be achieved by distributing sources of strength ϕ per unit area, over S. If a suitable distribution of ϕ can be found then potentials and velocities within S must necessarily be identical to those within S^*. The boundary element method solves problem 16.1a by discretizing S and calculating the necessary ϕ distribution to solve problem 16.1(b).

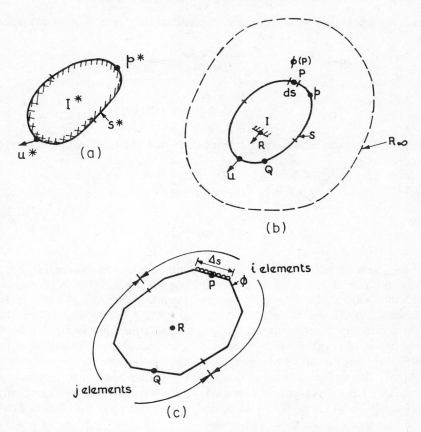

Figure 16.1   (a) The real body; (b) the fictitious body; and (c) its boundary element discretization

In Figure 16.1(b) the potential $dp(R)$ and flow velocity component $du(R)$, at any internal point R, due to a source $\phi(P)\,ds(P)$ at P can be written as

$$dp(R) = f(R, P)\phi(P)\,ds(P) \qquad du(R) = g(R, P)\phi(P)\,ds(P) \quad (16.1)$$

where $f(R, P)$ and $g(R, P)$ are known functions of the positions of R and P (the distance $\overline{RP}$) calculated from the unit excitation solutions referred to previously. For example in an isotropic two-dimensional region $f(R, P) = (\tfrac{1}{2}\pi k)\log(d_0/|\overline{RP}|)$; whereas for three-dimensional problems $f(R, P) = (\tfrac{1}{4}\pi k)(1/\overline{RP})$ and $g(R, P) = -k\,\partial f(R, P)/\partial\mu$ where μ is the outward normal direction to the surface S, d_0 is an arbitrary distance at which $f(R, P) = 0$ and k is the coefficient of permeability. Consequently for any distribution of ϕ

over the whole of S we can integrate Equation (16.1) to obtain for any point R

$$\left.\begin{array}{l} p(R) = \displaystyle\int_S f(R, P)\phi(P)\,ds(P) \\[3mm] u(R) = \displaystyle\int_S g(R, P)\phi(P)\,ds(P) \end{array}\right\} \tag{16.2}$$

If now R is taken onto S, from inside, at a point Q Equation (16.2) can be written as

$$\left.\begin{array}{l} p(Q) = \displaystyle\int_S f(Q, P)\phi(P)\,d(P) \\[3mm] u(Q) = \displaystyle\int_S g(Q, P)\phi(P)\,ds(P) + \tfrac{1}{2}\phi(Q) \end{array}\right\} \tag{16.2a}$$

where the term $\tfrac{1}{2}\phi(Q)$ appears in the second equation as a consequence of the continuity of flow requirements at the boundary when P and Q coincide, and the integral for $u(Q)$ is interpreted as a contour integral around S. However, $p(Q)$ will be known along one part of S and $u(Q)$ along the remainder and therefore the resulting system of equations forms an infinite set of scalar integral equations which can be solved for the unknown function $\phi(P)$. We shall do this by writing the equations in discrete numerical form as follows. The surface S is approximated by n planar boundary elements, of area $\Delta S(P)$ at P, over each of which ϕ is uniformly distributed with intensity $\phi(P)$ at P. The n elements are made up from i on the p specified boundaries and j on the u boundaries $(i + j = n)$.

We can now write algebraic equations equivalent to Equation (16.2) for $p_n(Q)$ and $u_n(Q)$ at any point Q on S as

$$\left.\begin{array}{l} p_n(Q) = \displaystyle\sum_{m=1}^{n} F_{nm}(Q, P)[\phi(P)\,\Delta S(P)]_m \\[3mm] u_n(Q) = \displaystyle\sum_{m=1}^{n} G_{nm}(Q, P)[\phi(P)\,\Delta S(P)]_m \end{array}\right\} \tag{16.3}$$

Whereas $f(Q, P)$, $g(Q, P)$ provided the values of $p(Q)$, $u(Q)$ respectively for a point source $[\phi(P)\,ds(P)]$, $F(Q, P)$ and $G(Q, P)$ are the equivalent expressions for a uniform source $\phi(P)$ distributed over an element $\Delta S(P)$. Evaluation of $F(Q, P)$ and $G(Q, P)$ is elaborated in the Appendix. We have generally taken $p(Q)$, $u(Q)$ to be the values at the mid-point of $\Delta s(Q)$. Tomlin (1972) additionally used $\bar{p}(Q)$, $\bar{u}(Q)$ to typify the values on $\Delta s(Q)$, these being the mean values of p and u over $\Delta S(Q)$, and found no worthwhile improvement in precision from the additional computation involved. He also solved problems using a uniform distribution of potential rather than of source strength along $\Delta S(P)$ and found a slight drop in solution accuracy.

Since we know the values of the $p_i(Q)$ and $u_j(Q)$ components we can extract these from Equation (16.3) and by writing

$$p_i(Q) = \mathbf{p} \qquad u_j(Q) = \mathbf{u} \qquad F_{im}(Q, P) = \mathbf{F} \qquad G_{jm}(Q, P) = \mathbf{G}$$

and $[\phi(P)\,\Delta S(P)]_n = \mathbf{\Phi}$ these equations become

$$\mathbf{p} = \mathbf{F\Phi}$$
$$\mathbf{u} = \mathbf{G\Phi}$$

(16.4)

in which only $\mathbf{\Phi}$ is unknown. By combining $\mathbf{p}$ and $\mathbf{u}$ into one long vector $\mathbf{q}$ and combining $\mathbf{F}$ and $\mathbf{G}$ correspondingly to form $\mathbf{K}$ we have

$$\mathbf{q} = \mathbf{K\Phi} \tag{16.5}$$

which may be solved for $\mathbf{\Phi}$. Equations (16.3) will now provide the remaining $p(Q)$ and $u(Q)$ values. Discrete equations equivalent to Equation (16.2) can then be used to calculate $p(R)$ and $u(R)$ at any internal point R.

The algorithm for generating Equation (16.5) involves the direct compilation of $\mathbf{K}$ from the relevant $F_{im}(Q, P)$ and $G_{jm}(Q, P)$ values. The given boundary information provides $p_i(Q)$ and $u_j(Q)$ and hence q and Equation (16.5) have to be solved for $\mathbf{\Phi}$ with $\mathbf{K}$ a fully populated $(n \times n)$ matrix only.

If I^* contains known internal sources of strength say $\psi^*(R)$ per unit volume then clearly identical sources $\psi(R)$ must be incorporated in I. This is achieved via equations analogous to Equation (16.3), viz.

$$\left.\begin{aligned}
p_i^\psi(Q) &= \sum_{l=1}^{l} H_{il}(Q, R)[\psi(R)\,\Delta V(R)]_l \\
u_j^\psi(Q) &= \sum_{l=1}^{l} J_{jl}(Q, R)[\psi(R)\,\Delta V(R)]_l
\end{aligned}\right\} \tag{16.6}$$

where p_i^ψ and u_j^ψ will be additional to those produced by ϕ, say p_i^ϕ, u_j^ϕ. The H (Q, R) and J(Q, R) components are again obtained from the point source solution (see Appendix). If $\psi(R)$ are merely point sources then H(Q, R), J(Q, R) are identical to f(Q, R) and g(Q, R) otherwise the point source has to be integrated over a discrete volume $\Delta V(R)$. The matrix equivalent of Equation (16.6) becomes

$$\mathbf{p}^\psi = \mathbf{H\psi} \qquad \text{and} \qquad \mathbf{u}^\psi = \mathbf{J\psi} \tag{16.7}$$

which combine to form $\mathbf{q}^\psi = \mathbf{L\psi}$ say.

If the problem boundary conditions are still represented by $\mathbf{q} = \mathbf{q}^{\phi} + \mathbf{q}^{\psi}$ then from Equations (16.5) and (16.7) the value $\mathbf{\Phi}$ can now be obtained from

$$\mathbf{K}\mathbf{\Phi} = \mathbf{q} - \mathbf{L}\mathbf{\Psi} \tag{16.8}$$

If I is anisotropic, then the standard simple geometric transformation must be applied initially to transform I into an equivalent isotropic region. This point is of importance when we wish to apply the B.E.M. to a multi-zone problem as sketched in Figure 16.2a since each zone must be so transformed initially. Every zone $I_1^*, I_2^* \ldots$ will have its own fictitious counterpart $I_1, I_2, \ldots$ embedded in its own finite region $R_1, R_2, \ldots$. In the

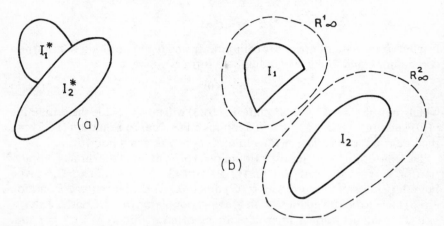

Figure 16.2 (a) The two-zone body; (b) each fictitious zone in its own infinite region

absence of internal point sources we can write equations analogous to Equation (16.5) for each zone as

$$\mathbf{q}_1 = \mathbf{K}_1\mathbf{\Phi}_1 \qquad \mathbf{q}_2 = \mathbf{K}_2\mathbf{\Phi}_2, \qquad \text{etc.} \tag{16.9}$$

where p will be specified on i_1 elements of I_1 and u along j_1 elements of I_1, say, and $k_1 = k_2 = k$ interface elements will make up the total n_1 for zone I_1 (i.e. $i_1 + j_1 + k_1 = n_1$). Along the $I_1 - I_2$ interface the potentials will be identical and the outward normal velocities equal and opposite thus

$$p_k(Q_1) = p_k(Q_2) \qquad u_k(Q_1) = -u_k(Q_2) \tag{16.10}$$

Equations (16.10) and (16.9) taken together are sufficient to eliminate the unknown p_k and u_k interface values and simple matrix algebra will again produce a set of equations of the form

$$\mathbf{q} = \mathbf{K}\mathbf{\Phi}$$

where, for such a two-zone problem, $\mathbf{q}$ and $\mathbf{\Phi}$ have $(i_1 + i_2 + j_1 + j_2 + 2k = h)$, say, components representing once more the total number of boundary elements and K will be $(h \times h)$ not fully populated but block banded. Once $\mathbf{\Phi}$ has been found back substitution in matrix equivalents of Equation (16.2) for each individual zone will provide the values of u and p everywhere. A simple extension of this procedure leads to the solution of problems involving any number of zones.

Clearly all the foregoing applies directly to planar flow problems by considering ΔS to be line elements etc. and using the corresponding planar point source solutions (see the Appendix).

Figure 16.3 (Butterfield and Tomlin, 1972) is an example of a homogeneous anisotropic problem for which an analytical solution is available. In order to test the zoned media algorithm the region was analyzed as if it comprised five zones of identical material. The continuous equipotentials shown were obtained analytically and the discrepancy between these and the boundary element solution is generally less than 2 per cent. The solution to a much more complex problem including twelve different anisotropic zones is shown in Figures 16.4(a) and (b). The boundary element solution, Figure 16.4b is compared with a finite difference solution, Figure 16.4a [obtained by S.O.R. with a triangular mesh network (Tomlin, 1972)]. The maximum discrepancy occurs at the corner of the dam and is about 4 per cent. Generally the difference is less than 2 per cent.

16.4 THE SOLUTION OF TRANSIENT POTENTIAL FLOW PROBLEMS

We now turn to the solution of the classical diffusion equation $c\nabla \cdot \nabla p = \dot{p}$, where $\dot{p}$ represents $\partial p/\partial t$, which is of particular interest to geotechnical engineers as an approximation to the equation governing the time dependent dissipation of excess pore pressures p in porous elastic media.

Again the analytical point source solutions required by the B.E.M. are available (see Appendix). The governing differential equation is now parabolic and in applying B.E.M. we are obliged to further discretise our system along the time axis and obtain our solution using a marching process along this axis (Tomlin, 1972).

The boundary data will generally comprise $p_i^*(Q, t)$ specified around part of S^* and $u_j^*(Q, t)$ specified around the remainder for all values of t. The transient process will be initiated by a known internal distribution of p-values, $p^*(R, 0)$ within I^* specified at $t = 0$ and possibly augmented by a known continuous internal source distribution $\psi^*(R, t)$ per unit volume. If these conditions are to be identically satisfied in the fictitious region (I, S) our problem is to find the distribution of $\phi_n(Q, t)$ which will achieve this.

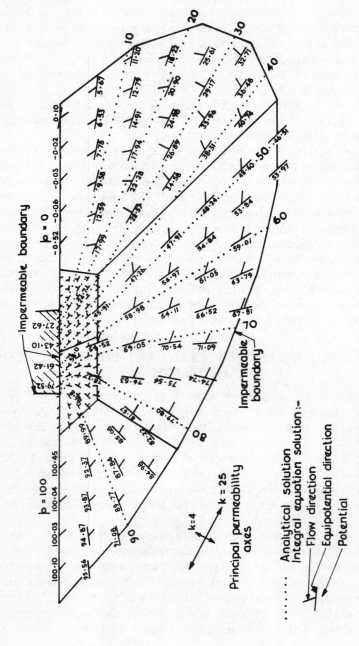

Figure 16.3 Steady-state potential distribution in a homogeneous anisotropic body

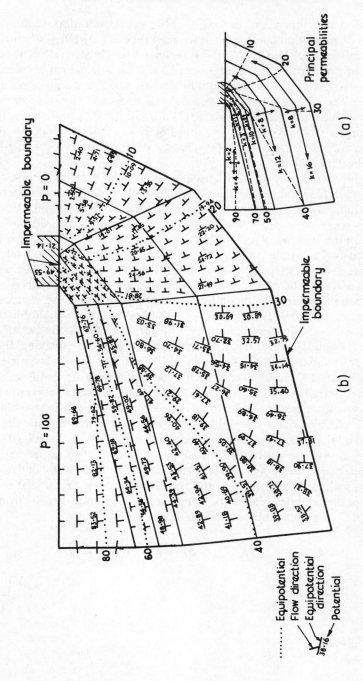

Figure 16.4 Two-dimensional steady-state flow in a 13-zone anisotropic body; (a) finite difference solution; (b) boundary element solution

The solution algorithm requires the use of two point excitation solutions. That due to an instantaneously applied source (Type A), $\Delta\chi(R, t)$ say such that $\Delta\chi(R, 0) = \Delta\chi(R)$ and $\Delta\chi(R, t) = 0$ when $t > 0$. Thus its effect is to produce an instantaneous source intensity of $\Delta\chi(R)$ at $t = 0$ which becomes more and more diffused with time until finally at $t = \infty$ it has zero effect at any point R. The second solution (Type B) is that for a continuous source $\Delta\phi(Q, t)$ say such that $\Delta\phi(Q, t) = \Delta\phi(Q)$ for all $t > 0$. This is clearly indistinguishable from Type A at $t = 0$ but finally at $t = \infty$ its effect at any point R becomes identical to that of a steady state point source of strength $\Delta\phi(Q)$ as used previously.

It should be noted that $p(R, 0)$ will usually be a continuous distribution of values and therefore lumped sources can not really provide an adequate approximation. This fact adds appreciably to the computational effort required to solve such problems and is the main source of additional complexity in the solution algorithm. In the simplest procedure, which will be described for a planar problem, type A sources are integrated over arbitrary internal area elements to approximate the known initial internal distribution $p(R, 0)$. The most convenient areas to use are triangles, Figure 16.5(a), which therefore provide uniform instantaneous triangular sources, say l of them, of intensity $\Delta\chi_l(R, 0) = p_l(R, 0)$ as an approximation to $p(R, 0)$. Since the potential gradient perpendicular to an outer boundary of a triangle is infinite (Tomlin, 1972) a convenient way of satisfying the $t = 0$ outer boundary conditions is to augment I by further external triangles as shown in Figure 16.5a. When each additional triangle is a mirror image of the adjacent internal one and has the same distributed source strength then clearly a zero flux boundary condition is being satisfied. If, in a similar triangle, the external source strength is the negative of the internal one then a zero potential boundary is being modelled, etc. Thus if $\Delta\chi_h(R, 0) = p_h(R, 0) = \Delta\chi_0$ say, this procedure can ensure that $q_n(Q, 0) = q_0$, and the initial boundary conditions are satisfied. At a later time Δt the total of these sources $\Delta\chi_0$ will produce potentials and velocities $\Delta r(\Delta t) \equiv \Delta r_1$, say, at the mid points of the boundary elements. These can be calculated directly from the distributed triangular source solution as

$$\Delta r_n(Q, \Delta t) = \sum_{l=1}^{l} H_{nl}(Q, R, \Delta t)[\Delta\chi(R, 0) \, \Delta A(R)]_l$$

i.e.

$$\Delta r(\Delta t) = H(\Delta t) \, \Delta\chi(0) \qquad (16.11)$$

or

$$\Delta r_1 = H_1 \, \Delta\chi_0$$

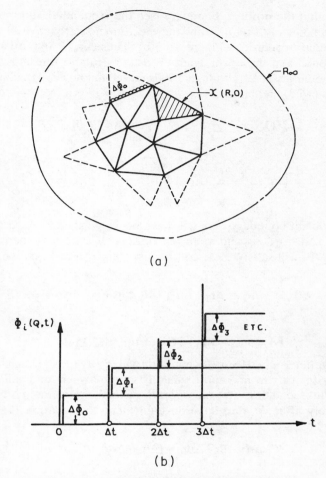

(a)

(b)

Figure 16.5 (a) Discretization scheme for plane diffusion problem; (b) time sequence of fictitious source increment applications

If the applied 'loading' $\chi(R, t)$ varies with time such that say $\Delta\chi_1$ is added at $t = \Delta t$ then the change in $\mathbf{r}$ between Δt and $2\Delta t$ will be

$$\Delta\mathbf{r}(2\Delta t) = \mathbf{H}(2\Delta t)\,\Delta\chi_0 + \mathbf{H}(\Delta t)\,\Delta\chi_1$$

i.e.

$$\Delta\mathbf{r}_2 = \mathbf{H}_2\,\Delta\chi_0 + \mathbf{H}_1\,\Delta\chi_1 \tag{16.12}$$

We now utilize type B solutions integrated along boundary line elements to provide continuous source increments of strength $\Delta\phi_n(P, t)$ per unit length around the problem boundary (see the Appendix). One such set is applied immediately after $t = 0$ and therefore has no retroactive effect on the $t = 0$ boundary conditions Figure 16.5(b). Thus $\Delta\phi_n(P, 0) = \Delta\mathbf{\Phi}(0) \equiv \Delta\mathbf{\Phi}_0$ say, is applied and these will again produce calculable effects around the problem boundary at Δt (although $\Delta\mathbf{\Phi}_0$ is, as yet, unknown). By analogy with Equations (16.3) and (16.5)

$$\Delta q_n^\phi(Q, \Delta t) = \sum_{l=1}^{l} K_{lm}^\phi(Q, P \cdot \Delta t)[\Delta\phi(P, 0) \, \Delta S(P)]_l$$

i.e.

$$\Delta\mathbf{q}^\phi(\Delta t) = \mathbf{K}^\phi(\Delta t) \, \Delta\mathbf{\Phi}(0) \tag{16.13}$$

$$\Delta\mathbf{q}_1^\phi = \mathbf{K}_1^\phi \, \Delta\mathbf{\Phi}_0$$

The problem boundary data will have been specified at Δt, $q_n(Q, \Delta t) = \mathbf{q}(\Delta t) \equiv \mathbf{q}_1$, $\Delta\mathbf{q}_1 = \mathbf{q}_1 - \mathbf{q}_0$ and we have to ensure that the combined effects of $\Delta\boldsymbol{\chi}_0$ and $\Delta\mathbf{\Phi}_0$ will satisfy these conditions. Hence from Equations (16.11) and (16.13)

$$\Delta\mathbf{q}_1 = \Delta\mathbf{r}_1 + \Delta\mathbf{q}^\phi = \mathbf{H}_1 \, \Delta\boldsymbol{\chi}_0 + \mathbf{K}_1^\phi \, \Delta\mathbf{\Phi}_0$$

i.e. $\tag{16.14}$

$$\mathbf{K}_1^\phi \, \Delta\mathbf{\Phi}_0 = (\Delta\mathbf{q}_1 - \Delta\mathbf{r}_1) = (\Delta\mathbf{q}_1 - \mathbf{H}_1 \, \Delta\boldsymbol{\chi}_0)$$

The $\Delta\mathbf{\Phi}_0$ determined from this equation will satisfy the specified boundary data at $t = 0$, at $t = \Delta t$ and approximately so in between for small Δt.

After the second time-step incorporating a further increment $\Delta\mathbf{\Phi}_1$ applied immediately after Δt the equation equivalent to Equation (16.14) will obviously be

$$\mathbf{K}_1^\phi \, \Delta\mathbf{\Phi}_1 + \mathbf{K}_2^\phi \, \Delta\mathbf{\Phi}_0 = (\Delta\mathbf{q}_2 - \Delta\mathbf{r}_2)$$

i.e.

$$\mathbf{K}_1^\phi \, \Delta\mathbf{\Phi}_1 = (\Delta\mathbf{q}_2 - \Delta\mathbf{r}_2 - \mathbf{K}_2^\phi \, \Delta\mathbf{\Phi}_0)$$

and after N time-steps

$$\mathbf{K}_1^\phi \, \Delta\mathbf{\Phi}_{N-1} = [\Delta\mathbf{q}_N - \Delta\mathbf{r}_N - (\mathbf{K}_N^\phi \, \Delta\mathbf{\Phi}_0 + \mathbf{K}_{N-1}^\phi \, \Delta\mathbf{\Phi}_1 \ldots \mathbf{K}_2^\phi \, \Delta\mathbf{\Phi}_{N-2})] \tag{16.15}$$

where $\Delta\mathbf{r}_N = (\mathbf{H}_N \, \Delta\boldsymbol{\chi}_0 + \mathbf{H}_{N-1} \, \Delta\boldsymbol{\chi}_1 \ldots \mathbf{H}_1 \, \Delta\boldsymbol{\chi}_{N-1})$

These equations assume that all time steps are equal and that all incremental sources $\Delta\mathbf{\Phi}$ are maintained as continuous sources once applied.

In most problems $\Delta\mathbf{q}_i = 0$ when $i \neq 0$ (i.e. the boundary conditions do not vary with time) and in many problems the 'loading' is also constant in time

$\Delta\chi_i = 0$, $i \neq 0$ in which case Equation (16.15) is very considerably simplified. In any event it should be noted that only the matrix $\mathbf{K}_1^\phi$ has to be inverted in order to calculate all the increments and the dimensions of $\mathbf{K}_1^\phi$ depend only on the boundary discretization and not the number of internal cells used. Once all the $\Delta\mathbf{\Phi}$ vectors have been calculated up to any time step then any internal $p(R)$, $u(R)$ values can be calculated as before.

Tomlin (1972) has used this scheme successfully with an additional improvement in that his source strengths, $\Psi_l(R, 0)$ varied linearly over the internal triangular elements. Figure 16.6 shows his test problem for diffusion in a plane radially symmetric hollow cylinder. The B.E.M. solution is practically indistinguishable from the exact analytical one. Multi-zoned problems are tackled as explained previously after any anisotropic regions have been transformed into their isotropic equivalents. Solutions to problems of this kind will be found in (Butterfield and Tomlin, 1972; Tomlin, 1972). The fact that the numerical procedure seemed to be quite stable in these problems is probably due to the implicit nature of the solution scheme adopted.

It is clearly possible to extend the above algorithm to include continuous internal sources $\psi(R, t)$ as outlined previously. Three-dimensional problems of this kind have not been programmed although the foregoing procedure would still be applicable. In fact three-dimensional potential theory problems are no more difficult than two-dimensional problems because here we are only dealing with scalar quantities.

The solution algorithm for diffusion problems can be simplified very considerably by not incorporating the image sources mentioned previously. This introduces errors of about 10 per cent in the solutions for small values of t. Tomlin (1972) investigated such an approach for one-dimensional diffusion problems and obtained errors of this magnitude at small values of t, these were entirely removed by using the algorithm described above.

16.5   THE SOLUTION OF ELASTO-STATIC PROBLEMS

The major part of the solution procedure is essentially identical to that already described for potential flow problems. In this case the governing differential equation for a homogeneous isotropic elastic region is Navier's equation in terms of the displacement vector $\mathbf{u}$ (in the absence of the body forces)

$$G\nabla . \nabla\mathbf{u} + (\lambda + G)\nabla . \mathbf{u} = 0 \qquad (16.16)$$

where λ and G are elastic constants.

One of the fundamental solutions of Equation (16.16) is the displacement field generated by a concentrated force vector within an infinite plane (in two

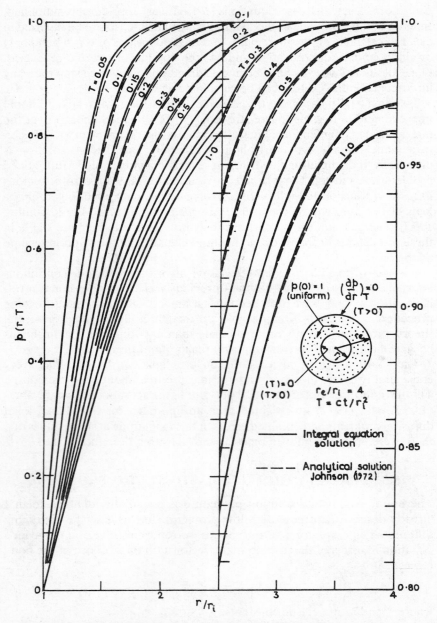

Figure 16.6 Plane-radially symmetric diffusion problem. Boundary element test case

dimensions) or within an infinite space (in three dimensions). Such solutions provide the displacements $u_\alpha(R)$ at a point R due to a force vector $E_\beta(P)$ acting at a point P as

$$u_\alpha(R) = f_{\alpha\beta}(R, P) \cdot E_\beta(P) \tag{16.17}$$

where α, β range 1 to 3 for three-dimensional problems and 1 to 2 for two-dimensional problems; $f_{\alpha\beta}(R, P)$ is defined in the Appendix. We can obtain the stresses $\sigma_{\alpha\beta}(R)$ by use of the stress strain relationships as

$$\sigma_{\alpha\beta}(R) = M_{\alpha\beta\gamma}(R, P) \cdot E_\gamma(P) \tag{16.18}$$

and the traction vector $p_\alpha(R)$ on a surface through R with an outward normal $\mu_\beta(R)$ from

$$P_\alpha(R) = \sigma_{\alpha\beta}(R) \cdot \mu_\beta(R)$$

$$= M_{\alpha\beta\gamma}(R, P)\mu_\beta(R) \cdot E_\gamma(P)$$

Substituting $g_{\alpha\gamma}(R, P) = M_{\alpha\beta\gamma}(R, P) \cdot \mu_\beta(R)$ in the above we obtain

$$p_\alpha(R) = g_{\alpha\gamma}(R, P)E_\gamma(P) \tag{16.19}$$

where $g_{\alpha\gamma}(R, P)$ and $M_{\alpha\beta\gamma}(R, P)$ are also defined in the Appendix.

If we distribute the fictitious surface tractions $\phi_\beta(P)$ over the surface S and let s be an element of S we can obtain the displacements $u_\alpha(R)$ at a point R due to all such elements from Equation 16.17 as

$$u_\alpha(R) = \int_S \phi_\beta(P)f_{\alpha\beta}(R, P)\,\mathrm{d}s(P) \tag{16.20}$$

Similarly the stress resultants at a point on a surface through R can be obtained from Equation (16.19)

$$p_\alpha(R) = \int_S \phi_\beta(P)\,g_{\alpha\beta}(R, P)\,\mathrm{d}s(P) \tag{16.21}$$

These solutions satisfy equilibrium and compatibility everywhere except at $(R = P)$. The functions $f_{\alpha\beta}$ and $g_{\alpha\beta}$ satisfy the radiation condition at infinity for three-dimensional problems but once again in two-dimensional problems logarithmic terms appear which involve a little extra effort to satisfy this condition, as explained in the Appendix.

By moving the point R onto S at Q, as before and considering the equilibrium of the tangent plane at Q we have

$$u_\alpha(Q) = \int_S \phi_\beta(P)\,f_{\alpha\beta}(Q, P)\,\mathrm{d}s(P)$$

$$p_\alpha(Q) = \int_S \phi_\beta(P)\,g_{\alpha\beta}(Q, P)\,\mathrm{d}s(P) + \tfrac{1}{2}\phi_\alpha(Q) \tag{16.22}$$

[It is worth noting that the kernel functions $f_{\alpha\beta}(Q, P)$ and $g_{\alpha\beta}(Q, P)$ although looking very similar to those introduced by Cruse and other workers using the direct integral equation methods are in fact different. The kernels used in the direct formulations are adjoint to those used here, i.e. they use $f_{\alpha\beta}(Q, P)$, $g_{\alpha\beta}(Q, P)$; where $f_{\alpha\beta}(P, Q) = f_{\alpha\beta}(Q, P)$ but $g_{\alpha\beta}(P, Q) \neq g_{\alpha\beta}(Q, P)$.]

In a well-posed problem $p_\alpha(Q)$ will be known on one part of the boundary and $u_\alpha(Q)$ over the remainder. For any boundary configuration the following system of equations can be obtained from the discretization of the surface geometry data as shown in the potential problem.

$$\mathbf{u} = \mathbf{F\Phi}$$
$$\mathbf{p} = \mathbf{G\Phi}$$

(16.23)

The algorithm for generating $\mathbf{F}$ and $\mathbf{G}$ matrices involves the integration of the respective kernel functions $f_{\alpha\beta}(Q, P)$ and $g_{\alpha\beta}(Q, P)$ over individual surface elements. These operations involve two types of integrals (i) for components generated when P and Q coincide, which have been evaluated by using an exact integration scheme proposed by Cruse (1969) (ii) for all other components (i.e. where $P \neq Q$), which have been evaluated by using numerical integration fromulae. Having compiled the $\mathbf{F}$ and $\mathbf{G}$ matrices the boundary conditions for $\mathbf{u}$ and $\mathbf{p}$ over S can be incorporated in Equation (16.23) the solution of which yields all $\mathbf{\Phi}$ values for the n boundary elements. The stresses and displacements at any interior point R can then be obtained from the matrix equivalents of

$$u_\alpha(R) = \int_S f_{\alpha\beta}(R, P) \cdot \phi_\beta(P) \, ds(P)$$

$$\sigma_{\alpha\beta}(R) = \int_S M_{\alpha\beta\gamma}(R, P) \cdot \phi_\gamma(P) \, ds(P)$$

i.e.   (16.24)

$$u_\alpha(R) = \sum_{m=1}^{n} f_{\alpha\beta}(R, P_m)\phi_\beta(P_m)\Delta S(P_m)$$

$$\sigma_{\alpha\beta}(R) = \sum_{m=1}^{n} M_{\alpha\beta\gamma}(R, P_m)\phi_\gamma(P_m)\Delta S(P_m)$$

We can derive one very important relationship from Equation (16.23). Eliminating $\mathbf{\Phi}$ between the set of equations gives the following relationship between $\mathbf{p}$ and $\mathbf{u}$

$$\mathbf{p} = (\mathbf{GF}^{-1})\mathbf{u}$$

(16.25)

An equation which relates the surface tractions and the surface displacements for a solid of any shape. We have therefore just described, in the terminology of the Finite Element analysis, a method for deriving the local stiffness matrix for an element of arbitrary shape. Instead of the conventional relationship between the nodal forces and nodal displacements we have a relationship between the surface tractions applied over each element and the displacements of the element centroids. The boundary conditions can therefore be included with greater ease because the calculations of the equivalent nodal forces are eliminated. Moreover because the governing differential equations are satisfied within the element we can make the element as large as we like.

In the presence of a known body force $\Psi_\alpha(R)$ per unit volume the displacements and the tractions over the surface S can be obtained from (Banerjee, Commons, and Mustoe, 1976)

$$u_\alpha(Q) = \int_S \phi_\beta(P)f_{\alpha\beta}(Q, P)\, ds(P) + \int_V \Psi_\beta(R)f_{\alpha\beta}(Q, R)\, dv(R)$$

$$(16.26)$$

$$p_\alpha(Q) = \int_S \phi_\beta(P)g_{\alpha\beta}(Q, P)\, ds(P) + \int_V \Psi_\beta(R)g_{\alpha\beta}(Q, R)\, dv(R)$$

$$+ \tfrac{1}{2}\phi(Q)$$

which can again be written for n discrete elements of S and l discrete interior cells as

$$\mathbf{F\Phi} = \mathbf{u} - \mathbf{H\psi}$$
$$\mathbf{G\Phi} = \mathbf{p} - \mathbf{J\psi}$$
$$(16.27)$$

It is worth noting that the internal sub-division into cells required in order to include body forces is quite arbitrary. The body forces can be either 'lumped' at specific points or more satisfactorily included as known distributions over internal volume elements. In neither case does their inclusion increase the dimensions of the final matrix system generating $\mathbf{\Phi}$ (Equation 16.23).

Again the development for multizone problems duplicates that already given for the potential problem even to the interface compatibility conditions (16.10), if $u \equiv u_\alpha$ and $p \equiv p_\alpha$ is understood. In the absence of body forces $\mathbf{q} = \mathbf{K\Phi}$ is finally obtained which once more yields $\mathbf{\Phi}$, which is now a $(2h \times 1)$ vector for two-dimensional problems and $(3h \times 1)$ for three-dimensional ones.

Anisotropy cannot be overcome in elasticity problems by simple transformation and within each zone $I_1, I_2, \ldots$ the point load solution for the corresponding anisotropic continuum must be used. These are well known for transversely anisotropic bodies. Various useful solutions are described in (de Urena, 1966) and a plane strain solution for point loads in an infinite orthotropic lamina is given in (Tomlin and Butterfield, 1974).

Figure 16.7 summarizes results obtained (Butterfield and Banerjee, 1971) from the three dimensional analysis of the load displacement behaviour of groups of rigid piles with a rigid pile cap both resting on isotropic elastic ground and clear of the ground. Apart from the intrinsic interest of the results in Figure 16.7(b) to geotechnical engineers (settlement ratio is defined as the ratio of the settlement of an N pile group to that of a single pile when each carry the same average load per pile), the presentation of the solution of a complicated rigid inclusion problem and the fact that Poisson's ratio = 0·5 has been used for the elastic ground illustrates two further most important capabilities of the boundary element method. In addition it is worth noting that:

(1) The extreme boundaries of the problem are at infinity. This is not only the very simplest boundary condition to include in the B.E.M., since conditions there are satisfied automatically without discretization, but also it is a condition which has to be approximated by all other numerical techniques.

(2) The particular solution used to form the kernels of the **K** matrices was that due to Mindlin described in (Butterfield and Banerjee, 1971) where the point load acts at an arbitrary depth below the free surface of a semi-infinite elastic space, and not the Kelvin point load solution mentioned previously. Consequently the free surface boundary conditions are automatically satisfied and only the pile group–soil interfaces have to be discretized. The number of algebraic equations developed was reduced even further by relaxing the radial displacement compatibility condition at the pile–soil interfaces and by assuming radially symmetric direct stress distributions on them (Butterfield and Banerjee, 1971).

Both of these assumptions have very small effects on the group stiffness calculations for axially loaded groups and reduce the dimensions of **K** to (50 × 50) for a 3 × 3 capped pile group problem.

An advanced version of this programme incorporating general loadings is now being issued by the Department of the Environment (U.K.) for the analysis of pile groups in bridge abutments, etc. (Banerjee and Driscoll, 1975).

An example of a multi-zone two-dimensional orthotropic problem is illustrated in Figure 16.8. Only the calculated displacement vectors are shown in Figure 16.8(b). Full details of the solution and the particular solution used for the kernel function are given in (Tomlin and Butterfield, 1972, 1974). A point of particular interest is the inclusion of boundary

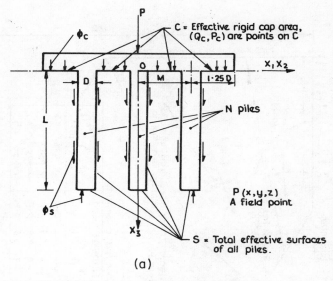

(a)

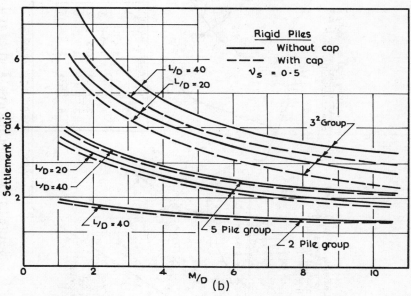

Figure 16.7 Three-dimensional elasticity problem; (a) geometry of rigid pile and cap system; (b) calculated settlement ratios for different geometries

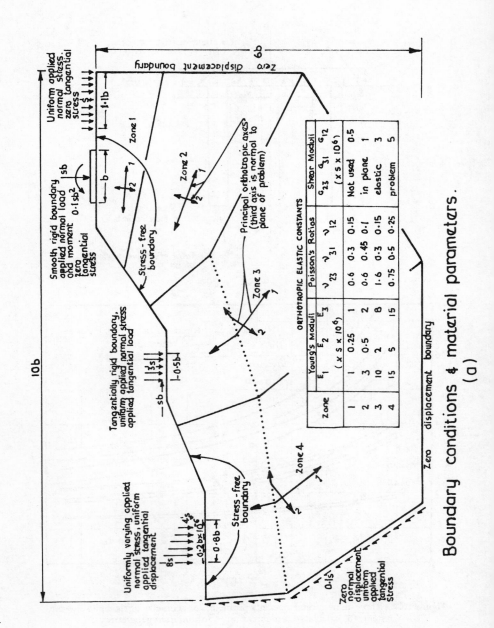

Boundary conditions & material parameters.

(a)

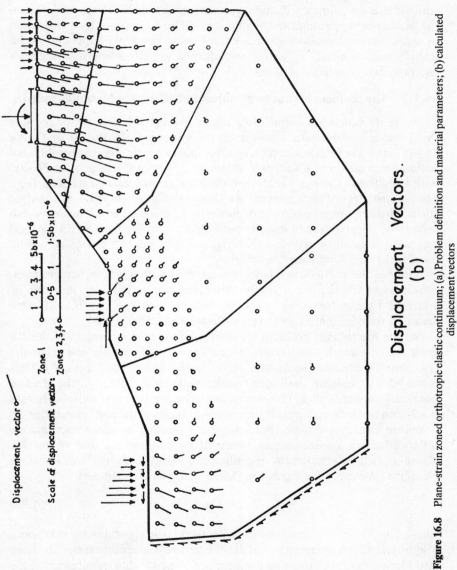

Displacement vector ○———

Scale of displacement vector:

Zone 1

Zones 2,3,4

Displacement Vectors.
(b)

Figure 16.8 Plane-strain zoned orthotropic elastic continuum; (a) Problem definition and material parameters; (b) calculated displacement vectors

conditions, Figure 16.8(a), common in geotechnical engineering, a region of rigid boundary under specified total normal (or tangential) forces which in effect, specified an inter-relationship between the normal (or shear) stress components on boundary elements under such a load. For each such region the total system of equations for solution will be augmented by a maximum of three further equations of this kind. Elastic boundary supports can be incorporated similarly by equations interrelating stress and displacement components on individual elements.

16.5.1 The problem of structures embedded in irregularly stratified media

Many geotechnical problems arise which involve the analysis of two- or three-dimensional elastic systems of the general form shown in Figure 16.9(a). The key features of such systems are an elastic structure embedded within a succession of different isotropic or anisotropic strata (A to N, say) with irregular interfaces each of which connect only two strata (e.g. $I-J$). Special instances of such systems are shown in Figure 16.9(b)—a non-rigid surface footing on an isotropic or anisotropic material with elastic moduli increasing approximately linearly with depth, and Figure 16.9(c)—a rigid cap piled foundation within a material possessing a stiff crust and a rigid basal layer enclosing softer materials.

Whereas the multi-zone algorithm can deal with any number of zones, problems which involve a singly connected succession of layers can be analysed by the following algorithm which combines the B.E.M. with standard transfer matrix techniques (Pestel and Leckie, 1961).

For the multi-layer problem we shall subdivide the boundary of the Ith layer, into a elements on the $(H-I)$ interface above I, into b elements on the $(I-J)$ interface below I and a total of $2e$ elements on the end faces of I. Thus $n = a + b + 2e$ and we shall also require that $a = b$, (although the sizes of boundary elements along the interfaces do not need to correspond) whereas the $2e$ can be made up from arbitrary sub-divisions of the end boundaries.

Within the layer I itself there may be a number of zones each having different elastic constants and bounded by suitable number of surface elements (which are already included in a and b above) and interface elements. We can write Equation (16.25) for one such zone as

$$\mathbf{p} = \mathbf{Cu} \qquad (16.28)$$

where $\mathbf{C} = (G \cdot F^{-1})$ is obtained by using the elastic constants for that zone. The matrix $\mathbf{C}$ is a symmetric matrix. We can now assemble these matrices into a larger matrix by utilizing the interface compatibility requirements [see Equation (16.10)] between the zones. This assembly process is exactly similar to that used in the Finite Element Method. By eliminating the

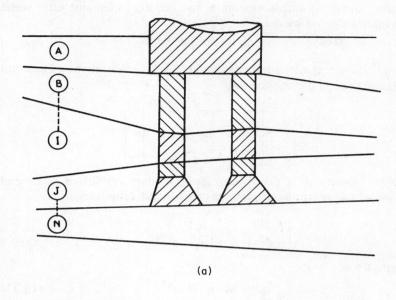

(a)

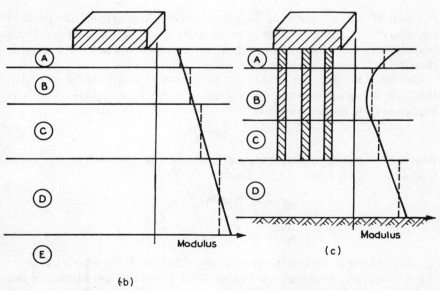

(b)

(c)

Figure 16.9 (a) An irregularly stratified multi-zone medium; (b) a typical footing problem; (c) a typical pile group problem

conditions, unknown displacements at the interface elements after some simple matrix algebra we get

$$\mathbf{p}^{(I)} = \mathbf{C}^{(I)} \mathbf{u}^{(I)} \tag{16.29}$$

where $\mathbf{p}^{(I)}$ and $\mathbf{u}^{(I)}$ are $3n \times 1$ vectors and $\mathbf{C}^{(I)}$ is a $3n \times 3n$ matrix. Equation (16.29) can now be partitioned into

$$\begin{Bmatrix} p_1 \\ p_b \\ p_e \end{Bmatrix}^{(I)} = \begin{bmatrix} C_{aa} & C_{ab} & C_{ae} \\ C_{ba} & C_{bb} & C_{be} \\ C_{ea} & C_{eb} & C_{ee} \end{bmatrix}^{(I)} \begin{Bmatrix} u_a \\ u_b \\ u_e \end{Bmatrix}^{(I)} \tag{16.30}$$

Now by incorporating the appropriate boundary conditions of $2e$ end elements we can rearrange Equations (16.30) and write them as

$$\begin{Bmatrix} p_a \\ u_a \end{Bmatrix}^{(I)} = \mathbf{M}^{(I)} \begin{Bmatrix} p_b \\ u_b \end{Bmatrix}^{(I)} + m^{(I)}$$

or compactly as

$$\mathbf{q}_b^{(I)} = \mathbf{M}^{(I)} \mathbf{q}_a^{(I)} + \mathbf{m}^{(I)} \tag{16.31}$$

in which $\mathbf{M}^{(I)}$ is known and $\mathbf{m}^{(I)}$ is a known vector arising from the specified boundary conditions on the extreme ends of I. In cases where these boundaries are so distant from the region that their influence is negligible then the $\mathbf{m}^{(I)}$ vector becomes zero.

One more the boundary conditions on the top of zone J will be related to those on the base of zone I by interface compatibility equations such as Equations (16.10) i.e. generally

$$\mathbf{q}_a^{(J)} = \mathbf{B}^{(JI)} \mathbf{q}_b^{(I)} \tag{16.32}$$

where $\mathbf{B}^{(JI)}$ will be a diagonal matrix containing only ± 1 terms. From Equation (16.31) and (16.32) we have

$$\mathbf{q}_a^{(J)} = \mathbf{B}^{(JI)} (\mathbf{M}^{(J)} \mathbf{q}_a^{(I)} + \mathbf{m}^{(I)})$$

i.e. $\tag{16.33}$

$$\mathbf{q}_a^{(J)} = \mathbf{T}^{(JI)} \mathbf{q}_a^{(J)} + \mathbf{t}^{(JI)}$$

an equation which expresses a transfer matrix relationship between boundary information on the top surface of layer I and the top surface of the underlying layer J. Consequently we can now proceed from the top boundary of the top layer A of the system through to the bottom of the bottom layer N by repeated application of Equation (16.33). The $\mathbf{T}$ and $\mathbf{t}$ matrices need to be calculated for all dissimilar layers and the chain of transfer matrix operations then establishes the following pattern

$$\mathbf{q}_b^{(N)} = \mathbf{M}^{(N)}\{\mathbf{T}^{(NM)}[\mathbf{T}^{(ML)} \ldots (\mathbf{T}^{(BA)}\mathbf{q}_a^{(A)} + \mathbf{t}^{(BA)}) \ldots + \mathbf{t}^{(ML)}] + \mathbf{t}^{(NM)}\}$$

$$+ \mathbf{m}^{(N)} \qquad (16.34)$$

i.e.

$$\mathbf{q}_b^{(N)} = \mathbf{T}\mathbf{q}_a^{(A)} + \mathbf{t}, \qquad \text{say} \qquad (16.35)$$

As before admissible boundary condition data will provide numerical values of either half of the components $\mathbf{q}_a^{(A)}$ and $\mathbf{q}_b^{(N)}$ or linear relationships between the stresses and displacement components within them. Then, providing that $\mathbf{T}$ is square and non-singular, Equation (16.35) can be used to obtain the unknown components of the $\mathbf{q}$ vectors. Back substitution within the chain of transfer matrix operations determines all other vectors $\mathbf{q}$ for each main zone and Equation (16.23) provides the $\boldsymbol{\Phi}$, etc. The stresses and displacements at any subseqently chosen internal points can be calculated as explained previously.

It is again a simple matter to reduce the order of many of the matrices involved in these operations by relaxing some of the interface compatibility requirements, for example a smooth interface assumption will essentially halve the size of the problem. Although the solution algorithm involves chains of matrix multiplication operations only a very modest series of matrix inversions arises.

This algorithm has been used in a computer program written specifically to solve boundary value problems involving multiple inclusions within a stratified half space. The transfer matrices for individual layers were formed in the central processor and transmitted in sequence, A to N, into a back-up storage device. Thus the central processor stores only two $6a \times 6a$ arrays at a given time. The remaining arrays that are needed have been defined within the various partitions of all of these $6a \times 6a$ arrays. The chain of multiplication of the transfer matrices was carried out by bringing only one of these matrices at a given time into the central processor. The final system of Equations (16.35) was solved by standard Gaussian elimination. It is of interest to note that the matrix $\mathbf{T}$ in these equations is not symmetrical for a mixed boundary value problem.

Figure 16.10a shows the details of a typical pile group problem analysed using this computer program and Figure 16.10b the scheme of discretization adopted. The individual coefficients of the off-diagonal blocks of Equation (16.23) were evaluated numerically from a series of non-singular integrals and those for the diagonal blocks by using an exact integration scheme described by Cruse (1969) as mentioned previously.

Having obtained $\boldsymbol{\Phi}$ values from Equation (16.23), the vertical stresses and displacements at various points within the individual zones can be calculated

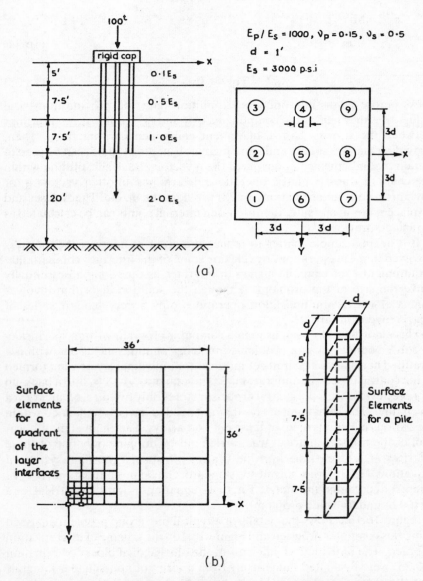

Figure 16.10 (a) A compressible pile group in a multilayered elastic medium; (b) boundary element discretization scheme used

from Equation (16.24). Figure 11(a) shows the average vertical stress over each pile cross-section plotted against distance along the pile. The actual distribution of the vertical stress over the cross-section was found to be non-uniform as expected near the pile head becoming gradually more uniform towards their base. The pile cap carries only some 4 per cent of the total applied load whereas in homogeneous conditions it would carry over 50 per cent (Butterfield and Banerjee, 1971). Figure 16.11(b) shows the displacements of the ground surface. These become very small beyond some twelve pile diameters from the group centreline which corresponds to the behaviour of an elastic medium approximating a Gibson material (Gibson, 1974) in contra-distinction to the surface displacements in a comparable system in a homogeneous material which, at this distance, are still some 40 per cent of their maximum value. Incidentally, the vertical stiffness of the Figure 16.10 pile group is 388 tonf/inch which would be the value for a similar group in a homogeneous material with a modulus $E_s = 2760 \, lbf/in^2$ whereas the simple average modulus over the pile length in Figure 16.11a is only $1760 \, lbf/in^2$.

The computational time used for the solution of the problem described above was approximately 30 minutes of an ICL 4/70 computer. It is interesting to note that a similar problem involving nine piles embedded within a homogeneous layer, analysed by using a three-dimensional finite element program on an approximately equivalent Univac 1108 computer, required a computing time of approximately 200 minutes (Ottovian, 1975). The ratio of computing time is approximately 10 to 1 in favour of the B.E.M.

Lachat (1975) also quotes a number of comparative studies one of which involves the elastic analysis of a gear tooth in which the ratio of total computer time (CDC 7600) between a finite element and a simple integral equation analysis is approximately 8 to 1 in favour of the latter with a difference of only some 2 per cent in the calculated stresses.

16.6 APPLICATIONS TO ELASTO-PLASTIC SOLIDS

An elasto-plastic body must obey the equilibrium equations

$$\partial \dot{\sigma}_{ij} / \partial x_j = 0 \tag{16.36}$$

where $\dot{\sigma}_{ij}$ denotes the total stress rate.

The total strain rate $\dot{\varepsilon}_{ij}$ can be written as

$$\dot{\varepsilon}_{ij} = \dot{\varepsilon}^e_{ij} + \dot{\varepsilon}^p_{ij} = \tfrac{1}{2}(\partial \dot{u}_i / \partial x_j + \partial \dot{u}_j / \partial x_i) \tag{16.37}$$

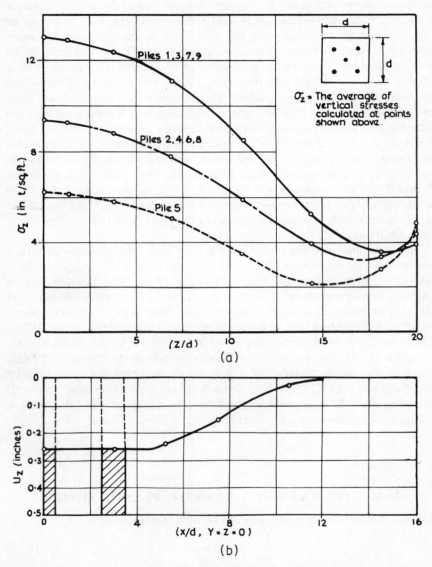

Figure 16.11 (a) Distribution of vertical stresses in piles; (b) vertical displacement of ground surface.

where

$$\dot{\varepsilon}_{ij}^e = \text{the elastic strain rate}$$

$$\dot{\varepsilon}_{ij}^p = \text{the plastic strain rate}$$

$$\dot{u} = \text{the displacement rate}$$

The elastic strain rate for an isotropic body is given by

$$2G\dot{\varepsilon}_{ij}^e = \dot{\sigma}_{ij} - [\nu/(1+\nu)]\dot{\sigma}_{kk}\delta_{ij} \tag{16.38}$$

where G and ν are elastic constants

$$\delta_{ij} = 0, \qquad i \neq j$$

$$= 1, \qquad i = j$$

In order to express the plastic strain rate we may choose a strain hardening Von Mises–Prandtl–Reuss material for which the flow rule may be written as either (Fung, 1965; Swedlow and Cruse, 1971)

$$2G\dot{\varepsilon}_{ij} = \dot{\sigma}_{ij} - [\nu/(1+\nu)]\dot{\sigma}_{kk}\,\delta_{ij}$$

$$+ (G/G_0)S_{ij}S_{kl}\dot{\sigma}_{kl}/(3\sigma_0^2) \tag{16.39}$$

or

$$\dot{\sigma}_{ij}/2G = \dot{\varepsilon}_{ij} + [\nu/(1-2\nu)]\dot{\varepsilon}_{kk}\,\delta_{ij}$$

$$- S_{ij}S_{kl}\dot{\varepsilon}_{kl}/[3\sigma_0^2(1+G_0/G)] \tag{16.40}$$

where

$$\sigma_0 = \surd(S_{ij}S_{ij}/3)$$

$$\varepsilon_0^p = \int \dot{\varepsilon}_0^p \text{ over the entire loading history,}$$

$$\dot{\varepsilon}_0^p = \surd(\dot{\varepsilon}_{ij}^p\dot{\varepsilon}_{ij}^p/3)$$

$$2G_0 = \dot{\sigma}_0/\dot{\varepsilon}_0, \text{ an instantaneous plastic shear modulus}$$

$$S_{ij} = \sigma_{ij} - \delta_{ij}(\sigma_{kk}/3)$$

By substituting Equation (16.10) in (16.36) and using Equation (16.37) we obtain the governing differential equations for elasto-plastic flow:

$$[1/(1-2\nu)]\,\partial^2\dot{u}_j/\partial x_i\partial x_j + \partial^2\dot{u}_i/\partial x_j^2 - 2\partial F_{ij}/\partial x_j = 0 \tag{16.41}$$

where

$$F_{ij} = (S_{ij}S_{kl}\,\partial\dot{u}_k/\partial x_l)/\{3\sigma_0^2(1+G_0/G)\} \tag{16.42}$$

By defining a new body force $\psi_1 = -2G \, \partial F_{ij}/\partial x_j$ we can rewrite Equation (16.41) as

$$[1/(1-2\nu)] \, \partial^2 \dot{u}_j/\partial x_i \partial x_j + \partial^2 \dot{u}_i/\partial x_j^2 + \psi_i/G = 0 \qquad (16.43)$$

Equation (16.43) is identical to Navier's equations for elastic displacements if ψ_i is known. Thus we see that the 'plasticity' takes the role of a body force and Equation (16.43) is quasi-linear in character.

Thus to solve any plasticity problem we have in effect to solve a problem with surface forces and modified body forces. This is analogous to the well-known Duhamel–Neuman analogy for thermo-elastic problems, where the thermal gradient takes on the role of a body force (Fung, 1965).

If the body forces were known Equation (16.43) would yield the correct displacement field provided of course we satisfy the boundary conditions. Therefore any method of analysis which can cope with an elastic body with body forces can be used to solve plasticity problems.

It should be noted the the body force in Equation (16.43) is not known *a priori* for a given increment of loading. Therefore the solution process is essentially an iterative one. We can write Equation (16.27) for this purpose as

$$\mathbf{F\dot{\Phi}} = \dot{\mathbf{u}} - \mathbf{H}(\mathbf{\Psi} + \Delta\mathbf{\Psi})$$

$$\mathbf{G\dot{\Phi}} = \dot{\mathbf{p}} - \mathbf{J}(\mathbf{\Psi} + \Delta\mathbf{\Psi}) \qquad (16.44)$$

where $\dot{\mathbf{\Phi}}$ is the vector of fictitious traction rates
  $\dot{\mathbf{u}}$ is the vector of surface displacement rates
  $\dot{\mathbf{p}}$ is the vector of surface traction rates
  $\mathbf{\Psi}$ is the vector of accumulated body forces up to but not including the current increment of loading
  $\Delta\mathbf{\Psi}$ is the vector of current increment of body forces which has to be determined as a part of the iterative solution.

A complete algorithm for these calculations has been given by Banerjee, Commons and Mustoe (1976). It is also instructive to note that such an iterative process is exactly analogous to the various methods such as the initial stress approach or the initial strain approach which are used in the finite element analysis for nonlinear solids.

16.7 DISCUSSIONS AND CONCLUSIONS

It has been shown that the Boundary Element Method (B.E.M.) is a practical numerical tool which can be used to obtain solutions to a number of geotechnical problems of considerable complexity. The method can, in fact model regions having low relative specific surface such as those found in foundation engineering problems better than other popular numerical methods which use a volume discretization scheme. The use of relatively elaborate analytical formulation does pay off in computer costs.

The method can also be used to derive the local stiffness matrix for an element of arbitrary shape for use in a finite element analysis. It can therefore be incorporated within an existing finite element computer program. Perhaps the best features of both the differential and the integral methods can be combined to advantage in soil–structure interaction problems, in which a finite size structure can be represented by a differential method discretization and the extensive soil medium by large boundary element zones. Such an application is in fact described by Banerjee and Driscoll (1975).

ACKNOWLEDGEMENTS

The authors wish to thank various post-graduate research students, notably Dr G. R. Tomlin, formerly of Southampton University, Mr P. E. Commons and Mr T. G. Davies of University College, Cardiff who carried out some of the development work presented in this chapter.

APPENDIX

A1   Steady state flow problems

A point source, at P, of strength $\phi(P)$ in a homogeneous infinite lamina of isotropic material, permeability $= k$, will produce at a field point Q, (x_1, x_2) (as shown in Figure 16.A1(a)), a potential $p(Q)$ and a flow velocity $u^{(\theta)}(Q)$ in the θ direction given by

$$p(Q) = f(Q, P)\phi(P) = \frac{1}{2\pi k} \ln (d/r)\phi(P)$$

$$u^{(\theta)}(Q) = g(Q, P)\phi(P) = \frac{\cos (\beta - \theta)}{2\pi r} \phi(P)$$

(16.1A)

where $\beta = \tan^{-1} (x_2/x_1)$ and $r^2 = x_\alpha x_\alpha$ $(\alpha = 1, 2)$ and d is the distance to a quite arbitrarily chosen circular boundary in the lamina on which $p(Q) = 0$.

If such a source is uniformly distributed, at ϕ per unit length, along a line segment $\Delta S(P) = 2b$ in the x_1 direction centred on the origin, Figure 16.A1(b), then integration of Equation (16.1A) along the segment yields the

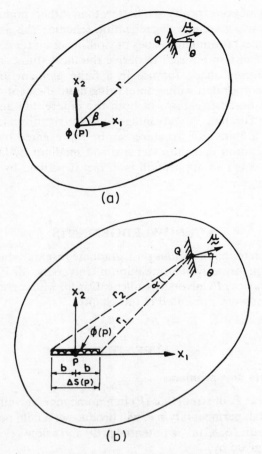

Figure 16.A1 Internal (a) point source; (b) line
source nomenclature for steady-state flow

$p(Q)$ and $u(Q)$ values relevant to this case as

$$p(Q) = F(Q, P)\phi(P) = \frac{\phi(P)}{4\pi bk}\left\{(x_1 - d)\ln\frac{r_1}{r_2} + (b+d)\ln\frac{b+d}{r_2}\right.$$

$$\left. + (b-d)\ln\frac{|b-d|}{r_1} - x_2\alpha\right\}$$

and

$$u^{(\theta)}(Q) = G(Q, P)\phi(P) = \frac{\phi(P)}{4\pi b}\left\{\alpha\sin\theta - \ln\frac{r_1}{r_2}\cos\theta\right\} \qquad (16.2\text{A})$$

When the source point P and the field point Q coincide at the mid-point of any segment then the integration of $f(Q, P)$ is carried across an infinite value which in this case is suppressed and leads to:

$$F(P, P) = \frac{1}{4\pi bk}\left\{(b+d)\ln\frac{b+d}{b} + (b-d)\ln\frac{|b-d|}{b}\right\} \quad (16.3A)$$

The corresponding limiting value of $G(P, P)$, obtained as $x_2 \to \pm 0$, $\theta = \pi/2$ and $-b < x_1 < b$, is

$$G(P, P) = \pm\frac{1}{4b} \quad (16.4A)$$

i.e. there is a step change in flux of $\pm \Phi(P)/2$, where

$$\Phi(P) = \phi(P)2b = \phi(P)\Delta S(P)$$

as the element is crossed corresponding to the influx bifurcating symmetrically into the infinite lamina. This is the physical explanation underlying the $\frac{1}{2}$ components which appear on the leading diagonal of **G**.

A complication arises due to the fact that $p(Q)$, Equation (16.2A) does not approach zero as Q goes to infinity but becomes logarithmically infinite. This has to be overcome by the following device in order that the fictitious potential distribution shall have zero influence at infinity as required (Jaswan, 1963; Butterfield and Tomlin, 1972). Since the datum from which the potentials are measured is quite arbitrary it can be adjusted by an amount C (initially unknown) so as to ensure that

$$\sum_{n=1}^{n} [\phi(P)\,\Delta S(P)]_n = 0$$

which will therefore clearly have zero effect on infinite boundaries. This requirement adds one further equation to the set of Equation (16.5) and the solution vector (Φ, C) has to be found from the augmented Equation 16.16

$$\begin{bmatrix} \mathbf{F} & \mathbf{1} \\ \mathbf{G} & \mathbf{0} \\ \mathbf{1} & \mathbf{0} \end{bmatrix}\begin{Bmatrix} \mathbf{\Phi} \\ C \end{Bmatrix} = \begin{Bmatrix} \mathbf{p} \\ \mathbf{u} \\ \mathbf{0} \end{Bmatrix} \quad (16.5A)$$

where **1** and **0** are unit and zero vectors of the appropriate dimensions.

This complication does not arise in three-dimensional problems for which a point source $\phi(P)$ at P produces $p(Q)$ and $u(Q)$, say, at Q given by

$$p(Q) = f(Q, P)\phi(P) = \frac{1}{4\pi k}\cdot\frac{1}{R}\cdot\phi(P)$$

$$u^{(\theta)}(Q) = g(Q, P)\phi P = \frac{1}{4\pi}\cdot\frac{1}{R^2}(\eta_\alpha\mu_\alpha)\phi(P)$$

$$(16.6A)$$

which both approach zero as $R = \sqrt{(x_\beta x_\beta)}$, $\beta = 1, 2, 3$, goes to infinity. Here η_α and μ_α are the components of a unit vector $\boldsymbol{\eta}$ along R and of the unit vector $\boldsymbol{\mu}$ along the outward normal to the surface element $\Delta S(Q)$ respectively. In order to obtain $F(Q, P)$ and $G(Q, P)$ for uniform sources distributed over $\Delta S(P)$ then, in general, $\Delta S(P)$ has to be further discretized and the distributed point sources integrated by numerical quadrature.

A2 Diffusion problem

The basic solution (type A) of the governing differential equation to the plane problem is,

$$p(Q, t) = \frac{\phi(P)}{4\pi ct} \cdot \exp\left(-r^2|4ct\right)$$

where

$$r = |PQ| = \sqrt{(x_\alpha x_\alpha)} \qquad (\alpha = 1, 2) \qquad (16.7\text{A})$$

By integrating Equation (16.7A) over a line an instantaneous line segment source can be obtained as described in Section 16.4. Integration over a triangular area will produce an instantaneous triangular source. The expressions for triangular sources are too lengthy to include here but comprehensive details, including triangular sources with linearly varying source strength can be found in Tomlin (1972).

The starting point for type B solutions, (i.e. a continuously applied source of strength $\phi(P)$ applied from $t = 0$) is Equation (16.7A) integrated in time from 0 to t. Further integration can be performed along a line to generate the continuous line segment source solution in closed form (Tomlin, 1972).

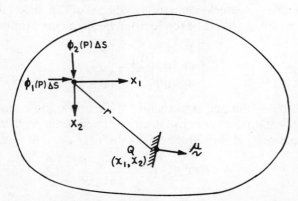

Figure 16.A2 Nomenclature for plane-strain internal line
load in elasto-statics

The flow velocities required at points on boundaries and interfaces can be calculated as in Section 16.4 via the gradients of all the above solutions normal to such boundaries precisely as for steady state solutions.

A3   Two-dimensional (x_1, x_2) plane-strain problems

The stress $\sigma_{\alpha\beta}$ and displacement v_α components at a point Q due to a line load of intensity say E_2 per unit length along x_3 and acting in the x_2 direction (Figure 16.A2) are given by Sokolnikoff (1956) as:

$$\sigma_{11} = A_1 \frac{x_2}{r^2}\left(\frac{2\nu-1}{2} + \frac{(x_1)^2}{r^2}\right)$$

$$\sigma_{22} = A_1 \frac{x_2}{r^2}\left(\frac{1-2\nu}{2} + \frac{(x_2)^2}{r^2}\right)$$

$$\sigma_{33} = A_1 \frac{\nu x_2}{r^2} \tag{16.7A}$$

$$\sigma_{12} = A_1 \frac{x_1}{r^2}\left(\frac{1-2\nu}{2} + \frac{x_2 x_1}{r^2}\right)$$

$$v_1 = -\frac{\dot{B}(x_1 x_2)}{r^2}$$

$$v_2 = B_1\left\{(3-4\nu)\ln\left|\frac{r}{d}\right| - \frac{(x_1)^2}{r^2}\right\}$$

where

$$A_1 = \frac{E_2(P)}{2\pi(1-\nu)} \quad \text{and} \quad B_1 = \frac{E_2(P)}{4\pi G}\frac{1}{(1-\nu)}, \quad r^2 = x_\alpha x_\alpha$$

If $\boldsymbol{\mu}$ is again the outward unit normal vector to a boundary element at Q then the contribution $E_2(P)$ to $\mathbf{p}(Q)$ and $\mathbf{u}(Q)$ are given by $P_\alpha^{(2)}(Q) = \sigma_{\alpha\beta}\mu_\beta$ and $u^{(2)}(Q) = V_\beta\mu_\beta$. The contributions of $E_1(P)$ acting in the x_1 direction at P, to $\mathbf{p}(Q)$ and $\mathbf{u}(Q)$ can be evaluated similarly by interchanging x_1 and x_2 in Equation (16.7A). The result of these operations provides $f_{\alpha\beta}(Q, P)$ and $g_{\alpha\beta}(Q, P)$ where $\phi_\beta(P)$ is the vector of the E_1, E_2 forces at P.

$$p_\alpha(Q) = f_{\alpha\beta}(Q, P)\phi_\beta(P)$$
$$g_\alpha(Q) = g_{\alpha\beta}(Q, P)\phi_\beta(P) \qquad (\beta = 1, 2) \tag{16.8A}$$

Precisely analogous expressions for line loads in an orthotropic elastic continuum involving nine compliances are given by Tomlin and Butterfield (1974).

When $\phi_\alpha(P)$ is uniformly distributed along $\Delta S(P)$ the corresponding kernels $F_{\alpha\beta}(Q, P)$ and $G_{\alpha\beta}(Q, P)$ have again to be evaluated by numerical quadrature (Banerjee, 1975; Tomlin, 1972; Tomlin and Butterfield, 1974).

In all cases there is a jump across each boundary element when P and Q coincide. In elasticity problems the jump occurs in the value of $p_2(P, P)$. This arises from the direct stresses of $\pm \phi_2(P)/2$ produced by $\phi_2(P)$ immediately 'outside' and 'inside' the boundary element here aligned along x_1, to which it is applied.

Once more logarithmically infinite values arise in the two dimensional problem this time in the displacement components in the direction of the applied loading. Thus in Equations (16.7A) v_2 is specified only in relation to its value at $(\pm d, 0)$, d being a quite arbitrary distance for each source element $\Delta S(P)$. This problem can be circumvented by applying a rigid body displacement to the fictitious body (i.e. a two component vector **c**) and requiring the resultant of all the fictitious tractions be adjusted, via **c**, to have a zero sum. Thus if

$$\sum_{n=1}^{n} [\phi_\alpha(P) \, \Delta S(P)]_n = 0$$

their net effect at an infinite boundary will be zero. The unknown vector **c** has to be incorporated within Equation (23) which now becomes

$$\begin{bmatrix} \mathbf{F} & \mathbf{0} \\ \mathbf{G} & \mathbf{I} \\ \mathbf{I} & \mathbf{0} \end{bmatrix} \begin{Bmatrix} \mathbf{\Phi} \\ \mathbf{c} \end{Bmatrix} = \begin{Bmatrix} \mathbf{p} \\ \mathbf{u} \\ \mathbf{0} \end{Bmatrix} \tag{16.9A}$$

where in the bottom block row the **I** is a row of 2×2 unit matrices and the **0** a 2×2 null matrix. The remaining **I** and **0** matrices are also built up from 2×2 sub-matrices as necessary.

For three-dimensional problems such adjustments are not necessary because the kernel functions satisfy the radiation conditions at infinity directly.

The functions for displacements $u_\alpha(Q)$, the tractions $p_\alpha(Q)$ and the stresses $\sigma_{\alpha\beta}(Q)$ are given by

$$f_{\alpha\beta}(Q, P) = B_2 \cdot \left(\frac{1}{r}\right)\left[(3 - 4\nu)\delta_{\alpha\beta} + \frac{\zeta_\alpha\zeta_\beta}{r^2}\right] \tag{16.10A}$$

$$g_{\alpha\beta}(Q, P) = A_2 \cdot \left(\frac{1}{r^2}\right)\left[\frac{(1 - 2\nu)}{r}\{-\mu_\alpha\zeta_\beta + \mu_\beta\zeta_\alpha\}\right.$$

$$\left. + \left\{(1 - 2\nu)\delta_{\alpha\beta} + \left(\frac{3}{r^2}\right)\zeta_\alpha\zeta_\beta\right\}\frac{\zeta_\gamma\mu_\gamma}{r}\right] \tag{16.11A}$$

$$M_{\alpha\beta\gamma}(Q, P) = A_2 \cdot \left(\frac{1}{r^2}\right)\left[\frac{(1-2\nu)}{r}\{-\delta_{\alpha\beta}\zeta_\gamma + \delta_{\alpha\gamma}\zeta_\beta + \delta_{\beta\gamma}\zeta_\alpha\}\right.$$

$$\left. +\frac{3}{r^3} \cdot \zeta_\alpha\zeta_\beta\zeta_\gamma\right] \hspace{3cm} \text{(16.12A)}$$

where α, β, γ range from 1 to 3

$A_2 = \{1/[8\pi(1-\nu)]\}$

$B_2 = \{1/[16\pi G(1-\nu)]\}$

$\zeta_\alpha = (y_\alpha - x_\alpha); \qquad \zeta_\beta = (y_\beta - x_\beta); \qquad \zeta_\gamma = (y_\gamma - x_\gamma)$

for points $P(y_1, y_2, y_3); \qquad Q(x_1, x_2, x_3)$

$r^2 = \zeta_\alpha\zeta_\alpha$

$\delta_{\alpha\beta}$ is the Kronecker delta.

REFERENCES

Banaugh, R. P. and Goldsmith, W. (1962). 'Diffraction of steady acoustic waves by surfaces of arbitrary shape', *Jour. Acoust. Soc. Amer.* **35**.

Banerjee, P. K. (1971). 'Foundations within a finite elastic layer—an application of the integral equation method', *Civil Engineering*, 1197–1202.

Banerjee, P. K. (1975a). 'Effects of the pile cap on the load-displacement behaviour of pile groups when subjected to eccentric loading', *Proc. 2nd Aust.-NZ Conference on Geomechanics, Brisbane*, Session IV.

Banerjee, P. K. (1975b). 'Load displacement behaviour of batter piles subjected to combined vertical load, horizontal load and moment', *Proc. 5th Pan American Conference on S.M.F.E., Buenos Aires*.

Banerjee, P. K. (1975c). 'Integral equation methods for the analysis of three-dimensional piece-wise non-homogeneous solids of arbitrary shape', *Report No. S.M./Int./2/1975*. Department of Civil Engineering, University College, Cardiff.

Banerjee, P. K. and Driscoll, R. (1975). 'Analysis of raked pile groups', *Publication No. HECB/B/8*, Department of the Environment, Highway Directorate, London.

Banerjee, P. K. (1976). 'Analysis of vertical pile groups embedded in non-homogeneous soil', *Proc. 6th European Conference on Soil Mech. Found. Eng.'*, Vienna, Austria.

Banerjee, P. K., Commons, P. E. and Mustoe, G. (1976). 'An indirect integral equation method for elasto-plasticity', (to be published).

Benjumea, R. and Sikarskie, D. L. (1972). 'On the solutions of plane, orthotropic elasticity problems by an integral equation method', *Jour. of Applied Mechanics*, 801–808.

Boissenot, J. M., Lachat, J. C., and Watson, J. (1974). 'Étude par equations integrales d'une eprouvette C.T. 15', Dept. D.T.E.—CETIM, Senlis, France. *Revue de Physique*, **9**, 611–615.

Butterfield, R. (1971). 'The application of integral equation methods to continuum problems in Soil Mechanics', *Roscoe Memorial Symposium, Cambridge*, 573–587.

Butterfield, R. and Banerjee, P. K. (1970). 'The problem of pile reinforced half space', *Geotechnique*, 100–103.

Butterfield, R. and Banerjee, P. K. (1971a). 'The elastic analysis of compressible piles and pile groups', *Geotechnique*, **21**, 43–60.

Butterfield, R. and Banerjee, P. K. (1971b). 'The problem of pile cap-pile group interaction', *Geotechnique*, **21**, 2, 135–142.

Butterfield, R. and Banerjee, P. K. (1971c). 'A rigid disc of any shape embedded in an elastic half space', *Geotechnical Engineering*, **2**, 35–52.

Butterfield, R. and Tomlin, G. R. (1972). 'Integral techniques for solving zoned anisotropic continuum problems', *Proc. Int. Conf. on Variational Methods in Engineering, Southampton University*, **2**, 9/13–9/15.

Byatt-Smith, J. G. B. (1971). 'An integral equation for unsteady surface waves and comment on Boussinesq equation', *Jour. Fluid Mech.*, **49**, 4, 625–633.

Chen, L. H. and Schweikert, H. (1963). 'Sound radiation from an arbitrary body', *Journal Acoust. Soc. Amer.* **35**.

Cruse, T. A. (1968a). 'The direct potential method in three-dimensional elasto-statics', *Dept. of Mech. Eng., Carnegie Inst. of Tech.* **SM-13**.

Cruse, T. A. (1968b). 'A direct formulation and numerical solution of the general transient elasto-dynamic problem—II', *Journ. Math. Anal. Appl.* **22**, 341–355.

Cruse, T. A. (1969). 'Numerical solutions in three-dimensional elasto-statics', *Int. Jour. Solids and Structures*, **5**, 1259–1274.

Cruse, T. A. (1972). 'Application of boundary integral equation method in Solid Mechanics', *Proc. Int. Conf. on Variational Methods in Engineering, Southampton University*, **2**, 9/1–9/30.

Cruse, T. A. (1973). 'Application of boundary integral equation method in three-dimensional stress analysis', *Jour. of Computers and Structures*, **3**, 509–527.

Cruse, T. A. (1974). 'An improved boundary integral equation method for three-dimensional elastic stress analysis', *Jour. of Computers and Structures*, **4**, 741–757.

Cruse, T. A. and Rizzo, F. J. (1968). 'A direct formulation and numerical solution of the general transient elasto-dynamic problem—I', *Jour. Maths. Anal. Appl.* **22**, 244–259.

Cruse, T. A. and Rizzo, F. J. (1975) (eds.). *Proc. A.S.M.E. Conf. on Boundary Integral Equation Method'*, New York.

Cruse, T. A. and Van Bauren, W. (1971). 'Three-dimensional elastic stress analysis of a fractured specimen with edge crack', *Int. Jour. Fract. Mech.* **7**, 1–15.

de Urena, R., Pigier, J. S., Muzas, F., and Sanz Sanado, I. M. (1966). 'Stress-distribution in cross-anisotropic media', *Proc. 1st Cong. Int. Soc. Rock Mech., Lisbon*, **V-I**, 313–317.

Fung, Y. C. (1965). '*Foundations of Solid Mechanics'*, Prentice Hall.

Gibson, R. E. (1974). 'The analytical method in soil mechanics', *Geotechnique*, **24**, 2, 113–140.

Hess, J. L. (1973). 'Higher order numerical solutions of the integral equation for two-dimensional Neuman problem', *Computer Methods in Applied Mech. and Eng.* **2**, 1–15.

Jaswan, M. A. (1963). 'Integral equation methods in potential theory—I', *Proc. Royal Soc.* **A 275**, 23–32.

Jaswan, M. A. and Ponter, A. R. (1963). 'An integral equation solution of the torsion problem', *Proc. Royal Soc.* **A 273**, 237–246.

Johnson, I. W. (1972). 'Electro-osmosis and pore water pressures; their effect on the stresses acting on driven piles', *Ph.D. Thesis*, Southampton University.

Kellog, O. D. (1929). *Foundations of Potential Theory*, Dover, New York.

Kupradze, V. D. (1964). *Potential Methods in Theory of Elasticity*, Davey, New York.

Kupradze, V. D. (1964). 'Dynamic problems in elasticity', *Progress in Solid Mechanics*, **3**, Sneddon, I. (ed.), N4 Hill, R., North Holland.

Lachat, J. C. (1975). 'Further development of the boundary integral equation methods for elasto-statics', *Ph.D. Thesis*, Southampton University.

Massonnet, C. E. (1965). *Numerical Use of Integral Procedures*, Chapter 10, Stress Analysis: Zienkiewicz & Hollister (eds.). John Wiley and Sons, London.

Mikhlin, S. G. (1957). *Integral Equations*, Pergamon.

Mikhlin, S. G. (1965). *Multi-dimensional Singular Integrals and Integral Equations*, Pergamon.

Mikhlin, S. G. (1965). *Approximate Methods for Solutions of Differential and Integral Equations*, Pergamon.

Mitzner, K. M. (1967). 'Numerical solution for transient scattering from a hard surface of arbitrary shape by retarded potential technique', *Jour. Acoust. Soc. Amer.*, **42**, 391.

Muskhelishvili, N. I. (1953). *Some Basic Problems of Mathematical Theory of Elasticity*, E. P. Noordhoff Ltd., Groningen, Nederlands.

Oliveira, E. R. A. (1968). 'Plane stress analysis by a general integral method', *Jour. A.S.C.E., Eng. Mech.* 79–85.

Ottaviani, M. (1975). 'Three-dimensional finite element analysis of vertically loaded pile groups', *Geotechnique*, **25**, 2, 159–174.

Pestel, E. and Leckie, F. A. (1961). *Matrix Methods of Elasto-mechanics*, McGraw-Hill, New York.

Ricardella, P. C. (1972). *An Improved Boundary Integral Equation Method for Two-dimensional Elasticity Problems*, Carnegie–Mellon University, September 1972.

Ricardella, P. C. (1973). *An Implementation of the Boundary-integral Techniques for Plane Problems in Elasticity and Elasto-plasticity*, Report SM. 73-10, Mech. Eng. Carnegie–Mellon University.

Rim, K. and Henry, A. S. (1967). *An Integral Equation Method in Plane Elasticity*, NASA CR-779, 1967.

Rim, K. and Henry, A. S. (1969). *Improvement of an Integral Equation Method in Plane Elasticity Through Modification of Source Density Representation*, NASA CR-1273.

Silvester, P. and Hsieh, M. S. (1971). 'Projective solution of integral equations arising in electric and magnetic field problems', *Jour. Comp. Physics.* **8**, 73–81.

Sokolnikoff, I. S. (1956). *Mathematical Theory of Elasticity*, McGraw-Hill.

Swedlow, J. L. and Cruse, T. A. (1971). 'Formulation of boundary integral equations for three-dimensional elasto-plastic flow', *Int. Jour. Solids and Structures*, **7**, 1673–1681.

Symm, G. T. (1963). 'Integral equation methods in potential theory, II', *Proc. Royal Soc.* **A 275**, 33–46.

Tomlin, G. R. (1972). 'Numerical analysis of continuum problems in zoned anisotropic media', *Ph.D. Thesis*, Southampton University.

Tomlin, G. R. and Butterfield, R. (1974). 'Elastic analysis of zoned orthotropic continua', *Jour. of A.S.C.E., Eng. Mech. Divn.*, **EM3**, 511–529.

Van Buren, W. (1968). *The Indirect Potential Method for Three-dimensional Boundary Value Problems of Classical Elastic Equilibrium*, Res. report 68-ID7-MEKMA-R2, Westinghouse Research Labs., Pittsburg, 1968.

Watson, J. O. (1968). *An Integral Representation of the Displacement of an Elastic Body*, Report CE/18/1968, Southampton University.

Watson, J. O. (1972a). 'The analysis of three-dimensional problems of elasticity by integral representation of displacements', *Proc. Int. Conf. on Variational methods in engineering*, **2**, 9/52–9/56.

Watson, J. O. (1972b). 'Analysis of thick shells with holes by using integral equation methods', *Ph.D. Thesis*, Southampton University.

Subject Index